THE INTERNATIONAL SERIES OF MONOGRAPHS ON PHYSICS

GENERAL EDITORS

N. F. MOTT E. C. BULLARD

THE INTERNATIONAL SERIES OF MONOGRAPHS ON PHYSICS

GENERAL EDITORS

N. F. MOTT E. C. BULLARD

Already Published

THE THEORY OF ELECTRIC AND MAGNETIC SUSCEPTIBILITIES. By J. H. VAN VLECK. 1932.
THE THEORY OF ATOMIC COLLISIONS. By N. F. MOTT and H. S. W. MASSEY. *Second edition.* 1949.
RELATIVITY, THERMODYNAMICS, AND COSMOLOGY. By R. C. TOLMAN. 1934.
KINEMATIC RELATIVITY. A sequel to *Relativity, Gravitation, and World-Structure.* By E. A. MILNE. 1948.
THE PRINCIPLES OF STATISTICAL MECHANICS. By R. C. TOLMAN. 1938.
ELECTRONIC PROCESSES IN IONIC CRYSTALS. By N. F. MOTT and R. W. GURNEY. *Second edition.* 1948.
GEOMAGNETISM. By S. CHAPMAN and J. BARTELS. 1940. 2 vols.
THE SEPARATION OF GASES. By M. RUHEMANN. *Second edition.* 1949.
THE PRINCIPLES OF QUANTUM MECHANICS. By P. A. M. DIRAC. *Third edition.* 1947.
THEORY OF ATOMIC NUCLEUS AND NUCLEAR ENERGY-SOURCES. By G. GAMOW and C. L. CRITCHFIELD. 1949. *Being the third edition of* STRUCTURE OF ATOMIC NUCLEUS AND NUCLEAR TRANSFORMATIONS.
THE PULSATION THEORY OF VARIABLE STARS. By S. ROSSELAND. 1949.
THEORY OF PROBABILITY. By HAROLD JEFFREYS. *Second edition.* 1948.
COSMICAL ELECTRODYNAMICS. By H. ALFVÉN. 1950.
COSMIC RAYS. By L. JÁNOSSY. *Second edition.* 1950.
THE FRICTION AND LUBRICATION OF SOLIDS. By F. P. BOWDEN and D. TABOR. 1950.
ELECTRONIC AND IONIC IMPACT PHENOMENA. By H. S. W. MASSEY and E. H. S. BURHOP. 1952.
MIXTURES. By E. A. GUGGENHEIM. 1952.
BASIC METHODS IN TRANSFER PROBLEMS. By V. KOURGANOFF with the collaboration of IDA W. BUSBRIDGE. 1952.
THE OUTER LAYERS OF A STAR. By R. v. d. R. WOOLLEY and D. W. N. STIBBS. 1953.
DISLOCATIONS AND PLASTIC FLOW IN CRYSTALS. By A. H. COTTRELL. 1953.
ELECTRICAL BREAKDOWN OF GASES. By J. M. MEEK and J. D. CRAGGS. 1953.
GEOCHEMISTRY. By the late V. M. GOLDSCHMIDT. Edited by ALEX MUIR. 1954.
THE QUANTUM THEORY OF RADIATION. By W. HEITLER. *Third edition.* 1954.
ON THE ORIGIN OF THE SOLAR SYSTEM. By H. ALFVÉN. 1954.
DYNAMICAL THEORY OF CRYSTAL LATTICES. By M. BORN and K. HUANG. 1954.
METEOR ASTRONOMY. By A. C. B. LOVELL. 1954.
RECENT ADVANCES IN OPTICS. By E. H. LINFOOT. 1955.
QUANTUM THEORY OF SOLIDS. By R. E. PEIERLS. 1955.
MOLECULAR BEAMS. By NORMAN F. RAMSEY. 1956.
RECTIFYING SEMI-CONDUCTOR CONTACTS. By H. K. HENISCH. 1957.
NEUTRON TRANSPORT THEORY. By B. DAVISON with the collaboration of J. B. SYKES. 1957.

THE THEORY OF ELEMENTARY PARTICLES

BY

J. HAMILTON
FELLOW OF CHRIST'S COLLEGE
CAMBRIDGE

OXFORD
AT THE CLARENDON PRESS
1959

CONTENTS

FIRST READING

The following sections are recommended as a suitable first course for those who are not already familiar with the subject.

Chap. I, §§ 1–5, 7, 9–11, 14, 16, 18 (pp. 46–48), 19, 21 (pp. 52–54)
Chap. II, §§ 1–5, 7–10, 13 (pp. 106–10, 114–16)
Chap. III, §§ 1–11, 14–17
Chap. IV, §§ 1–7, 10–14
Chap. V, §§ 1–3, 5–13, 14 (pp. 291–2)
Chap. VI, §§ 4, 6 (pp. 334–5), 7, 8 (pp. 345–6)
Chap. VII, §§ 1–3, 4 (pp. 363–4), 6, 7
Chap. VIII, §§ 1–4, 7, 8 (pp. 401–8)
Chap. IX, §§ 1, 2 (pp. 428–33), 3, 4 (pp. 437–44)
Appendix

INTRODUCTION

THE object of this book is to give an account of the more important theoretical methods which are used in describing the properties of the elementary particles, and in explaining their observed interactions. It is necessary to assume that the reader is familiar with the simpler phenomena of elementary particle physics; however, when discussing recent experiments or less well-known phenomena, references to the experimental material will be given.

The theoretical techniques are of two distinct kinds: on the one hand there are the methods of field quantization, renormalization, dispersion relations, etc.; on the other the numerous invariance and symmetry properties, and the selection rules. Although we cannot calculate transition probabilities and lifetimes without adequate techniques of the first kind, the symmetry properties are of increasing importance in understanding the modern complex of elementary particles. A discussion of the field quantization and renormalization methods without some account of the symmetry properties would be one-sided and unpractical. We shall therefore develop these two kinds of technique side by side. Examples of the application of the symmetry properties and the selection rules to important physical phenomena will be given immediately after the more general discussions of the various kinds of fields. Other selection rules of a more subtle character, such as charge conjugation, time reversal, and the attribute, or 'strangeness', are treated in detail in Chapter VII. The polarization properties of beams of particles are closely related to the angular momentum properties of the particles; a description of polarized assemblies is to be found in a later chapter.

We discuss in some detail the theory and properties of fermions of spin $\frac{1}{2}$, and of bosons of spin zero, as well as the theory of the electromagnetic field. Elementary particles having other spin values have not been identified, and comparatively little work has been done on the theory of such particles. In dealing with the interactions of elementary particles, only those theories are given which are well established, or which, at least, have had reasonable success in explaining observed phenomena.

The classical theory of fields is given in Chapter I together with the basic Lorentz invariance and angular momentum properties of boson fields. The use of the classical field techniques in deriving the optical model for the passage of pions, or nucleons, through a nucleus is

form; for example, a rotation of the axes system through an angle θ_3 about the O_3 axis gives

$$\left.\begin{array}{ll} x_1' = x_1\cos\theta_3+x_2\sin\theta_3, & x_3' = x_3 \\ x_2' = -x_1\sin\theta_3+x_2\cos\theta_3, & t' = t \end{array}\right\}. \tag{2}$$

Other linear relations between the two coordinate systems are the spatial inversion ($\mathbf{x}' = -\mathbf{x}$, $t' = t$, where $\mathbf{x} = (x_1, x_2, x_3)$), and the time reflection ($t' = -t$, $\mathbf{x}' = \mathbf{x}$). In general the equations of interacting fields are not invariant under spatial inversion; an example is the β-decay process which is discussed in Chapter III, § 15. The two-component neutrino theory (Chapter III, § 16) has a free particle equation which is not invariant under inversion.† Strong interactions, such as the pion-nucleon interaction and the electromagnetic interaction, do appear (to a high order of accuracy) to be invariant under spatial inversion and time reflection. For such interactions, space inversion and time reflection are important symmetry properties giving rise to selection rules, etc.

These various linear relations can be written

$$x_\mu' = a_{\mu\nu} x_\nu \quad (\mu = 1,2,3,4). \tag{3}$$

where the $a_{\mu\nu}$ are constants and $x_4 = ict$.‡ The summation convention applies to the repeated index in (3). We allow Greek indices to run from 1 to 4 and Roman indices to run from 1 to 3.

The transformations we have discussed all leave invariant the form

$$x_\mu^2 = \mathbf{x}^2 - c^2t^2.$$

This requires that the coefficients $a_{\mu\nu}$ (with a_{ij}, a_{44} real, and a_{i4}, a_{4j} pure imaginary) obey the relations

$$a_{\mu\nu} a_{\mu\lambda} = \delta_{\nu\lambda} \quad (\nu, \lambda = 1,2,3,4), \tag{4}$$

where
$$\delta_{\nu\lambda} = \begin{cases} 1 \text{ if } \nu = \lambda, \\ 0 \text{ otherwise.} \end{cases}$$

The field equations must be unaltered under the transformations (3), provided (4) is satisfied. It is convenient to denote the 4×4 matrix $a_{\mu\nu}$ by A; eqn. (4) is now written

$$A_T A = I, \tag{5}$$

where I is the identity 4×4 matrix $(\delta_{\mu\nu})$ and the subscript T denotes the transpose. Eqn. (5) gives§ $A_T = A^{-1}$ and $(\det A)^2 = 1$; therefore

† In Chapter VII, §§ 3–5, the general nature of parity and time reversal invariance is discussed.

‡ It is sometimes convenient to write $x_4 = ix_0$, $x_0 = ct$.

§ $AA_T = I$ gives the relations $a_{\nu\mu} a_{\lambda\mu} = \delta_{\nu\lambda}$.

INTRODUCTION

THE object of this book is to give an account of the more important theoretical methods which are used in describing the properties of the elementary particles, and in explaining their observed interactions. It is necessary to assume that the reader is familiar with the simpler phenomena of elementary particle physics; however, when discussing recent experiments or less well-known phenomena, references to the experimental material will be given.

The theoretical techniques are of two distinct kinds: on the one hand there are the methods of field quantization, renormalization, dispersion relations, etc.; on the other the numerous invariance and symmetry properties, and the selection rules. Although we cannot calculate transition probabilities and lifetimes without adequate techniques of the first kind, the symmetry properties are of increasing importance in understanding the modern complex of elementary particles. A discussion of the field quantization and renormalization methods without some account of the symmetry properties would be one-sided and unpractical. We shall therefore develop these two kinds of technique side by side. Examples of the application of the symmetry properties and the selection rules to important physical phenomena will be given immediately after the more general discussions of the various kinds of fields. Other selection rules of a more subtle character, such as charge conjugation, time reversal, and the attribute, or 'strangeness', are treated in detail in Chapter VII. The polarization properties of beams of particles are closely related to the angular momentum properties of the particles; a description of polarized assemblies is to be found in a later chapter.

We discuss in some detail the theory and properties of fermions of spin $\frac{1}{2}$, and of bosons of spin zero, as well as the theory of the electromagnetic field. Elementary particles having other spin values have not been identified, and comparatively little work has been done on the theory of such particles. In dealing with the interactions of elementary particles, only those theories are given which are well established, or which, at least, have had reasonable success in explaining observed phenomena.

The classical theory of fields is given in Chapter I together with the basic Lorentz invariance and angular momentum properties of boson fields. The use of the classical field techniques in deriving the optical model for the passage of pions, or nucleons, through a nucleus is discussed as an example. Dirac's theory of spin-$\frac{1}{2}$ particles, and some account of the interactions of these particles, is given in Chapter III.

In Chapters II and IV respectively, the quantization of boson and fermion fields is shown; the method which is used is designed to keep the mathematical manipulations as simple as possible, and at the same time give a ready physical understanding. In the latter part of Chapter IV the general problem of interacting quantized fields is discussed. The detailed techniques for solving interacting field problems are given in Chapters V and VI; the properties of the S-matrix are examined and illustrated.

The renormalization method is discussed, and it is applied to quantum electrodynamics problems. For the pion-nucleon interaction, the Chew–Low method and the dispersion relations are given. The interactions of K-mesons and hyperons will, no doubt, be investigated by similar methods; however, our knowledge of these interactions is at present so limited that it only seemed worth while to discuss their selection rules. For the same reason, the structure of nucleons and the mass differences of the elementary particles within the same family are not discussed.

A description of the foundations of field quantization will be found in Chapter IX.

Units. In the discussion of the classical theory of radiation which is contained in Chapter I, Gaussian units are used; this is in agreement with the usual practice. In subsequent chapters where the quantized electromagnetic field is discussed, Heaviside units are used; again, this is the usual practice. There is little chance of confusion if it is remembered that the fine structure constant $\alpha \simeq \frac{1}{137}$ is $e^2/\hbar c$ in Gaussian units, and $e^2/4\pi\hbar c$ in Heaviside units.

The scale of the pion field $\phi(x)$ is chosen so that

$$[\phi(x_\mu), \phi(x'_\mu)] = (i\hbar/c)D(x_\mu - x'_\mu);$$

this gives the convenient expression (2.20) for the energy.

The convention for scattering matrices is that initial state vectors are to the right and final state vectors are to the left.

The reader is reminded that selected sections which are suitable for a first reading are indicated at the end of the Table of Contents on p. ix.

I

CLASSICAL FIELDS: LORENTZ AND ROTATION INVARIANCE

1. General

IN discussing the equations of the fields associated with elementary particles we require consistency with special relativity† because the particles may move with any velocity up to the velocity of light. This requirement turns out to be useful in classifying the types of free field which are possible, and it severely restricts the possible equations of motion.‡ The relativity requirement is also of value in limiting the types of interactions which are possible between elementary particles. In practice the requirement is satisfied if the field equations are derived from a Lagrangian function which is a relativistic invariant.

Another important invariance property—rotation invariance—comes from the requirement that the field equations should be independent of the orientation of the (spatial) coordinate system.§ This leads to the angular momentum analysis of the fields which is an important tool for studying the actual interactions between particles.

We now discuss these invariance requirements in more detail. The simple Lorentz transformation relates the position (x_1, x_2, x_3) and time t of an event as seen by an observer A to the position (x_1', x_2', x_3') and time t' of the same event as seen by an observer B who is moving with a uniform velocity relative to A. If this relative velocity is v along the axis O_1 then||

$$\left.\begin{aligned} x_1' &= \eta(x_1 - vt), \quad x_2' = x_2, \quad x_3' = x_3 \\ t' &= \eta(t - vx_1/c) \end{aligned}\right\}, \tag{1}$$

where c is the velocity of light and $\eta = (1-v^2/c^2)^{-\frac{1}{2}}$. Spatial rotations about the origin of coordinates can conveniently be written in a similar

† General relativity effects are ignored throughout. At the shortest distances investigated at present ($\sim 10^{-14}$ cm) the gravitational potential of a particle is very weak compared with other interactions.

‡ Field equations containing partial derivatives of higher order than the second, or non-linear free-field equations, have not been intensively studied.

§ The equations of motion of a closed interacting system of particles should be independent of the position of the origin of coordinates. As is well known, this implies that the total momentum of the system is constant.

|| For a discussion of special relativity see C. Møller, *The Theory of Relativity* (Clarendon Press, 1952), chs. i and ii.

form; for example, a rotation of the axes system through an angle θ_3 about the O_3 axis gives

$$\left.\begin{aligned} x_1' &= x_1\cos\theta_3 + x_2\sin\theta_3, & x_3' &= x_3 \\ x_2' &= -x_1\sin\theta_3 + x_2\cos\theta_3, & t' &= t \end{aligned}\right\}. \tag{2}$$

Other linear relations between the two coordinate systems are the spatial inversion ($\mathbf{x}' = -\mathbf{x}$, $t' = t$, where $\mathbf{x} = (x_1, x_2, x_3)$), and the time reflection ($t' = -t$, $\mathbf{x}' = \mathbf{x}$). In general the equations of interacting fields are not invariant under spatial inversion; an example is the β-decay process which is discussed in Chapter III, § 15. The two-component neutrino theory (Chapter III, § 16) has a free particle equation which is not invariant under inversion.† Strong interactions, such as the pion-nucleon interaction and the electromagnetic interaction, do appear (to a high order of accuracy) to be invariant under spatial inversion and time reflection. For such interactions, space inversion and time reflection are important symmetry properties giving rise to selection rules, etc.

These various linear relations can be written

$$x_\mu' = a_{\mu\nu} x_\nu \quad (\mu = 1, 2, 3, 4). \tag{3}$$

where the $a_{\mu\nu}$ are constants and $x_4 = ict$.‡ The summation convention applies to the repeated index in (3). We allow Greek indices to run from 1 to 4 and Roman indices to run from 1 to 3.

The transformations we have discussed all leave invariant the form

$$x_\mu^2 = \mathbf{x}^2 - c^2t^2.$$

This requires that the coefficients $a_{\mu\nu}$ (with a_{ij}, a_{44} real, and a_{i4}, a_{4j} pure imaginary) obey the relations

$$a_{\mu\nu} a_{\mu\lambda} = \delta_{\nu\lambda} \quad (\nu, \lambda = 1, 2, 3, 4), \tag{4}$$

where $$\delta_{\nu\lambda} = \begin{cases} 1 \text{ if } \nu = \lambda, \\ 0 \text{ otherwise.} \end{cases}$$

The field equations must be unaltered under the transformations (3), provided (4) is satisfied. It is convenient to denote the 4×4 matrix $a_{\mu\nu}$ by A; eqn. (4) is now written

$$A_T A = I, \tag{5}$$

where I is the identity 4×4 matrix $(\delta_{\mu\nu})$ and the subscript T denotes the transpose. Eqn. (5) gives§ $A_T = A^{-1}$ and $(\det A)^2 = 1$; therefore

† In Chapter VII, §§ 3–5, the general nature of parity and time reversal invariance is discussed.

‡ It is sometimes convenient to write $x_4 = ix_0$, $x_0 = ct$.

§ $AA_T = I$ gives the relations $a_{\nu\mu} a_{\lambda\mu} = \delta_{\nu\lambda}$.

$\det A = \pm 1$. Transformations which can be brought together by continuous variation of $a_{\mu\nu}$ cannot have opposite values for $\det A$. Clearly the *simple* Lorentz transformations (such as (1)) and the rotations (such as (2)) can be altered continuously into the identity; hence they have $\det A = 1$. Transformations having $\det A = -1$ may all be obtained either from spatial inversion or from time reflection by superimposing simple Lorentz transformations and rotations.†

2. Invariant and covariant quantities

The nature and properties of the simpler quantities which are invariant or are tensors under the transformations (3), (4) are well known and will only be mentioned briefly here.

Invariants or *scalars* are rest mass, the charge of particles, the proper time interval $[-(x_\mu^{(1)}-x_\mu^{(2)})^2]^{\frac{1}{2}}$ between the events $x_\mu^{(1)}$, $x_\mu^{(2)}$, etc.

4-vectors are x_μ, p_μ the energy-momentum of a particle ($p_4 = iE/c$, $E = c(\mathbf{p}^2+m^2c^2)^{\frac{1}{2}}$).

Tensors. Any second-rank tensor can be split, in an invariant way, into the sum of a symmetric tensor $k_{\mu\nu}$ (having ten independent components) and an anti-symmetric tensor $t_{\mu\nu}$ (having six independent components). The electric and magnetic field strengths *in vacuo* form an anti-symmetric tensor of second rank (cf. p. 8).

Among tensors of higher rank, the completely anti-symmetric parts—which are themselves tensors—have especially simple properties, and they are of considerable physical importance. There are two such tensors: that of third rank, $M_{\lambda\mu\nu}$ ($M_{\lambda\mu\nu} = -M_{\mu\lambda\nu} = M_{\mu\nu\lambda}$) which has four independent components, and that of fourth rank $N_{\lambda\mu\nu\rho}$ ($N_{\lambda\mu\nu\rho} = -N_{\mu\lambda\nu\rho} = N_{\mu\nu\lambda\rho} = -N_{\mu\nu\rho\lambda}$) which has one component.‡ We introduce a useful symbol $\epsilon_{\lambda\mu\nu\rho}$ (which is not a tensor); it is defined by $\epsilon_{\lambda\mu\nu\rho} = 0$ if λ, μ, ν, ρ are not distinct, $\epsilon_{\lambda\mu\nu\rho} = +1\ (-1)$ if $\lambda\mu\nu\rho$ is obtained from 1234 by an even (odd) number of exchanges. Then

$$\det A = \epsilon_{\lambda\mu\nu\rho}\, a_{\lambda 1}\, a_{\mu 2}\, a_{\nu 3}\, a_{\rho 4} = \frac{1}{4!}\epsilon_{\lambda\mu\nu\rho}\,\epsilon_{\lambda'\mu'\nu'\rho'}\, a_{\lambda\lambda'}\, a_{\mu\mu'}\, a_{\nu\nu'}\, a_{\rho\rho'}. \tag{6}$$

The tensor $N_{\lambda\mu\nu\rho}$ may be written

$$N_{\lambda\mu\nu\rho} = \epsilon_{\lambda\mu\nu\rho} N, \quad \text{where } N = (1/4!)\epsilon_{\lambda\mu\nu\rho} N_{\lambda\mu\nu\rho}.$$

† From (4) and the pure imaginary nature of a_{k4},

$$a_{44} = \pm\Big(1+\sum_k |a_{k4}|^2\Big)^{\frac{1}{2}};$$

for each set of values a_{k4} there is a transformation ($a_{44} < 0$) which reverses time, as well as the orthochronous type ($a_{44} > 0$).

‡ There can be no completely anti-symmetric tensor of rank greater than four.

It is easy to see on using (6) that the transformation properties of N are

$$N' = (\det A)N. \tag{7}$$

Thus N behaves as a scalar for transformations having $\det A = +1$, but it changes sign under transformations having $\det A = -1$. N (or $N_{\lambda\mu\nu\rho}$) is called a *pseudo-scalar*.† The distinction between scalars and pseudo-scalars with respect to the transformations (3) is analogous to the distinction in three-dimensional geometry between scalars like $|\mathbf{x}|$ and triple scalar products like $(\mathbf{a}.\mathbf{b}\times\mathbf{c})$ or the *element* of volume; the latter change sign on going from a right-handed set of axes to a left-handed set.

The third rank anti-symmetric tensor $M_{\lambda\mu\nu}$ is examined in the same way. We write

$$M_{\lambda\mu\nu} = \epsilon_{\lambda\mu\nu\rho} m_\rho, \quad \text{where } m_\rho = \frac{1}{3!}\epsilon_{\lambda\mu\nu\rho} M_{\lambda\mu\nu}.$$

Using (6) it is easy to see that the transformation property of m_ρ is

$$m'_\rho = (\det A)\, a_{\rho\sigma} m_\sigma; \tag{8}$$

m_ρ is called a *pseudo-vector* because it transforms like a 4-vector so long as $\det A = +1$, but it changes sign in any transformation having $\det A = -1$. The distinction between 4-vector and pseudo-vector is analogous to the distinction in three-dimensional geometry between polar vectors, such as the position $\mathbf{x}$, and axial vectors, such as the angular momentum $\mathbf{x}\times\mathbf{p}$; the former changes sign under an inversion, the latter is unaltered. The gradient operator $\partial_\mu \equiv \partial/\partial x_\mu$ is a 4-vector,‡ the gradient of a scalar is a 4-vector and the gradient of a pseudo-scalar is a pseudo-vector. The pion is a spinless particle, but its field amplitude ϕ is a pseudo-scalar;§ hence the physical importance of the concepts we have just discussed.

There is a special *tensor* $\bar{\epsilon}_{\lambda\mu\nu\rho}$ defined by putting $\bar{\epsilon}_{\lambda\mu\nu\rho} = \epsilon_{\lambda\mu\nu\rho}$ in the conventional right-handed axes system. This tensor may be used to form the dual tensor to any anti-symmetric tensor; the dual of $N_{\lambda\mu\nu\rho}$ is a scalar, etc. The dual $\bar{t}_{\lambda\mu}$ of the anti-symmetric tensor $t_{\lambda\mu}$ is defined by‖

$$\bar{t}_{\lambda\mu} = \frac{i}{2!}\bar{\epsilon}_{\lambda\mu\nu\rho} t_{\nu\rho}; \tag{9}$$

$\bar{t}_{\lambda\mu}$ is an anti-symmetric tensor. The transformation $\mathbf{E}\rightarrow\mathbf{H}$, $\mathbf{H}\rightarrow-\mathbf{E}$

† Obviously N has negative parity.

‡ By (3) and (4), $\partial'_\mu = a_{\mu\nu}\partial_\nu \quad \left(\partial_4 \equiv \dfrac{1}{ic}\dfrac{\partial}{\partial t}\right)$.

§ For the proof of this assertion see Chapter VII, § 1.

‖ The factor i is included to give a real tensor a real dual tensor.

of the electromagnetic field vectors *in vacuo* is an example of the dual relationship.

Besides the quantities mentioned, there is an important class of double valued quantities whose transformation properties under the general Lorentz transformations are of physical importance; these are the four-component *spinors*. They are discussed in Chapter III.

3. Example: The centre of mass system

An important Lorentz frame of reference for studying the behaviour of elementary particles is the centre of mass system (c.m.s.) in which the total momentum of the particles is zero. When, for example, a photon and a nucleon collide, they may, if they have enough energy, produce a pion. In any particular frame of reference, the least energy required to produce a pion is called the *threshold energy* for that frame. The threshold energy is least for the c.m.s. in which the nucleon and the pion (at the threshold) are at rest after the collision; in any other frame of reference kinetic energy is taken up by the particles remaining after the collision, and the threshold is higher than in the c.m.s.

Elastic scattering of particles, such as, for example, pion-nucleon scattering, and the spontaneous disintegration of particles, should both be analysed in the c.m.s., so that the angular distributions of the end products depend on the structure of the interacting system rather than on the reference frame of the observer. We give a few examples of the c.m.s.

Consider two particles of masses M_1, M_2 and parallel (laboratory) momenta $\mathbf{p}^{(1)}$, $\mathbf{p}^{(2)}$ respectively. The c.m.s. moves in the same direction with velocity $v = \beta c$. The momenta in this system are

$$\mathbf{p}^{(1)\prime} = \eta\{\mathbf{p}^{(1)}-(\beta/c)E^{(1)}\}, \qquad \mathbf{p}^{(2)\prime} = \eta\{\mathbf{p}^{(2)}-(\beta/c)E^{(2)}\}.$$

$E^{(1)}$, $E^{(2)}$ are the laboratory energies of the particles. The value of β required to give $\mathbf{p}^{(1)\prime}+\mathbf{p}^{(2)\prime} = 0$ is

$$c|\mathbf{p}^{(1)}+\mathbf{p}^{(2)}|/(E^{(1)}+E^{(2)}).$$

The total energy in the c.m.s. is†‡

$$E^{(1)\prime}+E^{(2)\prime} = \{c^4(M_1^2+M_2^2)+2(E^{(1)}E^{(2)}-c^2p^{(1)}p^{(2)})\}^{\frac{1}{2}}. \tag{10}$$

† Using $E^{(1)\prime} = \eta(E^{(1)}-\beta c\mathbf{p}^{(1)})$, etc.

‡ It is sometimes useful to notice that

$$\eta = (E^{(1)}+E^{(2)})/(E^{(1)\prime}+E^{(2)\prime}),$$

where $E^{(i)}$ are laboratory values and $E^{(i)\prime}$ are c.m. values.

Suppose that in the laboratory system a nucleon of momentum $\mathbf{p}^{(1)}$ strikes a nucleon at rest ($\mathbf{p}^{(2)} = 0$, $E^{(2)} = Mc^2$). The threshold for the reaction

$$P+P \rightarrow D+\pi^+$$

in which a deuteron having binding energy Δ and a pion of mass μ are formed, is given by

$$E^{(1)'}+E^{(2)'} = 2Mc^2-\Delta+\mu c^2.$$

Using (10) the laboratory threshold is

$$E^{(1)} = Mc^2+2(\mu c^2-\Delta)+(\mu c^2-\Delta)^2/2Mc^2; \tag{11}$$

this means that the proton must have a kinetic energy of about 280 MeV.

When a nucleon strikes a nucleon at rest ($\mathbf{p}^{(2)} = 0$) the energy available in the c.m.s. is

$$E^{(1)'}+E^{(2)'} = \{2Mc^2(E^{(1)}+Mc^2)\}^{\frac{1}{2}} \quad (M = \text{nucleon mass}). \tag{12}$$

In proton synchrotrons operating at (kinetic) energies appreciably greater than Mc^2 ($\sim$ 1 GeV) the energy available for creating new particles when the beam is directed on a stationary target is approximately $(2E^{(1)}.Mc^2)^{\frac{1}{2}}$; at very high energies most of the energy goes into the forward motion and is not available for particle production. The kinetic energy required (using the exact formula (12)) for the production of an anti-proton in the collision of a moving nucleon with a nucleon at rest is† $6Mc^2 \simeq 5{\cdot}6$ GeV. It is, however, necessary to remember that (12) is inaccurate when the target nucleon moves; the inaccuracy can be appreciable. If the beam proton strikes a fairly large nucleus, the target nucleon may well have a kinetic energy of around 25 MeV (the Fermi energy)‡ due to its motion in the nucleus. This gives a value for $p^{(2)}$ of 220 MeV/c. From (10), this changes the threshold by $\delta E^{(1)} \simeq p^{(1)}p^{(2)}/M$; when the nucleons move in opposite directions the threshold $E^{(1)}$ is reduced. For anti-proton production the threshold is reduced§ to about 4·3 GeV.

Finally we notice the relation between the angular distributions of a particle after the reaction has taken place, as measured in the laboratory system and in the c.m.s. Let the energy-momentum of the

† A pair consisting of anti-proton and nucleon must be created.

‡ See J. M. Blatt and V. F. Weisskopf, *Theoretical Nuclear Physics* (J. Wiley, New York, 1952), ch. 7.

§ G. Feldman, *Phys. Rev.* **95** (1954) 1697, suggests that the anti-proton threshold may be further reduced if the production is a two-stage process in which an energetic pion is first emitted.

particle be $(p_1, p_2, 0, E)$, $(p_1', p_2', 0, E')$ in the respective systems. The inclination θ to the O_1 axis in the laboratory system is given by

$$\tan\theta = p_2/p_1 = \frac{p_2'}{\eta(p_1'+\beta E'/c)}, \tag{13}$$

where βc is the velocity of the c.m.s. reference frame (along the O_1 axis). Assuming $\beta \simeq +1$, laboratory angles in the range $\frac{1}{2}\pi < \theta < \pi$ can only occur for particles which in the c.m.s. move with velocity close to the velocity of light backwards along O_1. Because η is large, particles which do not move this way in the c.m.s. are in a forward cone in the laboratory system; for example if $p_1' = 0$, $\tan\theta = p_2'/\eta\beta E' \simeq 1/\eta$.

4. The electromagnetic field

Maxwell's equations for the electromagnetic field in the presence of charge density ρ, current density $\mathbf{j}$, and magnetization density $\mathbf{M}$ are

$$\left.\begin{aligned} \operatorname{div}\mathbf{E} &= 4\pi\rho \\ \operatorname{div}(\mathbf{H}+4\pi\mathbf{M}) &= 0 \\ \operatorname{curl}\mathbf{E} &= -\frac{1}{c}\frac{\partial}{\partial t}(\mathbf{H}+4\pi\mathbf{M}) \\ \operatorname{curl}\mathbf{H} &= \frac{4\pi}{c}\mathbf{j}+\frac{1}{c}\frac{\partial\mathbf{E}}{\partial t} \end{aligned}\right\}. \tag{14}$$

Gaussian units have been used here. The magnetization density $\mathbf{M}$ is included in eqns. (14) to make them convenient for calculating the radiation produced by the intrinsic magnetic moments of particles. A disadvantage in writing Maxwell's equations in this form is that, unless further terms are included, the equations are not Lorentz invariant. A moving magnetization density gives rise to an electric polarization density, and, to secure Lorentz invariance, electric polarization terms have to be added to the first and fourth equations.† When we examine the Lorentz invariance we shall simplify the discussion by omitting both the magnetization density $\mathbf{M}$ and the electric polarization. The Maxwell eqns. (14) hold both in classical (unquantized) theory and in quantum field theory; in the latter case the source functions ρ, $\mathbf{j}$, $\mathbf{M}$ require redefinition. For the present we discuss the unquantized theory.

It is possible to express the solutions of (14) in terms of a vector

† For a detailed discussion see C. Møller (p. 1, note ||) or W. K. H. Panofsky and M. Phillips, *Classical Electricity and Magnetism* (Addison-Wesley, Cambridge, Mass., 1955), ch. 22.

potential **A** and a scalar potential ϕ. The second equation shows that a vector function **A** exists such that

$$\mathbf{H}+4\pi\mathbf{M} = \operatorname{curl}\mathbf{A}, \tag{15}$$

and from the third equation,

$$\mathbf{E} = -\frac{1}{c}\partial\mathbf{A}/\partial t-\operatorname{grad}\phi, \tag{16}$$

where ϕ is some scalar function. These equations do not determine **A**, ϕ; we can require that they also obey the Lorentz gauge condition

$$\operatorname{div}\mathbf{A}+\frac{1}{c}\partial\phi/\partial t = 0. \tag{17}$$

With condition (17), the equations for **A**, ϕ in terms of the source functions are particularly simple,

$$\left.\begin{aligned} \nabla^2\mathbf{A}-\frac{1}{c^2}\frac{\partial^2\mathbf{A}}{\partial t^2} &= -\frac{4\pi}{c}(\mathbf{j}+c\operatorname{curl}\mathbf{M}) \\ \nabla^2\phi-\frac{1}{c^2}\frac{\partial^2\phi}{\partial t^2} &= -4\pi\rho \end{aligned}\right\}. \tag{18}$$

The charge and current sources are related by the conservation equation

$$\frac{\partial\rho}{\partial t}+\operatorname{div}\mathbf{j} = 0. \tag{19}$$

Now we omit **M** and show the tensor form of the equations. Charge is an invariant under Lorentz transformation, but charge density is not invariant, because of the deformation of the element of volume. It is easily shown† that **j**, ρ are the components of a 4-vector j_μ,

$$j_\mu = (\mathbf{j}, ic\rho).$$

This is consistent with the conservation equation (19), which is now written

$$\partial_\mu j_\mu = 0. \tag{20}$$

The operator appearing in (18) is the invariant operator ∂_μ^2, so **A**, ϕ are components of a 4-vector $A_\mu = (\mathbf{A}, i\phi)$; eqns. (18) (with $\mathbf{M} = 0$) may be written

$$\partial_\mu^2 A_\nu = -\frac{4\pi}{c}j_\nu. \tag{21}$$

Eqn. (17) becomes $\partial_\mu A_\mu = 0$. From (15) and (16) (again with $\mathbf{M} = 0$) the field amplitudes **E** and **H** are components of an anti-symmetric second-rank tensor,

$$f_{\mu\nu} = \partial_\mu A_\nu-\partial_\nu A_\mu, \tag{22}$$

$$\left.\begin{aligned} E_k &= if_{k4} \\ H_k &= \tfrac{1}{2}\epsilon_{klm}f_{lm} \end{aligned}\right\}, \tag{23}$$

† See p. 7, n. †.

where $\epsilon_{klm} = +1\ (-1)$ if k, l, m is an even (odd) permutation of 1, 2, 3 and $\epsilon_{klm} = 0$ otherwise. If the tensor $f_{\mu\nu}$ is replaced by its dual $\bar{f}_{\mu\nu}$ (cf. eqn. (9)), the vectors **E**, **H** are replaced by $-$**H**, **E** respectively.

Eqn. (22) shows that the same physical situation is given by different functions A_μ; replacing A_μ by $A_\mu + \partial_\mu \chi$, where χ is a scalar, leaves the field strength tensor $f_{\mu\nu}$ unaltered. The Lorentz gauge condition (17), and hence the source equations (18), are obeyed by the new potentials, provided

$$\partial_\mu^2 \chi = 0. \tag{24}$$

This replacement of the potentials, which is called a *gauge transformation of the second kind*,† is valuable in subsequent developments; physical results should be invariant under such transformations. A special gauge which is useful for discussing the electromagnetic field away from sources (i.e. where ρ, **j**, **M** are zero) is the *solenoidal gauge* having $\operatorname{div} \mathbf{A} = 0$; this is obtained by putting $\partial\chi/\partial t = c\phi$.

Maxwell's equations (with $\mathbf{M} = 0$) may be written in the Lorentz invariant form‡

$$\left.\begin{aligned} \partial_\mu f_{\mu\nu} &= -\frac{4\pi}{c} j_\nu \\ \partial_\lambda f_{\mu\nu} + \partial_\mu f_{\nu\lambda} + \partial_\nu f_{\lambda\mu} &= 0 \end{aligned}\right\}. \tag{25}$$

The simpler solutions of Maxwell's equations are well known; a brief discussion of multipole waves will be given in §§ 15, 16. The Green's functions required to solve the basic eqns. (21) under various boundary conditions are given in the Appendix.

5. The pion equation

Some useful information about the behaviour of pions can be obtained from the wave equation for the unquantized pion amplitude ϕ: of course, the use of the unquantized amplitude ignores all effects arising from quantum fluctuations in the field amplitude and it ignores some effects arising from the discrete nature of the particles.

The total energy of a free pion E is related to its momentum **p** and rest mass μ by the equation

$$E^2 = c^2(\mathbf{p}^2 + \mu^2 c^2). \tag{26}$$

The invariant wave equation for the pion amplitude ϕ (the Klein–Gordon equation) is formed by acting on the pseudo-scalar ϕ with (26), replacing the 4-vector p_μ by $(\hbar/i)\partial_\mu$:

$$(\partial_\mu^2 - \kappa^2)\phi = 0. \tag{27}$$

† Gauge transformations of the first kind are discussed in Chapter IX, § 2.

‡ The form for $\mathrm{M} \neq 0$ is given by Panofsky and Phillips, op. cit.

Here $\kappa = \mu c/\hbar$ is the inverse Compton wavelength of the pion (for $\mu_\pi = 273m_e$, $1/\kappa = 1{\cdot}42\times 10^{-13}$ cm).

A plane pion wave of the form $\exp[i(\mathbf{k}.\mathbf{x}-\omega t)]$ has the dispersive relation

$$\mathbf{k}^2+\kappa^2 = \omega^2/c^2. \tag{28}$$

The phase velocity is $$\frac{\omega}{|\mathbf{k}|} = c(1+\kappa^2/\mathbf{k}^2)^{\frac{1}{2}},$$

and the group velocity is

$$\frac{d\omega}{d\mathbf{k}} = \frac{c\mathbf{k}}{\sqrt{(\mathbf{k}^2+\kappa^2)}} = \frac{c^2\mathbf{p}}{E} = \mathbf{v},$$

where $\mathbf{v}$ is the particle velocity. Green's functions for solving the inhomogeneous equation†

$$(\partial_\mu^2-\kappa^2)\phi = -\delta^4(x)$$

are given in the Appendix: they enable us to express the pion field in terms of its sources.

Results of considerable physical importance may be obtained by using simple solutions of (27) or of the related equation for a pion moving in an external potential energy. Some examples follow.

6. Example: The optical disk

We consider the propagation of a pion wave through a medium having both a refractive and an absorptive effect. The analysis is a crude approximation to the propagation of a pion through a nucleus; similar considerations also apply to the propagation of a nucleon through a nucleus.‡ The refractive and absorptive effects can both be described by a complex potential energy function.§ This is easily seen on replacing (26) and (27) by the non-relativistic form

$$\{E-\mathbf{p}^2/2\mu-V(\mathbf{x})\}\phi = 0, \tag{29}$$

where $V(\mathbf{x})$ is the potential energy of the pion in the medium and E is its total (non-relativistic) energy. Considering plane wave solutions of the form $\phi = \exp[i(\mathbf{k}.\mathbf{x}-\omega t)]$, a constant potential well $V(\mathbf{x}) = -V$ alters the free particle propagation vector $\mathbf{k}$ to $\mathbf{k}+\mathbf{k}_1$, where

$$\mathbf{k}_1 = \mathbf{k}\{(1+V/E)^{\frac{1}{2}}-1\}.$$

† $\delta^4(x) \equiv \delta^3(\mathbf{x})\delta(x_0)$, where $x_0 = ct$, and $\delta^3(\mathbf{x}) = \delta(x_1)\delta(x_2)\delta(x_3)$.

‡ The nucleon wave components each obey (27) in free space. In this example the spin is ignored and the interaction with the nucleus is described by a scalar potential energy. In a further extension of the method (which will be mentioned in Chapter VIII, § 4) a complex potential together with a spin orbital interaction is used to describe the polarization of nucleons when scattered by nuclei.

§ For neutrons penetrating into a nucleus, the complex potential energy was used by H. A. Bethe, *Phys. Rev.* **57** (1940) 1125.

A positive real part of V increases the propagation vector and thus decreases the pion wavelength; a positive imaginary part of V gives a damping factor $\exp[-\mathrm{im}(\mathbf{k}_1.\mathbf{x})]$ in the pion wave. These arguments can be extended to the relativistic case.

It is convenient to specify both effects by *real* constants k_1, K associated with the particle and the medium. These constants are defined for the propagation of a plane wave in an infinite block of the material; in moving forward through a distance h the plane wave differs from what its amplitude would be after a similar motion *in vacuo* by a factor $\exp[(-\frac{1}{2}K+ik_1)h]$. Thus the complex refractive index n is given by

$$(n-1)k = k_1+\tfrac{1}{2}iK,$$

where $\mathbf{k}$ is the propagation vector in vacuum.† The relation of the refractive index n (or the complex well depth) to the more fundamental phenomena of scattering by individual nucleons is discussed in § 7 below and in Chapter V, § 4. The quantities k_1, K are, in general, functions of the energy of the incident particle.

It should be emphasized that this crude form of the optical model which is based on propagation in an infinite nuclear medium, takes no account of the structure of the actual nucleus. In its simple form it is only valid provided the energy of the incoming particle (pion or nucleon) is much greater than the binding energy of a nucleon in the nucleus; and this form is not expected to be useful for incident particle energies of less than, say, 50 MeV. In the calculations which follow, incident particle energies greater than 50 MeV are assumed.

However, the optical model using a complex potential $V(\mathbf{x})$ which has a real and an imaginary part, can be adapted for use at lower energies. The potential $V(\mathbf{x})$ is now a function both of the energy of the incident particle and of the actual nucleus involved. It is desirable to use a potential well with a rounded-off edge so as to avoid spurious surface scattering effects. Exact numerical solutions of Schrödinger's equation can be used to describe the elastic scattering (by the nucleus as a whole) of pions and nucleons according to this model.‡

Consider a high-energy ($\geqslant$ 50 MeV) plane wave pion beam which moves through a large piece of nuclear matter. We can attempt to

† In terms of a complex well depth V, in the non-relativistic case $n = (1+V/E)^{\frac{1}{2}}$, where E is the (non-relativistic) energy.

‡ For the case of pions see p. 20, n. ||. For nucleons see H. Feshbach, C. E. Porter, and V. F. Weisskopf, *Phys. Rev.* **96** (1954) 446.

describe the *attenuation* coefficient K in terms of elementary particle interactions by writing†

$$K = K_a + K_{sc}.$$

The coefficient K_a arises from the absorption of pions by nuclear matter‡ and K_{sc} describes the depletion of the (infinite plane wave) beam due to the scattering of pions by individual nucleons. Because we are dealing with high-energy incident pions it can be assumed that the absorbing and scattering nucleons are in the lowest energy states; the incident particle is always ahead of the disturbance it has created. In an actual nucleus, the coefficient|| K_{sc} includes inelastic scattering of the pions; this is because the scattering nucleon has a recoil energy, so it might either escape from the nucleus or else excite the nucleus. (The same holds for the passage of a high-energy nucleon through a nucleus.)

Attenuation and diffraction scattering

Now we discuss what happens when a plane-wave pion beam (of high energy) $\exp\{i(kx_3 - \omega t)\}$ hits a nucleus. The nucleus is first assumed to be a cylindrical disk of nuclear matter whose plane faces are normal to the beam. (A spherical nucleus is discussed in § 8.) The radius of the disk is R and its thickness is T. It is also assumed that the surface of the disk is smeared out so that k_1 and K rise gradually from the outside to their constant values inside the disk. This is necessary if scattering from surface discontinuities is to be avoided.§ It is a good first approximation at these energies to ignore any Coulomb force between the pion and the nucleus.

With these assumptions, an approximate solution to the problem may be given by using the simple diffraction theory of Kirchhoff. The portion of the beam which has passed through the disk has the amplitude

$$\phi = a\exp\{i(kx_3 - \omega t)\},$$

† For incident pions of several hundred MeV, production of one or more pions can occur during a collision with an individual nucleon. This gives a further contribution to the absorption coefficient K_a.

‡ K_a may be evaluated by a simple theory based on the absorption of a pion by the deuteron.

|| A rough estimate is $K_{sc} = 3A\sigma\gamma/4\pi R^3$, where A, R are the weight and radius of the nucleus, and σ is the average total cross-section for scattering of a free pion by a nucleon; γ is a numerical factor allowing for the effect of the exclusion principle. (Nucleons cannot be scattered into occupied states.)

§ A sufficient condition is that the fractional changes in k_1 or K in a length $1/k$ are not great. For high energies this condition is easy to satisfy. At a discontinuity at which the propagation vector abruptly changes from k to k' reflection will occur. The intensity of a plane wave crossing such a discontinuity is $4kk'/(k+k')^2$ times the intensity of the incident wave.

where $$a = \exp\{(-\tfrac{1}{2}K+ik_1)T\}.$$

The total cross-section for the *attenuation* of the pion beam in the disk is therefore
$$\sigma_a = \pi R^2(1-|a|^2) = \pi R^2(1-e^{-KT}). \tag{30}$$

If $a = 0$, we say the disk is *black* (for such pions).

Behind the disk the amplitude ϕ is no longer identical with the plane-wave form. In the language of optics, diffraction occurs at the disk. The diffraction pattern arises from a wave amplitude $(a-1)\exp(-i\omega t)$ at all points on the shadow face of the disk. In this way the disk acts as a pion scatterer, producing what is called *diffraction scattering* or *shadow scattering*; this scattering is elastic (the nucleus remaining in its ground state). The total cross-section for this scattering is†
$$\sigma_{\rm sh} = \pi R^2|1-a|^2; \tag{31}$$
for a black disk, $\sigma_{\rm sh}$ and σ_a are equal.

We now find the angular distribution of this shadow effect. Let P be a point at a distance r from the centre of the shadow face of the disk, such that OP makes angle θ with the O_3 axis. The amplitude $\phi(P)$ of the scattered wave at P is given by Kirchhoff's‡ diffraction formula
$$\phi(P) = e^{-i\omega t}(a-1)\frac{k}{2\pi i}\int\limits_{\rm (disk)} \frac{e^{ikd}}{d}\,dS, \tag{32}$$
where d is the distance from P to a variable point on the shadow face of the disk.

The edge of the shadow region remains fairly sharp up to a distance of the order $R.(kR)$ from the disk; beyond that distance Fraunhofer diffraction sets in, and the disturbance may be treated as scattering from a point (the centre of the disk). Remembering that the radius of a nucleus of atomic weight A is $R = 1{\cdot}2A^{\frac{1}{3}}\times 10^{-13}$ cm, it is obvious that, experimentally, only the Fraunhofer region is of interest. In that case (32) becomes
$$\phi(P) = e^{i(kr-\omega t)}f(\theta)/r,$$
where the scattering amplitude is given by§
$$f(\theta) = i(1-a)k\int\limits_0^R J_0(k\rho\sin\theta)\rho\,d\rho = i(1-a)RJ_1(kR\sin\theta)/\sin\theta. \tag{33}$$

† Because the surface effect has been ignored, the elastic scattering included in σ_a and the shadow scattering give the only elastic scattering in this approximation.

‡ See, for example, G. Joos, *Theoretical Physics* (Blackie, London, 1951), ch. 20.

§ J_0, J_1 are Bessel's ordinary functions of order zero and one. They are defined in E. Jahnke and F. Emde, *Funktionentafeln* (B. G. Teubner, Leipzig, 1933).

The differential cross-section $Q(\theta)\,d\Omega$ for scattering into the element of solid angle $d\Omega$ is†

$$Q(\theta)\,d\Omega = |f(\theta)|^2 d\Omega = d\Omega \frac{\sigma_{\text{sh}}}{4\pi}\{2J_1(kR\sin\theta)/\sin\theta\}^2. \tag{34}$$

$2J_1(kR\sin\theta)/\sin\theta$ is a typical diffraction pattern function which has its maximum value of (kR) at $\theta = 0$, and for increasing θ it oscillates with decreasing amplitude; the first zero of the diffraction pattern occurs for $\sin\theta = (3{\cdot}8)/(kR)$. The angular spread of the diffraction pattern can be estimated by remembering typical values of k^{-1}: (a) for a 60 MeV (kinetic energy) pion $k^{-1} \simeq 1{\cdot}4\times 10^{-13}$ cm; (b) for a 100 MeV neutron, $k^{-1} \simeq 5\times 10^{-14}$ cm. The slower the particle the larger is the angular spread of the pattern.

Typical values of the nuclear well constants k_1, K are as follows. For 100 MeV nucleons the mean free path in the nucleus is of the order of nuclear dimensions ($K^{-1} \simeq 4\times 10^{-13}$ cm); the real part of the well depth V is about 20 MeV, i.e. $k_1^{-1} \simeq 5\times 10^{-13}$ cm. For data at other energies the reader is referred to the literature.‡

For pions it is estimated that for an incident kinetic energy of 200 MeV, $K^{-1} = 1{\cdot}4\times 10^{-13}$ cm;§ for somewhat lower energies the mean free path is appreciably greater. The real part of the well depth V in the pion case has a more complicated energy dependence,§ but its absolute value is not large. (For details the reader is referred to the literature.§)

The estimation of k_1 and K in terms of nucleon-nucleon and pion-nucleon scattering is discussed in Chapter V, § 4.

7. The scattering amplitude and the refractive index

The formulae (30), (31), (33) illustrate the important general relation‖ (the 'optical theorem')

$$\text{im}\{f(0)\} = \frac{k}{4\pi}\sigma_{\text{tot}}, \tag{35}$$

where $\sigma_{\text{tot}} = \sigma_{\text{sh}}+\sigma_a$ is the total cross-section for the scattering (elastic and inelastic) and the absorption of pions. In the particular case above†† $\sigma_{\text{tot}} = 2\pi R^2\{1-e^{-\frac{1}{2}KT}\cos(k_1 T)\}$. Now we show how (35) can be proved

† This formula was derived for the scattering of high-energy neutrons by nuclei by S. Fernbach, R. Serber, and T. B. Taylor, *Phys. Rev.* **75** (1949) 1352.

‡ References are given in Chapters V, § 4, and VIII, § 4.

§ R. M. Frank, J. L. Gammel, and K. M. Watson, *Phys. Rev.* **101** (1956) 891; K. M. Watson, *Phys. Rev.* **89** (1953) 576.

‖ See N. Bohr, R. Peierls, and G. Placzek, *Nature*, **144** (1939) 200; E. Feenberg, *Phys. Rev.* **40** (1932) 40.

†† Using $J_1(x) \to \frac{1}{2}x$ as $x \to 0$ in (33).

for any scattering process.† Suppose for the moment that the spin (if any) of the scattered particle is ignored, and assume that the spatial distribution of the incident beam and the *elastically* scattered part is given by

$$\psi = e^{ikx_3} + \frac{e^{ikr}}{r} f(\theta) \tag{36}$$

where r is the distance from the scattering centre (this distance is assumed to be large compared with the dimensions of the scattering system and compared with k^{-1}). The form of the scattering amplitude $f(\theta)$ depends on the details of the scattering process. All terms in ψ have the same propagation number k; thus particles which have been scattered inelastically do not contribute to ψ.

Consider a large sphere S having radius r', with its centre at the scatterer. If ψ is used to calculate the net flux of particles entering S, the result gives the flux of particles being absorbed or scattered inelastically. This flux equals the flux of momentum across S divided by $\hbar k$. It is

$$N = -\frac{\pi(r')^2}{\hbar k} \int\limits_0^\pi \sin\theta \, d\theta \left\{ \psi^* \frac{\hbar}{i} \frac{\partial\psi}{\partial r} - \frac{\hbar}{i} \frac{\partial\psi^*}{\partial r} \psi \right\}$$

(θ is measured from the O_3 axis).

The incident beam term e^{ikx_3} by itself gives no contribution, but by interference with the scattered wave it does contribute. In fact

$$N = -2\pi \int\limits_0^\pi \sin\theta \, d\theta |f(\theta)|^2 -$$
$$-\pi r' \int\limits_0^\pi \sin\theta \, d\theta \{f(\theta)(1+\cos\theta)\exp[ikr'(1-\cos\theta)] + \text{comp. conj.}\}. \tag{37}$$

The first term on the right is (minus) the total elastic scattering cross-section σ_{sc}. By definition, $N+\sigma_{sc} = \sigma_{tot}$, where σ_{tot} is the total cross-section for elastic, inelastic, and absorption processes. For kr' large, the integrand in the second term on the right of (37) oscillates rapidly. The phase is stationary at $\theta = 0$, $\theta = \pi$, but due to the factor $(1+\cos\theta)$, the neighbourhood of $\theta = 0$ gives the predominant contribution. Integrating by parts and neglecting terms of relative order $(1/kr')$,

$$\sigma_{tot} = \frac{2\pi i}{k} \{f^*(0) - f(0)\}.$$

This is relation (35). If the particle which is scattered has spin or charge

† Coulomb scattering is ignored in order to avoid complications.

only the component of the scattered wave for *no change of spin or charge* can interfere with the incident beam. In this case, the *elastic* scattering amplitude $f(0)$ for no spin-flip appears on the right of (35).

The refractive index

The proof of (35) is of a general and fundamental character, and it shows the wide range of validity of the formula. We now discuss how (35) can be related to another set of physical ideas, namely the connexion between the (complex) refractive index n of a homogeneous medium and the forward scattering amplitude for the individual scatterers which make up the medium. The relation between the refractive index and the properties of the individual scatterer is important in studying the passage of electromagnetic radiation or slow neutrons through matter. It also suggests a similar connexion between the optical model for the passage of fast particles through a nucleus and the individual pion-nucleon or nucleon-nucleon collisions. A form of multiple scattering theory suitable for investigating these high-energy phenomena is discussed in Chapter V, § 4.

The derivation† which is now given is only suitable for the passage of radiation or particles through a medium which is neither strongly absorbing nor strongly refractive. Suppose the medium consists of identical scattering centres which are spread uniformly‡ so that there are N/unit volume. We assume this medium has a plane face $x_3 = 0$ and that it occupies the region $x_3 > 0$. A plane wave whose form outside the medium is $\exp[i(kx_3-\omega t)]$ gives rise to a *coherent* wave inside the medium which is approximately of the form $A\exp[i(k'x_3-\omega t)]$, where A and k' are constants. This expression gives the correct propagation of the main component of the coherent wave, but the true wave form differs from this in the neighbourhood of individual scatterers. The propagation constant k' in general has a positive imaginary part to allow for absorption and for scattering out of the beam. The refractive index of the medium n is defined by $k' = nk$.

We consider the propagation of a plane-wave $\exp(ikx_3)$ from left to right through a thin infinite slab of the medium lying between the planes $x_3 = 0$ and $x_3 = \delta h$ (Fig. 1). It is assumed that between scat-

† For light a dynamical derivation is given by M. Born, *Optik* (J. Springer, Berlin, 1933) 313. For slow neutrons see O. Halpern, M. Hamermesh, and M. H. Johnson, *Phys. Rev.* **59** (1941) 981, and E. Fermi, *Nuclear Physics* (University of Chicago Press, 1950) 201. A survey of multiple scattering theory is given by M. Lax, *Rev. Mod. Phys.* **23** (1951) 287.

‡ It is assumed that the scatterers are not arranged in a regular array. For crystal propagation see P. P. Ewald, *Ann. Physik*, **49** (1916) 4.

tering centres the waves travel with the same phase velocity as in free space. For each scattering centre the incident and the elastically scattered waves are related, as in eqn. (36), in the form

$$\psi = e^{ikx_3} + \frac{e^{ikr}}{r} f(\theta).$$

The scattering amplitude $f(\theta)$ must tend to a finite value $f(0)$ as $\theta \to 0$: Coulomb scattering is excluded.

The width of the slab δh must be chosen so that it is unnecessary to

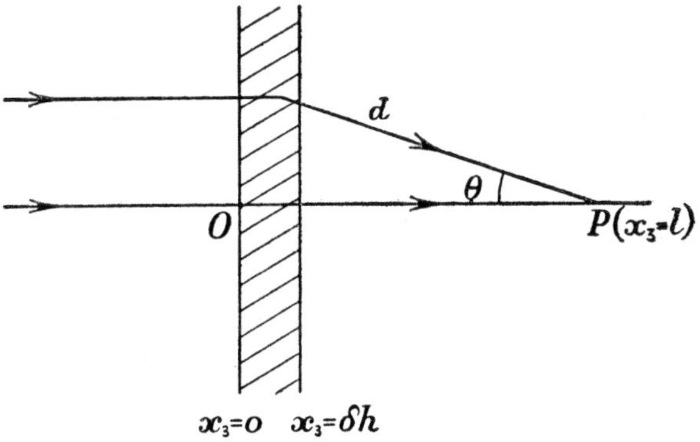

FIG. 1. Scattering of a plane wave in a thin slab of nuclear material.

consider double scattering within the slab; this will be seen to require that $2\pi N f(0)\delta h/k$ be small.† If this is satisfied, and if the influence of scatterers on their neighbours may be ignored, the wave incident on each scatterer is of the form $\exp(ikx_3)$. If also $k\delta h$ is small it is possible to assume that all the scatterers are situated on the plane $x_3 = 0$. This latter condition is not essential; it is introduced to simplify the calculation.‡

The total coherent amplitude reaching a point P at a distance l from the left face of the slab is readily found if kl is large. It is

$$e^{ikl}\left\{1 + \frac{2\pi i}{k} N\delta h f(0)\right\}. \tag{38}$$

The first term in (38) is the incident wave contribution; the second term

† By (35) this condition gives $\delta h \leqslant 2/N\sigma_{\text{tot}}$; i.e. δh should not be greater than the mean free path.

‡ In fact, only the forward scattering is important for the coherent wave, so this condition can be appreciably relaxed.

is the sum of the contributions from all scatterers in the slab. In the notation used in Fig. 1 this is

$$N\,\delta h \int\limits_{(x_3=0)} \frac{e^{ikd}}{d} f(\theta)\,d\theta = N\,\delta h \int\limits_0^\infty \frac{\exp[ik(l^2+r^2)^{\frac{1}{2}}]}{(l^2+r^2)^{\frac{1}{2}}} f(\theta) 2\pi r\,dr.$$

Using the stationary phase method, or integrating by parts and expanding in powers of $1/(kl)$, the result (38) follows. It should be noted that only in the forward direction do the scattered waves interfere constructively; large angle scattering does not give a contribution to the coherent wave.

The refractive index of the medium is found by comparing (38) with the propagation of a plane wave (having propagation vector k *in vacuo*) through a thin slab in which its propagation vector is k'. It is easy to see that if the incident wave is $\exp(ikx_3)$, the transmitted wave is†

$$\exp(ikx_3).\{1+i\delta h(k'^2-k^2)/2k\}.$$

Comparing with (38) gives‡

$$k'^2 = k^2+4\pi Nf(0). \tag{39 a}$$

The refractive index n is therefore related to the forward scattering amplitude by

$$n = 1+\frac{2\pi}{k^2}Nf(0). \tag{39 b}$$

Here we have used the fact that the derivation which has been given is only valid provided $|n-1| \ll 1$. For larger values of $Nf(0)/k^2$, a more accurate form of multiple scattering theory must be used.§

The attenuation coefficient $K = 2k\,\mathrm{im}(n)$ is related to the total cross-section σ_{tot} for the individual scatterers by $K = N\sigma_{\mathrm{tot}}$. This is because all absorbed and scattered particles are lost to the coherent beam.‖ Taking the imaginary part of (39 b) and substituting for K now gives eqn. (35). Of course, eqn. (35) is of much wider validity than eqn. (39 b); however, the latter equation is of interest in connexion with

† Because ψ obeys a second-order differential equation both ψ and grad ψ must be continuous across the interfaces. A straightforward calculation gives the transmission coefficient.

‡ An alternative treatment is to consider m thin slabs placed together. If the plane wave (38) is incident on the second slab, and so on, the phase change of the coherent wave in passing through a slab of thickness $d = m\delta h$ is

$$\left\{1+\frac{2\pi i}{k}N\,\delta h f(0)\right\}^m \simeq \exp\left\{\frac{2\pi i}{k}Nf(0)\,d\right\}.$$

This gives $k'-k = 2\pi Nf(0)/k$.

§ See, for example, M. Lax, *Rev. Mod. Phys.* **23** (1951) 287.

‖ The assumption that $f(\theta) \to f(0)$ as $\theta \to 0$, where $f(0)$ is finite, is implicit here.

dispersion relations for elementary particle collisions which are discussed in Chapter VI.

For nucleon-nucleus and pion-nucleus collisions eqn. (39 b) is replaced by expressions for the potential well depth which are derived from elementary particle interactions by an accurate form of multiple scattering theory (see Chapter V, § 4).

8. Example: The optical sphere

The optical disk model for the passage of high-energy particles through the nucleus which was given above can readily be replaced by an optical sphere model; this extension leads to an interesting comparison with the conventional partial wave analysis of scattering. Suppose the sphere, of radius R, has the propagation constants k_1, K, and assume again that these functions rise gradually to their interior values,† in order that surface scattering should not occur. Let the O_3 axis be a diameter of the sphere. The portion of the plane wave $\exp(ikx_3)$ which strikes the sphere at a distance ρ from the O_3 axis has to penetrate a depth of material $2s$, where $s = (R^2-\rho^2)^{\frac{1}{2}}$. Its amplitude factor on emerging is $a = \exp[(2ik_1-K)s]$; it is now easy to calculate the attenuation cross-section σ_a.‡ The scattering amplitude $f(\theta)$ which describes the shadow scattering§ is found by applying (33):

$$f(\theta) = ik\int\limits_0^R (1-e^{(2ik_1-K)s})J_0(k\rho\sin\theta)\rho\,d\rho. \tag{40}$$

This gives the same general form of the diffraction scattering pattern as eqn. (34).

We consider the case of kR large, i.e. the incident particles have large momentum. The diffraction pattern is now confined to small values of θ, and we use the approximation‖ that for small θ,

$$P_l(\cos\theta) = J_0[\{l(l+1)\}^{\frac{1}{2}}\theta]. \tag{41 a}$$

Writing $\{l(l+1)\}^{\frac{1}{2}} \sim l+\frac{1}{2}$, putting $k\rho = (l+\frac{1}{2})$, and replacing the integral in (40) by a summation over the intervals $\Delta\rho = (1/k)$ gives

$$f(\theta) = \frac{1}{2ik}\sum_{l=0}^{L}(2l+1)(e^{(2ik-K)S_l}-1)P_l(\cos\theta), \tag{41 b}$$

where $$S_l = \{k^2R^2-(l+\tfrac{1}{2})^2\}^{\frac{1}{2}}/k$$

and L is the greatest integer less than or equal to $(kR-\frac{1}{2})$.

† This rise is ignored in the following formulae. ‡ See p. 14, n. †.

§ Cf. H. A. Bethe and R. Wilson, *Phys. Rev.* **83** (1951) 690.

‖ Eqn. (41 a) results from comparing the respective differential equations for small θ.

Eqn. (41 b) has the same form as the usual partial wave analysis expression for the scattering amplitude of a spinless particle.† By this comparison the phase shift η_l for the partial wave of angular momentum l is

$$\eta_l = \begin{cases} (k_1+\tfrac{1}{2}iK)S_l & (l \leqslant L), \\ 0 & (l > L). \end{cases} \tag{41 c}$$

We can say that the partial wave of angular momentum l arises from values of the impact parameter ρ in the range $l/k < \rho < (l+1)/k$. The phase shift η_l is the change in phase, due to the nuclear matter, of that part of the wave having impact parameter $\rho = (l+\frac{1}{2})k$, as it passes from the diametral plane O_{12} to the surface. A direct calculation‡ for the complex potential well using the J.W.K.B. approximation method to solve Schrödinger's equation gives the same value of the phase shifts η_l as (41 c). This is an additional indication that the simple calculations which have been given in §§ 6 and 8 are reasonably accurate for high-energy incident particles.§

The exact solution of Schrödinger's equation for the optical model of nucleons passing through nuclei has been extensively used to discuss scattering and polarization phenomena.|| Details are given in Chapter VIII.

9. Angular momentum and spin

Under a rotation of the axes about the origin (such as given by (2) above) any scalar or pseudo-scalar function of position $\psi(\mathbf{x})$, such as the pion wave function, is transformed into a function $\psi'(\mathbf{x})$. If $R\mathbf{x}$ denotes the vector in the new coordinate system which is called $\mathbf{x}$ in the original system, then $\psi'(R\mathbf{x}) = \psi(\mathbf{x})$. Written in the equivalent form $\psi'(\mathbf{x}) = \psi(R^{-1}\mathbf{x})$, this relation is used to find the differential relation between the functions ψ and ψ' for a small rotation $\delta\theta$ of the axes about the O_3 direction. Using (2),

$$\begin{aligned} \psi'(x_1 x_2 x_3) &= \psi(x_1 - x_2\,\delta\theta,\, x_2 + x_1\,\delta\theta,\, x_3) \\ &= \{1 + I_3\,\delta\theta\}\psi(x_1, x_2, x_3), \end{aligned} \tag{42}$$

where $I_3 = x_1\partial_2 - x_2\partial_1$ is the third component of the 3-vector operator

† Cf. N. F. Mott and H. S. W. Massey, *Theory of Atomic Collisions* (Clarendon Press, 2nd edn., 1949), ch. 2.

‡ See p. 14, n. †; also S. Fernbach, W. Heckrotte, and J. V. Lepore, *Phys. Rev.* **97** (1955) 1059.

§ In the discussion in §§ 6 and 8 no allowance is made for the effect of a Coulomb interaction between the fast particle and the nucleus. This can alter the diffraction pattern by modifying the phase of the incident wave outside the nucleus (i.e. for $\rho > R$); the effect cannot be important at high energies.

|| The Schrödinger equation for the propagation of 60 MeV pions in carbon has been solved by H. Byfield, J. Kessler, and L. M. Lederman, *Phys. Rev.* **86** (1952) 17.

$\mathbf{I} = \mathbf{x} \times \text{grad}$. The other components of $\mathbf{I}$ are similarly *generators* for rotations about the other coordinate axes. They obey the commutation rules $\mathbf{I} \times \mathbf{I} = -\mathbf{I}$.

The angular momentum $\mathbf{L}$ in wave mechanics is given by

$$\mathbf{L} = \mathbf{x} \times \mathbf{p} = (\hbar/i)\mathbf{I},$$

where $\mathbf{p}$ is the momentum of the particle. This relation between $\mathbf{L}$ and $\mathbf{I}$ is of a fundamental character. If the Hamiltonian H is independent of the orientation of the coordinate axes, then $\psi'(\mathbf{x})$ must be an eigenstate of H provided $\psi(\mathbf{x})$ is an eigenstate; therefore the functions $\mathbf{I}\psi(\mathbf{x})$ are eigenstates of H. This means that the rotation generating operators $\mathbf{I}$ commute with H ($[\mathbf{I}, H] = 0$). The pion's angular momentum is described in this way. For particles which are described by wave functions having several components, the angular momentum $\mathbf{J}$ is again related to the rotation generator which we now write $\mathbf{I}''$. We have $\mathbf{J} = (\hbar/i)\mathbf{I}''$. Such particles are the Dirac electron, which at low velocities has two components, and the photon, which is described by the vector potential $\mathbf{A}$. The rotation of the axes, as well as altering the individual components of the wave function, will also cause a mixing of the components (this is particularly obvious for the vector potential $\mathbf{A}$). The change in the individual components is given by $\mathbf{I}$, as in the scalar case, and the mixing of components is given by a matrix $\mathbf{I}'$. For example, for a low energy electron $\mathbf{I}'$ is the 2×2 Pauli matrix $(\frac{1}{2}i\boldsymbol{\sigma})$. Then $\mathbf{I}'' = \mathbf{I} + \mathbf{I}'$ and

$$\mathbf{J} = (\hbar/i)\mathbf{I}'' = \mathbf{L} + \mathbf{S}, \tag{43}$$

where $\mathbf{L}$ is the orbital angular momentum ($\mathbf{L} = (\hbar/i)\mathbf{I}$) and $\mathbf{S}$ ($\mathbf{S} = (\hbar/i)\mathbf{I}'$) is the spin, or intrinsic angular momentum. A particle which is spread uniformly in space cannot have orbital angular momentum, but the $\mathbf{I}'$ term, and hence the spin, still occur. The invariance of the Hamiltonian for rotations of the axes implies the conservation of the total angular momentum $\mathbf{J}$. The pion, which has a single component wave function, has spin 0, the electron has spin $\frac{1}{2}$, and the photon has spin 1.† The details of the angular momentum analysis for the Dirac particle are given in Chapter III.

10. Spherical harmonics and vector addition

We give some notations and formulae which are used later. Using spherical polar coordinates‡ (r, θ, ϕ) and writing $\nabla^2_{(\theta,\phi)}$ for the terms in

† For a general discussion on the relation between angular momentum and representations of the rotation group see B. L. van der Waerden, *Gruppentheoretische Methode in Quantenmechanik* (Edwards, Ann Arbor, 1944).

‡ The O_3 axis is the axis of the spherical polar coordinates.

the Laplacian operator ∇^2 which do not contain $\partial/\partial r$, we have

$$\mathbf{l}^2 = r^2\nabla^2_{(\theta,\phi)}.$$

Therefore the orbital angular momentum eigenfunctions for a single particle, or the total angular momentum eigenfunctions for a spinless particle like the pion, are the spherical harmonics $Y_l(\theta,\phi)$; they obey

$$\left.\begin{aligned} L_3 Y_l^{(m)} &= m\hbar Y_l^{(m)} \qquad (m = l, l-1,..., -l) \\ \mathbf{L}^2 Y_l^{(m)} &= l(l+1)\hbar^2 Y_l^{(m)} \qquad (l = 0, 1, 2,...) \end{aligned}\right\}. \tag{44}$$

Explicit formulae are†

$$Y_l^{(m)}(\theta,\phi) = \frac{(-1)^{(m+l)}}{2^l.l!}\left[\frac{(2l+1)}{4\pi}\frac{(l-m)!}{(l+m)!}\right]^{\frac{1}{2}}(\sin\theta)^m\left(\frac{d}{d\cos\theta}\right)^{(l+m)}(\sin\theta)^{2l}e^{im\phi}. \tag{45}$$

A related function is

$$P_l^{|m|}(\mu) = \frac{1}{2^l.l!}(1-\mu^2)^{\frac{1}{2}|m|}\left(\frac{d}{d\mu}\right)^{l+|m|}(\mu^2-1)^l. \tag{46}$$

The spherical harmonics $Y_l^{(m)}$ form a normal orthogonal set on the unit sphere,

$$\int Y_l^{(m)*}(\theta,\phi)Y_{l'}^{(m')}(\theta,\phi)\,d\Omega = \delta_{ll'}\delta_{mm'}.$$

As defined above they obey

$$Y_l^{(m)*}(\theta,\phi) = (-1)^m Y_l^{(-m)}(\theta,\phi). \tag{47}$$

Particular cases are $\quad Y_0 = (4\pi)^{-\frac{1}{2}},$

$$\left.\begin{aligned} Y_1^{(1)} &= -\left(\frac{3}{8\pi}\right)^{\frac{1}{2}}\sin\theta\, e^{i\phi}, \qquad Y_1^{(0)} = \left(\frac{3}{4\pi}\right)^{\frac{1}{2}}\cos\theta, \\ Y_1^{(-1)} &= \left(\frac{3}{8\pi}\right)^{\frac{1}{2}}\sin\theta\, e^{-i\phi}, \end{aligned}\right\}$$

also

$$Y_l^{(0)}(\theta) = \left(\frac{2l+1}{4\pi}\right)^{\frac{1}{2}}P_l(\cos\theta). \tag{48}$$

Two particles with orbital angular momentum operators $\mathbf{L}^{(1)}$ and $\mathbf{L}^{(2)}$ have a total orbital angular momentum operator $\mathbf{L} = \mathbf{L}^{(1)}+\mathbf{L}^{(2)}$. The eigenstates of $\mathbf{L}$ are functions of the angles (θ_1,ϕ_1) and (θ_2,ϕ_2) of both particles; we write them $\mathscr{Y}_L^{(M)}(1,2)$ $(M = L, L-1,..., -L)$. Angular momenta $l_1\hbar$, $l_2\hbar$ of the individual particles can be combined by the quantum law of addition of angular momentum‡ to give total angular momentum $L\hbar$, where $L = l_1+l_2, l_1+l_2-1,..., |l_1-l_2|$. The eigenstates

† The phase of $Y_l^{(m)}$ in (45) agrees with E. U. Condon and G. H. Shortley, *Theory of Atomic Spectra* (Cambridge University Press, 1935), and with J. M. Blatt and V. F. Weisskopf, *Theoretical Nuclear Physics* (Wiley, New York, 1952). It does not agree with the definition by H. A. Bethe, *Handbuch der Physik* (Springer, Berlin, 1933), vol. xxiv/1.

‡ P. A. M. Dirac, *Quantum Mechanics* (Clarendon Press, 3rd edn., 1947), ch. 7.

$\mathscr{Y}_L^M(1,2)$ of $\mathbf{L}$ are expressed in terms of the products $Y_{l_1}^{(m_1)}(1)Y_{l_2}^{(m_2)}(2)$ of the eigenstates of $\mathbf{L}_1$ and $\mathbf{L}_2$ by a unitary transformation,

$$\mathscr{Y}_L^{(M)}(1,2) = \sum_{m_1,m_2} (l_1\, l_2\, m_1\, m_2 \mid LM) Y_{l_1}^{(m_1)}(1) Y_{l_2}^{(m_2)}(2). \tag{49}$$

The real constants $(l_1\, l_2\, m_1\, m_2 \mid LM)$, which vanish if $m_1+m_2 \neq M$, are the Clebsch–Gordan vector coupling coefficients.† Because of the unitary nature of the transformation, the eigenfunctions $\mathscr{Y}_L^{(M)}(1,2)$ form a normal orthogonal set,

$$\int \mathscr{Y}_L^{(M)*}(1,2)\mathscr{Y}_{L'}^{(M')}(1,2)\, d\Omega_1\, d\Omega_2 = \delta_{LL'}\delta_{MM'}.$$

Again by the unitary nature‡ of (49), the inverse transformation is

$$Y_{l_1}^{(m_1)}(1)Y_{l_2}^{(m_2)}(2) = \sum_{L=|l_1-l_2|}^{l_1+l_2} (l_1\, l_2\, m_1\, m_2 \mid L\,(m_1+m_2))\mathscr{Y}_L^{(m_1+m_2)}(1,2). \tag{50}$$

Values of the coefficients $(l_1\, 1\, m_1\, m_2 \mid LM)$ are given in Table 4 (Chapter VIII, § 8). As an example, the angular momentum eigenstates $\mathscr{Y}_L^{(M)}(1,2)$ of two particles each of which is in a p-state ($l_1 = 1$, $l_2 = 1$) are

$L = 2$:

$$M = 2,\quad Y_1^{(1)}(1)Y_1^{(1)}(2);$$

$$M = 1,\quad \frac{1}{\sqrt{2}}\{Y_1^{(1)}(1)Y_1^{(0)}(2)+Y_1^{(0)}(1)Y_1^{(1)}(2)\};$$

$$M = 0,\quad \frac{1}{\sqrt{6}}\{Y_1^{(1)}(1)Y_1^{(-1)}(2)+Y_1^{(-1)}(1)Y_1^{(1)}(2)+2Y_1^{(0)}(1)Y_1^{(0)}(2)\};$$

$$M = -1,\quad \frac{1}{\sqrt{2}}\{Y_1^{(0)}(1)Y_1^{(-1)}(2)+Y_1^{(-1)}(1)Y_1^{(0)}(2)\};$$

$$M = -2,\quad Y_1^{(-1)}(1)Y_1^{(-1)}(2).$$

$L = 1$:

$$M = 1,\quad \frac{1}{\sqrt{2}}\{Y_1^{(1)}(1)Y_1^{(0)}(2)-Y_1^{(0)}(1)Y_1^{(1)}(2)\};$$

$$M = 0,\quad \frac{1}{\sqrt{2}}\{Y_1^{(1)}(1)Y_1^{(-1)}(2)-Y_1^{(-1)}(1)Y_1^{(1)}(2)\};$$

$$M = -1,\quad \frac{1}{\sqrt{2}}\{Y_1^{(0)}(1)Y_1^{(-1)}(2)-Y_1^{(-1)}(1)Y_1^{(0)}(2)\}.$$

$L = 0$:

$$M = 0,\quad \frac{1}{\sqrt{3}}\{Y_1^{(1)}(1)Y_1^{(-1)}(2)+Y_1^{(-1)}(1)Y_1^{(1)}(2)-Y_1^{(0)}(1)Y_1^{(0)}(2)\}. \tag{51}$$

† Cf. E. U. Condon and G. H. Shortley, p. 22, n. †.

‡ For fixed M, M', $\sum_{m_1,m_2} (l_1\, l_2\, m_1\, m_2 \mid LM)(l_1\, l_2\, m_1\, m_2 \mid L'M') = \delta_{LL'}\delta_{MM'}$.

There are $5+3+1 = 9$ independent terms here corresponding to the $3\times 3 = 9$ independent functions $Y_1^{(m_1)}(1)Y_1^{(m_2)}(2)$. The last function ($L = 0, M = 0$) equals $-(\sqrt{3}/4\pi)\cos(\omega_{12})$, where ω_{12} is the angle between the directions (θ_1, ϕ_1) and (θ_2, ϕ_2). Under any rotation or inversion of the axes $\cos(\omega_{12})$ is invariant.

The spherical harmonics $Y_l^{(m)}(\theta, \phi)$ have parity, or inversion character, $(-1)^l$, so the functions $\mathscr{Y}_L^{(M)}(1,2)$ have parity $(-1)^{(l_1+l_2)}$.

Eigenstates of total angular momentum $\mathscr{Y}_L^{(M)}(1,2)$ can be formed by coupling other individual angular momenta values l_1', l_2' with the coefficients $(l_1' l_2' m_1' m_2' \mid LM)$ provided $|l_1'-l_2'| \leqslant L \leqslant l_1'+l_2'$. Such functions are orthogonal to the functions $\mathscr{Y}_L^{(M)}(1,2)$ of (49) when integrated over the angles of both particles, provided $l_1' \neq l_1$, or $l_2' \neq l_2$.

The vector coupling (49) can be used to combine spin eigenstates with orbital angular momentum. In the same way spin state vectors can be coupled together. The coupling is independent of whether the $Y_l^{(m)}$ are replaced by spin-state vectors, because it is the transformation of the $Y_l^{(m)}$, or the spin vectors, under a rotation of the axes which determines the Clebsch–Gordan coefficients.† To include all spin vectors, it is necessary to include angular momentum values $J = \frac{1}{2}, \frac{3}{2},\ldots$. The simplest spin-state vectors are the pair $s_{\frac{1}{2}}$, $s_{-\frac{1}{2}}$ for the spinning electron. In the state $s_{\pm\frac{1}{2}}$ the electron spin is $\pm\frac{1}{2}\hbar$ along the O_3 axis. The spin and the orbital angular momentum l are combined to give eigenstates of the total angular momentum $W_{lj}^{(m)}$, where $j = l+\frac{1}{2}$, or $|l-\frac{1}{2}|$ and $m = j, j-1,\ldots, -j$:

$$W_{lj}^{(m)} = \sum_{m'=-l}^{l} \sum_{m''=-\frac{1}{2}}^{\frac{1}{2}} (l\tfrac{1}{2}m'm'' \mid jm)Y_l^{(m')}(\theta,\phi)s_{m''}. \tag{52}$$

The values of the coefficients $(l\frac{1}{2}m'm'' \mid jm)$ are given in Table 2, p. 131. $s_{m''}$ is a two-component vector, so $W_{lj}^{(m)}$ is a two-component vector. The transformation (52) is unitary, and the eigenstates $W_{lj}^{(m)}$ obey the relation

$$\int \tilde{W}_{lj}^{(m)}.\, W_{l'j'}^{(m')}\, d\Omega = \delta_{ll'}\delta_{jj'}\delta_{mm'}.$$

Here $\tilde{W}$ is the Hermitian transpose of W, and $\tilde{W}.W$ denotes the scalar product of the two-component vectors.

11. Example: Addition of isotopic spins

Under rotations in isotopic (or charge) space the state vectors $|\pi^+, \mathbf{p}\rangle$, $|\pi^0, \mathbf{p}\rangle$, $|\pi^-, \mathbf{p}\rangle$ for positive, neutral, and negative pions of momentum $\mathbf{p}$ transform in the same way as $Y_1^{(1)}$, $Y_1^{(0)}$, $Y_1^{(-1)}$ (cf. Chapter

† The coefficients only depend on the representation of the rotation group.

II, § 8). The eigenvalue T_3 of the related generating operator $(-i)I_3$ is the charge of the state. State vectors for two pions can therefore have total isotopic spin $T = 2$, 1, or 0; the form of these state vectors can be written down using (51). If $|\pi^+(1)\pi^0(2)\rangle$ is the state vector indicating that the first pion is positive and the second is neutral, the $T = 0$ state vector is

$$\frac{1}{\sqrt{3}}|\pi^+(1)\pi^-(2)+\pi^-(1)\pi^+(2)-\pi^0(1)\pi^0(2)\rangle. \tag{53}$$

The $T = 1$ state vectors are

$$T_3 = 1, \quad \frac{1}{\sqrt{2}}|\pi^+(1)\pi^0(2)-\pi^0(1)\pi^+(2)\rangle;$$

$$T_3 = 0, \quad \frac{1}{\sqrt{2}}|\pi^+(1)\pi^-(2)-\pi^-(1)\pi^+(2)\rangle;$$

$$T_3 = -1, \frac{1}{\sqrt{2}}|\pi^0(1)\pi^-(2)-\pi^-(1)\pi^0(2)\rangle. \tag{54}$$

The eigenvalue of T_3 is the total charge. It follows from (53), (54), and the corresponding formula for the case $T = 2$, that in a two-pion state of zero charge ($T_3 = 0$) the pair (π^0, π^0) occur in one-third of all observations in the state $T = 0$, in two-thirds of all events in state $T = 2$, and never in the state $T = 1$. In this way the charge distribution in a two-pion state can give information about charge-independent reactions.†

The states $T = 0$ and $T = 2$ are symmetric with respect to exchange of the two pions; the $T = 1$ states are anti-symmetric. It follows, because pions are bosons, that the remaining factors in the two-pion state vectors have definite exchange character. For example, if the two pions are in an eigenstate of relative angular momentum L (i.e. angular momentum L about their centre of mass), for $T = 0$, 2, only even L is allowed, while for $T = 1$ only odd L is allowed.

The state vectors $|P, \mathbf{p}, s\rangle$, $|N, \mathbf{p}, s\rangle$, for a proton and a neutron of momentum $\mathbf{p}$ and spin s transform, under rotations of isotopic space, like spin-$\frac{1}{2}$ state vectors.‡ Two nucleons, therefore, can form an isotopic spin triplet ($T = 1$) having state vectors,§

$$T_3 = 1, \quad |P(1)P(2)\rangle; \qquad T_3 = 0, \quad \frac{1}{\sqrt{2}}|P(1)N(2)+N(1)P(2)\rangle;$$

$$T_3 = -1, \quad |N(1)N(2)\rangle;$$

† Charge-independent reactions conserve the total isotopic spin.

‡ We do not discuss anti-nucleons at present.

§ For nucleons the charge is $\frac{1}{2}(T_3+N)$, where N is the excess of the number of nucleons over anti-nucleons (cf. Chapter IV, § 6).

and a singlet ($T = 0$),

$$\frac{1}{\sqrt{2}}\,|\,P(1)N(2)-N(1)P(2)\rangle.$$

A pion and a nucleon give rise to states of total isotopic spin $T = \frac{3}{2}$ and $T = \frac{1}{2}$. The form of these eigenstates is shown in eqn. (74) of Chapter VI.

12. Example: The product of spherical harmonics

In calculating differential cross-sections it is often necessary to evaluate the product of two spherical harmonics arising from the interference of two partial waves.† Putting $1 = 2$ in eqn. (50) gives the functions $\mathscr{Y}_L^{(M)}(1,1)$. For fixed L, these $(2L+1)$ functions must transform into each other under a rotation of the axes in exactly the same way as the spherical harmonics $Y_L^{(M)}(1)$ (for example, a rotation through ϕ about O_3 multiplies both by $e^{iM\phi}$).

It follows that $$\mathscr{Y}_L^{(M)}(1,1) = \alpha_L . Y_L^{(M)}(1). \tag{55}$$

The constant α_L cannot depend on M if the relation (55) is to be independent of the axes. Putting $\theta_1 = 0$ and using (cf. (48))

$$Y_l^{(0)}(\theta = 0) = \left(\frac{2l+1}{4\pi}\right)^{\frac{1}{2}},$$

the constant α_L is determined. This gives

$$Y_{l_1}^{(m_1)}(1)Y_{l_2}^{(m_2)}(1) = \sum_{L=|l_1-l_2|}^{(l_1+l_2)} \left\{\frac{(2l_1+1)(2l_2+1)}{4\pi(2L+1)}\right\}^{\frac{1}{2}} \times$$
$$\times (l_1\, l_2\, 00\,|\,L0)(l_1\, l_2\, m_1\, m_2\,|\,LM)Y_L^{(M)}(1) \quad (M = m_1+m_2). \tag{56}$$

It follows from the parity that only terms having even (l_1+l_2-L) can occur.‡

In evaluating the differential cross-section $|f(\theta)|^2\,d\Omega$ for an elastic scattering problem without spin, where $f(\theta)$ is of the usual form (with *real* phase shifts η_l)

$$f(\theta) = \frac{1}{2ik}\sum_{l=0}^{\infty}(2l+1)(e^{2i\eta_l}-1)P_l(\cos\theta),$$

use of (48) and (56) gives§

$$|f(\theta)|^2 = \frac{1}{k^2}\sum_{l=0}^{\infty}(2l+1)\sin^2\eta_l + \frac{1}{k^2}\sum_{L=1}^{\infty}B_L P_L(\cos\theta), \tag{57}$$

† Remembering that by (47), $Y_l^{(m)*} = Y_l^{(-m)}.(-1)^m$.

‡ For l_1+l_2+L odd, $(l_1\, l_2\, 00\,|\,L0)$ vanishes. Cf. eqn. (60).

§ Cf. J. M. Blatt and L. C. Biedenharn, *Rev. Mod. Phys.* **24** (1952) 258.

where

$$B_L = 2\sum_{l=1}^{\infty}\sum_{l'<l}(2l+1)(2l'+1)\{(ll'00\mid L0)\}^2\sin\eta_l\sin\eta_{l'}\cos(\eta_l-\eta_{l'}).$$

The first term is the total cross-section divided by 4π.

13. Clebsch-Gordan and Racah coefficients

We give some relations which are frequently of use when manipulating angular momenta. Using the explicit form† of the Clebsch–Gordan coefficients, Racah‡ deduced the following simple relations:

$$(ll'mm'\mid LM) = (l'l,-m',-m\mid L,-M) = (-1)^{(l+l'-L)}(l'lm'm\mid LM) \tag{58}$$

and

$$\frac{1}{\sqrt{(2L+1)}}(ll'mm'\mid LM) = (-1)^{(l-m)}\frac{1}{\sqrt{(2l'+1)}}(lL\,m,-M\mid l',-m')$$
$$= (-1)^{(l'+m')}\frac{1}{\sqrt{(2l+1)}}(L\,l',-M\,m'\mid l,-m). \tag{59}$$

These formulae and the others in this section hold for half-integral as well as integral values of l, l', L.

The coefficient $(ll'00\mid L0)$ is zero if $(l+l'+L)$ is odd; if $(l+l'+L)$ is even,‡

$$\left.\begin{aligned}&(ll'00\mid L0) = (-1)^{(g+L)}\sqrt{(2L+1)}\,.\,\Delta(l\,l'\,L)\frac{g!}{(g-l)!\,(g-l')!\,(g-L)!}\\ &\text{where } 2g = l+l'+L, \text{ and}\\ &\qquad\Delta(l\,l'L) = \left\{\frac{(l+l'-L)!\,(l'+L-l)!\,(L+l-l')!}{(l+l'+L+1)!}\right\}^{\frac{1}{2}}\end{aligned}\right\} \tag{60}$$

(here $0! \equiv 1$ and $(-n)! \equiv 0$ for $n > 0$).

Vector addition of three angular momenta can be carried out by using formula (49) twice. Eigenstates of angular momentum j_1 and j_2 are combined to give eigenstates of angular momentum J_a. The latter eigenstates are then combined with eigenstates of angular momentum j_3 to give eigenstates of angular momentum J. The resulting state vector is a function of three variables (directions or spin coordinates). It may be written

$$|((j_1,j_2)J_a,j_3)JM\rangle. \tag{61}$$

The notation $(A,B)\,C$ means that A and B are added (by (49)) to give C. M is the O_3 component of the total angular momentum.§ State

† E. P. Wigner, *Gruppentheorie* (F. Vieweg, Braunschweig, 1931).

‡ G. Racah, *Phys. Rev.* **62** (1942) 438.

§ The order of the symbols is significant: by (58), exchanging j_1 and j_2 in (61) changes the sign by $(-1)^{j_1+j_2-J_a}$.

vector (61) is orthogonal to the state vectors obtained by altering one or more of j_1, j_2, J_a, j_3, J, M. For fixed j_1, j_2, j_3 the state vectors (61) form a complete set of $(2j_1+1)(2j_2+1)(2j_3+1)$ independent functions.†

It is possible to couple the individual angular momenta in another way, first adding j_2 and j_3 to give J_b and then adding j_1 to J_b. The result may be written

$$|(j_1,(j_2,j_3)J_b)JM\rangle. \tag{62}$$

The range of values J is the same as for (61). State vector (62) must be a linear combination of state vectors (61), and, because both (61) and (62) have the same transformation properties under rotation, the coefficients of the linear relation are independent of the magnetic quantum number M. The relation is written

$$|(j_1,(j_2,j_3)J_b)JM\rangle = \sum_{J_a} |((j_1,j_2)J_a,j_3)JM\rangle(2J_a+1)^{\frac{1}{2}}(2J_b+1)^{\frac{1}{2}}W(j_1j_2\,Jj_3;\,J_aJ_b). \tag{63}$$

The constants W are Racah's coefficients;‡ they have been studied and tabulated by Biedenharn and others.§ The coefficients on the right of (63) connect two orthonormal sets of eigenstates. Because W is real (as follows from (64) below) the unitary property gives

$$\sum_{J_a}(2J_a+1)(2J_b+1)W(j_1j_2\,Jj_3;\,J_aJ_b)W(j_1j_2\,Jj_3;\,J_aJ'_b) = \delta_{J_bJ'_b}.$$

(Here, as in (63), J_a is summed over all possible values.)

Finally, we notice that on using the vector addition law and equating coefficients of the basic eigenstates of j_1, j_2, j_3, eqn. (63) gives

$$(j_2j_3\,m_2m_3\,|\,J_b\,m_2+m_3)(j_1\,J_b\,m_1\,m_2+m_3\,|\,JM) = \sum_{J_a}(j_1j_2\,m_1m_2\,|\,J_a\,m_1+m_2)(J_aj_3\,m_1+m_2,m_3\,|\,JM)\times$$
$$\times(2J_a+1)^{\frac{1}{2}}(2J_b+1)^{\frac{1}{2}}W(j_1j_2\,Jj_3;\,J_aJ_b). \tag{64}$$

Multiplying (64) by $(j_1j_2\,m_1m_2\,|\,J'_a\,m_1+m_2)$ and summing over m_1 and m_2 (while keeping M and m fixed), the unitary property of the coupling coefficients‖ gives

$$\sum_{m_1,m_2}(j_2j_3\,m_2m_3\,|\,J_b\,m_2+m_3)(j_1\,J_b\,m_1\,m_2+m_3\,|\,JM)(j_1j_2\,m_1m_2\,|\,J'_a\,M-m_3)$$
$$= (2J'_a+1)^{\frac{1}{2}}(2J_b+1)^{\frac{1}{2}}(J'_aj_3\,M-m_3,m_3\,|\,JM)W(j_1j_2\,Jj_3;\,J'_aJ_b). \tag{65}$$

Using (65) (and (64)) it is frequently possible to evaluate the compli-

† For each value of J_a there are $(2J_a+1)(2j_3+1)$ state vectors. Also
$$\sum(2J_a+1) = (2j_1+1)(2j_2+1).$$

‡ G. Racah, *Phys. Rev.* **62** (1942) 438, and **63** (1943) 367.

§ L. C. Biedenharn, *J. Math. Phys.* (M.I.T.), **31** (1952) 286; see also L. C. Biedenharn, J. M. Blatt, and M. E. Rose, *Rev. Mod. Phys.* **24** (1952) 249, and M. E. Rose, *Multipole Fields* (Wiley, New York, 1955).

‖ This unitary relation (which was used in deriving (50)) follows from the unitary character of the transformation (49), or its extension to half-integral indices (p. 23, n. ‡).

cated sums† over magnetic quantum numbers which occur in evaluating differential cross-sections‡ for the collision of spinning particles, and in angular correlation and similar problems.

14. Angular momentum of radiation

Most of the angular momentum properties of electromagnetic radiation can be adequately discussed in terms of the classical theory, provided we use the exponential notation for the time dependence. In this notation, the vector potential $\mathbf{A}(\mathbf{x},t)$ is written

$$\mathbf{A}(\mathbf{x},t) = \mathbf{A}(\mathbf{x},\omega)e^{-i\omega t}+\mathbf{A}^*(\mathbf{x},\omega)e^{i\omega t}. \tag{66}$$

On going over to quantum theory (cf. Chapter II) this form appears naturally; the exponential $e^{-i\omega t}$ then indicates that the operator $\mathbf{A}(\mathbf{x},\omega)$ is associated with a transition between states whose energies differ by $\hbar\omega$. In the present chapter we develop the theory as though the variables in (66) were classical quantities; the results can be taken over to quantum radiation theory almost directly.

It is convenient to describe the electromagnetic field in free space in terms of the solenoidal gauge vector potential $\mathbf{A}(\mathbf{x},t)$; then

$$\mathbf{H} = \operatorname{curl}\mathbf{A}(\mathbf{x},t), \qquad \mathbf{E} = -\frac{1}{c}\frac{\partial}{\partial t}\mathbf{A}(\mathbf{x},t), \tag{67}$$

where $\operatorname{div}\mathbf{A} = 0$. The transformation of the electric and magnetic fields under a rotation of the axes is therefore obtained by studying the transformation properties of $\mathbf{A}(\mathbf{x},t)$. Under a rotation of the axes the coordinate vector $\mathbf{x}$ becomes $\mathbf{x}' = R\mathbf{x}$, and the vector field $\mathbf{A}(\mathbf{x})$ is replaced§ by the field $\mathbf{A}'(\mathbf{x})$, where

$$\mathbf{A}'(\mathbf{x}') = \mathbf{A}'(R\mathbf{x}) = R\mathbf{A}(\mathbf{x}).$$

It is more convenient to write this in the form

$$\mathbf{A}'(\mathbf{x}) = R\mathbf{A}(R^{-1}\mathbf{x}). \tag{68}$$

The first factor R in (68) rotates the vector $\mathbf{A}$, the second R allows for the change in the position. An infinitesimal rotation $\delta\theta$ about the O_3 axis gives

$$\left.\begin{aligned}
A_1'(x_1,x_2,x_3) &= A_1(x_1-x_2\,\delta\theta, x_2+x_1\,\delta\theta, x_3)+\\
&\qquad +\delta\theta A_2(x_1-x_2\,\delta\theta, x_2+x_1\,\delta\theta, x_3)\\
A_2'(x_1,x_2,x_3) &= -\delta\theta A_1(x_1-x_2\,\delta\theta, x_2+x_1\,\delta\theta, x_3)+\\
&\qquad +A_2(x_1-x_2\,\delta\theta, x_2+x_1\,\delta\theta, x_3)\\
A_3'(x_1,x_2,x_3) &= A_3(x_1-x_2\,\delta\theta, x_2+x_1\,\delta\theta, x_3)
\end{aligned}\right\}.$$

† Details are given by J. M. Blatt and L. C. Biedenharn, *Rev. Mod. Phys.* **24** (1952) 258.

‡ An example occurs in Chapter VIII, § 8.

§ Since rotations in space are being discussed, it is not necessary to specify whether $\mathbf{A}(\mathbf{x},t)$ or $\mathbf{A}(\mathbf{x},\omega)$ is being used; hence we write $\mathbf{A}(\mathbf{x})$.

Therefore $$\mathbf{A}'(x_1,x_2,x_3) = \{1+(I_3+I_3')\,\delta\theta\}\mathbf{A}(x_1,x_2,x_3), \tag{69}$$

where I_3 is the same operator as occurred in (42), and I_3' is a 3×3 matrix. As discussed in connexion with eqn. (43), the total angular momentum is $\mathbf{J} = \mathbf{L}+\mathbf{S}$, where $\mathbf{L}$ is the orbital angular momentum operator, and the spin, $\mathbf{S} = (\hbar/i)\mathbf{I}'$, is given by

$$S_1 = \frac{\hbar}{i}\begin{pmatrix} 0 & 0 & 0 \\ 0 & 0 & 1 \\ 0 & -1 & 0 \end{pmatrix}, \quad S_2 = \frac{\hbar}{i}\begin{pmatrix} 0 & 0 & -1 \\ 0 & 0 & 0 \\ 1 & 0 & 0 \end{pmatrix}, \quad S_3 = \frac{\hbar}{i}\begin{pmatrix} 0 & 1 & 0 \\ -1 & 0 & 0 \\ 0 & 0 & 0 \end{pmatrix}. \tag{70}$$

These spin operators obey the commutation rules†

$$\mathbf{S}\times\mathbf{S} = i\hbar\mathbf{S}. \tag{71}$$

Also it is easy to see that

$$\mathbf{S}^2 = \sum_{i=1}^{3} S_i^2 = 2\hbar^2, \tag{72}$$

These spin operators $\mathbf{S}$ therefore obey the usual commutation rules for angular momenta ($\mathbf{J}\times\mathbf{J} = i\hbar\mathbf{J}$), and comparing (72) with (44) it is seen that $\mathbf{S}$ is associated with unit angular momentum. Because $\mathbf{S}$ (which has constant coefficients) commutes with the differentiation operator, it follows from (67) that the spin properties of the electromagnetic field are given by the spin properties of the vector potential $\mathbf{A}$.

One component of the spin $\mathbf{S}$ can have eigenvalues $+\hbar$, 0, $-\hbar$; but it is obvious from (70) that a change of representation is required to make a component of $\mathbf{S}$ diagonal. We now set up eigenstates of the spin. Suppose a plane electromagnetic wave has a propagation vector $\mathbf{k} = |\mathbf{k}|\mathbf{e}_0$. There are two independent plane polarized waves whose vector potentials $\mathbf{A}$ are (apart from a constant factor)‡

$$\left.\begin{aligned} \mathbf{A}(\mathbf{x},t) &= \mathbf{e}_1\exp[i(k(\mathbf{e}_0.\mathbf{x})-\omega t)] \\ \mathbf{A}(\mathbf{x},t) &= \mathbf{e}_2\exp[i(k(\mathbf{e}_0.\mathbf{x})-\omega t)] \end{aligned}\right\}. \tag{73}$$

Here it is assumed that $\mathbf{e}_0$, $\mathbf{e}_1$, $\mathbf{e}_2$ form a right-handed orthogonal triad of unit vectors. For circularly polarized waves the polarization vectors $\mathbf{e}_1$, $\mathbf{e}_2$ in (73) are replaced by $\mathbf{e}_{+1}$ and $\mathbf{e}_{-1}$, where§

$$\mathbf{e}_{+1} = -\frac{1}{\sqrt{2}}(\mathbf{e}_1+i\mathbf{e}_2), \qquad \mathbf{e}_{-1} = \frac{1}{\sqrt{2}}(\mathbf{e}_1-i\mathbf{e}_2). \tag{74}$$

† This is a necessary consequence of their being rotation generators. Cf. B. L. van der Waerden, p. 21, n. †.

‡ Here the complex form of $\mathbf{A}(\mathbf{x}, t)$ appropriate to quantum theory is being used. The classical theory expression is just the real part of (73); taking the real part does not alter the argument.

§ The particular choice of signs used in (74) is related to $Y_1^{(\pm 1)}$ (eqn. 48).

These are complex unit vectors, obeying $\mathbf{e}^*_{+1}.\mathbf{e}_{+1} = \mathbf{e}^*_{-1}.\mathbf{e}_{-1} = 1$, $\mathbf{e}^*_{+1}.\mathbf{e}_{-1} = 0$. The waves

$$\mathbf{A}_{(+)} = \mathbf{e}_{+1}\exp[i(k(\mathbf{e}_0.\mathbf{x})-\omega t)] \quad \text{and} \quad \mathbf{A}_{(-)} = \mathbf{e}_{-1}\exp[i(k(\mathbf{e}_0.\mathbf{x})-\omega t)]$$

are right-handed and left-handed circularly polarized waves, respectively. Choosing the axes O_1, O_2, O_3 to be along $\mathbf{e}_1$, $\mathbf{e}_2$, $\mathbf{e}_0$ respectively, the spin operators $\mathbf{S}$ have the form (70); for example, in dyadic notation

$$S_3 = \left(\frac{\hbar}{i}\right)(\mathbf{e}_1\mathbf{e}_2-\mathbf{e}_2\mathbf{e}_1).$$

Changing over to the circular polarization representation, $\mathbf{e}_1$ and $\mathbf{e}_2$ must be replaced by $\mathbf{e}_{+1}$, $\mathbf{e}_{-1}$; thus

$$S_3 = \hbar(\mathbf{e}_{+1}\mathbf{e}^*_{+1}-\mathbf{e}_{-1}\mathbf{e}^*_{-1}). \tag{75}$$

(The operator S_3 has to be written in Hermitian form, hence the complex conjugate unit vectors appearing in (75).) It follows that the vector potentials $\mathbf{A}_{(+)}$, $\mathbf{A}_{(-)}$ for the circularly polarized waves are eigenstates of S_3:

$$S_3\mathbf{A}_{(+)} = \hbar\mathbf{A}_{(+)}, \qquad S_3\mathbf{A}_{(-)} = -\hbar\mathbf{A}_{(-)}; \tag{76}$$

hence these plane waves have angular momentum components $\hbar$ and $-\hbar$ respectively, about the direction of propagation. The coefficient of $\mathbf{e}_0\mathbf{e}_0^*$ in (75) is zero; therefore a plane wave having longitudinal polarization $\mathbf{e}_0$ would have zero eigenvalue of S_3. The solenoidal condition ($\operatorname{div}\mathbf{A} = 0$) does not permit a longitudinal plane wave in free space.

In addition to their spin, the circularly polarized plane waves have orbital angular momentum. Because the wave is plane, the component of orbital angular momentum about the direction of propagation $\mathbf{k}$ is zero.† This does not mean that the wave is an eigenstate of the orbital angular momentum operator $\mathbf{L}^2$; it is a superposition of eigenstates each of which has zero component of $\mathbf{L}$ along $\mathbf{k}$. This is seen on expanding the plane wave e^{ikx_3} in spherical polar coordinates (r,θ,ϕ) about the O_3 axis:‡

$$e^{ikx_3} = e^{ikr\cos\theta} = \sum_{l=0}^{\infty} i^l\{4\pi(2l+1)\}^{\frac{1}{2}}j_l(kr)Y_l^{(0)}(\theta), \tag{77}$$

where the spherical Bessel functions $j_l(kr)$ are related to the ordinary Bessel functions by

$$j_l(kr) = \left(\frac{\pi}{2kr}\right)^{\frac{1}{2}}J_{l+\frac{1}{2}}(kr). \tag{78}$$

For each value of l there is a partial wave having orbital angular

† This is because the motion in a plane wave is everywhere parallel to $\mathbf{k}$.

‡ Lord Rayleigh, *Theory of Sound* (Macmillan, London, 2nd edn., 1896), vol. ii, p. 273.

momentum l and zero component along the axis. The way in which the spin and the orbital angular momentum of electromagnetic radiation combine to give eigenstates of the total angular momentum will be discussed in the next section.

15. Electromagnetic multipoles

Suppose a source of electromagnetic radiation is placed at the origin of the coordinate system. The radiation emitted will have some angular distribution; for example, it may be the well-known electric dipole distribution. Under a rotation of the coordinate axes the electromagnetic field will change in two ways; the vector potential $\mathbf{A}(\mathbf{x},t)$ will be measured at a new point and the vector itself will be rotated. To find the eigenstates of the vector field $\mathbf{A}$ under rotations of the coordinate system about the origin, it is necessary to place an orthogonal triad of unit vectors $\mathbf{e}_1$, $\mathbf{e}_2$, $\mathbf{e}_3$ at the origin. These vectors are imagined to be fixed relative to the field, so that under a rotation of the coordinate axes they behave as if they were rigidly attached to the source of the radiation.

If the coordinate axes are rotated through an infinitesimal angle $\delta\theta$ about O_3, the new values $\mathbf{e}_1'$, $\mathbf{e}_2'$, $\mathbf{e}_3'$ of the triad of vectors are

$$\left.\begin{aligned} \mathbf{e}_1' &= \mathbf{e}_1 - \delta\theta\, \mathbf{e}_2 \\ \mathbf{e}_2' &= \mathbf{e}_2 + \delta\theta\, \mathbf{e}_1 \\ \mathbf{e}_3' &= \mathbf{e}_3 \end{aligned}\right\}. \tag{79}$$

Therefore the vectors $\mathbf{e}_1$, $\mathbf{e}_2$, $\mathbf{e}_3$ transform under rotations in the same way as the components x_1, x_2, x_3 of the position vector $\mathbf{x}$. Now comparing with (48) it follows that the vectors

$$\mathbf{e}_{+1} = -\frac{1}{\sqrt{2}}(\mathbf{e}_1 + i\mathbf{e}_2), \qquad \mathbf{e}_0 = \mathbf{e}_3, \qquad \mathbf{e}_{-1} = \frac{1}{\sqrt{2}}(\mathbf{e}_1 - i\mathbf{e}_2) \tag{80}$$

are eigenstates of unit angular momentum† having components of angular momentum $\hbar$, 0, $-\hbar$, respectively, along the direction $\mathbf{e}_0$. The vectors (80) may be compared with Pauli's binary vectors $s_{\frac{1}{2}} = \begin{pmatrix}1\\0\end{pmatrix}$, $s_{-\frac{1}{2}} = \begin{pmatrix}0\\1\end{pmatrix}$ which are eigenstates with angular momentum components $+\frac{1}{2}\hbar$, $-\frac{1}{2}\hbar$, respectively. Circularly polarized plane waves discussed above provide an example of the use of the spin eigenvectors (80).

† The angular momentum is always $(\hbar/i)$ times the rotation generating operator.

The vector set

Vector fields $\mathbf{A}(\mathbf{x})$ which are eigenstates of the total angular momentum $\mathbf{J}$ are formed by combining the spin vectors (80) and spherical harmonics $Y_l^{(m)}(\theta,\phi)$ using the vector addition formula. The basic eigenstates are

$$\mathbf{T}_{J,l}^{(M)}(\theta,\phi) = \sum_{s=-1}^{+1} (1\,l\,s\,M-s \mid JM) Y_l^{(M-s)}(\theta,\phi)\mathbf{e}_s, \tag{81}$$

where $-1 \leqslant s \leqslant 1$, and $|l-1| \leqslant J \leqslant l+1$. $\mathbf{T}_{J,l}^{(M)}(\theta,\phi)$ is a vector field which has total angular momentum J with component M in the direction $\mathbf{e}_0$ and arises from orbital angular momentum l.† The $\mathbf{T}_{J,l}^{(M)}$ are a complete ortho-normal vector set obeying‡

$$\int (\mathbf{T}_{J,l}^{(M)})^*.\mathbf{T}_{J'l'}^{(M')}\, d\Omega_{(\theta\phi)} = \delta_{JJ'}\delta_{MM'}\delta_{ll'}, \tag{82}$$

the integration being over the surface of the unit sphere. Using (51) and (48) we see that the simplest function is

$$\mathbf{T}_{0,1}^{(0)} = -\frac{1}{(4\pi)^{\frac{1}{2}}}(\mathbf{e}_1 x_1+\mathbf{e}_2 x_2+\mathbf{e}_3 x_3)/\,|\mathbf{x}| = -\frac{1}{(4\pi)^{\frac{1}{2}}}\hat{\mathbf{x}}, \tag{83}$$

where $\hat{\mathbf{x}}$ is the unit radial vector. Other functions are easily formed, for example

$$\mathbf{T}_{2,1}^{(2)} = \frac{1}{4}\left(\frac{3}{\pi}\right)^{\frac{1}{2}} \sin\theta\, e^{i\phi}(\mathbf{e}_1+i\mathbf{e}_2).$$

The vector potential field (on dropping the exponential time component $\exp(-i\omega t)$) can be written

$$\mathbf{A}(\mathbf{x}) = \sum_{J,l,M} f_{JlM}(r)\mathbf{T}_{J,l}^{(M)}(\theta,\phi), \tag{84}$$

where $r = |\mathbf{x}|$ is the radial distance, and $f_{JlM}(r)$ are functions to be determined. It is now clear that the term (83) gives rise to a spherically symmetric field $\mathbf{A}$.

In free space the vector potential $\mathbf{A}(\mathbf{x},t)$ obeys the wave equation; on dropping the time factor,

$$\nabla^2\mathbf{A}(\mathbf{x})+k^2\mathbf{A}(\mathbf{x}) = 0 \quad (k = \omega/c). \tag{85}$$

Because

$$\nabla^2\mathbf{T}_{J,l}^{(M)} = 0,$$

the radial functions f_{JlM} can be written $f_{JlM}(r) = C_{JlM} f_l(r)$, where C_{JlM} is an arbitrary constant, and

$$\frac{1}{r^2}\frac{d}{dr}\left(r^2\frac{df_l(r)}{dr}\right)+\left(k^2-\frac{l(l+1)}{r^2}\right)f_l(r) = 0. \tag{86}$$

† Notice that $\mathbf{T}_{J,l}^{(M)*} = (-1)^{(1+l+J-M)}\mathbf{T}_{J,l}^{(-M)}$ (cf. (47)).

‡ The vector eigenstates $\mathbf{T}_{J,l}^{(M)}$ have been defined by H. C. Corben and J. Schwinger, *Phys. Rev.* **58** (1940) 953; G. Goertzel, ibid. **70** (1946) 897; V. B. Berestetski, *J. Phys. U.S.S.R.* **11** (1947) 85. See also M. E. Rose, *Multipole Fields* (Wiley, New York, 1955), for a detailed account.

The general solution of (86) is

$$f_l(r) = \frac{1}{r^{\frac{1}{2}}}\{aJ_{l+\frac{1}{2}}(kr)+bN_{l+\frac{1}{2}}(kr)\}, \tag{87}$$

where a, b are arbitrary constants and $J_{l+\frac{1}{2}}$, $N_{l+\frac{1}{2}}$ are Bessel functions of the first and second kinds respectively.† It is more convenient to use the spherical Bessel function $j_l(kr)$ given by (78), and the spherical Neumann function‡

$$n_l(kr) = \left(\frac{\pi}{2kr}\right)^{\frac{1}{2}} N_{l+\frac{1}{2}}(kr). \tag{88}$$

Near the origin $j_l(kr)$ is proportional to r^l, but $n_l(kr)$ is singular, being proportional to $r^{-(l+1)}$. The asymptotic forms at large distances ($kr \gg l$) are

$$j_l(kr) \simeq \frac{1}{kr}\sin(kr-\tfrac{1}{2}l\pi); \qquad n_l(kr) \simeq -\frac{1}{kr}\cos(kr-\tfrac{1}{2}l\pi). \tag{89}$$

Different combinations of these solutions of (86) are used according to the physical problem being discussed. If we wish to expand the free radiation field in terms of electromagnetic multipoles, the functions $j_l(kr)$, which are everywhere finite, will be used (as, for example, in (77)). As they stand, the functions $j_l(kr)$ are normalized by their asymptotic form (89); alternatively, we can use the functions (cf. Chapter II, § 6)

$$g_{lk}(r) = k\left(\frac{2}{\mathscr{R}}\right)^{\frac{1}{2}} j_l(kr) \tag{90}$$

which are normalized in a large sphere of radius $\mathscr{R}$ so that

$$\int\limits_0^{\mathscr{R}} [g_{lk}(r)]^2 r^2\,dr = 1.$$

This form is useful if it is desired to normalize the field strengths so that the energy in the sphere equals that of one photon. Whenever the physical problem involves the creation (or scattering) of a photon it is necessary to have a factor in the vector potential which for large r takes the form $\exp[i(kr-\omega t)]$, so as to give an outgoing wave. The required solution of (86) is written§

$$\frac{1}{kr}u_l^{(+)}(r) = -n_l(kr)+ij_l(kr). \tag{91}$$

† See, for example, E. Jahnke and F. Emde, *Funktionentafeln* (B. G. Teubner, Leipzig, 1933).

‡ See, for example, L. I. Schiff, *Quantum Mechanics* (McGraw-Hill, New York, 1949), ch. iv.

§ J. M. Blatt and V. F. Weisskopf, *Theoretical Nuclear Physics* (Wiley, New York, 1952), ch. 8.

By (89) the asymptotic form of $u_l^{(+)}(r)$ is

$$u_l^{(+)}(r) \simeq \exp[i(kr-\tfrac{1}{2}l\pi)]. \tag{92}$$

It is possible to discuss the electromagnetic multipoles without, for the moment, specifying the normalization of the radial factor in $\mathbf{A}(\mathbf{x})$. In what follows, the symbol $f_l(r)$ is used to denote any one of the solutions of (86) as specified by (89), (90), or (91). Functions $f_l(r)$ having different indices are, as a result, related by†

$$\frac{d}{dr}\{r^{(l+1)}f_l(r)\} = kr^{(l+1)}f_{l-1}(r); \qquad \frac{d}{dr}\{r^{-l}f_l(r)\} = -kr^{-l}f_{l+1}(r). \tag{93}$$

The solenoidal condition

It is necessary to find solutions (84) of the wave equation which are solenoidal. The operation of taking the divergence of a vector commutes with the operation R of rotating the coordinate axes; this is because the divergence of the rotated vector equals the divergence of the original vector, due allowance being made for the different labelling of the point of observation. Therefore the divergence operation commutes with the generating operators for rotations; using (70) it is easy to verify that for any vector $\mathbf{A}$,

$$\operatorname{div}(J_i\,\mathbf{A}) = L_i \operatorname{div}\mathbf{A} \quad (i = 1,2,3).$$

Hence $\psi \equiv \operatorname{div}\{f_l(r)\mathbf{T}_{J,l}^{(M)}(\theta,\phi)\}$ will have the eigenvalues J and M of angular momentum. Because ψ has only one component it must contain $Y_J^{(M)}(\theta,\phi)$ as a factor. Also, by (85), it obeys

$$\nabla^2\psi + k^2\psi = 0,$$

so ψ must be a multiple of $f'_J(r)Y_J^{(M)}(\theta,\phi)$, where $f'_J(r)$ is some solution of (86) (inserting J). Differentiation of a function whose asymptotic form (cf. (89)) is e^{ikr}/kr cannot give a function with asymptotic form e^{-ikr}/kr, and vice versa.‡ Therefore the radial function $f'_J(r)$ appearing in $\operatorname{div}\{f_l(r)\mathbf{T}_{J,l}^{(M)}(\theta,\phi)\}$ is of the same asymptotic type as $f_l(r)$; they are related as in eqn. (93). It follows that

$$\operatorname{div}\{f_l(r)\mathbf{T}_{J,l}^{(M)}(\theta,\phi)\} = \alpha(J,l)f_J(r)Y_J^{(M)}(\theta,\phi), \tag{94}$$

where $\alpha(J,l)$ is a constant which is necessarily independent of M.§

The operator div reverses the parity, therefore the parity on the left and right sides of (94) is $(-1)^{(l-1)}$ and $(-1)^J$ respectively. It follows that $\alpha(J,J) = 0$. The coefficients $\alpha(J,J\pm 1)$ are found by a simple

† See p. 34, n. †.

‡ Differentiation of an outgoing wave cannot give an incoming wave.

§ This is because a rotation about the O_1 or O_2 axis must, on both sides of (94), introduce the same mixture of terms having different values of M.

calculation. At great distances from the origin on the polar axis $\mathbf{e}_0$ (i.e. $\theta = 0$), by (81) and (48),

$$f_l(r)\mathbf{T}^{(0)}_{J,l}(0) = f_l(r)(1l00 \mid J0)\left(\frac{2l+1}{4\pi}\right)^{\frac{1}{2}}\mathbf{e}_0.$$

Again, for large r and $\theta = 0$, the predominant contribution to $\operatorname{div}(f_l \mathbf{T}^{(0)}_{J,l})$ arises from the derivative along the polar axis.† Eqn. (94) becomes (for large r)

$$(2l+1)^{\frac{1}{2}}(1l00 \mid J0)\frac{df_l(r)}{dr} = \alpha(J,l)(2J+1)^{\frac{1}{2}}f_J(r). \tag{95}$$

For large r, by (93)‡

$$\frac{df_l(r)}{dr} \simeq kf_{l-1}(r), \qquad \frac{df_l(r)}{dr} \simeq -kf_{l+1}(r). \tag{96}$$

Using (60) gives

$$\left.\begin{aligned} \alpha(J,J+1) = -k\left(\frac{J+1}{2J+1}\right)^{\frac{1}{2}}, \qquad \alpha(J,J-1) = -k\left(\frac{J}{2J+1}\right)^{\frac{1}{2}}, \\ \text{and (as above)} \qquad \alpha(J,J) = 0. \end{aligned}\right\} \tag{97}$$

The solenoidal vector potentials which have total angular momentum eigenvalues (J, M) can therefore be written

$$\mathbf{A}^{(M)}_J(\mathscr{M}) = f_J(r)\mathbf{T}^{(M)}_{J,J}(\theta,\phi) \tag{98}$$

and

$$\mathbf{A}^{(M)}_J(\mathscr{E}) = \left(\frac{J+1}{2J+1}\right)^{\frac{1}{2}} f_{J-1}(r)\mathbf{T}^{(M)}_{J,J-1}(\theta,\phi) - \left(\frac{J}{2J+1}\right)^{\frac{1}{2}} f_{J+1}(r)\mathbf{T}^{(M)}_{J,J+1}(\theta,\phi). \tag{99}$$

The notation $\mathbf{A}^{(M)}_J(\mathscr{M})$, $\mathbf{A}^{(M)}_J(\mathscr{E})$ indicates that these vector potentials will be shown to give the magnetic and electric multipoles (2^J-poles) respectively.§ The vector fields given by (98) and (99) form the complete set of solutions of the wave equation (85) subject to the solenoidal condition $\operatorname{div}\mathbf{A} = 0$.‖ In the magnetic case the smallest value of the angular momentum is $J = 1$ giving the magnetic dipole; in the electric case the electric dipole with $J = 1$ has the least angular momentum. The electric *monopole* solution ($J = 0$) is excluded by the solenoidal condition.††

† Noticing relations (96) it is seen that other components of $\mathbf{T}^{(0)}_{Jl}$ give contributions which are down by a factor $1/r$.

‡ The errors in (95) and (96) are terms of order $1/r^2$, that is of relative order $1/r$.

§ The notation MJ, EJ is frequently used for magnetic and electric 2^J-poles respectively.

‖ Orthogonal to $\mathbf{A}^{(M)}_J(\mathscr{M})$ and $\mathbf{A}^{(M)}_J(\mathscr{E})$ there is a third set $\mathbf{A}^{M}_J(\mathscr{L})$ which is not solenoidal and does not correspond to any electromagnetic waves *in vacuo*. Its form is similar to (99) with different coefficients (cf. eqn. (120)).

†† Monopole emission can occur as a first step in the ejection of a conversion electron.

The multipole field strengths

The electric and magnetic field strengths are deduced by (67). Using (66), the electric field strength is given by $\mathbf{E} = ik\mathbf{A}$, where $\mathbf{A}$ is defined by (98) or (99). In finding curl $\mathbf{A}_J^{(M)}$ we notice that the operation curl commutes with rotation of the coordinate axes; by (70) we can verify that for any vector $\mathbf{A}$,

$$J_i \operatorname{curl} \mathbf{A} = \operatorname{curl}(J_i \mathbf{A}) \quad (i = 1, 2, 3).$$

Therefore curl $\mathbf{A}_J^{(M)}$ has the same eigenvalues (J, M) of total angular momentum. The vector $\operatorname{curl}\{f_l(r)\mathbf{T}_{J,l}^{(M)}(\theta,\phi)\}$ is again a solution of the wave equation (85) and it is solenoidal.† The operation curl changes the parity from $(-1)^l$ to $(-1)^{(l-1)}$. It follows that curl $\mathbf{A}_J^{(M)}(\mathscr{M})$ is a constant multiple of $\mathbf{A}_J^{(M)}(\mathscr{E})$, and vice versa.‡ This constant which must§ be independent of M is found by working out the case $M = 1$ on the polar axis $(\theta = 0)$ for large r. Using Table 4 (p. 404) we get

$$f_l(r)\mathbf{T}_{J,l}^{(+1)}(\theta = 0) = -\frac{1}{2\sqrt{(4\pi)}}(\mathbf{e}_1 + i\mathbf{e}_2)f_l(r)a_l,$$

where $a_{J-1} = (J+1)^{\frac{1}{2}}$, $a_J = (2J+1)^{\frac{1}{2}}$, $a_{J+1} = J^{\frac{1}{2}}$. The dominant contribution to the curl for large r is $\operatorname{curl}(f\mathbf{T}) \simeq (\operatorname{grad} f)\times\mathbf{T}$, giving

$$\operatorname{curl}\{f_l(r)\mathbf{T}_{J,J}^{(+1)}\}_{(\theta=0)} \simeq \frac{i}{2}(\mathbf{e}_1 + i\mathbf{e}_2)\left(\frac{2J+1}{4\pi}\right)^{\frac{1}{2}}\frac{df_J}{dr}.$$

Using (96) it follows that

$$\left.\begin{aligned} \operatorname{curl} \mathbf{A}_J^{(M)}(\mathscr{M}) &= -ik\mathbf{A}_J^{(M)}(\mathscr{E}) \\ \text{and hence‡} \qquad \operatorname{curl} \mathbf{A}_J^{(M)}(\mathscr{E}) &= ik\mathbf{A}_J^{(M)}(\mathscr{M}) \end{aligned}\right\}. \tag{100}$$

Finally, the electric and magnetic field strengths in the electric and magnetic multipoles having total angular momentum (J, M) are

$$\left.\begin{aligned} &\mathbf{H}_J^{(M)}(\mathscr{M}) = -ik\mathbf{A}_J^{(M)}(\mathscr{E}), \qquad \mathbf{E}_J^{(M)}(\mathscr{M}) = ik\mathbf{A}_J^{(M)}(\mathscr{M}) \\ \text{and} \qquad &\mathbf{H}_J^{(M)}(\mathscr{E}) = ik\mathbf{A}_J^{(M)}(\mathscr{M}), \qquad \mathbf{E}_J^{(M)}(\mathscr{E}) = ik\mathbf{A}_J^{(M)}(\mathscr{E}) \end{aligned}\right\}, \tag{101}$$

where the potentials are defined by (98) and (99). The exchange $\mathbf{E} \to \mathbf{H}$, $\mathbf{H} \to -\mathbf{E}$ on going from the electric to the magnetic 2^L-pole shows that the relation between these solutions is the dual transformation (9).

In evaluating the field strengths it is sometimes convenient to use the relation

$$\mathbf{T}_{JJ}^{(M)}(\theta,\phi) = -\frac{1}{\hbar}\frac{\mathbf{L}Y_J^{(M)}(\theta,\phi)}{\sqrt{\{J(J+1)\}}}, \tag{102}$$

† Again, differentiation of a radial function $f_l(r)$ having asymptotic form $1/kr \exp(\pm ikr)$ cannot give a function having asymptotic form $1/kr \exp(\mp ikr)$.

‡ One relation follows from the other by curl curl $\mathbf{A} = k^2\mathbf{A}$.

§ Cf. with footnote ‡, p. 33.

where **L** is the orbital angular momentum operator. This relation may be worked out by detailed manipulation,† or it can be seen directly as follows. The total angular momentum operator **J** obeys the relation

$$J_i \mathbf{L} = (L_i + S_i)\mathbf{L} = \mathbf{L}L_i \quad (i = 1, 2, 3) \tag{103}$$

(this follows from the commutation rule $\mathbf{L}\times\mathbf{L} = i\hbar\mathbf{L}$ and the expressions (70) for S_i). Therefore $\mathbf{L}Y_J^{(M)}(\theta,\phi)$ is a vector having total angular momenta (J, M); also it has parity $(-1)^J$, so it must be a multiple of $\mathbf{T}_{JJ}^{(M)}(\theta,\phi)$. The relation (102) follows on comparing the O_3 components ($\mathbf{e}_3 = \mathbf{e}_0$) of $\mathbf{T}_{JJ}^{(M)}$ and $\mathbf{L}Y_J^{(M)}$, using (81), (58), and Table 4 (Chapter VIII, § 8).

16. Properties of the multipole solutions

The parity of a multipole is defined to be the parity of the magnetic field **H**. The reason for this definition can easily be seen by looking at the wave-mechanical matrix element for the emission of radiation by a dynamical system containing moving charges. If ψ_α and ψ_β are the wave functions of the initial and final states of the system respectively, the matrix element‡ is

$$H' = -\frac{1}{c}\int \tilde{\psi}_\beta(\mathbf{j}\,.\,\mathbf{A})\psi_\alpha\, d^3\mathbf{x},$$

where **j** is the current operator. For multipole radiation ψ_α and ψ_β can both have definite parity; the product of their parities must be opposite to the parity of **A**, because **j** is a polar vector. The parity of the magnetic field of the multipole is opposite to the parity of the corresponding vector potential (by (67)); thus the above convention for the parity of a multipole gives conservation of parity in multipole emission or absorption. From (98) and (99) the magnetic 2^J-pole has parity§ $(-1)^{J-1}$ and the electric 2^J-pole has parity $(-1)^J$.

The classical expression for the energy in a radiation multipole is

$$W = \frac{1}{8\pi}\int \{(\mathbf{E}(\mathbf{x},t))^2 + (\mathbf{H}(\mathbf{x},t))^2\}\, d^3\mathbf{x}. \tag{104}$$

The field strengths $\mathbf{H}(\mathbf{x},t)$ (and $\mathbf{E}(\mathbf{x},t)$) must be written in the form (as in (66))

$$\mathbf{H}(\mathbf{x},t) = \mathbf{H}(\mathbf{x},\omega)e^{-i\omega t} + \mathbf{H}^*(\mathbf{x},\omega)e^{i\omega t}, \tag{105}$$

† See p. 33, n. ‡.

‡ The interaction Hamiltonian density for radiation and matter is

$$H = -\frac{1}{c}j_\mu A_\mu \quad \text{(cf. Chapter II, § 12).}$$

§ The basic vectors $\mathbf{e}_s$ of (74) and (81) are axial vectors because they describe spin or angular momentum. They do not change sign on inversion of the axes.

where $\mathbf{H}(\mathbf{x},\omega)$ (and $\mathbf{E}(\mathbf{x},\omega)$) are given by (101). Substituting into (104), the time independent term (which corresponds to the diagonal value, or the expectation value, in quantum theory) is

$$W = \frac{1}{4\pi}\int \{\mathbf{E}^*(\mathbf{x},\omega).\mathbf{E}(\mathbf{x},\omega)+\mathbf{H}^*(\mathbf{x},\omega).\mathbf{H}(\mathbf{x},\omega)\}\, d^3\mathbf{x}. \qquad (106)$$

By (101), for either the electric or the magnetic 2^J-pole this gives

$$W = \frac{k^2}{4\pi}\int \{|\mathbf{A}_J^{(M)}(\mathscr{M})|^2+|\mathbf{A}_J^{(M)}(\mathscr{E})|^2\}\, d^3\mathbf{x},$$

where the integral extends over the space containing the multipole. Using (82) and remembering that the normalization of the radial functions $f_l(r)$ is independent of l gives

$$W = \frac{k^2}{2\pi}\int |f_l(r)|^2 r^2\, dr. \qquad (107)$$

Choosing $f_l(r)$ to be a multiple of the finite function $j_l(kr)$ (eqn. (78)) we can imagine the field to be confined to a large sphere centred on the source (suitable boundary conditions are imposed on the field strengths at the surface of the sphere). Choosing a suitable multiple of $j_l(kr)$, the right-hand side of (107) can be equated to $\hbar\omega$, the energy of one photon; solutions (85) obtained in this way form a basic set of functions for quantizing the electromagnetic field in the angular momentum representation.

It has been shown by Franz† that in such a sphere, the time average $\langle\mathbf{G}\rangle_{\text{av}}$ of the classical angular momentum

$$\mathbf{G} = \frac{1}{4\pi c}\int \mathbf{x}\times\{\mathbf{E}(\mathbf{x},t)\times\mathbf{H}(\mathbf{x},t)\}\, d^3\mathbf{x}$$

has zero component perpendicular to the axis $\mathbf{e}_0$ of the multipole. Along the multipole axis $\langle\mathbf{G}\rangle_{\text{av}_0} = MW/\omega$, where M is the magnetic quantum number and W is the energy (107). The vanishing of the components of $\langle\mathbf{G}\rangle_{\text{av}}$ perpendicular to $\mathbf{e}_0$ corresponds to their having zero expectation value in quantum theory.

It follows from (102) (because $\mathbf{x}.\mathbf{L} = 0$) that $\mathbf{A}_J^{(M)}(\mathscr{M})$ has no component in the direction of the radius vector $\mathbf{x}$; hence $\mathbf{E}_J^{(M)}(\mathscr{M})$ and $\mathbf{H}_J^{(M)}(\mathscr{E})$ are entirely transverse to $\mathbf{x}$ for all values of $r = |\mathbf{x}|$. The other field strengths (101) have radial components; these are found by evaluating $(\mathbf{A}_J^{(M)}(\mathscr{E}).\hat{\mathbf{x}})$, where $\hat{\mathbf{x}}$ is the unit radial vector. The operation of taking the radial component of a vector commutes with the

† W. Franz, *Z. Phys.* **127** (1950) 363. The details of this calculation can readily be worked out (see also M. E. Rose, p. 33, n. ‡).

operation of rotating the coordinate axes; therefore $(\mathbf{A}_J^{(M)}(\mathscr{E}).\hat{\mathbf{x}})$ must be of the form $F(r)Y_J^{(M)}(\theta,\phi)$, where $F(r)$ is to be determined. Letting $\hat{\mathbf{x}}$ point along $\mathbf{e}_0$, a calculation using (99), (60), and (93) gives

$$(\mathbf{A}_J^{(M)}(\mathscr{E}).\hat{\mathbf{x}}) = \frac{1}{k}\sqrt{\{J(J+1)\}}\frac{f_J(r)}{r}Y_J^{(M)}(\theta,\phi). \tag{108}$$

The radial components of $\mathbf{E}_J^{(M)}(\mathscr{E})$ and $\mathbf{H}_J^{(M)}(\mathscr{M})$ are therefore of order $(1/r^2)$ for large r; the transverse components of these fields are of order $(1/r)$ for large r.

Angular distributions

If the outgoing wave form (91) is used for the radial function $f_l(r)$, the strength of the multipole solutions can conveniently be measured by the outward flux of energy. The flux of energy per unit area is given by the Poynting vector

$$\mathbf{S} = \frac{c}{4\pi}\{\mathbf{E}(\mathbf{x},t)\times\mathbf{H}(\mathbf{x},t)\}.$$

Substituting (105) for $\mathbf{H}(\mathbf{x},t)$ and the corresponding expression for $\mathbf{E}(\mathbf{x},t)$, the time average of the Poynting vector is

$$\langle\mathbf{S}\rangle_{\text{av}} = \frac{c}{4\pi}\{\mathbf{E}^*(\mathbf{x},\omega)\times\mathbf{H}(\mathbf{x},\omega)+\mathbf{E}(\mathbf{x},\omega)\times\mathbf{H}^*(\mathbf{x},\omega)\}. \tag{109}$$

Remembering that the radial function in the outgoing solution has (cf. (92)) the form $e^{i(kr-l\pi/2)}/kr$, it follows that for large r the predominant term in the magnetic field (for any multipole) is

$$\mathbf{H} = \operatorname{curl}\mathbf{A} \simeq ik\hat{\mathbf{x}}\times\mathbf{A}, \tag{110}$$

where $\hat{\mathbf{x}}$ is the unit radial vector. Using $\mathbf{E} = +ik\mathbf{A}$ (from (66))† gives

$$\mathbf{E}^*\times\mathbf{H}+\mathbf{E}\times\mathbf{H}^* = k^2\{\mathbf{A}^*\times(\hat{\mathbf{x}}\times\mathbf{A})+\mathbf{A}\times(\hat{\mathbf{x}}\times\mathbf{A}^*)\} \simeq 2k^2(\mathbf{A}^*.\mathbf{A})\hat{\mathbf{x}}. \tag{111}$$

Here we have used the fact that for magnetic multipoles $(\mathbf{A}.\hat{\mathbf{x}})$ is zero, and, by (108), for electric multipoles $(\mathbf{A}.\hat{\mathbf{x}})$ is of order $(1/r^2)$. Hence for large r,

$$\langle\mathbf{S}\rangle_{\text{av}} = \frac{c}{2\pi}k^2(\mathbf{A}^*.\mathbf{A})\hat{\mathbf{x}}. \tag{112}$$

$|\langle\mathbf{S}\rangle_{\text{av}}|$ gives the angular distribution of the outgoing radiation. By the duality relation, or by (101), it follows that the angular distributions for the electric and the magnetic multipoles having quantum numbers (J,M) are identical. Writing $I(\theta,\phi)\,d\Omega$ for the rate of flow

† From (110) and $\mathbf{E} = ik\mathbf{A}$ it follows that the electric and magnetic field strengths are orthogonal for large r.

of energy in the solid angle $d\Omega$, we have $I(\theta,\phi) = r^2|\langle \mathbf{S}\rangle_{\rm av}|$. For a multipole (J, M), by (98) and (91),

$$I_{(J,M)}(\theta,\phi) = \frac{c}{2\pi}|\mathbf{T}_{J,J}^{(M)}(\theta,\phi)|^2 \tag{113}$$

$$= \frac{c}{2\pi}\sum_{s=-1}^{1}|(1Js\,M-s\mid JM)|^2|Y^{(M-s)}(\theta,\phi)|^2. \tag{114}$$

In deriving (114), eqn. (81) and the relation $\mathbf{e}_s^*.\mathbf{e}_{s'} = \delta_{ss'}$ have been used. The Clebsch–Gordan coefficients are given in Table 4 (Chapter VIII, § 8). For dipoles the angular distributions (113) are

$$I_{(1,0)} = \frac{c}{2\pi}\frac{3}{8\pi}\sin^2\theta,$$

$$I_{(1,\pm 1)} = \frac{c}{2\pi}\frac{3}{16\pi}(1+\cos^2\theta). \tag{115}$$

These are the well-known distributions for electric dipole radiation in atomic transitions. For any values (J, M) the total intensity integrated over all angles is $c/2\pi$ (this follows from (113) and the orthogonality relation (82)).

A general *outgoing* electromagnetic wave can be written in the form

$$\mathbf{A}(\mathbf{x},\omega) = \sum_{J,M}\{A(J,M;\mathscr{E})\mathbf{A}_J^{(M)}(\mathscr{E})+A(J,M;\mathscr{M})\mathbf{A}_J^{(M)}(\mathscr{M})\}, \tag{116}$$

where $A(J,M;\mathscr{E})$, $A(J,M;\mathscr{M})$ are constant complex coefficients and the multipole potentials $\mathbf{A}_J^{(M)}(\mathscr{E})$, $\mathbf{A}_J^{(M)}(\mathscr{M})$ are given by (98) and (99) with $f_l(r)$ put equal to the function (91). The time average of the Poynting vector is again (at large r) given by (112). The intensity distribution becomes

$$I(\theta,\phi) = \frac{c}{2\pi}\Bigg|\sum_{J,M} i^{-J}\Bigg[A(J,M;\mathscr{M})\mathbf{T}_{J,J}^{(M)}+ +iA(J,M;\mathscr{E})\Bigg\{\Big(\frac{J+1}{2J+1}\Big)^{\frac{1}{2}}\mathbf{T}_{J,J-1}^{(M)}+\Big(\frac{J}{2J+1}\Big)^{\frac{1}{2}}\mathbf{T}_{J,J+1}^{(M)}\Bigg\}\Bigg]\Bigg|^2. \tag{117}$$

The angular distribution can show interference between the various multipoles. If the system producing the radiation jumps from a state of definite parity to another such state, only multipoles having the same parity can appear on the right of (116); this is frequently the case in nuclear problems. In such a situation, if an electric dipole occurs in (116), a magnetic dipole or electric quadrupole cannot occur.

The total intensity is (by (82))

$$\int I(\theta,\phi)\,d\Omega = \frac{c}{2\pi}\sum_{J,M}\{|A(J,M;\mathscr{M})|^2+|A(J,M;\mathscr{E})|^2\}. \tag{118}$$

17. Multipole moments

The generation of radiation multipoles can be understood by looking at the outgoing wave solution of eqn. (18) for $\mathbf{A}(\mathbf{x}, t)$. Because radiation can be generated by the intrinsic magnetic moments of particles the intensity of magnetization $\mathbf{M}$ will be retained. Writing $\mathbf{M}$ and $\mathbf{j}$ in the exponential time-dependent form (105), we have

$$\nabla^2\mathbf{A}(\mathbf{x}, \omega)+k^2\mathbf{A}(\mathbf{x}, \omega) = -\frac{4\pi}{c}\mathbf{j}'(\mathbf{x}, \omega), \qquad (119)$$

where $\mathbf{j}' = \mathbf{j}+c\,\mathrm{curl}\,\mathbf{M}$.

Because $\mathrm{div}\,\mathbf{j}'(\mathbf{x}, \omega)$ need not be zero,† the solution of (119) cannot everywhere be expressed in terms of solenoidal vectors. The solenoidal solutions of the *homogeneous* wave equation (85) are $\mathbf{A}_J^{(M)}(\mathscr{M})$ and $\mathbf{A}_J^{(M)}(\mathscr{E})$ given in (98) and (99); a solution of the same equation which is not solenoidal‡ is

$$\mathbf{A}_J^{(M)}(\mathscr{L}) = \left(\frac{J+1}{2J+1}\right)^{\frac{1}{2}} f_{J+1}(r)\mathbf{T}_{J,J+1}^{(M)}(\theta,\phi)+ \\ +\left(\frac{J}{2J+1}\right)^{\frac{1}{2}} f_{J-1}(r)\mathbf{T}_{J,J-1}^{(M)}(\theta,\phi). \qquad (120)$$

This solution has been chosen so that (using (82))

$$\int \mathbf{A}_J^{(M)}(\lambda)^*.\mathbf{A}_{J'}^{(M')}(\lambda')\,d\Omega = 0 \qquad (121)$$

unless $J = J'$, $M = M'$, and $\lambda = \lambda'$, where λ is $\mathscr{M}$, $\mathscr{E}$, or $\mathscr{L}$.

The vector field $\mathbf{A}_J^{(M)}(\mathscr{L})$ has the same transformation properties under rotations of the coordinate system as the vector

$$\mathrm{grad}\{f_J(r)Y_J^{(M)}(\theta,\phi)\};$$

neither vector is solenoidal and similar arguments§ to those in § 15 above show that

$$\mathbf{A}_J^{(M)}(\mathscr{L}) = C\,\mathrm{grad}\{f_J(r)Y_J^{(M)}(\theta,\phi)\}, \qquad (122)$$

where C is a constant.‖ (It is easy to verify, using (43) and (70), that

$$J_i\,\mathrm{grad} = \mathrm{grad}\,L_i \quad (i = 1,2,3).)$$

† $\mathrm{div}\,\mathbf{j}'(\mathbf{x}, \omega) = i\omega\rho(\mathbf{x}, \omega)$ by the continuity equation. Outside the source $\mathbf{A}$ may be chosen solenoidal.

‡ $\mathbf{A}_J^{(M)}(\mathscr{L})$ is not solenoidal because $\mathbf{A}_J^{(M)}(\mathscr{M})$, $\mathbf{A}_J^{(M)}(\mathscr{E})$ exhaust the solenoidal vectors having angular momentum eigenvalues (J, M).

§ For large r the term of order $(1/r)$ in $\mathrm{grad}\{f_J(r)Y_J^{(M)}(\theta,\phi)\}$ is in the radial direction. Therefore this vector is independent of $\mathbf{A}_J^{(M)}(\mathscr{M})$ and $\mathbf{A}_J^{(M)}(\mathscr{E})$.

‖ In fact, $C = 1/k$.

The outgoing wave solution of (119) can be written in the form (116) where

$$A(J,M;\mathscr{M}) = \frac{4\pi k}{c}\int \mathbf{A}_J^{\prime(M)*}(\mathscr{M}).\,\mathbf{j}'(\mathbf{x})\,d^3\mathbf{x}, \tag{123}$$

$$A(J,M;\mathscr{E}) = \frac{4\pi}{ic}\int \mathbf{A}_J^{\prime(M)*}(\mathscr{M}).\operatorname{curl}\mathbf{j}'(\mathbf{x})\,d^3\mathbf{x}. \tag{124}$$

The integrals on the right of these equations are taken over all space, and

$$\mathbf{A}_J^{\prime(M)}(\mathscr{M}) = j_J(kr)\mathbf{T}_{J,J}^{(M)}(\theta,\phi); \tag{125}$$

$j_J(kr)$ is the spherical Bessel function (78).

Verification of the solution

This solution of (119) is found with the aid of the Green's function† (written in dyadic form)

$$\mathbf{G}(\mathbf{x},\mathbf{x}') = \begin{cases} k\sum_{J,M,\lambda} \mathbf{A}_J^{(M)}(\lambda,\mathbf{x})\mathbf{A}_J^{\prime(M)*}(\lambda,\mathbf{x}') & (r>r') \\ k\sum_{J,M,\lambda} \mathbf{A}_J^{\prime(M)}(\lambda,\mathbf{x})\mathbf{A}_J^{(M)*}(\lambda,\mathbf{x}') & (r<r') \end{cases}. \tag{126}$$

Here λ runs over $\mathscr{M}$, $\mathscr{E}$, and $\mathscr{L}$. $\mathbf{A}_J^{(M)}(\lambda)$ and $\mathbf{A}_J^{\prime(M)}(\lambda)$ are given by (98), (99), and (120) on substituting respectively $(1/kr)u_l^+(r)$ and $j_l(kr)$ for $f_l(r)$. Summing over λ gives, for $r>r'$,

$$\mathbf{G}(\mathbf{x},\mathbf{x}') = k\sum_{l=0}^{\infty}\frac{u_l^{(+)}(kr)}{kr}j_l(kr')\sum_{J=|l-1|}^{l+1}\sum_{M=-J}^{J}\mathbf{T}_{J,l}^{(M)}(\theta,\phi)\mathbf{T}_{J,l}^{(M)*}(\theta',\phi') \quad (r>r'). \tag{127}$$

The value of $\mathbf{G}(\mathbf{x},\mathbf{x}')$ for $r<r'$ is obtained by exchanging r and r' in (127). Using (81) and the unitary property of the vector coupling coefficients gives

$$\sum_{J=|l-1|}^{l+1}\sum_{M=-J}^{J}\mathbf{T}_{J,l}^{(M)}(\theta,\phi)\mathbf{T}_{J,l}^{(M)*}(\theta',\phi') = \sum_{s=-1}^{+1}\mathbf{e}_s\,\mathbf{e}_s^*\sum_{m=-l}^{l}Y_l^{(m)}(\theta,\phi)Y_l^{(m)*}(\theta',\phi').$$

By (80)‡

$$\sum_{s=-1}^{+1}\mathbf{e}_s\,\mathbf{e}_s^* = \sum_{i=1}^{3}\mathbf{e}_i\,\mathbf{e}_i = \mathbf{I},$$

where **I** is the unit matrix, or dyadic, in three-dimensional space.

† Cf. M. E. Rose, p. 33, n. ‡, and J. M. Blatt and V. F. Weisskopf, p. 22, n. †.

‡ $\mathbf{e}_s$ denotes $\mathbf{e}_{-1}$, $\mathbf{e}_0$, $\mathbf{e}_{+1}$; $\mathbf{e}_i$ denotes $\mathbf{e}_1$, $\mathbf{e}_2$, $\mathbf{e}_3$ ($\mathbf{e}_3=\mathbf{e}_0$).

Acting on $\mathbf{G}(\mathbf{x},\mathbf{x}')$ with $(\nabla_{\mathbf{x}}^2+k^2)$ gives zero except for $r = r'$. Writing

$$g_l(r,r') = \begin{cases} k\dfrac{u_l^{(+)}(kr)}{kr}\,j_l(kr') & (r > r'), \\ k\dfrac{u_l^{(+)}(kr')}{kr'}\,j_l(kr) & (r < r') \end{cases}$$

we find the value of†

$$\frac{1}{r^2}\frac{d}{dr}\left(\frac{r^2 dg_l(r,r')}{dr}\right)$$

at $r = r'$ by integrating across $r = r'$:

$$\int\limits_{(r'-\epsilon)}^{(r'+\epsilon)} dr\, r^2 \frac{1}{r^2}\frac{d}{dr}\left\{\frac{r^2 dg_l(r,r')}{dr}\right\} = \left[r^2\frac{dg_l(r,r')}{dr}\right]_{r=(r'-\epsilon)}^{r=(r'+\epsilon)}$$

where ϵ is small. The Wronskian property (which follows from (86)),

$$kr^2\left\{\frac{d}{dr}\left(\frac{u_l^{(+)}(r)}{kr}\right)j_l(kr)-\frac{u_l^{(+)}(r)}{kr}\frac{d}{dr}j_l(kr)\right\} = -1 \quad (\text{all } r > 0),$$

gives

$$\frac{d}{dr}\left(r^2\frac{dg_l(r,r')}{dr}\right) = -\delta(r-r'). \tag{128}$$

Noticing that (128) is independent of l, and using the relation‡

$$\sin\theta \sum_{l=0}^{\infty}\sum_{m=-l}^{l} Y^{(m)}(\theta,\phi)Y^{(m)*}(\theta',\phi') = \delta(\theta-\theta')\delta(\phi-\phi'), \tag{129}$$

gives

$$(\nabla_{\mathbf{x}}^2+k^2)\mathbf{G}(\mathbf{x},\mathbf{x}') = -\mathbf{I}\,\delta^3(\mathbf{x}-\mathbf{x}'). \tag{130}$$

The outgoing wave solution of (119) is therefore

$$\mathbf{A}(\mathbf{x},\omega) = \frac{4\pi}{c}\int \mathbf{G}(\mathbf{x},\mathbf{x}').\mathbf{j}'(\mathbf{x}',\omega)\,d^3\mathbf{x}'. \tag{131}$$

Letting $|\mathbf{x}|\to\infty$ and picking out the electric or magnetic multipole term (J, M), gives the coefficients (123), (124).§ The solution (131) contains terms in $\mathbf{A}_J^{M)}(\mathscr{L})$, the longitudinal potential. Because of (122) these terms give no magnetic field outside the source and therefore give no radiation. The outgoing scalar potential solution of the second equation in (18) cancels the electrical effect of the $\mathbf{A}_J^{(M)}(\mathscr{L})$ terms outside the source. A gauge transformation could be made to eliminate $\mathbf{A}_J^{(M)}(\mathscr{L})$ outside the source.

† This is the radial term in $\nabla_{\mathbf{x}}^2$.

‡ Cf. H. A. Bethe, *Handbuch der Physik* (J. Springer, Berlin, 1933), vol. xxiv/1, § 65. By expanding any function $f(\theta,\phi)$ in spherical harmonics and integrating over the unit sphere, relation (129) is obvious.

§ Eqn. (124) is obtained by using the first of eqns. (100) and the relation

$$(\text{curl}\,\mathbf{A}'^*).\mathbf{j}' = \mathbf{A}'^*.\text{curl}\,\mathbf{j}'+\text{div}(\mathbf{A}'^*\times\mathbf{j}').$$

The divergence term gives no contribution to the integral.

Application of the formulae

The explicit form of (123) is

$$A(J,M;\mathscr{M}) = \frac{4\pi k}{c}\int j_J(kr)\mathbf{T}_{J,J}^{(M)*}(\theta,\phi).(\mathbf{j}+c\,\mathrm{curl}\,\mathbf{M})\,d^3\mathbf{x} \quad (132)$$

and after integration by parts (124) gives

$$A(J,M;\mathscr{E}) = \frac{4\pi}{ic}\int j_J(kr)\mathbf{T}_{J,J}^{(M)*}(\theta,\phi).(\mathrm{curl}\,\mathbf{j}+ck^2\mathbf{M})\,d^3\mathbf{x}. \quad (133)$$

The source functions $\mathbf{j}$ and $\mathbf{M}$ appearing on the right of (119) should be given by the quantum-mechanical values of the current density and the magnetization within the source. The justification for using the classical equation (119) to find the radiation emitted by a quantized system, is that the quantum electrodynamic field variables propagate according to the same equation.† The subtleties of field theory arise in the definition of $\mathbf{j}'(\mathbf{x})$. For many purposes, such as, for example, the emission of γ-rays by a nucleus, it is sufficiently accurate to replace $\mathbf{j}(\mathbf{x})$ and $\mathbf{M}(\mathbf{x})$ by their wave-mechanical forms $\psi_\beta^*(\mathbf{x})\mathbf{j}\psi_\alpha(\mathbf{x})$ and $\psi_\beta^*(\mathbf{x})\mathbf{M}\psi_\alpha(\mathbf{x})$, where ψ_α, ψ_β are the wave functions of the initial and final states respectively and $\mathbf{j}$, $\mathbf{M}$ are the current and magnetic moment *operators*.‡ In other problems such as the photo-production of pions on nucleons, the form of $\mathbf{j}(\mathbf{x})$ requires special consideration.§ The life-time T for the transition is (by (118)) given by

$$1/T = \frac{c}{2\pi\hbar\omega}|A|^2, \quad (134)$$

where A is the amplitude for the transition, and is given by (132) or (133).

A useful approximation to the multipole moments (132) and (133) can be made for sources whose linear dimensions are much smaller than $(1/k)$; this is in general true for the emission of γ-rays by nuclei.‖ Using (102) and the Hermitian property†† of $\mathbf{L}$ gives (after partial

† Actually the positive frequency component $\mathbf{A}(\mathbf{x},\omega)$ of the operator $\mathbf{A}(\mathbf{x},t)$ is associated with the destruction of photons of energy $\hbar\omega$, and the Hermitian conjugate variable $\bar{\mathbf{A}}(\mathbf{x},\omega)$ is associated with their creation (cf. Chapter II).

‡ For example, for a nucleon $\mathbf{M} = e\hbar\mu\boldsymbol{\sigma}/2Mc$, where μ is the intrinsic magnetic moment (in units of the Bohr magneton of the proton), $\boldsymbol{\sigma}$ is the Pauli spin operator, and M the proton mass. For non-relativistic motion of a particle of mass M we can use

$$\psi_\beta^*(\mathbf{x})\mathbf{j}\psi_\alpha(\mathbf{x}) = \frac{e}{2M}[\psi_\beta^*(\mathbf{x})\{\mathbf{p}\psi_\alpha(\mathbf{x})\}+\{\mathbf{p}\psi_\beta(\mathbf{x})\}^*\psi_\alpha(\mathbf{x})].$$

§ e.g. G. Bernardini, *Suppl. Nuovo Cim.* **1** (1955) 104.

‖ Roughly, the nuclear radius $R = 0{\cdot}85A^{\frac{1}{3}}(\hbar/\mu c)$ (μ = pion mass). Then $kR = 0{\cdot}85A^{\frac{1}{3}}(\Delta E/\mu c^2)$, where ΔE is the energy of the emitted γ-ray. Even for $\Delta E = 10$ MeV, kR is small.

†† $\int (L_i\phi)^*\psi\,d^3\mathbf{x} = \int \phi^*(L_i\psi)\,d^3\mathbf{x}$.

integration and neglect of all but the lowest order in (kr))†

$$A(J,M;\mathscr{E}) \simeq \frac{1}{i}\frac{4\pi}{(2J+1)!!}\left(\frac{J+1}{J}\right)^{\frac{1}{2}} k^{(J+1)} \int r^J Y_J^{(M)*}(\theta,\phi) \times \times \left(\rho(\mathbf{x}) - \frac{ik}{J+1}\,\mathrm{div}\{\mathbf{x}\times\mathbf{M}(\mathbf{x})\}\right) d^3\mathbf{x} \tag{135}$$

and

$$A(J,M;\mathscr{M}) \simeq \frac{1}{i}\frac{4\pi}{(2J+1)!!}\left(\frac{J+1}{J}\right)^{\frac{1}{2}} k^{(J+1)} \int r^J Y_J^{(M)*}(\theta,\phi) \times \times \left(\frac{1}{J+1}\frac{1}{c}\,\mathrm{div}\{\mathbf{x}\times\mathbf{j}(\mathbf{x})\} + \mathrm{div}\,\mathbf{M}(\mathbf{x})\right) d^3\mathbf{x}, \tag{136}$$

where $(2J+1)!! = (2J+1)(2J-1)...3.1$. The charge density $\rho(\mathbf{x})$ is to be replaced by $\psi^*_\beta(\mathbf{x})\rho\psi_\alpha(\mathbf{x})$, where ρ is the charge density operator (in the non-relativistic case for one particle of charge e, we have $e\psi^*_\beta(\mathbf{x})\psi_\alpha(\mathbf{x})$).

Obviously for these comparatively long wavelengths, the probability of emission of higher multipoles falls off rapidly. Comparing (135) and (136) it is seen that in general the magnetic multipole moment of order J is smaller than the electric multipole moment of the same order, selection rules apart,‡ by a factor (v/c), where v is a mean speed of the charged particles.§ Using the non-relativistic expression for $\mathbf{j}(\mathbf{x})$ (cf. p. 45, n. ‡) the magnetic multipole moment term $(1/c)\mathbf{x}\times\mathbf{j}(\mathbf{x})$ can be replaced by $(e/Mc)\mathbf{L}$, where $\mathbf{L}$ is the angular momentum of the charged particles; this term is therefore (for a nucleus) of the same order as the contribution to the magnetic multipole moment arising from the intrinsic moments $\mathbf{M}$. Typical nuclear lifetimes for the emission of γ-rays having energies of order 0·1 MeV to 1 MeV are: $E1$, 10^{-15} sec; $M1$, 10^{-13} sec; $E2$, 10^{-9} sec; there is, however, a considerable spread in the observed values.‖ There is a general tendency for higher multipoles to be relatively more important for larger nuclei and for greater γ-ray energy.

18. Example: Angular correlation

Knowledge of the relative angular distribution, or angular correlation, of two particles which are emitted in succession by a nucleus can

† Details are given in references on p. 43, n. †. See also J. B. French and Y. Shimamoto, *Phys. Rev.* **91** (1953) 898.

‡ Of course the two moments cannot be non-zero between the *same* pair of definite parity states.

§ In a nucleus, if the EJ transition is forbidden the MJ transition may well be appreciably more probable than the $E(J+1)$ transition because $(v/c)^2$ is in many cases much larger than the decrease in $|A(\mathscr{E})|^2$ on going from J to $J+1$.

‖ A survey is given by M. Goldhaber and J. Weneser, *Ann. Rev. Nuclear Sci.* **5** (Annual Reviews, Inc., Stanford, Cal., 1955).

be used to determine the angular momentum of one of the three nuclear states involved.† Suppose a nucleus, which is originally in an excited state, having angular momentum values (J_1, M_1), makes a transition to a state of angular momentum (J_2, M_2) by emitting a particle A whose total angular momentum is (J_A, M_A); subsequently the nucleus makes another transition to the ground state which has angular momentum (J_3, M_3) by emitting a particle B with angular momentum (J_B, M_B). For simplicity we assume J_2 and J_3 are known.

Assume that originally the nucleus is not orientated so that the states (J_1, M_1) for all values of the magnetic quantum number M_1 $(-J_1 \leqslant M_1 \leqslant J_1)$ are equally occupied. Observing the direction in which particle A is emitted gives information about M_A; this is because a particle has zero component of orbital angular momentum about its direction of motion. The direction of emission of A is taken to be the polar axis $\theta = 0$. Knowing the value, or values, of M_A enables us to determine how the occupation of the states (J_2, M_2) varies with M_2 $(-J_2 \leqslant M_2 \leqslant J_2)$. This distribution, which can depend markedly on the value we assume for J_1, determines the angular distribution of the particle B which is emitted in the final transition. Clearly if all values of M_2 were equally probable, the distribution of B would be isotropic and there would be no angular correlation between A and B.

Consider the case in which $J_2 = 1$, $J_3 = 0$, and J_1 is known to be either 0 or 2. Particle A is scalar or pseudo-scalar, e.g. an α-particle,‡ particle B is an electromagnetic dipole (electric or magnetic).§ Because A is scalar, the angular component of its wave function is $Y_{JA}^{(MA)}(\theta, \phi)$; hence along $\theta = 0$, only $M_A = 0$ can occur. The possible transitions in the two cases $J_1 = 0$, $J_1 = 2$ are shown in Fig. 2. For $J_1 = 0$ only $M_2 = 0$ out of the states (J_2, M_2) is occupied, therefore by (115) the angular distribution of the γ-ray B is $\sin^2\theta$; for $J_1 = 2$, the states $M_2 = +1, 0, -1$ are equally occupied, and the angular distribution of the γ-ray B is isotropic. For $J_1 = 2$ there is no correlation.

† Angular correlation was investigated by D. R. Hamilton, *Phys. Rev.* **58** (1940) 122, and ibid. **74** (1948) 782. See also J. V. Dunworth, *Rev. Sci. Instrum.* **11** (1940) 167. A detailed discussion is given by D. L. Falkoff and G. E. Uhlenbeck, *Phys. Rev.* **79** (1950) 323; see also the article by H. Frauenfelder in *β- and γ-Ray Spectroscopy* (North-Holland, Amsterdam, 1955), p. 531.

‡ An internal conversion electron ejected from an *s*-shell without spin-flip could, for this purpose, be treated as scalar. Cf. J. W. Gardner, *Proc. Phys. Soc.* A **62** (1949) 763, and ibid. A **64** (1951) 238, for the calculation of correlation between conversion electrons.

§ As was seen in § 16, *EJ* and *MJ* have the same angular distribution; only by polarization analysis can their distributions be distinguished.

It is assumed throughout this section that there is no interference between emitted particles having different values of M_B. This is true if we observe the directions of the particles, but it would not be true if we were also to observe their polarizations.

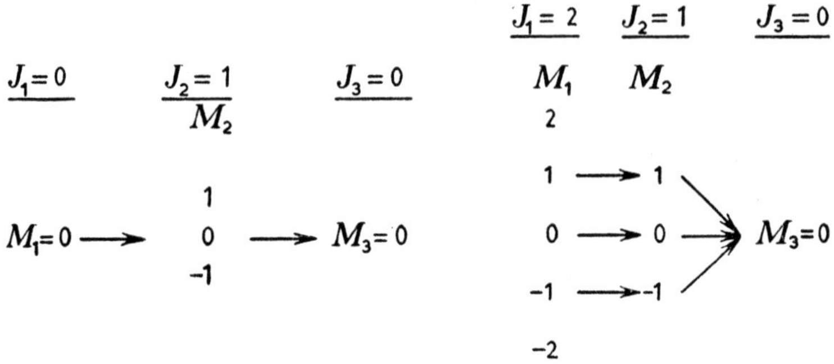

FIG. 2. Angular correlation for the emission of a scalar particle followed by an electromagnetic dipole; on the left the nuclear levels are $J_1 = 0$, $J_2 = 1$, $J_3 = 0$; on the right, $J_1 = 2$, $J_2 = 1$, $J_3 = 0$.

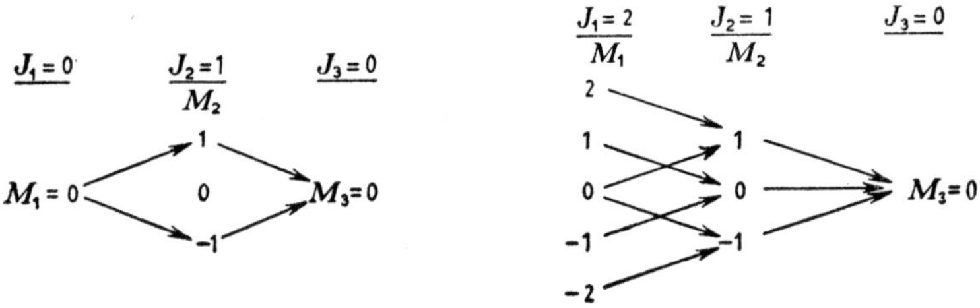

FIG. 3. Angular correlation for the successive emission of two electromagnetic dipoles; on the left the nuclear levels are $J_1 = 0$, $J_2 = 1$, $J_3 = 0$; on the right, $J_1 = 2$, $J_2 = 1$, $J_3 = 0$.

The case when A and B are both γ-rays and the nuclear states have the same angular momenta is illustrated in Fig. 3. Only $M_A = \pm 1$ is possible, and for $J_1 = 0$ the distribution of the second γ-ray is $(1+\cos^2\theta)$; for $J_1 = 2$ the distribution is of the form

$$\alpha' \sin^2\theta + \beta'(1+\cos^2\theta) \quad (\alpha' \neq 0). \tag{137}$$

The constants α', β' are determined by general arguments below.

General angular correlation analysis

The interaction Hamiltonian H_{int} for the emission of a particle, or particles, by a nucleus must be invariant under rotations; for example, for γ-rays it is of the form $-(1/c)(\mathbf{A}.\mathbf{j}')$, where $\mathbf{j}' = \mathbf{j}+c\,\text{curl}\,\mathbf{M}$. This rotation invariance makes it possible to deduce the dependence of the matrix elements on the magnetic quantum numbers. The electromagnetic interaction will be used as an illustration.† The interaction for a charged particle of (non-relativistic) momentum **p** emitting a photon, in the direction **k** with polarization **e**, is (apart from a constant) $(\mathbf{p}.\mathbf{e})\exp[i(\mathbf{k}.\mathbf{x})]$, where **x** is the position of the particle. The first term in the expansion of this matrix element in powers of $(\mathbf{k}.\mathbf{x})$ gives the electric dipole interaction $(\mathbf{p}.\mathbf{e})$. Using (80) this may be written

$$(\mathbf{p}.\mathbf{e}) = \sum_{s=-1}^{1} \mathbf{e}_s^*.\mathbf{p}_s, \tag{138}$$

where $\mathbf{p}_s$ $(s = +1, 0, -1)$ is defined similarly to $\mathbf{e}_s$. The next term in the expansion may be written

$$\sum_{i,j} p_i x_j e_i k_j = \left(\frac{4\pi}{3}\right) \sum_{s=-1}^{1} \mathbf{p}_s^*.\mathbf{e}_s \sum_{m=-1}^{1} Y_1^{(m)*}(\mathbf{x}) Y_1^{(m)}(\mathbf{k}), \tag{139}$$

where $Y_1^{(m)}(\mathbf{x})$, $Y_1^{(m)}(\mathbf{k})$ are spherical harmonics formed from the vectors **x** and **k**. By the inverse of the combination law (81), and the unitary property of the Clebsch–Gordan coefficients, (139) can be written

$$\sum_{i,j} p_i x_j e_i k_j = \left(\frac{4\pi}{3}\right) \sum_{J=1}^{2} \sum_{M=-J}^{J} \mathbf{T}_{J,1}^{(M)*}(N).\mathbf{T}_{J,1}^{(M)}(R), \tag{140}$$

where $\mathbf{T}_{J,1}^{(M)}(N)$ is formed like (81) from $\mathbf{p}_s$ and $Y_1^{(m)}(\mathbf{x})$ while $\mathbf{T}_{J,1}^{(M)}(R)$ is formed from $\mathbf{e}_s$ and $Y_1^{(m)}(\mathbf{k})$.

The term $J = 2$ gives the electric quadripole and $J = 1$ gives the magnetic dipole.‡ The term $J = 0$ does not occur because $(\mathbf{k}.\mathbf{e}) = 0$. Both (139) and (140) can be written as a sum of terms of the form

$$\sum_{M=-J}^{J} \mathscr{Y}_J^{(M)*}(\mathscr{A}).\mathscr{Y}_J^{(M)}(\mathscr{J}) \quad (J = 1, 2), \tag{141}$$

where the $\mathscr{Y}_J^{(M)}$ are generalized spherical harmonics and $\mathscr{J}, \mathscr{A}$ are some variables associated with the nucleus and the emitted particle, or particles, respectively. Eqn. (141) is the general form of the component of H_{int} which gives rise to the emission of a particle of angular momentum (J, M); this is because the component of H_{int} for the emission of such particles with any value of J $(-J \leqslant M \leqslant J)$ must be an invariant.§

† Cf. D. L. Falkoff and G. E. Uhlenbeck, p. 47, n. †.

‡ The $J = 1$ term, expressed in ordinary vector coordinates, is $(p_i x_j - p_j x_i)$; this gives $(\mathbf{x}\times\mathbf{j})$.

§ By the laws of vector addition (49), $\mathscr{Y}_J^{(M)}(A)$ can only give an invariant if combined with other functions of total angular momentum $(J, -M)$. By (59),

$$(JJM-M\,|\,00) = (-1)^{(J-M)}\frac{(J0M0\,|\,JM)}{\sqrt{(2J+1)}} = (-1)^{(J-M)}/\sqrt{(2J+1)}.$$

In general, $\mathscr{Y}_J^{(-M)} \propto (-1)^M \mathscr{Y}_J^{(M)*}$, and it follows that (141) is the only invariant which can be formed.

The matrix element for the emission of a particle (J, M) during a nuclear transition from a state of angular momentum (J_1, M_1) to a state (J_2, M_2) is therefore proportional to

$$\mathscr{Y}_J^{(M)*}(\mathscr{A}).(J_2, M_2 \mid \mathscr{Y}_J^{(M)}(\mathscr{J}) \mid J_1, M_1). \tag{142}$$

The last term in (142) indicates a matrix element which contains an integration and summation over the nuclear variables only. By the law of composition of angular momenta it can be written

$$(J_2 M_2 \mid \mathscr{Y}_J^{(M)}(\mathscr{J}) \mid J_1 M_1) = (J_1 J M_1 M \mid J_2 M_2)(J_1 \| J, \mathscr{J} \| J_2), \tag{143}$$

where the last factor is independent of the magnetic quantum numbers.†

It follows that the angular correlation function in the general case is given by

$$F(\theta) = \sum_{M_A M_B} \sum_{M_1 M_2 M_3} (J_1 J_A M_1 M_A \mid J_2 M_2)^2 I_{J_A}^{(M_A)}(A; \theta = 0) \times \\ \times (J_2 J_B M_2 M_B \mid J_3 M_3)^2 I_{J_B}^{(M_B)}(B; \theta), \tag{144}$$

where $I_{J_A}^{(M_A)}(A; \theta)$ is the angular distribution of particles A in the angular momentum or multipole state (J_A, M_A), etc. The formula (144) is independent of the detailed nature of the interaction of the nucleus with the emitted particles and it is applicable to the successive emission of any particles.‡ A wide variety of examples of (144) for γ–γ correlations§ and conversion electron correlations|| have been worked out. We only give the form for successive dipole emission between levels $J_1 = 2$, $J_2 = 1$, $J_3 = 0$ (i.e. the detailed form of (137)); a simple calculation using (144) gives

$$F(\theta) = 1 + \tfrac{1}{13}\cos^2\theta.$$

Detailed correlation data for nuclear β–γ emission have also been evaluated.†† The effect on γ–γ correlation of the magnetic field of the atomic electrons has been investigated by Goertzel.‡‡

Another form of angular correlation occurs when particles are emitted in the same event; these correlations depend on the structure of a single matrix element. Examples are the β-neutrino correlation in β-decay

† Eqn. (143) is frequently called Eckart's theorem. See C. Eckart, *Rev. Mod. Phys.* **2** (1930) 305, and E. P. Wigner, *Gruppentheorie* (Vieweg & Sohn, Braunschweig, 1931).

‡ General methods for angular correlation have been discussed by R. D. Myers, *Phys. Rev.* **54** (1938) 361; C. N. Yang, *Phys. Rev.* **74** (1948) 764; F. Coester and J. M. Jauch, *Helv. phys. Acta*, **26** (1953) 3. A comprehensive formulation is given by G. Racah, *Phys. Rev.* **84** (1951) 910.

§ I. Zinnes, *Phys. Rev.* **80** (1950) 386; L. C. Biedenharn and M. E. Rose, *Rev. Mod. Phys.* **25** (1953) 729.

|| See p. 47, n. † and J. W. Gardner, p. 47, n. ‡; also D. L. Falkoff, *Phys. Rev.* **82** (1951) 98.

†† D. L. Falkoff and G. E. Uhlenbeck, *Phys. Rev.* **79** (1950) 334.

‡‡ G. Goertzel, *Phys. Rev.* **70** (1946) 897.

processes,† and the correlation between the three pions emitted in the decay of a τ-meson.‡

19. Example: Capture of a slow neutron by a proton

Because of the attraction between a proton and a neutron, slow neutrons can be captured by the process

$$P+N \rightarrow D+\gamma.$$

For thermal neutrons the capture cross-section is appreciable; for example, it is about 0·3 barns§ per proton for (1/40) eV neutrons. Here we briefly discuss the selection rules governing the emission of the γ-ray. At such low energies capture will only be appreciable|| from a state of relative orbital angular momentum $l = 0$, i.e. from the ${}^1S_0$ or ${}^3S_1$ state of the two nucleons. These states both have positive parity. The deuteron ground state is ${}^3S_1$ and has positive parity. Because the γ-ray energy is of the order of 2 MeV, only dipole radiation is considered. The conservation of parity allows only the magnetic dipole.

Putting $J = 1$ in (136) and integrating by parts, it is seen that the magnetic dipole moments are just††

$$\mathbf{A} \equiv C \int \psi_\beta^*(\mathbf{x})\Big(\frac{1}{2c}\mathbf{x}\times\mathbf{j}+\mathbf{M}\Big)\psi_\alpha(\mathbf{x})\, d^3\mathbf{x}, \tag{145}$$

where $\mathbf{j}$ and $\mathbf{M}$ are the current and magnetic moment operators. $\psi_\alpha(\mathbf{x})$, $\psi_\beta(\mathbf{x})$ are the wave functions of the initial and final states of the two nucleons. We replace $\mathbf{x}\times\mathbf{j}/c$ by $(e/Mc)\mathbf{L}_P$, where $\mathbf{L}_P$ is the proton's orbital angular momentum. Also $\mathbf{M} = (e\hbar/2Mc)(\mu_P\boldsymbol{\sigma}_P+\mu_N\boldsymbol{\sigma}_N)$, where $\boldsymbol{\sigma}_P$, $\boldsymbol{\sigma}_N$ are the Pauli spin operators for the proton and neutron and μ_P, μ_N are their magnetic moments (in terms of the proton magneton). In the centre of mass system we may put

$$\mathbf{L}_P = \mathbf{L}_N = \tfrac{1}{2}\mathbf{L},$$

where $\mathbf{L}$ is the nucleon orbital angular momentum; it vanishes. The magnetic moment term $\mathbf{M}$ can be split into two parts

$$\mu_P\boldsymbol{\sigma}_P+\mu_N\boldsymbol{\sigma}_N = \tfrac{1}{2}(\mu_P+\mu_N)(\boldsymbol{\sigma}_P+\boldsymbol{\sigma}_N)+\tfrac{1}{2}(\mu_P-\mu_N)(\boldsymbol{\sigma}_P-\boldsymbol{\sigma}_N). \tag{145 a}$$

† See p. 156, especially n.‡

‡ R. H. Dalitz, *Phil. Mag.* **44** (1953) 1068; E. Fabri, *Nuovo Cim.* **11** (1954) 479.

§ 1 barn $= 10^{-24}$ cm^2.

|| In the centre of mass system, the relative orbital angular momentum and the spin make up the total angular momentum. The radial distribution of P and N in a state of relative angular momentum l is determined by $j_l(kr) \sim (kr)^l$ for (kr) small. For the energies mentioned, (kr) is very small for any value of r at which nuclear forces are not negligible.

†† The usual combinations $-(1/\sqrt{2})(A_1+iA_2)$, A_3, $(1/\sqrt{2})(A_1-iA_2)$ are to be used. C is a constant.

The first part acting on a triplet state gives a triplet state; therefore it cannot give a non-zero matrix element between two S wave triplet nucleon states of different energy. The second term on the right of (145a) converts a $^3S_1$ state into a $^1S_0$ state and vice versa.

Thus only the $^1S_0$ initial state contributes, and the magnetic dipole emission gives a spin change leading to the $^3S_1$ deuteron state.† On inserting numerical values in (145), good agreement with the experimental results is obtained.‡

20. Example: Expansion of circularly polarized waves in multipoles

The circularly polarized plane waves

$$\mathbf{A}_{\pm}(\mathbf{x}, \omega) = \mathbf{e}_{\pm}\, e^{ikx_3}$$

are expanded in terms of multipoles by using the series (77). The relation

$$\mathbf{e}_s Y_l^{(M-s)}(\theta, \phi) = \sum_{J=|l-1|}^{l+1} (1\, l\, s\, M-s \mid JM)\mathbf{T}_{J,l}^{(M)}$$

together with (98) and (99) gives

$$\mathbf{A}_{\pm}(\mathbf{x}, \omega) = \sqrt{(2\pi)} \sum_{J=1}^{\infty} i^J(2J+1)^{\frac{1}{2}}\{\pm\mathbf{A}_J^{(\pm1)}(\mathscr{M}) - i\mathbf{A}_J^{(\pm1)}(\mathscr{E})\}. \quad (146)$$

Using (146) the multipole components in a plane electromagnetic wave can be picked out. This separation is of value in studying photon induced transitions.

21. Example: Angular distribution of photo-pions

Pions can be produced by the process

$$(\gamma\text{-ray}) + (\text{nucleon}) \rightarrow (\text{nucleon}) + (\text{pion}).$$

Eqn. (10) shows that if the nucleon is initially at rest, the γ-ray threshold is $\mu c^2(1+\mu/2M)$, where μ, M are the pion and nucleon masses; this threshold is around 150 MeV. For incident γ-rays of up to about 350 MeV we assume that (on account of the comparatively long pion wavelength in the final state) it is only necessary to consider S, P, and D wave pions; for a similar reason only the electric dipole, magnetic dipole, and electric quadripole radiation components are considered.

Because the pion has negative intrinsic parity, a final state in which

† E. Fermi, *Phys. Rev.* **48** (1935) 570.

‡ For details see J. M. Blatt and V. F. Weisskopf, *Theoretical Nuclear Physics* (J. Wiley, New York, 1952).

the pion has orbital angular momentum l has parity $(-1)^{l+1}$. The nucleon's recoil is neglected, so only its spin contributes to the angular momentum. The *electric dipole* component in the incident electromagnetic wave has angular momentum unity, and, adding the nucleon spin, initial states having total angular momentum $J = \frac{1}{2}$ and $\frac{3}{2}$ can be formed; each has parity (-1) (coming from $E1$). Because of the parity, the pion must be in a state of even angular momentum; of these only the S and D states can give (respectively) $J = \frac{1}{2}, \frac{3}{2}$. The *magnetic dipole* component has parity $(+1)$ and angular momentum unity; therefore it can only give $J = \frac{1}{2}, \frac{3}{2}$ states with the pion in a P state. Similarly

TABLE 1

γ-ray component	*Total a.m. and parity*	*Pion orbital a.m.*	*Spin-flip*	*Pion angular distribution*
$E1$	$\frac{1}{2}, -$	S	Yes	Constant
	$\frac{3}{2}, -$	D	Yes	$2+3\sin^2\theta$
$M1$	$\frac{1}{2}, +$	P	No	Constant
	$\frac{3}{2}, +$	P	No	$2+3\sin^2\theta$
$E2$	$\frac{3}{2}, +$	P	Yes	$1+\cos^2\theta$

the $E2$ radiation can give $J = \frac{3}{2}, \frac{5}{2}$ states of parity $(+1)$; the pion can be in a P (or F) state. These rules are given in Table 1 together with information about whether the nucleon spin is or is not reversed (relative to the γ-ray beam) during the photo-production. Spin-flip necessarily occurs if the γ-ray and the pion have different angular momenta.

In the last column, the angular distribution of the pion relative to the γ-ray beam is given. It has been assumed that the polarization of the γ-ray and the nucleon is random, and it is further assumed that interference between different modes can be ignored.†

As an example of the angular distribution calculation, the $E1 \rightarrow D$ wave case is given. The $E1$ component has angular momentum $\hbar$ and can have the components $\pm\hbar$ along the beam direction. By symmetry it is only necessary to consider the component $+\hbar$ (right-handed circularly polarized radiation). This is characterized by the spherical harmonic $Y_1^{(1)}$; if $u_{\pm\frac{1}{2}}$ are the nucleon spin state vectors,‡ the initial state gives a $J = \frac{3}{2}$ component which (with the notation of § 11, eqn.

† This analysis has been given by B. T. Feld, *Phys. Rev.* **89** (1953) 330. The interference between different modes has been discussed by G. Bernardini, *Suppl. Nuovo Cim.* **2** (1955) 104. Writing the differential cross-section in the form

$$A_0+A_1\cos\theta+A_2\cos^2\theta,$$

the interference term A_1 is small for $\gamma+P \rightarrow P+\pi^0$ (a P-wave pion predominates), but for $\gamma+P \rightarrow N+\pi^+$, A_1 is of the same order as A_2 in the energy region $E\gamma < 300$ MeV.

‡ These two-component state vectors are discussed in Chapter III.

(52), and of eqns. (3.50), (3.51))† we write $W_{1,\frac{3}{2}}^{(M)}$, where $-\frac{3}{2} \leqslant M \leqslant \frac{3}{2}$. Using formula (50) above, and Table 2, p. 131, gives

$$\left.\begin{aligned} Y_1^{(1)}u_{+\frac{1}{2}} &= W_{1,\frac{3}{2}}^{(\frac{3}{2})} \\ Y_1^{(1)}u_{-\frac{1}{2}} &= \frac{1}{\sqrt{3}}W_{1,\frac{3}{2}}^{(\frac{1}{2})} + (J=\tfrac{1}{2},\ \text{term}) \end{aligned}\right\}. \tag{147}$$

The final state is of the type $W_{2,\frac{3}{2}}^{(M)}$ because the pion is in a D state. The actual distribution is a statistical mixture (the polarizations are random) of the form

$$|W_{2,\frac{3}{2}}^{(\frac{3}{2})}|^2 + \tfrac{1}{3}|W_{2,\frac{3}{2}}^{(\frac{1}{2})}|^2. \tag{148}$$

The factor $\frac{1}{3}$ comes from the ratio of the $J = \frac{3}{2}$ terms in (147). By Table 2,

$$W_{2,\frac{3}{2}}^{(\frac{3}{2})} = -\frac{1}{\sqrt{5}}Y_2^{(1)}u_{+\frac{1}{2}} + \frac{2}{\sqrt{5}}Y_2^{(2)}u_{-\frac{1}{2}},$$

$$W_{2,\frac{3}{2}}^{(\frac{1}{2})} = -\sqrt{\tfrac{2}{5}}\,Y_2^{(0)}u_{+\frac{1}{2}} + \sqrt{\tfrac{3}{5}}\,Y_2^{(1)}u_{-\frac{1}{2}}.$$

The expression (148) is evaluated, using the normal-orthogonal property of the spin vectors: $(u^*_{\pm\frac{1}{2}}.u_{\pm\frac{1}{2}}) = 1$, $(u^*_{+\frac{1}{2}}.u_{-\frac{1}{2}}) = 0$. This gives the form

$$(\text{const.}) \times (2+3\sin^2\theta).$$

The isotropic distribution of $J = \frac{1}{2}$ states

The $M1$ component with $J = \frac{1}{2}$ gives uniform pion distribution, in spite of the pion being in a P-wave. This is a general property of $J = \frac{1}{2}$ states; it arises because the angular distribution cannot contain a power of $\cos\theta$ higher than $(\cos\theta)^{2J}$. For a single mode of definite parity, the angular distribution must be an even function of $\cos\theta$, hence for $J = \frac{1}{2}$ only a uniform distribution is possible. The result is not true if the process violates parity.

The assertion that the angular dependence cannot vary more rapidly than $(\cos\theta)^{2J}$ is proved as follows. Consider the sum over the spin directions s of the product $W_{l,j}^{(m)*}.W_{l',j'}^{(m')}$, where m, m' are fixed. We have

$$W_{lj}^{(m)*}.W_{l'j'}^{(m')} = \sum_{sm_1m_2} (l\tfrac{1}{2}\,m_1 s\,|\,jm)(l'\tfrac{1}{2}\,m_2 s\,|\,j'm')\{Y_l^{(m_1)}(\theta,\phi)\}^* Y_{l'}^{(m_2)}(\theta,\phi).$$

Using (56) the product of spherical harmonics can be written as a sum of terms $Y_L^{(M)}(\theta,\phi)$ $(M = m_2 - m_1)$ with $|l-l'| \leqslant L \leqslant (l+l')$. Now applying (59) and (65), the summation over s, m_1, m_2 (with m, m', M fixed) is evaluated, giving

$$\begin{aligned} W_{lj}^{(m)*}.W_{l'j'}^{(m')} &= (-1)^{(l+j+m)} \sum_L \left\{\frac{(2j+1)(2j'+1)}{4\pi(2L+1)}\right\}^{\frac{1}{2}} (ll'00\,|\,L0)\,W(Llj'\tfrac{1}{2};\,l'j) \times \\ &\quad \times (2l+1)^{\frac{1}{2}}(2l'+1)^{\frac{1}{2}}(jj',-m,m'\,|\,LM)\,Y_L^{(M)}(\theta,\phi). \end{aligned} \tag{149}$$

† The notation is $W_{l,J}^{(M)}$, where (J, M) is the total a.m. and $l = |J \pm \frac{1}{2}|$ is the photon or pion a.m.

The last Clebsch–Gordan coefficient in (149) shows that L is also restricted by $|j-j'| \leqslant L \leqslant (j+j')$. Putting $j = j' = J$, the assertion is proved. Because we have not summed over m or m', this result is also applicable to the angular distribution of particles scattered from polarized targets.† The derivation of (149) is readily extended to particles of spin greater than $\frac{1}{2}$; the restrictions on L are again

$$|l-l'| \leqslant L \leqslant (l+l'), \qquad |j-j'| \leqslant L \leqslant (j+j').$$

The hyperon decay $\Lambda^0 \rightarrow P+\pi^-$ is parity violating. If Λ^0 has spin $J = \frac{1}{2}$, the decay of *aligned* Λ^0 gives a π^- distribution $(A+B\cos\theta)\,d\Omega$, where A, B are constants. As a function of $|\cos\theta|$ this has the isotropic form $2A\,d\Omega$. For $J = \frac{3}{2}$ a term in $\cos^2\theta$ would also appear. The experimental data‡ give isotropy in $|\cos\theta|$, suggesting that Λ^0 has spin $\frac{1}{2}$.

† Cf. eqn. (116), Chapter VIII.

‡ *Annual Conference on High Energy Physics* (CERN, Geneva, 1958), 266–7. J. Steinberger *et al.*, *Nuovo Cim.* 7 (1958) 272.

II

QUANTIZATION OF BOSON FIELDS

1. The need for quantization

MAXWELL's electromagnetic theory and the classical meson propagation equation, which have been discussed and used in Chapter I, do not describe any of the essentially quantum properties of these fields. For example, the electromagnetic multipole solutions did not show that energy could only occur in packets of amount $\hbar\omega$; we had to add that idea in order to count the number of γ-ray quanta emitted in various directions by an assembly of excited nuclei.† The classical pion theory used in Chapter I gives no indication that the charge in a pion field can only be $\pm ne$ where n is an integer. These classical theories also allow us (by using the Poynting vector and its analogue for the pion field) to calculate precisely what is the mechanical momentum of the field within a small volume; this is in disagreement with the uncertainty relation $\Delta p_1 . \Delta x_1 \geqslant \hbar$, which must apply to all physical entities if quantum theory is to be a consistent scheme. The deficiency of the classical theories may be summed up by the remark that they do not enable us to see both the particle and the wave aspects of photons or pions in a consistent way.

Heisenberg has discussed in detail‡ the uncertainties which necessarily occur in the values of the electric and magnetic field strengths if the wave and particle aspects of electromagnetic radiation are combined. The field strengths $\mathbf{E}(\mathbf{x})$, $\mathbf{H}(\mathbf{x})$, although they are written as point functions, cannot really be measured at a space-time point; actual measurements, at the best, can give an average value over a small volume of space and an interval of time. Assuming the small volume is a cube of edge δl, the classical field energy and momenta are§

$$W = \frac{(\delta l)^3}{2}(\mathbf{E}^2 + \mathbf{H}^2), \qquad \mathbf{P} = \frac{(\delta l)^3}{c}(\mathbf{E} \times \mathbf{H})$$

respectively. According to the particle aspect, the number of photons

† As discussed in Chapter I, § 17, the propagation equations in the Maxwell case and the quantum electrodynamic case are identical in form; hence eqn. (1.119) gives the correct radiated intensity provided the appropriate source $\mathbf{j}'$ is used.

‡ W. Heisenberg, *Physical Principles of Quantum Theory* (University of Chicago Press, Chicago, 1930), ch. 3.

§ We use Heaviside units for quantum electrodynamics—see § 9 below for further details.

in the small cube must be zero or integral. Frequencies up to the order of $(c/\delta l)$ can be detected over the cube,† so there must be uncertainties $\Delta\mathbf{E}$, $\Delta\mathbf{H}$ in the values of **E** and **H** such that W and **P** cannot be specified precisely to within amounts $(hc/\delta l)$ and $(h/\delta l)$ respectively. The values $\Delta\mathbf{E}$, $\Delta\mathbf{H}$ which are required for this purpose can be estimated from the expressions

$$\Delta W = \tfrac{1}{2}(\delta l)^3\{(\Delta\mathbf{E})^2+(\Delta\mathbf{H})^2\}, \qquad \Delta\mathbf{P} = \frac{1}{c}(\delta l)^3\Delta\mathbf{E}\times\Delta\mathbf{H}, \tag{1}$$

which are applicable when the mean field strengths **E** and **H** are zero. There are still, necessarily, fluctuations in this zero-field case; the statement that the average fields over the cube vanish does not imply that their high-frequency components vanish, or that the fields are zero outside the cube. Heisenberg shows‡ that on using (1) the inequalities $\Delta W \geqslant hc/\delta l$, $|\Delta\mathbf{P}| \geqslant h/\delta l$ are satisfied provided

$$\Delta E_i.\Delta H_j \geqslant \hbar c/(\delta l)^4 \quad (i \neq j). \tag{2}$$

In an ideal experiment the field strength components E_1 and H_2 are measured simultaneously in the same small volume by examining the deflexion of beams of charged particles passing through the volume. This experiment has the same limitation (2) on the optimum accuracy of measurement.§ The inaccuracy in the results of the ideal experiment arises because the charged test particles obey the uncertainty relation $\Delta p_1.\Delta x_1 \geqslant \hbar$; the deflected beams therefore show a fuzziness which prevents accurate measurement of the deflexion.

The uncertainty relations (2) can be obtained from electromagnetic theory, provided the classical field strengths **E** and **H** are replaced by quantum mechanical operators which do not commute with each other. We shall not give the derivation of the uncertainty relations from the general commutation relations: the reader is referred to the literature.§ It is sufficient for our purpose to state that the commutation relations for the field strengths are readily deduced from the simple form of field quantization which is given below. This quantization also gives

† That is, wavelengths greater than δl.

‡ Cf. p. 56, n. ‡. See also P. Jordan and W. Pauli, *Z. Phys.* **47** (1928) 151, who first gave the commutation relations for electromagnetic field strengths.

§ W. Heisenberg, loc. cit. N. Bohr and L. Rosenfeld, *K. danske vidensk. Selsk.* (*Math.-fys. Medd.*) **12** (1933), No. 8, have given a critical analysis of the limitations on the measurements of two field strengths at various points in space-time. In a further paper (*Phys. Rev.* **78** (1950) 794) they have considered the measurement of charge-current. See also W. Heitler, *Quantum Theory of Radiation* (Clarendon Press, 3rd edn., 1954), ch. 2.

a satisfactory detailed description of the particle-wave duality for the free electromagnetic field or the free pion field.†

The quantum field theory will be developed by the method of Jordan and Pauli.‡ This is a simple extension of the quantum mechanics of an atomic system to the case of a system having an infinite number of degrees of freedom. The method is used here because it leads quickly and directly to the quantum description of free fields; a more profound discussion of the *basis* of quantum field theory, with the action principle as a starting-point, is given in Chapter IX.

2. Field quantization

In classical mechanics the equations of motion of a system having n degrees of freedom can be written in the very general—but simple—form

$$\frac{d}{dt}\left(\frac{\partial L}{\partial \dot{q}_r}\right) = \frac{\partial L}{\partial q_r} \quad (r = 1, 2,..., n), \tag{3}$$

where $q_1,..., q_n$ are generalized coordinates for the system and $L(q_r, \dot{q}_s)$ is its Lagrangian function. Eqns. (3) result from the more fundamental extremum condition

$$\delta \int\limits_A^B L\, dt = 0,$$

where the integral is to be taken over varied paths between the fixed end positions A and B; this is the *action principle*.§ In setting up quantum mechanics, Dirac|| postulated the commutation relations††

$$\left.\begin{aligned} [p_r, q_s] &= (\hbar/i)\delta_{rs} \\ [p_r, p_s] = 0, &\qquad [q_r, q_s] = 0 \end{aligned}\right\}, \tag{4}$$

where p_r is the *canonical* momentum defined classically by $p_r = \partial L/\partial \dot{q}_r$. This quantization scheme now has to be extended to a continuous dynamical system.

For a continuous classical system, such as a vibrating membrane or the Maxwell field, eqns. (3) are not sufficiently general because the system has an infinite number of degrees of freedom. There is a displacement $Z(\mathbf{x})$ of the membrane corresponding to each point $\mathbf{x}$ in its plane; for the electromagnetic field there is (subject to the Lorentz condition) a 4-potential $A_\mu(\mathbf{x}) = (\mathbf{A}(\mathbf{x}), i\phi(\mathbf{x}))$ at each point of space. In general, we may have N independent variables $\phi^{(\alpha)}(\mathbf{x})$ $(\alpha = 1, 2,.., N)$

† By 'free' we mean 'non-interacting'. ‡ Cf. p. 57, n. ‡.

§ For details see Chapter IX, § 1.

|| P. A. M. Dirac, *Proc. Roy. Soc.* A, **109** (1925) 642.

†† The notation is $[A, B] = AB-BA$.

at *each* point $\mathbf{x}$ at a fixed time t. The Lagrangian L of the simple dynamical system has to be replaced by an integral over all the points $\mathbf{x}$, so

$$L = \int d^3\mathbf{x}\,\mathscr{L}, \tag{5}$$

where $\mathscr{L}$ is called the Lagrangian density. $\mathscr{L}$ is a function of the $\phi^{(\alpha)}(\mathbf{x})$ and their first derivatives:†

$$\mathscr{L} \equiv \mathscr{L}\{\phi^{(\alpha)}(\mathbf{x}), \partial_\mu \phi^{(\beta)}(\mathbf{x})\}.$$

The action principle is now written

$$\delta \int \mathscr{L}\{\phi^{(\alpha)}(\mathbf{x}), \partial_\mu \phi^{(\beta)}(\mathbf{x})\}\, d^3\mathbf{x}dt = 0, \tag{6}$$

where suitable boundary conditions for the space integral are to be used.‡ The equations of motion are therefore a simple generalization§ of (3):

$$\partial_\mu\left(\frac{\partial\mathscr{L}}{\partial(\partial_\mu \phi^{(\alpha)})}\right) = \frac{\partial\mathscr{L}}{\partial\phi^{(\alpha)}} \quad (\alpha = 1, 2,..., N), \tag{7}$$

where $\partial_\mu \equiv \partial/\partial x_\mu$ and $x_4 = ict$. (The relativity notation is here used solely for convenience; it has not yet got any special significance.) The Lagrangian L is an integral over all points $\mathbf{x}$ of space (cf. eqn. (5)) because there are N independent variables $\phi^{(\alpha)}(\mathbf{x})$ at each point $\mathbf{x}$. The canonical momentum $p^{(\alpha)}(\mathbf{x})$ which is conjugate to $\phi^{(\alpha)}(\mathbf{x})$ is therefore given by

$$p^{(\alpha)}(\mathbf{x}) = d^3\mathbf{x}(\partial\mathscr{L}/\partial\dot{\phi}^{(\alpha)}), \tag{8}$$

where $d^3\mathbf{x}$ is the element of volume appearing in the integral (5). This awkward notation is avoided if, instead of $p^{(\alpha)}(\mathbf{x})$, we use the canonical momentum *density* $\pi^{(\alpha)}(\mathbf{x})$. It is defined by||

$$\pi^{(\alpha)}(\mathbf{x}) = (\partial\mathscr{L}/\partial\dot{\phi}^{(\alpha)}), \tag{9}$$

where $\mathscr{L}$ is regarded as a function of the independent variables $\phi^{(\alpha)}(\mathbf{x})$, $\dot{\phi}^{(\alpha)}(\mathbf{x})$.

The canonical commutation relations for a field theory may now be written down by analogy with (4). Because the commutation relations (4) are independent of time, it is to be expected that the analogous

† For a uniform membrane of surface density ρ which is under a constant surface tension T/unit length, L is an integral ($L = \int dx_1\, dx_2\, \mathscr{L}$) taken over all points (x_1, x_2) of the equilibrium plane. The Lagrangian density $\mathscr{L}$ is a function of the displacement $Z(x_1, x_2)$ and its derivatives. It is

$$\mathscr{L} = \tfrac{1}{2}\rho\{\dot{Z}(x_1, x_2)\}^2 - T\left[\sqrt{\left\{1+\left(\frac{\partial Z}{\partial x_1}\right)^2+\left(\frac{\partial Z}{\partial x_2}\right)^2\right\}}-1\right].$$

‡ For a discussion of the general action integral for a field see Chapter IX.

§ For the membrane example, the equation of motion is, for a small displacement,

$$\frac{\partial^2 Z}{\partial x_1^2}+\frac{\partial^2 Z}{\partial x_2^2}-\frac{\rho}{T}\frac{\partial^2 Z}{\partial t^2} = 0.$$

|| For the uniform membrane, $\pi(x_1, x_2) = \rho\dot{Z}(x_1, x_2)$.

relations for the field are independent of time;† however, for preciseness the time dependence is explicitly written in the form $\phi^{(\alpha)}(\mathbf{x},t)$. For the present (up to eqn. (13)) only field variables at one time are considered.

Because field variables at different points are to be regarded as independent variables, the last two relations in (4) give

$$[\phi^{(\alpha)}(\mathbf{x},t),\, \phi^{(\alpha')}(\mathbf{x}',t)] = 0, \qquad [\pi^{(\alpha)}(\mathbf{x},t),\, \pi^{(\alpha')}(\mathbf{x}',t)] = 0. \tag{10}$$

Similarly the first relation gives

$$[\pi^{(\alpha)}(\mathbf{x},t),\, \phi^{(\alpha')}(\mathbf{x}',t)] = 0, \quad \text{if } either\ \mathbf{x} \neq \mathbf{x}' \ or\ \alpha \neq \alpha'. \tag{11}$$

The equation

$$\int d^3\mathbf{x}\, [\pi^{(\alpha)}(\mathbf{x},t),\, \phi^{(\alpha)}(\mathbf{x}',t)] = \hbar/i \tag{12}$$

follows from the first relation in (4) on remembering that

$$p^{(\alpha)}(\mathbf{x}) = d^3\mathbf{x}\, \pi^{(\alpha)}(\mathbf{x}),$$

and replacing the integral by a sum over the elements of volume $d^3\mathbf{x}$. Eqns. (11) and (12) may be written in the concise form

$$[\pi^{(\alpha)}(\mathbf{x},t),\, \phi^{(\alpha')}(\mathbf{x}',t)] = (\hbar/i)\delta_{\alpha\alpha'}\, \delta^3(\mathbf{x}-\mathbf{x}'), \tag{13}$$

where $\delta^3(\mathbf{x}) = \delta(x_1).\delta(x_2).\delta(x_3)$. From (10) and (13) the commutator of any field variables (at time t) can be found.

In quantum mechanics there are various ways of expressing the behaviour of a system as time varies. The two best-known methods are the Schrödinger and the Heisenberg representations. In the Schrödinger representation, the dynamical variables (like p_r, q_s) stay constant and the wave functions $\psi(t)$ or the state vectors $|\,,t\rangle$ vary with time. In the Heisenberg representation the opposite is the case; the state vector $|\,\rangle$ for any state of the physical system is independent of time while the operators $q_r(t)$, $p_s(t)$ vary with time. In discussing the motion of fields the Heisenberg representation is frequently used because the time-dependent field operators $\phi^{(\alpha)}(\mathbf{x},t)$ give a picture of the field motion which is in many ways similar to classical wave propagation. For example, the Heisenberg equations of motion for the electromagnetic field are just the Maxwell equations (with suitably defined source functions): the quantities which are propagated are now operators.

The Heisenberg equations of motion for a dynamical system are‡

$$\frac{df}{dt} = \frac{i}{\hbar}[\mathbf{H},f]. \tag{14}$$

† The Heisenberg equations of motion ((14) below) ensure that $[A(t), B(t)]$ is independent of the time t, if for some time, $[A, B]$ commutes with H. Therefore relations (4) are time independent.

‡ P. A. M. Dirac, *Quantum Mechanics* (Clarendon Press, 3rd edn., 1947), ch. 6.

Here f is any function of the dynamical variables† and $\mathbf{H}$ is the Hamiltonian for the system, which is in general obtained by writing the classical Hamiltonian‡ in operator form. The classical expression is

$$\mathbf{H} = \sum_{r=1}^{n} p_r \dot{q}_r - L$$

and $\mathbf{H}$ is to be written as a function $\mathbf{H}(p_r, q_s)$ of the dynamical variables q_r and their canonical momenta p_r. In field theory the analogous expression is

$$\mathbf{H} = \int d^3\mathbf{x} \Big\{ \sum_{\alpha=1}^{N} \pi^{(\alpha)}(\mathbf{x})\dot{\phi}^{(\alpha)}(\mathbf{x}) - \mathscr{L} \Big\}. \tag{15}$$

[Starting from the action principle for fields, a direct derivation of this Hamiltonian and of the Heisenberg equation of motion (14) is given in Chapter IX (see especially §§ 2, 3, 4 and eqns. (9.37), (9.39)). The use of the action principle method of Chapter IX has the advantage that all the equations and properties of the quantized field are derived from the simple fundamental equation (9.26) in a way which is obviously self-consistent and Lorentz invariant. The method is also applicable to the interaction of several fields; the Lagrangian density $\mathscr{L}$ appearing in (15) has to be replaced by a sum of terms $\mathscr{L}^{(f)}$—one for each field f—together with terms $\mathscr{L}_{\text{int}}$ which describe the interactions of the fields.]

When discussing a relativistic field theory by means of the Heisenberg representation it is desirable to express the spatial variation of the operators by equations similar to (14); in this way the Lorentz transformation properties of the derivatives of operators are easily seen. Remembering that the state vector for a particular physical situation is constant for all positions and times, we have (9.39) which shows that the derivative $\partial_\mu A(x_\nu)$ of any Heisenberg field operator $A(x_\nu)$ is given by

$$(\hbar/i)\partial_\mu A(x_\nu) = [A(x_\nu), \mathbf{P}_\mu], \tag{16}$$

where $\mathbf{P}_\mu$ is the total energy-momentum 4-vector operator which is defined by (9.37). In particular $\mathbf{P}_4 = (i/c)\mathbf{H}$; the spatial components $\mathbf{P}_k$ $(k = 1,2,3)$ are the components of the total momentum operator for the field.§

† If f is a function of the dynamical variables and in addition is an *explicit* function of t, eqn. (14) has to be modified. An example is given by eqn. (37) below where $A(\mathbf{k})$ is defined as a function of $\phi^{(+)}(x_\mu)$ by the relation (35) which contains the time explicitly.

‡ Possible ambiguities in the order of operators in $\mathbf{H}$ are discussed in Chapter X.

§ The consistency of eqns. (16) requires that $(\partial_\mu \partial_{\mu'} - \partial_{\mu'} \partial_\mu)A = 0$. This is guaranteed by the relation $[\mathbf{P}_\mu, \mathbf{P}_{\mu'}] = 0$. These commutators vanish by (9.39) when $\mu = 4$; when neither μ nor $\mu' = 4$, they must vanish because $\partial_k \mathbf{P}_{k'} = 0$ since $\mathbf{P}_{\mu'}$ is an integral over all space.

3. The free neutral pion field

The neutral pion field is considered first because there is only one independent field amplitude $\phi(\mathbf{x})$ at each point $\mathbf{x}$ of space (in charged pion theory it is necessary to have two independent field amplitudes at each point $\mathbf{x}$, so as to allow for the doubling of the degrees of freedom arising from the two possible signs of the charge of a pion).

The classical equation of motion (eqn. (1.27))

$$(\partial_\mu^2-\kappa^2)\phi(x_\mu) = 0 \tag{17}$$

of the pseudo-scalar wave amplitude $\phi(x_\mu)$ is given by the Lagrangian density,†

$$\mathscr{L} = -\tfrac{1}{2}c^2\{\partial_\mu\phi\,\partial_\mu\phi+\kappa^2\phi^2\}. \tag{18}$$

The canonical momentum density is therefore

$$\pi(x_\mu) = \dot{\phi}(x_\mu) \tag{19}$$

and the Hamiltonian‡ becomes

$$\mathbf{H} = \tfrac{1}{2}\int d^3\mathbf{x}[\pi^2(\mathbf{x},t)+c^2\kappa^2\phi^2(\mathbf{x},t)+c^2\{\operatorname{grad}\phi(\mathbf{x},t)\}^2]. \tag{20}$$

On going over to quantum theory $\phi(x_\mu)$ has to be replaced by a Hermitian operator;§ similarly $\pi(x_\mu)$ is to be a Hermitian operator. The commutation rules for variables at the same time are, by (10) and (13),

$$\left.\begin{aligned}[\phi(\mathbf{x},t),\,\phi(\mathbf{x}',t)] = 0, \qquad [\pi(\mathbf{x},t),\,\pi(\mathbf{x}',t)] = 0\\ [\pi(\mathbf{x},t),\,\phi(\mathbf{x}',t)] = (\hbar/i)\delta^3(\mathbf{x}-\mathbf{x}')\end{aligned}\right\}. \tag{21}$$

The quantum equations of motion are now readily written down. By (14) and (20),

$$\frac{\partial\pi(\mathbf{x},t)}{\partial t} = \frac{i}{\hbar}\frac{1}{2}\int d^3\mathbf{x}'[c^2\{\operatorname{grad}\phi(\mathbf{x}',t)\}^2+c^2\kappa^2\{\phi(\mathbf{x}',t)\}^2,\,\pi(\mathbf{x},t)].$$

Using (21) and integrating by parts‖ gives

$$\frac{\partial\pi(\mathbf{x},t)}{\partial t} = c^2\nabla^2\phi(\mathbf{x},t)-c^2\kappa^2\phi(\mathbf{x},t). \tag{22}$$

† The factor $(-\tfrac{1}{2}c^2)$ is inserted in (18) so that the Hamiltonian will readily agree with the usual expression for the energy.

‡ The Hamiltonian density $H(x)$ is given by $\mathbf{H} = \int d^3\mathbf{x}H(\mathbf{x})$.

§ Strictly speaking, in the classical theory of the neutral pion $\phi(x)$ is everywhere real, because if it were complex there would be two independent components at each point x. However, in Chapter I we used complex ϕ for convenience, just as complex A was used in Maxwell theory.

‖ The integration by parts assumes either that $\phi(\mathbf{x})$ vanishes sufficiently quickly as $|\mathbf{x}| \to \infty$, or that a periodicity condition is imposed on $\phi(\mathbf{x})$ on the walls of a very large cubic box. The periodicity condition is mentioned on p. 68 below.

The equation
$$\frac{\partial\phi(\mathbf{x},t)}{\partial t} = \frac{i}{\hbar}[\mathbf{H},\phi(\mathbf{x},t)]$$

gives (19) as a relation between operators (as it must, for consistency). Combining these two equations, it is seen that the Heisenberg operator $\phi(x_\mu)$ obeys the equation of motion (17).

It is frequently necessary to know the value of the commutator $[\phi(x'_\mu),\phi(x_\mu)]$ of the field amplitudes at arbitrary space-time points x'_μ x_μ. The commutator of ϕ at points having different space and time coordinates is involved in working out how a disturbance at one point propagates and alters the field measured at another point. The commutator in question (by (17)) obeys the equation

$$(\partial^2_{x'\mu}-\kappa^2)[\phi(x'_\mu),\phi(x_\mu)] = 0 \quad (\text{all } x_\mu, x'_\mu). \tag{23}$$

Also, by (21), it satisfies

$$\left.\begin{aligned} [\phi(\mathbf{x}',t),\ \phi(\mathbf{x},t)] &= 0 \\ \frac{\partial}{\partial t'}[\phi(\mathbf{x}',t'),\ \phi(\mathbf{x},t)]\Big|_{t=t'} &= (\hbar/i)\delta^3(\mathbf{x}-\mathbf{x}') \end{aligned}\right\}. \tag{24}$$

Keeping x_μ fixed, we may regard relations (24) as initial conditions (on the plane $t' = t$) which are sufficient to determine the solution of the homogeneous wave equation (23). In the Appendix, the solution of the equation

$$(\partial^2_{x'\mu}-\kappa^2)f(x'_\mu) = 0 \quad (\text{all } x'_\mu),$$

which takes the values $f(\mathbf{x},t)$, $\partial f(\mathbf{x},t)/\partial t$ on the plane $t' = t$, is determined in explicit form. Eqn. (A.70), which gives this solution, can be written

$$f(\mathbf{x}',t') = \frac{1}{c}\int\limits_{(t)} d^3\mathbf{x}\left\{D_{(\kappa)}(\mathbf{x}-\mathbf{x}',t-t')\frac{\partial f(\mathbf{x},t)}{\partial t} - f(\mathbf{x},t)\frac{\partial}{\partial t}D_{(\kappa)}(\mathbf{x}-\mathbf{x}',t-t')\right\}, \tag{25}$$

where $D_{(\kappa)}(x_\mu)$ is the Lorentz invariant function given by (A.49) or (A.62). $D_{(\kappa)}(x_\mu)$ obeys the homogeneous wave equation (A.54),

$$(\partial^2_\mu-\kappa^2)D_{(\kappa)}(x_\nu) = 0$$

and it has the properties (A.49), (A.55), (A.57),

$$\left.\begin{aligned} D_{(\kappa)}(\mathbf{x},t) = 0,\ \mathbf{x}^2 > c^2t^2; \qquad \frac{1}{c}\frac{\partial}{\partial t}D_{(\kappa)}(\mathbf{x},t)\,|_{t=0} = -\delta^3(\mathbf{x}) \\ D_{(\kappa)}(\mathbf{x},t) = D_{(\kappa)}(-\mathbf{x},t) = -D_{(\kappa)}(\mathbf{x},-t) \end{aligned}\right\}. \tag{26}$$

Substituting (24) into (25) gives the general commutator

$$[\phi(x'_\mu), \phi(x_\mu)] = (i\hbar/c)D_{(\kappa)}(x'_\mu - x_\mu). \tag{27}$$

This is a Lorentz invariant expression,† and on using (26) it is seen to contain relations (21) as special cases.

4. The particle aspect

The particle aspect‡ of the field is derived on expanding the operator $\phi(x_\mu)$ in terms of a complete set of solutions $f^{(n)}(x_\mu)$ of the free-field equation

$$(\partial_\mu^2 - \kappa^2)f^{(n)}(x_\nu) = 0. \tag{28}$$

The expansion is

$$\phi(x_\mu) = \sum_{(n)} q_{(n)} f^{(n)}(x_\mu), \tag{29}$$

where $q_{(n)}$ are constant operator coefficients. Examples are the expansion in terms of the plane-wave solutions $\exp(ik_\mu x_\mu)$ of (28) (having $k_\mu^2 + \kappa^2 = 0$)§ which describes particles in eigenstates of momentum, and the expansion in terms of the spherical harmonic solutions|| of (28),

$$e^{\mp i\omega t} g_{lk}(r) Y_l^{(m)}(\theta, \phi)$$

(having $\omega^2 = c^2(k^2 + \kappa^2)$) which describes particles in eigenstates of angular momentum.

The expansion in terms of plane waves is the simplest, and will now be discussed. The eigensolutions $\exp(ik_\mu x_\mu)$ exist for a continuum of values of k_μ, and it is convenient to write the expansion (29) in the form

$$\phi(x_\mu) = \frac{1}{(2\pi)^2} \int d^4k\, \delta(k_\mu^2 + \kappa^2) A(k_\mu) e^{ik_\mu x_\mu}, \tag{30}$$

where the integral is taken over the whole of the $(\mathbf{k}, k_0)$ space, and $A(k_\mu)$ are the operator coefficients.†† The presence of the δ-function in (30) ensures that the wave equation (17) is obeyed. Apart from $A(k_\mu)$, the integrand in (30) is a Lorentz invariant;‡‡ hence, because $\phi(x_\mu)$ is a pseudo-scalar, $A(k_\mu)$ must be a pseudo-scalar.

The operator $\phi(x_\mu)$ is Hermitian, so it is necessary that§§

$$\tilde{A}(k_\mu) = A(-k_\mu). \tag{31}$$

† The proof that $D_{(\kappa)}(x_\mu)$ is an invariant is given in the Appendix.

‡ The particle aspect of a scalar (or pseudo-scalar) field was discussed by W. Pauli and V. F. Weisskopf, *Helv. phys. Acta*, **7** (1934) 709.

§ $k_4 \equiv ik_0$, so that $k_\mu x_\mu = \mathbf{k}.\mathbf{x} - k_0 x_0 = \mathbf{k}.\mathbf{x} - ck_0 t$.

|| See eqn. (1.90) for the definition of $g_{lk}(r)$.

†† $A(k_\mu)$, like $\phi(x_\mu)$, is an operator which acts upon the state vector describing the particular physical situation in which we are interested.

‡‡ $\int d^4k.I$ is invariant provided I is invariant; $k_\mu x_\mu$ and k_μ^2 are invariants.

§§ $\tilde{A}$ is the Hermitian conjugate of A.

Using Dirac's relation†

$$\delta(y^2-a^2) = \frac{1}{2|a|}\{\delta(y-a)+\delta(y+a)\} \quad (a, y \text{ real}), \tag{32}$$

the δ-function in (30) becomes

$$\delta(k_\mu^2+\kappa^2) = \frac{c}{2\omega_k}\{\delta(k_0-\omega_k/c)+\delta(k_0+\omega_k/c)\}, \tag{33}$$

where $\omega_k = c(\mathbf{k}^2+\kappa^2)^{\frac{1}{2}}$. Using (31) and (33) and writing $A(\mathbf{k})$ for $A(\mathbf{k}, k_0 = \omega_k/c)$, the expansion (30) takes the form

$$\phi(x_\mu) = \frac{c}{8\pi^2}\int\limits_{-\infty}^{\infty}\frac{d^3\mathbf{k}}{\omega_k}\{A(\mathbf{k})e^{i(\mathbf{k}.\mathbf{x}-\omega_k t)}+\tilde{A}(\mathbf{k})e^{-i(\mathbf{k}.\mathbf{x}-\omega_k t)}\}. \tag{34}$$

The integral in (34) is taken over the whole three-dimensional space of the propagation vector $\mathbf{k}$.‡ The operators $A(\mathbf{k})$, $\tilde{A}(\mathbf{k})$ are independent; they appear in (34) as the operator coefficients of the positive and negative frequency parts of $\phi(x_\mu)$:

$$\left.\begin{aligned}\phi^{(+)}(x_\mu) &= \frac{c}{8\pi^2}\int\limits_{-\infty}^{\infty}\frac{d^3\mathbf{k}}{\omega_k}A(\mathbf{k})e^{i(\mathbf{k}.\mathbf{x}-\omega_k t)}\\ \phi^{(-)}(x_\mu) &= \frac{c}{8\pi^2}\int\limits_{-\infty}^{\infty}\frac{d^3\mathbf{k}}{\omega_k}\tilde{A}(\mathbf{k})e^{-i(\mathbf{k}.\mathbf{x}-\omega_k t)}\end{aligned}\right\} \tag{35}$$

with $\phi(x_\mu) = \phi^{(+)}(x_\mu)+\phi^{(-)}(x_\mu)$. The splitting of $\phi(x_\mu)$ into positive and negative frequency parts, $\phi^{(+)}(x_\mu)$ and $\phi^{(-)}(x_\mu)$ respectively, is a Lorentz invariant division. This follows from the relation§

$$\phi^{(+)}(x_\mu) = \frac{1}{(2\pi)^2}\int d^4k\; \theta(k_\mu)\delta(k_\mu^2+\kappa^2)A(k_\mu)e^{ik_\mu x_\mu}, \tag{36}$$

where
$$\theta(k_\mu) = \begin{cases}1, & k_0 > 0,\\ 0, & k_0 < 0;\end{cases}$$

$\theta(k_\mu)\delta(k_\mu^2+k^2)$ is invariant under any orthochronous Lorentz transformation, therefore $\phi^{(+)}(x_\mu)$ is a pseudo-scalar. The general conditions under which positive and negative frequency splitting is a unique and invariant operation are discussed in the Appendix (pp. 456–8).

The physical interpretation of the operators $A(\mathbf{k})$, $\tilde{A}(\mathbf{k})$ is closely associated with the positive and negative frequency splitting. Because

† P. A. M. Dirac, *Quantum Mechanics* (Clarendon Press, 1947), ch. 4.

‡ $\int (d^3\mathbf{k}/\omega_k)I$ is invariant, if I is an invariant.

§ There is a similar relation for $\phi^{(-)}(x_\mu)$ got by replacing $\theta(k_\mu)$ in (36) by $\theta(-k_\mu)$.

H is independent of time, taking the positive frequency part of the operator equation

$$\partial\phi(x_\mu)/\partial t = i/\hbar[\mathbf{H}, \phi(x_\mu)]$$

gives

$$\partial\phi^{(+)}(x_\mu)/\partial t = i/\hbar[\mathbf{H}, \phi^{(+)}(x_\mu)].$$

Substituting in (35) and equating the coefficients of the independent functions $\exp(i\mathbf{k}.\mathbf{x})$ gives

$$[\mathbf{H}, A(\mathbf{k})] = -\hbar\omega_k A(\mathbf{k}). \tag{37}$$

Similarly, using $\phi^{(-)}(x_\mu)$ gives

$$[\mathbf{H}, \tilde{A}(\mathbf{k})] = \hbar\omega_k \tilde{A}(\mathbf{k}). \tag{38}$$

If $|E'\rangle$ is an eigenstate of the Hamiltonian **H** having energy eigenvalue E', then either $A(\mathbf{k})|E'\rangle$ vanishes, or else it is also an eigenstate of **H** and has the energy eigenvalue $E'-\hbar\omega_k$. This follows from (37) because

$$\mathbf{H}.A(\mathbf{k})|E'\rangle = A(\mathbf{k})(\mathbf{H}-\hbar\omega_k)|E'\rangle = (E'-\hbar\omega_k)A(\mathbf{k})|E'\rangle.$$

Similarly (38) shows that $\tilde{A}(\mathbf{k})|E'\rangle$ is an eigenstate of **H** having the eigenvalue $(E'+\hbar\omega_k)$.

Because $[\mathbf{P}_\mu, \mathbf{P}_{\mu'}] = 0$,† it is possible to find state vectors which are eigenstates both of **H** and of the total momentum operator‡

$$\mathbf{P} = (\mathbf{P}_1, \mathbf{P}_2, \mathbf{P}_3).$$

The operator **P** is given by (9.60):

$$\mathbf{P} = -\tfrac{1}{2}\int d^3\mathbf{x}[\pi(\mathbf{x},t)\operatorname{grad}\phi(\mathbf{x},t)+\{\operatorname{grad}\phi(\mathbf{x},t)\}\pi(\mathbf{x},t)], \tag{39}$$

where the terms in the integrand have been written in both orders to ensure that **P** is Hermitian. It is easy to verify, using the commutation relations (21), that for any function§ of the field variables $f\{\phi(x_\mu), \pi(x_\mu)\}$

$$(\hbar/i)\operatorname{grad} f = [f, \mathbf{P}].$$

Substituting $\phi(x_\mu)$ for f, we take the positive (or negative) frequency part of the resulting equation, remembering that **P** is independent of time ($[\mathbf{P}, \mathbf{H}] = 0$). This gives

$$(\hbar/i)\operatorname{grad}\phi^{(+)}(x_\mu) = [\phi^{(+)}(x_\mu), \mathbf{P}].$$

Substituting (35) gives‖

$$\left.\begin{aligned} [\mathbf{P}, A(\mathbf{k})] &= -\hbar\mathbf{k}A(\mathbf{k}); \\ \text{similarly}\qquad [\mathbf{P}, \tilde{A}(\mathbf{k})] &= +\hbar\mathbf{k}\tilde{A}(\mathbf{k}). \end{aligned}\right\} \tag{40}$$

Hence acting with $A(\mathbf{k})$ on an eigenstate $|\mathbf{P}'\rangle$ of **P** changes its eigen-

† Cf. p. 61, n. §.

‡ Below, **P** denotes the *vector* momentum operator.

§ $f(x_\mu)$ should not depend *explicitly* on x_μ.

‖ Coefficients of the independent functions $\exp(i\mathbf{k}.\mathbf{x})$ are equated.

value of momentum $\mathbf{P}'$ to $(\mathbf{P}'-\hbar\mathbf{k})$, and acting on $|\mathbf{P}'\rangle$ with $\tilde{A}(\mathbf{k})$ changes its eigenvalue of momentum to $(\mathbf{P}'+\hbar\mathbf{k})$.

Using (37), (38), (40), and noticing that $\hbar\omega_k = c(\hbar^2\mathbf{k}^2+\mu^2c^2)^{\frac{1}{2}}$, where μ is the pion mass, it is reasonable to suggest the following physical interpretation of $A(\mathbf{k})$ and $\tilde{A}(\mathbf{k})$: $A(\mathbf{k})$ is an operator destroying a neutral pion of momentum $\hbar\mathbf{k}$, $\tilde{A}(\mathbf{k})$ is an operator creating such a pion. So far it has only been proved that this interpretation is consistent with the changes in energy and momentum which are produced by A and $\tilde{A}$; we now derive relations ((56) and (57)) which complete the proof.

It is first necessary to find the commutation relations of the $A(\mathbf{k})$ and $\tilde{A}(\mathbf{k})$. A Fourier inversion of (35) gives

$$\left.\begin{aligned} A(\mathbf{k}) &= \frac{\omega_k}{c\pi}\int\limits_{-\infty}^{\infty} d^3\mathbf{x}\, e^{-i\mathbf{k}.\mathbf{x}}\phi^{(+)}(\mathbf{x},0) \\ \tilde{A}(\mathbf{k}) &= \frac{\omega_k}{c\pi}\int\limits_{-\infty}^{\infty} d^3\mathbf{x}\, e^{i\mathbf{k}.\mathbf{x}}\phi^{(-)}(\mathbf{x},0) \end{aligned}\right\}. \tag{41}$$

From the general commutator (27) it follows (*since both sides of* (27) *obey the equation* $(\partial_\mu^2-\kappa^2)f = 0$) that

$$[\phi^{(+)}(x'_\mu), \phi(x_\mu)] = i\hbar/c.D^{(+)}_{(\kappa)}(x'_\mu-x_\mu). \tag{42}$$

The explicit forms of the positive and negative frequency parts $D^{(+)}_{(\kappa)}(x_\mu)$ and $D^{(-)}_{(\kappa)}(x_\mu)$ are given in (A.66). Because the function on the right of (42) has the argument $(x'_\mu-x_\mu)$, taking the negative frequency part of (42) with respect to x_μ is the same as taking the positive frequency part with respect to x'_μ. Thus, from (42),

$$[\phi^{(+)}(x'_\mu), \phi^{(-)}(x_\mu)] = i\hbar/c.D^{(+)}_{(\kappa)}(x'_\mu-x_\mu). \tag{43}$$

Subtracting (43) from (42) gives

$$\left.\begin{aligned} &[\phi^{(+)}(x'_\mu), \phi^{(+)}(x_\mu)] = 0 \\ \text{similarly}\qquad &[\phi^{(-)}(x'_\mu), \phi^{(-)}(x_\mu)] = 0 \end{aligned}\right\}. \tag{44}$$

Therefore all creation operators commute and all destruction operators commute; in particular, by (41),

$$[A(\mathbf{k}), A(\mathbf{k}')] = 0 = [\tilde{A}(\mathbf{k}), \tilde{A}(\mathbf{k}')]. \tag{45}$$

From (A.66) and (33),

$$D^{(+)}_{(\kappa)}(\mathbf{x},0) = \frac{-i}{(2\pi)^3}\frac{c}{2}\int\limits_{-\infty}^{\infty}\frac{d^3\mathbf{k}}{\omega_k}e^{i\mathbf{k}.\mathbf{x}}. \tag{46}$$

Using (41), (43), and (46) a simple calculation gives†

$$[A(\mathbf{k}'), \tilde{A}(\mathbf{k})] = \frac{4\pi\hbar\omega_k}{c^2}\delta^3(\mathbf{k}-\mathbf{k}'). \tag{47}$$

In general we use basic solutions of (28) whose spatial factors $\exp[i(\mathbf{k}.\mathbf{x})]$ are periodic on the faces of a large cube of edge L. The restriction on the values of $\mathbf{k}$ which is imposed in this way is of no physical consequence; by making L sufficiently large, we can use these functions to approximate, as accurately as may be wished, to any well-behaved field distribution. The periodicity condition is used in deriving (22) and in similar situations. The number of propagation vectors $\mathbf{k}$ lying in the volume $d^3\mathbf{k}$ about $\mathbf{k}$ is $\rho_\mathbf{k}\, d^3\mathbf{k}$ where $\rho_\mathbf{k} = (L/2\pi)^3$. In general the δ-function in (47) can be replaced by using‡

$$\delta^3(\mathbf{k}-\mathbf{k}') = \rho_\mathbf{k}\,\delta_{\mathbf{k},\mathbf{k}'}, \tag{48}$$

where
$$\delta_{\mathbf{k},\mathbf{k}'} = \begin{cases} 1, & \mathbf{k} = \mathbf{k}', \\ 0, & \mathbf{k} \neq \mathbf{k}'. \end{cases}$$

It is now possible to replace $A(\mathbf{k})$, $\tilde{A}(\mathbf{k})$ by the dimensionless operators $a(\mathbf{k})$, $\tilde{a}(\mathbf{k})$ defined by

$$A(\mathbf{k}) = \left(\frac{4\pi\hbar\omega_k}{c^2}\rho_\mathbf{k}\right)^{\frac{1}{2}} a(\mathbf{k}), \qquad \tilde{A}(\mathbf{k}) = \left(\frac{4\pi\hbar\omega_k}{c^2}\rho_\mathbf{k}\right)^{\frac{1}{2}} \tilde{a}(\mathbf{k}). \tag{49}$$

The commutators (45) and (47) are now written

$$\left.\begin{aligned} [a(\mathbf{k}), a(\mathbf{k}')] = 0, \qquad [\tilde{a}(\mathbf{k}), \tilde{a}(\mathbf{k}')] = 0 \\ [a(\mathbf{k}), \tilde{a}(\mathbf{k}')] = \delta_{\mathbf{k},\mathbf{k}'} \end{aligned}\right\}. \tag{50}$$

From (50) it follows that

$$\left.\begin{aligned} [\tilde{a}(\mathbf{k})a(\mathbf{k}), \tilde{a}(\mathbf{k}')] &= \tilde{a}(\mathbf{k})\delta_{\mathbf{k},\mathbf{k}'} \\ [\tilde{a}(\mathbf{k})a(\mathbf{k}), a(\mathbf{k}')] &= -a(\mathbf{k})\delta_{\mathbf{k},\mathbf{k}'} \end{aligned}\right\}. \tag{51}$$

Any function of the field variables is expressible in terms of the set of operators $a(\mathbf{k})$ and $\tilde{a}(\mathbf{k})$. Comparing (37) and (38) with (51) it is seen that the commutators of H with $a(\mathbf{k})$ and $\tilde{a}(\mathbf{k})$ are identical with the commutators of $\sum_{\mathbf{k}'} \hbar\omega_{k'}\tilde{a}(\mathbf{k}')a(\mathbf{k}')$ with $a(\mathbf{k})$ and $\tilde{a}(\mathbf{k})$ respectively. Therefore we may write§

$$\mathsf{H} = \sum_\mathbf{k} \hbar\omega_k \tilde{a}(\mathbf{k})a(\mathbf{k}), \tag{52}$$

† $\delta^3(\mathbf{k}) = \delta(k_1)\delta(k_2)\delta(k_3)$ is the three-dimensional δ-function in $\mathbf{k}$-space. It is useful to notice that

$$\int_{-\infty}^{\infty} d^3\mathbf{x}\, e^{i\mathbf{k}.\mathbf{x}} = (2\pi)^3\delta^3(\mathbf{k}).$$

‡ $\rho_\mathbf{k}$ may become infinite; for example, for $L \to \infty$.

§ To the right of (52) may be added any quantity C which commutes with all field variables; so far as the pion field variables are concerned, C is a number. It cannot enter the equations of motion, and although it can alter the eigenvalues of H, it cannot appear in the energy differences between states. If the vacuum is required to have zero energy then C must vanish (cf. eqn. (58)).

where the summation is over all allowed propagation vectors (as discussed on the opposite page).

The eigenvalues of the operators $n(\mathbf{k}) = \tilde{a}(\mathbf{k})a(\mathbf{k})$ must be positive or zero.† The first of equations (51) shows that if $|n'_{\mathbf{k}}\rangle$ is an eigenvector of $n(\mathbf{k})$ having eigenvalue $n'_{\mathbf{k}}$, then $\tilde{a}(\mathbf{k})|n'_{\mathbf{k}}\rangle$ is also an eigenvector of $n(\mathbf{k})$ and has eigenvalue $(n'_{\mathbf{k}}+1)$; the second equation shows that $a(\mathbf{k})|n'_{\mathbf{k}}\rangle$ is an eigenvector of $n(\mathbf{k})$ having eigenvalue $(n'_{\mathbf{k}}-1)$. Because a negative eigenvalue $(n'_{\mathbf{k}}-1)$ cannot exist, there must be a state, which we write as $|0_{\mathbf{k}}\rangle$, such that $a(\mathbf{k})|0_{\mathbf{k}}\rangle = 0$. Obviously this state is an eigenstate of $n(\mathbf{k})$ and has zero eigenvalue. Using the operator $\tilde{a}(\mathbf{k})$ repeatedly, the other eigenstates of $n(\mathbf{k})$ can be built up; clearly the eigenvalues of $n(\mathbf{k})$ are 0, 1, 2, 3,.... A little algebraic manipulation shows that the normalized eigenvector‡ having (integral) eigenvalue $n'_{\mathbf{k}}$ may be written

$$|n'_{\mathbf{k}}\rangle = \frac{1}{(n'_{\mathbf{k}}!)^{\frac{1}{2}}}\{\tilde{a}(\mathbf{k})\}^{n'_{\mathbf{k}}}|0_{\mathbf{k}}\rangle. \tag{53}$$

Because $\tilde{a}(\mathbf{k})$ increases the eigenvalue $n'_{\mathbf{k}}$ by unity, the only non-zero matrix elements of $\tilde{a}(\mathbf{k})$ (in the $n(\mathbf{k})$ representation) are $\langle n'_{\mathbf{k}}+1|\tilde{a}(\mathbf{k})|n'_{\mathbf{k}}\rangle$. By (53) they have the value

$$\langle n'_{\mathbf{k}}+1|\tilde{a}(\mathbf{k})|n'_{\mathbf{k}}\rangle = (n'_{\mathbf{k}}+1)^{\frac{1}{2}}. \tag{54}$$

The only non-zero matrix elements of the Hermitian conjugate operator $a(\mathbf{k})$ are therefore

$$\langle n'_{\mathbf{k}}|a(\mathbf{k})|n'_{\mathbf{k}}+1\rangle = (n'_{\mathbf{k}}+1)^{\frac{1}{2}}. \tag{55}$$

By (52) it follows that the Hamiltonian

$$\mathsf{H} = \sum_{\mathbf{k}} \hbar\omega_k n(\mathbf{k}) \tag{56}$$

has eigenvalues which are a sum of integral multiples of $\hbar\omega_k$. Similarly, from (40) it follows (by arguments analogous to those used in deriving (52)) that the total momentum operator may be written (on ignoring an additive constant)

$$\mathbf{P} = \sum_{\mathbf{k}} \hbar\mathbf{k}\, n(\mathbf{k}). \tag{57}$$

Its eigenvalues are a sum of integral multiples of $\hbar\mathbf{k}$. It is now clear that the interpretation given above for $\tilde{A}(\mathbf{k})$, $A(\mathbf{k})$ as operators creating and destroying pions of momentum $\hbar\mathbf{k}$ is correct.

† This is because

$$n'\langle n'|n'\rangle = \langle n'|\tilde{a}a|n'\rangle = |(a|n'\rangle)|^2 \geqslant 0.$$

‡ The normalized eigenvector obeys $\langle n'_{\mathbf{k}}|n'_{\mathbf{k}}\rangle = 1$.

5. The vacuum and the propagators

The vacuum is the state having the least energy, and we have chosen† the least energy eigenvalue to be zero. The vacuum state vector $|0\rangle$ is therefore defined by the condition

$$n(\mathbf{k})|0\rangle = 0, \quad \text{all } \mathbf{k}. \tag{58}$$

An equivalent definition which is frequently more convenient, comes from (58) on using (35) and (49):

$$\phi^{(+)}(x_\mu)|0\rangle = 0, \quad \text{all } x_\mu. \tag{59}$$

Definition (59) is obviously Lorentz invariant, and it is independent of the particular representation which is used (linear momentum, angular momentum, etc.). The Hermitian conjugate form of (59) is

$$\langle 0|\phi^{(-)}(x_\mu) = 0. \tag{60}$$

Looking at (35) we see that the state vector $\phi^{(-)}(x_\mu)|0\rangle$ is a linear superposition of single-pion states, and $\phi^{(-)}(x_\mu)\phi^{(-)}(x'_\mu)|0\rangle$ is a superposition of two-meson states, and so on. It would clearly be incorrect to regard $\phi^{(-)}(x_\mu)$ itself as an operator giving the production of a pion at x_μ; a special Schrödinger representation is required to localize the creation and destruction operators. However, the positive and negative frequency parts of $\phi(x_\mu)$ can be associated with the propagation of the field, as follows.

An ordering operator T is used to arrange products of pion operators $\phi(x_\mu)$ in chronological order so that the operator associated with the latest time is to the left; for example

$$T\{\phi(x_\mu)\phi(x'_\mu)\} = \begin{cases} \phi(x_\mu)\phi(x'_\mu), & x_0 > x'_0, \\ \phi(x'_\mu)\phi(x_\mu), & x_0 < x'_0. \end{cases}$$

This definition of chronological ordering is consistent with special relativity. This is because in the region of space-like separation, $(x_\mu - x'_\mu)^2 > 0$, where the statement $x_0 > x'_0$ is not invariant, the commutator (27) of the field variables vanishes; in this case the order of $\phi(x_\mu)\phi(x'_\mu)$ can be freely changed.

By (59) and (60) the vacuum expectation value of $T\{\phi(x_\mu)\phi(x'_\mu)\}$ is

$$\langle 0|T\{\phi(x_\mu)\phi(x'_\mu)\}|0\rangle = \begin{Bmatrix} \langle 0|\phi^{(+)}(x_\mu)\phi^{(-)}(x'_\mu)|0\rangle, & x_0 > x'_0 \\ \langle 0|\phi^{(+)}(x'_\mu)\phi^{(-)}(x_\mu)|0\rangle, & x_0 < x'_0 \end{Bmatrix}. \tag{61}$$

In both cases the creation operator occurs at the earlier time and the destruction operator at the later time; this suggests that (61) is asso-

† See p. 68, n. §.

ciated with the *causal* propagation of the pion field. The suggestion is borne out by the fact that (61) obeys the Green's function equation:†

$$(\partial^2_{x\mu} - \kappa^2)\langle 0|T\{\phi(x_\mu)\phi(x'_\mu)\}|0\rangle = (i\hbar/c)\delta^4(x_\mu - x'_\mu). \qquad (62)$$

As is shown in the Appendix, there is a Green's function $G(x_\mu - x'_\mu)$ which obeys the inhomogeneous equation

$$(\partial^2_{x\mu} - \kappa^2)G(x_\mu - x'_\mu) = -\delta^4(x_\mu - x'_\mu),$$

and which has the causal behaviour (as in (61)) $G(x_\mu) = -D^{(+)}_\kappa(x_\mu)$, $x_0 > 0$; $G(x_\mu) = D^{(-)}_{-\kappa}(x_\mu)$, $x_0 < 0$. It is commonly written

$$G(x_\mu) = \frac{i}{2} D_{F(\kappa)}(x_\mu),$$

where D_F is the Feynman function defined by (A.51). This causal Green's function is used to give the solution of scattering problems (cf. Appendix), and it plays an important role in the theory of interacting fields.

Now we prove relation (62). Using (61), the left-hand side of (62) vanishes, except for $x_0 = x'_0$. At $x_0 = x'_0$, the order of the operators is reversed, but by (24) this can only give a non-zero contribution on the left of (62) for $\mathbf{x} = \mathbf{x}'$. The contribution to the left of (62) arising from $x_\mu = x'_\mu$ is found by evaluating the integral

$$\frac{1}{c^2} \int \partial^2_t [T\{\phi(\mathbf{x}, t)\phi(\mathbf{x}', t')\}]\, d^4x$$

over the four-dimensional volume between the two time planes $t = (t' \pm \epsilon)$ (ϵ small). Using the commutator (27) we get

$$\frac{1}{c} \int d^3\mathbf{x} [\partial_t\{\phi(\mathbf{x}, t)\phi(\mathbf{x}', t')\}|_{t=t'+\epsilon} - \partial_t\{\phi(\mathbf{x}', t')\phi(\mathbf{x}, t)\}|_{t=t'-\epsilon}]$$

$$= i\hbar/c^2 \int d^3\mathbf{x}\, \partial_t D_{(\kappa)}(\mathbf{x} - \mathbf{x}', t - t')|_{t=t'} = -i\hbar/c.$$

Eqn. (62) follows. We deduce that

$$\langle 0|T\{\phi(x_\mu)\phi(x'_\mu)\}|0\rangle = \frac{1}{2}\frac{\hbar}{c} D_{F(\kappa)}(x_\mu - x'_\mu) \qquad (63)$$

because eqn. (62) and the causal conditions determine the Green's function, as is shown in the Appendix.

† $\delta^4(x_\mu) = \delta(x_0)\delta(x_1)\delta(x_2)\delta(x_3)$.

6. Example: Angular momentum representation†

The angular momentum operator $\mathbf{M}$ for the neutral pion field is given by the components $(\mathbf{P}_{23}, \mathbf{P}_{31}, \mathbf{P}_{12})$ of the tensor $\mathbf{P}_{\mu\nu}(\sigma)$ defined in (9.40). If σ is the space-like surface $t = \text{const}$, we have (9.61):

$$\mathbf{M} = -\tfrac{1}{2}\int d^3\mathbf{x}[\pi(\mathbf{x},t)\{\mathbf{x}\times\operatorname{grad}\phi(\mathbf{x},t)\}+\{\mathbf{x}\times\operatorname{grad}\phi(\mathbf{x},t)\}\pi(\mathbf{x},t)]. \tag{64}$$

In (64) both orders of the operators occur, since $\mathbf{M}$ must be Hermitian.

First we verify that

$$[\mathbf{M}, \mathbf{H}] = 0. \tag{65}$$

It is convenient to use the notation of Chapter I, eqn. (1.42):

$$\mathbf{I} = \mathbf{x}\times\operatorname{grad}.$$

Using (64), (20), and the commutation relations (21), it is easy to deduce that

$$[M_3, \mathbf{H}] = 2(\hbar/i)\int d^3\mathbf{x}\{\pi(\mathbf{x},t)I_3\,\pi(\mathbf{x},t)-c^2\kappa^2\phi(\mathbf{x},t)I_3\,\phi(\mathbf{x},t)-$$
$$-c^2\operatorname{grad}\phi(\mathbf{x},t).\operatorname{grad}I_3\,\phi(\mathbf{x},t)\}. \tag{66}$$

Also
$$\operatorname{grad}\phi.\operatorname{grad}(I_3\,\phi) = \operatorname{grad}\phi.I_3\operatorname{grad}\phi.$$

So (66) can be written

$$[M_3, \mathbf{H}] = \frac{\hbar}{i}\int d^3\mathbf{x}\; I_3[\{\pi(\mathbf{x},t)\}^2-c^2\kappa^2\{\phi(\mathbf{x},t)\}^2-c^2\{\operatorname{grad}\phi(\mathbf{x},t)\}^2].$$

The integral vanishes because $I_3 = \partial/\partial\alpha_3$, where α_3 is the azimuthal angle about the O_3 axis; hence (65) is true.‡ It is also easy to verify, using (64) and (21), that

$$[M_1, M_2] = i\hbar M_3. \tag{67}$$

It follows that the total angular momentum $\mathbf{M}^2$ and one of its components (say M_3) can be made diagonal together with the Hamiltonian $\mathbf{H}$. This will give the angular momentum representation of the field.

The angular momentum eigenstates for the free pion field are formed as a result of expanding the field operator $\phi(x_\mu)$ in terms of the complete set of functions

$$g_{lk}(r)Y_l^{(m)}(\theta,\phi). \tag{68}$$

Here (r,θ,ϕ) are spherical polar coordinates referred to the origin O of (spatial) coordinates, and $Y_l^{(m)}(\theta,\phi)$ are the spherical harmonics as defined in (1.45). The radial functions $g_{lk}(r)$ are the multiples of the spherical Bessel functions given by (1.90). The spherical Bessel functions are used rather than the spherical Neumann functions (1.88),

† The angular momentum representation has been discussed by R. G. Sachs, *Phys. Rev.* **87** (1952) 1100.

‡ The boundary conditions are assumed to have spherical symmetry.

because the field operator $\phi(x_\mu)$ which is to be expanded is everywhere finite; alternatively, we may say that it is necessary to derive state vectors which yield a finite probability for a pion being within a finite volume. The Neumann functions would not satisfy this condition because of their singularity at the origin. The functions $g_{lk}(r)$ are normalized in a large† sphere of radius $\mathscr{R}$ centred on O, by the condition

$$\int_0^{\mathscr{R}} dr\, r^2\{g_{lk}(r)\}^2 = 1.$$

The explicit form of these functions is

$$g_{lk}(r) = \left(\frac{\pi k}{r\mathscr{R}}\right)^{\frac{1}{2}} J_{l+\frac{1}{2}}(kr). \tag{69}$$

A discrete spectrum of values of the radial propagation number k is given by the boundary condition

$$g'_{lk}(\mathscr{R})/g_{lk}(\mathscr{R}) = \xi, \tag{70}$$

where ξ is any real constant; adjacent values of k are $(\pi/\mathscr{R})$ apart (for large $\mathscr{R}$). It follows from (70) that the radial functions $g_{lk}(r)$, $g_{lk'}(r)$ are orthogonal,‡ i.e.

$$\int_0^{\mathscr{R}} dr\, r^2 g_{lk}(r) g_{lk'}(r) = \delta_{kk'}. \tag{71}$$

Frequency splitting

The expansion of the field in terms of functions (68) is written in a form analogous to (35):

$$\left.\begin{aligned} \phi^{(+)}(x_\mu) &= \sum_{k,l,m} B_{klm}\, g_{lk}(r) Y_l^{(m)}(\theta,\phi) e^{-i\omega_k t} \\ \phi^{(-)}(x_\mu) &= \sum_{k,l,m} (-1)^m \tilde{B}_{klm}\, g_{lk}(r) Y_l^{(-m)}(\theta,\phi) e^{i\omega_k t} \end{aligned}\right\}. \tag{72}$$

Here B_{klm} and $\tilde{B}_{klm}$ are the (constant) operator coefficients of the expansion. The summations in (72) extend over all the discrete eigenvalues k, as well as all allowed values of (l, m). The second expansion is obtained from the first on noticing that, by (35), $\phi^{(-)}(x_\mu)$ is the Hermitian conjugate of $\phi^{(+)}(x_\mu)$; the factor $(-1)^m$ arises from using equation (1.47) for $Y_l^{(m)*}$. Splitting $\phi(x_\mu)$ into positive and negative frequency parts will, in any representation, give a division into destruction and creation operators; therefore it is expected that B_{klm}, $\tilde{B}_{klm}$ are destruction and creation operators respectively. It is easy to see that

† 'Large' means $k\mathscr{R} \gg 1$ for the values of k which are of interest in a particular problem.

‡ Cf. E. Jahnke and F. Emde, *Funktionentafeln* (B. G. Teubner, Leipzig, 1933).

$$\left.\begin{aligned}[\mathbf{H}, B_{klm}] &= -\hbar\omega_k B_{klm}\\ [\mathbf{H}, \tilde{B}_{klm}] &= \hbar\omega_k \tilde{B}_{klm}\end{aligned}\right\}. \tag{73}$$

These equations follow from (72) and the equations of motion by an argument identical with that leading to (37) and (38).

The commutation relations of the B, $\tilde{B}$ with themselves are readily found by expressing these operator coefficients in terms of the operators $A(\mathbf{k})$, $\tilde{A}(\mathbf{k})$. Using (71) and the orthogonality relation for the spherical harmonics (p. 22) gives the inverse relation to (72):

$$B_{klm} = \int\limits_0^{\mathscr{R}} r^2\,dr \int d\Omega_{(\theta\phi)}\, g_{lk}(r) Y_l^{(m)*}(\theta,\phi)\phi^{(+)}(\mathbf{x},0), \tag{74}$$

where $\mathbf{x} = (r,\theta,\phi)$ and $d\Omega_{(\theta\phi)}$ is the element of solid angle ($d\Omega = \sin\theta\,d\theta d\phi$). Using (1.77) and (1.90) we can write†

$$e^{i\mathbf{k}.\mathbf{x}} = (8\mathscr{R})^{\frac{1}{2}}\frac{\pi}{k}\sum_{l=0}^{\infty}\sum_{m=-l}^{l} i^l g_{lk}(r) Y_l^{(m)}(\theta,\phi) Y_l^{(m)*}(\alpha,\beta), \tag{75}$$

where (α,β) is the direction of the vector $\mathbf{k}$. Substituting (75) into the first of equations (35) for $\phi^{(+)}(\mathbf{x},0)$ and making the replacement‡

$$\int d^3\mathbf{k} \to \frac{\pi}{\mathscr{R}}\sum_k k^2 \int d\Omega_{(\alpha\beta)}$$

gives

$$\phi^{(+)}(\mathbf{x},0) = \frac{c}{(8\mathscr{R})^{\frac{1}{2}}}\sum_{k,l,m}\int \frac{k}{\omega_k}\, d\Omega_{(\alpha\beta)}\, i^l g_{lk}(r) Y_l^{(m)}(\theta,\phi) Y_l^{(m)*}(\alpha,\beta) A(\mathbf{k}).$$

Here the integral over $k = |\mathbf{k}|$ is replaced by a sum over the discrete values. Substituting into (74) gives the required relation between the operator coefficients

$$B_{klm} = \frac{c}{(8\mathscr{R})^{\frac{1}{2}}} i^l \frac{k}{\omega_k}\int d\Omega_{(\alpha\beta)}\, Y_l^{(m)*}(\alpha,\beta) A(\mathbf{k}). \tag{76}$$

Taking the Hermitian conjugate,§

$$\tilde{B}_{klm} = \frac{c}{(8\mathscr{R})^{\frac{1}{2}}} i^{-l} \frac{k}{\omega_k}\int d\Omega_{(\alpha\beta)}\, Y_l^{(m)}(\alpha,\beta) \tilde{A}(\mathbf{k}). \tag{77}$$

Eqns. (76) and (77) again show that B_{klm}, $\tilde{B}_{klm}$ are respectively related to the destruction and creation of pions. It may be objected that the

† By footnote §, p. 49, of Chapter I, $S = \sum_{m=-l}^{l} Y_l^{(m)}(\theta,\phi) Y_l^{(m)*}(\alpha,\beta)$ is invariant under rotations of the axes. Choosing the axes so that $\alpha = 0$, it follows that $S = \{(2l+1)/4\pi\}^{\frac{1}{2}} Y_l^{(0)}(\omega)$ where ω is the angle between the vectors $\mathbf{x}$ and $\mathbf{k}$.

‡ The interval between adjacent values of the radial propagation number k is $dk = \pi/\mathscr{R}$ (for large $\mathscr{R}$).

§ Eqns. (76) and (77) may be compared with similar relations given by J. Hamilton, *Proc. Camb. Phil. Soc.* **52** (1956) 97 (cf. eqn. (15)).

derivation of (76) is inconsistent because the set of functions $\exp[i(\mathbf{k}.\mathbf{x})]$ which is used in setting up (35) is not a normal† orthogonal set over the large sphere of radius $\mathscr{R}$. However, it should be noted that equation (76) is a direct consequence of the relation (75) between the plane wave and the spherical harmonic eigensolutions (68) of the wave equation; we may assume that in the limit $\mathscr{R} \to \infty$, eqn. (75) gives a unitary transformation.‡ This justifies relation (76), as we assume that $\mathscr{R}$ is always very large.

The number operators

Using (76), (77), and the commutation relations (45) for $A(\mathbf{k})$ and $\tilde{A}(\mathbf{k})$ gives

$$[B_{klm}, B_{k'l'm'}] = 0, \qquad [\tilde{B}_{klm}, \tilde{B}_{k'l'm'}] = 0. \tag{78}$$

Using (47) and making the replacement

$$\delta^3(\mathbf{k}-\mathbf{k}') \to \frac{1}{k^2}\frac{\mathscr{R}}{\pi}\delta_{k,k'}\,\delta(\hat{\mathbf{k}},\hat{\mathbf{k}}'),$$

where $\hat{\mathbf{k}}$, $\hat{\mathbf{k}}'$ are unit vectors, and $\delta(\hat{\mathbf{k}},\hat{\mathbf{k}}')$ is a δ-function on the unit sphere such that

$$\int \delta(\hat{\mathbf{k}},\hat{\mathbf{k}}')\,d\Omega_{(\alpha\beta)} = 1,$$

we get

$$[B_{klm}, \tilde{B}_{k'l'm'}] = \frac{\hbar}{2\omega_k}\delta_{kk'}\,\delta_{ll'}\,\delta_{mm'}. \tag{79}$$

It is now convenient, as in the linear momentum representation, to define dimensionless operators b_{klm}, $\tilde{b}_{klm}$,

$$B_{klm} = b_{klm}\sqrt{\left(\frac{\hbar}{2\omega_k}\right)}, \qquad \tilde{B}_{klm} = \tilde{b}_{klm}\sqrt{\left(\frac{\hbar}{2\omega_k}\right)}. \tag{80}$$

These operators have the commutation relations

$$\left.\begin{aligned}[b_{klm}, b_{k'l'm'}] = 0, \qquad [\tilde{b}_{klm}, \tilde{b}_{k'l'm'}] = 0\\ [b_{klm}, \tilde{b}_{k'l'm'}] = \delta_{kk'}\delta_{ll'}\delta_{mm'}\end{aligned}\right\}. \tag{81}$$

Comparing (81) with (50) it is clear that commutation relations similar to (51) hold for the operators $n(klm) \equiv \tilde{b}_{klm} b_{klm}$; it follows (as on p. 69) that the eigenvalues of these operators are zero and the positive integers. For each set of values k, l, m, there is a 'zero' state $|0_{klm}\rangle$ such that

$$b_{klm}|0_{klm}\rangle = 0;$$

the eigenstate of $n(klm)$ which has eigenvalue n'_{klm} is (cf. (53))

$$|n'_{klm}\rangle = (n'_{klm}!)^{-\frac{1}{2}}(\tilde{b}_{klm})^{n'_{klm}}|0_{klm}\rangle. \tag{82}$$

† For a finite volume the normalization agrees if the cube and the sphere have equal volumes.

‡ See also Hamilton, loc. cit., eqn. (17).

By arguments similar to those on p. 68, or else by direct calculation using (52), (49), (76), and (77), we see that the Hamiltonian

$$\mathsf{H} = \frac{c^2}{4\pi}\int d^3\mathbf{k}\ \tilde{A}(\mathbf{k})A(\mathbf{k})$$

can be written

$$\mathsf{H} = \sum_{k,l,m} \hbar\omega_k \tilde{b}_{klm} b_{klm} = \sum_{k,l,m} \hbar\omega_k n(klm). \tag{83}$$

Comparison of (59) and (72) shows that the vacuum state is that for which all eigenvalues n'_{klm} are zero. Eqns. (81) and (83) suggest that $\tilde{b}_{klm}$ and b_{klm} are operators which respectively create and destroy pions of energy $\hbar\omega_k$, whose angular momentum quantum numbers are (l, m). It only remains to prove this assertion about the angular momentum.

The angular momentum eigenstates

Remembering that the angular momentum operator **M** given by (64) is time independent (eqn. (65)), it follows from the commutation relations (21) that†

$$\left.\begin{aligned}(\hbar/i)\mathbf{I}\phi(\mathbf{x},t) &= [\phi(\mathbf{x},t), \mathbf{M}] \\ (\hbar/i)\mathbf{I}\pi(\mathbf{x},t) &= [\pi(\mathbf{x},t), \mathbf{M}]\end{aligned}\right\}, \tag{84}$$

where $\mathbf{I} = \mathbf{x}\times\text{grad}$ (cf. Chapter I, § 9). Hence for any function of the field variables $f(x_\mu)$,

$$(\hbar/i)\mathbf{I}f(x_\mu) = [f(x_\mu), \mathbf{M}]. \tag{85}$$

This result is now applied to (72) and the coefficients of the independent functions (68) are picked out.‡ Using I_3 and remembering (1.44) (where $\mathbf{L} = (\hbar/i)\mathbf{I}$), gives

$$\left.\begin{aligned}[M_3, B_{klm}] &= -m\hbar B_{klm} \\ [M_3, \tilde{B}_{klm}] &= m\hbar\tilde{B}_{klm}\end{aligned}\right\}. \tag{86}$$

Thus $\tilde{b}_{klm}$, b_{klm} respectively decrease and increase the total angular momentum in the field by $m\hbar$ ($|m| \leqslant l$). From (86) it follows (as for H in § 4) that apart from a constant number,§ we can write

$$M_3 = \sum_{k,l,m} m\hbar\, n(klm). \tag{87}$$

Using the relations||

$$(I_1 \pm iI_2)Y_l^{(m)}(\theta,\phi) = i\sqrt{\{(l\mp m)(l\pm m+1)\}}Y_l^{(m\pm 1)}(\theta,\phi), \tag{88}$$

† The second equation in (84) is obtained on integration by parts; this does not require special assumptions about boundary values.

‡ The operator coefficients B_{klm} are, of course, constants.

§ This constant number is determined by requiring that $M_3|0\rangle = 0$.

|| Cf. N. F. Mott and I. Sneddon, *Wave Mechanics* (Clarendon Press, 1948) 388. Apart from a phase factor, eqn. (88) can be deduced by the general methods of angular momentum addition used in Chapter I, § 10 (see, for example, E. P. Wigner, *Anwendungen der Gruppentheorie* (Vieweg, 1931)).

we deduce from (85) and (72)

$$\left.\begin{aligned}[M_1 \pm iM_2, B_{klm\pm1}] &= -\hbar\sqrt{\{(l\mp m)(l\pm m+1)\}}B_{klm}\\ \text{and}\qquad [M_1 \pm iM_2, \tilde{B}_{klm\mp1}] &= \hbar\sqrt{\{(l\pm m)(l\mp m+1)\}}\tilde{B}_{klm}\end{aligned}\right\}. \tag{89}$$

Here both the upper, or both the lower, signs are to be read together. It follows from (81) that

$$M_1 \pm iM_2 = \sum_{k,l,m} \hbar\tilde{b}_{klm\pm1}\, b_{klm}\sqrt{\{(l\mp m)(l\pm m+1)\}}. \tag{90}$$

(An arbitrary constant number in (90) has been equated to zero, so that for the vacuum state vector, $\mathbf{M}|0\rangle = 0$.) Eqns. (87) and (90) express the total angular momentum operator in terms of the dimensionless creation and annihilation constants $\tilde{b}$, b.

The physical interpretation of the eigenstates can now be completed. The state vector $\tilde{b}_{klm}|0\rangle$ is an eigenstate of energy $\hbar\omega_k$ (by (83)), and it is an eigenstate of the O_3 component of angular momentum M_3, with eigenvalue $m\hbar$ (by (87)). Using (90) and (81),

$$(M_1 \pm iM_2)\,\tilde{b}_{klm}|0\rangle = \hbar\sqrt{\{(l\mp m)(l\pm m+1)\}}\,\tilde{b}_{klm\pm1}|0\rangle. \tag{91}$$

Therefore the $(2l+1)$ state vectors $\tilde{b}_{klm}|0\rangle$ $(-l \leqslant m \leqslant l)$ transform among themselves under the action of the field angular momentum operator $\mathbf{M}$, in the same way as do the spherical harmonics $Y_l^{(m)}(\theta,\phi)$ under the influence of the angular momentum operator $\mathbf{L} = (\hbar/i)\mathbf{I}$ (cf. eqn. (88)). Hence the $(2l+1)$ state vectors $\tilde{b}_{klm}|0\rangle$ $(|m| \leqslant l)$ describe pions whose eigenvalues of the total angular momentum $\mathbf{M}^2$ are $l(l+1)\hbar^2$.

Outgoing waves

In our analysis of the angular momentum of the pion field, the spatial representatives of the pion state vectors $\tilde{b}_{klm}|0\rangle$ are of the form $g_{lk}(r)Y_l^{(m)}(\theta,\phi)$. Their asymptotic radial dependence is given by (1.89),

$$j_l(kr) \simeq \frac{1}{kr}\sin(kr-\tfrac{1}{2}l\pi). \tag{92}$$

It is not obvious that such state vectors can represent the outgoing waves which occur in scattering and creation processes; these have the asymptotic form

$$e^{ikr}/kr.$$

We now show how the functions $g_{lk}(r)$ can give outgoing waves.

The state vector $|I\rangle$ of an interacting system obeys

$$(H_0+H_I)|I\rangle = E_0|I\rangle, \tag{93}$$

where E_0 is the energy eigenstate of the interacting system, H_0 is the Hamiltonian of the free particles or fields, and H_I is the interaction

Hamiltonian. The expansion of $|I\rangle$ in terms of the eigenstates $|\alpha\rangle$ of the free particle system is

$$|I\rangle = \sum_{\alpha} |\alpha\rangle\langle\alpha|I\rangle.$$

Writing E_{α} for the energy eigenvalue of $|\alpha\rangle$, i.e.

$$H_0|\alpha\rangle = E_{\alpha}|\alpha\rangle,$$

eqn. (93) can be written (for fixed E_0)

$$(E_0-E_{\alpha})\langle\alpha|I\rangle = \sum_{\alpha'} \langle\alpha|H_I|\alpha'\rangle\langle\alpha'|I\rangle. \tag{94}$$

This is in general an integral equation; without going into detail we can say that, following the usual methods of quantum mechanics,† the solution is of the form‡

$$\langle\alpha|I\rangle = V_{\alpha}\left\{\frac{1}{E_{\alpha}-E_0}+\lambda\delta(E_{\alpha}-E_0)\right\}, \tag{95}$$

where V_{α} is a function which does not vary rapidly with E_{α} in the neighbourhood $E_{\alpha} \simeq E_0$; λ is an undetermined multiplier. Dirac shows§ that in the momentum representation outgoing waves are obtained by putting $\lambda = \pi i$. We shall use the same value for λ.

The production or scattering of a pion can be described by an equation like (93).‖ The representative $\langle\alpha|I\rangle$ now gives the amplitude and phase of the free pion states which are superimposed to give the actual pion wave. It is convenient to write $\alpha \equiv (klm)$, $E_{\alpha} \equiv E_k$; the form of the pion distribution in space is therefore written

$$\sum_{k,l,m} g_{lk}(r)Y_l^{(m)}(\theta,\phi)\langle klm|I\rangle. \tag{96}$$

The major contribution to the solution of (94) comes from the neighbourhood $E_k \simeq E_0$; hence to find the radial dependence of (96) we can replace

$$\int\limits_{\mu c^2}^{\infty} dE_k\left\{\frac{1}{E_k-E_0}+\pi i\delta(E_k-E_0)\right\}j_l(kr)$$

by

$$\int\limits_{0}^{\infty} dk\left\{\frac{1}{k-k_0}+\pi i\delta(k-k_0)\right\}j_l(kr), \tag{97}$$

† P. A. M. Dirac, *Quantum Mechanics* (Clarendon Press, 3rd edn., 1947), ch. 9.

‡ When renormalization is necessary, the energy E_0 in (94) may have to be replaced by a corrected value $E_0+\Delta E_0$.

§ See eqn. (A.39) in the Appendix.

‖ Eqns. (93) and (94) are the Tamm–Dancoff equations which are discussed in Chapter IV, § 8 (where α denotes pion and nucleon variables).

where $\hbar c k_0 = (E_0^2 - \mu^2 c^4)^{\frac{1}{2}}$. The principal value is to be taken at $k = k_0$ in the first term of the integrand. Using (92) this gives the required asymptotic form for outgoing waves,

$$\frac{1}{k_0 r} \exp[i(k_0 r - \tfrac{1}{2} l\pi)]. \tag{98}$$

Putting $\lambda = \pi i$ in (95), we can write

$$\langle \alpha | I \rangle = V_\alpha . 2\pi i . \delta^{(+)}(E_\alpha - E_0),$$

where $\delta^{(+)}$ is defined by (A.37). The use of the $\delta^{(+)}$ function is seen in the Appendix to be equivalent to using the causal Green's function D_F (cf. (63)).

7. Free charged pions

It appears to be a fundamental principle of physics that charged elementary particles occur with both signs of the elementary charge $(\pm e)$.† This principle can be ensured for boson fields by using a complex (in quantized theory a non-Hermitian) field amplitude and at the same time requiring that the Lagrangian density $\mathscr{L}$ be real (or Hermitian). The complex pion field has two independent components at each point $\mathbf{x}$; for these we can use ϕ and ϕ^* (in the quantum theory we use ϕ and $\tilde{\phi}$).‡ The real Lagrangian is unaltered if ϕ and ϕ^* are replaced by $\phi e^{i\alpha}$ and $\phi^* e^{-i\alpha}$ respectively (α is real), and this invariance of $\mathscr{L}$ gives a new constant of motion, just as the invariance of $\mathscr{L}$ under rotation of the coordinate axes gives the angular momentum $\mathbf{M}$ (eqn. (64)). This invariance principle—it is called gauge invariance of the first kind§ —gives the law of charge conservation. The details of this principle and its consequences are discussed in Chapter IX.

For charged pions the classical Lagrangian density (18) is replaced by

$$\mathscr{L} = -c^2\{\partial_\mu \phi^* \partial_\mu \phi + \kappa^2 \phi^* \phi\}. \tag{99}$$

This Lagrangian describes *free* pions; it takes no account of any interaction between the pions arising from the charge or from any other force. Such interactions can be discussed by the methods for treating interacting fields which are developed in Chapters IV, V, and VI.

† The principle can be stated in the more general form that both signs of any electric or magnetic moment of an elementary particle will occur; for example, it is expected that the neutron and the anti-neutron differ in the sign of their magnetic moment measured relative to their spin.

‡ $\tilde{\phi}$ denotes the Hermitian conjugate of ϕ.

§ W. Pauli, *Phys. Rev.* **58** (1940) 716.

Now $\mathscr{L}$ can be expressed in terms of real independent field variables $\phi_1(x_\mu)$, $\phi_2(x_\mu)$ by the relations†

$$\phi(x_\mu) = \frac{1}{\sqrt{2}}\{\phi_1(x_\mu)-i\phi_2(x_\mu)\}, \qquad \phi^*(x_\mu) = \frac{1}{\sqrt{2}}\{\phi_1(x_\mu)+i\phi_2(x_\mu)\}. \quad (100)$$

This gives
$$\mathscr{L} = -\tfrac{1}{2}c^2 \sum_{j=1}^{2} \{\partial_\mu \phi_j \partial_\mu \phi_j + \kappa^2 \phi_j \phi_j\}; \quad (101)$$

this form is merely a simple extension of the expression (18) for the neutral pion field. Eqn. (9) (or eqn. (19)) gives the canonical momentum densities π_1, π_2 which are conjugate to ϕ_1 and ϕ_2 respectively:

$$\pi_1(x_\mu) = \dot{\phi}_1(x_\mu), \qquad \pi_2(x_\mu) = \dot{\phi}_2(x_\mu). \quad (102)$$

The quantized field theory is obtained by using the commutation relations (10) and (13). At any given time t, all functions of $\pi_1(\mathbf{x},t)$ and $\phi_1(\mathbf{x},t)$ commute with all functions of $\pi_2(\mathbf{x},t)$ and $\phi_2(\mathbf{x},t)$. The function $\mathscr{L}$ in (101) is separable in the two fields (ϕ_1 and ϕ_2), therefore the two fields propagate independently; hence

$$[\phi_1(x_\mu), \phi_2(x'_\mu)] = 0 \quad (\text{all } x_\mu, x'_\mu). \quad (103)$$

Because $\mathscr{L}$ is separable, it follows that the individual fields ϕ_1, ϕ_2 each propagate like the neutral pion field, and by (27) their general commutation relations are

$$\left.\begin{aligned} [\phi_1(x'_\mu), \phi_1(x_\mu)] &= (i\hbar/c)D_{(\kappa)}(x'_\mu - x_\mu) \\ [\phi_2(x'_\mu), \phi_2(x_\mu)] &= (i\hbar/c)D_{(\kappa)}(x'_\mu - x_\mu) \end{aligned}\right\}. \quad (104)$$

In quantum theory eqn. (100) is replaced by

$$\phi = \frac{1}{\sqrt{2}}(\phi_1 - i\phi_2), \qquad \tilde{\phi} = \frac{1}{\sqrt{2}}(\phi_1 + i\phi_2),$$

and by (103), (104), these non-Hermitian operators obey the general commutation relations

$$\left.\begin{aligned} [\tilde{\phi}(x_\mu), \tilde{\phi}(x'_\mu)] = 0, \qquad [\phi(x_\mu), \phi(x'_\mu)] = 0 \\ [\tilde{\phi}(x'_\mu), \phi(x_\mu)] = (i\hbar/c)D_{(\kappa)}(x'_\mu - x_\mu) \end{aligned}\right\}. \quad (105)$$

Differentiating (105) with respect to time and using (26), it follows that

$$\left.\begin{aligned} [\pi(x'_\mu), \tilde{\phi}(x_\mu)] = 0, \qquad [\pi(\mathbf{x}',t), \phi(\mathbf{x},t)] = \frac{\hbar}{i}\delta^3(\mathbf{x}'-\mathbf{x}) \\ [\tilde{\pi}(x'_\mu), \phi(x_\mu)] = 0, \qquad [\tilde{\pi}(\mathbf{x}',t), \tilde{\phi}(\mathbf{x},t)] = \frac{\hbar}{i}\delta^3(\mathbf{x}'-\mathbf{x}) \end{aligned}\right\}, \quad (106)$$

† $\phi_1(x_\mu)$, $\phi_2(x_\mu)$ play the role of the independent field variables $\phi^{(\alpha)}(x_\mu)$ of § 2 above. ϕ_1 and ϕ_2 are both pseudo-scalar.

and† $$[\tilde{\pi}(\mathbf{x}',t),\pi(\mathbf{x},t)] = 0$$

where $$\pi(\mathbf{x},t) \equiv \dot{\tilde{\phi}}(\mathbf{x},t), \qquad \tilde{\pi}(\mathbf{x},t) \equiv \dot{\phi}(\mathbf{x},t). \tag{107}$$

Thus $\pi(\mathbf{x},t)$, $\tilde{\pi}(\mathbf{x},t)$ are the canonical momenta conjugate to $\phi(\mathbf{x},t)$, and $\tilde{\phi}(\mathbf{x},t)$ respectively.‡ In terms of these variables, the Hamiltonian may be written

$$\mathbf{H} = \int d^3\mathbf{x}\,\{\tilde{\pi}(\mathbf{x},t)\pi(\mathbf{x},t)+c^2\,\mathrm{grad}\,\tilde{\phi}(\mathbf{x},t).\mathrm{grad}\,\phi(\mathbf{x},t)+c^2\kappa^2\tilde{\phi}(\mathbf{x},t)\phi(\mathbf{x},t)\}. \tag{108}$$

Eqns. (107), and the wave equations

$$(\partial_\mu^2-\kappa^2)\phi(x_\mu) = 0, \qquad (\partial_\mu^2-\kappa^2)\tilde{\phi}(x_\mu) = 0, \tag{109}$$

are now given by the quantum equations of motion (eqn. (14)) using the Hamiltonian (108).

The charge-current 4-vector which results from the gauge invariance principle is obtained from (9.43) on substituting $\pi_\mu = -c\partial_\mu\tilde{\phi}$, etc. Thus

$$j_\mu = \frac{iec^2}{\hbar}\{(\partial_\mu\tilde{\phi})\phi-\tilde{\phi}(\partial_\mu\phi)\}. \tag{110}$$

The conservation law $$\partial_\mu j_\mu = 0$$

follows from (109). The *total charge* operator is (by (9.42))

$$Q = \frac{ie}{\hbar}\int d^3\mathbf{x}\,\{\tilde{\phi}(\mathbf{x},t)\tilde{\pi}(\mathbf{x},t)-\pi(\mathbf{x},t)\phi(\mathbf{x},t)\}. \tag{111}$$

It is easy to verify, using (106), that

$$[\mathbf{H},Q] = 0;$$

thus Q is a constant of motion. Also by (106) we have

$$\left.\begin{aligned}[Q,\phi(x_\mu)] &= -e\phi(x_\mu)\\ [Q,\tilde{\phi}(x_\mu)] &= +e\tilde{\phi}(x_\mu)\end{aligned}\right\}. \tag{112}$$

Thus $\phi(x_\mu)$, or $\tilde{\phi}(x_\mu)$, operating on an eigenstate of Q, respectively decrease or increase the eigenvalue of Q by an amount e.

The particle aspect of the charged pion field can be readily demonstrated in the linear momentum representation. Analogous to (30) we write

$$\left.\begin{aligned}\phi(x_\mu) &= \frac{1}{(2\pi)^2}\int d^4k\,\delta(k_\mu^2+\kappa^2)A(k_\mu)e^{ik_\mu x_\mu}\\ \tilde{\phi}(x_\mu) &= \frac{1}{(2\pi)^2}\int d^4k\,\delta(k_\mu^2+\kappa^2)\tilde{A}(k_\mu)e^{-ik_\mu x_\mu}\end{aligned}\right\}, \tag{113}$$

† The last relation comes from the last of eqns. (105), using $(\partial_\mu^2-\kappa^2)D_{(\kappa)}(x_\mu) = 0$ and (26).

‡ We also have, from (105), $[\phi(\mathbf{x},t),\tilde{\phi}(\mathbf{x}',t)] = 0$.

where $A(k_\mu)$, $\tilde{A}(k_\mu)$ are constant operators. For the charged field it is no longer true that $\tilde{A}(-k_\mu) = A(+k_\mu)$, and we shall use the notation

$$\left.\begin{aligned} A(\mathbf{k}, \omega_k) &\equiv A(\mathbf{k}) \\ \tilde{A}(-\mathbf{k}, -\omega_k) &\equiv B(\mathbf{k}) \end{aligned}\right\} \qquad (\omega_k = c(\mathbf{k}^2+\kappa^2)^{\frac{1}{2}}).$$

The possibility of having either sign of the charge makes it necessary to have two independent operator coefficients $A(\mathbf{k})$, $B(\mathbf{k})$ for each value of $\mathbf{k}$. The invariant splitting of the *free* field amplitudes into positive and negative frequency parts,†

$$\phi(x_\mu) = \phi^{(+)}(x_\mu)+\phi^{(-)}(x_\mu); \qquad \tilde{\phi}(x_\mu) = \tilde{\phi}^{(+)}(x_\mu)+\tilde{\phi}^{(-)}(x_\mu),$$

is given by (cf. (35))

$$\left.\begin{aligned} \phi^{(+)}(x_\mu) &= \frac{c}{8\pi^2}\int\limits_{-\infty}^{\infty}\frac{d^3\mathbf{k}}{\omega_k}A(\mathbf{k})e^{i(\mathbf{k}.\mathbf{x}-\omega_k t)} \\ \phi^{(-)}(x_\mu) &= \frac{c}{8\pi^2}\int\limits_{-\infty}^{\infty}\frac{d^3\mathbf{k}}{\omega_k}\tilde{B}(\mathbf{k})e^{-i(\mathbf{k}.\mathbf{x}-\omega_k t)} \\ \tilde{\phi}^{(+)}(x_\mu) &= \frac{c}{8\pi^2}\int\limits_{-\infty}^{\infty}\frac{d^3\mathbf{k}}{\omega_k}B(\mathbf{k})e^{i(\mathbf{k}.\mathbf{x}-\omega_k t)} \\ \tilde{\phi}^{(-)}(x_\mu) &= \frac{c}{8\pi^2}\int\limits_{-\infty}^{\infty}\frac{d^3\mathbf{k}}{\omega_k}\tilde{A}(\mathbf{k})e^{-i(\mathbf{k}.\mathbf{x}-\omega_k t)} \end{aligned}\right\}. \tag{114}$$

The quantum equation of motion applied to $\phi^{(\pm)}$, $\tilde{\phi}^{(\pm)}$ gives‡

$$\left.\begin{aligned} [\mathbf{H}, A(\mathbf{k})] &= -\hbar\omega_k A(\mathbf{k}), \qquad & [\mathbf{H}, B(\mathbf{k})] &= -\hbar\omega_k B(\mathbf{k}) \\ [\mathbf{H}, \tilde{A}(\mathbf{k})] &= \hbar\omega_k \tilde{A}(\mathbf{k}), & [\mathbf{H}, \tilde{B}(\mathbf{k})] &= \hbar\omega_k \tilde{B}(\mathbf{k}) \end{aligned}\right\}. \tag{115}$$

The charge operator Q (eqn. (111)) is independent of time; therefore it cannot mix up positive and negative frequency parts when it is commuted with a field operator as in eqns. (112). Hence, taking the positive and negative frequency parts of (112) gives

$$\left.\begin{aligned} [Q, A(\mathbf{k})] &= -eA(\mathbf{k}), \qquad & [Q, B(\mathbf{k})] &= eB(\mathbf{k}) \\ [Q, \tilde{A}(\mathbf{k})] &= e\tilde{A}(\mathbf{k}), & [Q, \tilde{B}(\mathbf{k})] &= -e\tilde{B}(\mathbf{k}) \end{aligned}\right\}. \tag{116}$$

The total momentum operator $\mathbf{P}$ for the charged field is obtained

† It is necessary to distinguish between $\tilde{\phi}^{(+)}$ and $\widetilde{\phi^{(+)}}$; the latter is a negative frequency part.

‡ Strictly, we write down the equations of motion for $\phi(x_\mu)$, $\tilde{\phi}(x_\mu)$ and split them into positive and negative frequency parts (as was done in § 4).

by using the sum of expression (39) evaluated for the Hermitian fields $\phi_1(x_\mu)$ and $\phi_2(x_\mu)$; this gives

$$\mathbf{P} = -\tfrac{1}{2}\int d^3\mathbf{x}\,\{\pi(\mathbf{x},t)\operatorname{grad}\phi(\mathbf{x},t)+\tilde{\pi}(\mathbf{x},t)\operatorname{grad}\tilde{\phi}(\mathbf{x},t)+ +[\operatorname{grad}\phi(\mathbf{x},t)]\pi(\mathbf{x},t)+[\operatorname{grad}\tilde{\phi}(\mathbf{x},t)]\tilde{\pi}(\mathbf{x},t)\}. \quad (117)$$

Using (117) and (106) it is easy to verify that if f is any function of the field variables (and if f is not *explicitly* dependent on x_μ) then

$$\left(\frac{\hbar}{i}\right)\operatorname{grad}f = [f, \mathbf{P}].$$

Applying this relation to (114) gives†

$$\left.\begin{aligned}[][\mathbf{P}, A(\mathbf{k})] &= -\hbar\mathbf{k}A(\mathbf{k}), &\quad [\mathbf{P}, \tilde{A}(\mathbf{k})] &= \hbar\mathbf{k}\tilde{A}(\mathbf{k}) \\ [\mathbf{P}, B(\mathbf{k})] &= -\hbar\mathbf{k}B(\mathbf{k}), &\quad [\mathbf{P}, \tilde{B}(\mathbf{k})] &= \hbar\mathbf{k}\tilde{B}(\mathbf{k})\end{aligned}\right\}. \quad (118)$$

The physical interpretation

Relations (115), (116), and (118) suggest that $A(\mathbf{k})$, $B(\mathbf{k})$ are operators which respectively destroy positive and negative pions of momentum $\hbar\mathbf{k}$, and that $\tilde{A}(\mathbf{k})$, $\tilde{B}(\mathbf{k})$ are operators which respectively create positive and negative pions of momentum $\hbar\mathbf{k}$. The verification of this interpretation is completed by deriving the number operators for positive and negative pions and by expressing $\mathbf{H}$, Q, and $\mathbf{P}$ in terms of the number operators. As a first step the commutators of the operators A, B, etc., are evaluated. By (114) and the first equation in (105), it follows that all the operators $\tilde{A}(\mathbf{k})$, $B(\mathbf{k}')$ commute with each other. Similarly, all the operators $A(\mathbf{k})$, $\tilde{B}(\mathbf{k}')$ commute with each other. By the last equation in (105) we have‡

$$[\tilde{\phi}^{(+)}(x'_\mu), \phi(x_\mu)] = [\tilde{\phi}(x'_\mu), \phi^{(-)}(x_\mu)] = [\tilde{\phi}^{(+)}(x'_\mu), \phi^{(-)}(x_\mu)].$$

Therefore $$[\tilde{\phi}^{(+)}(x'_\mu), \phi^{(+)}(x_\mu)] = 0,$$

so $$[A(\mathbf{k}), B(\mathbf{k}')] = 0,$$

and similarly $$[\tilde{A}(\mathbf{k}), \tilde{B}(\mathbf{k}')] = 0. \quad (119)$$

The only non-zero commutators arise from the relation§

$$[\tilde{\phi}^{(+)}(x'_\mu), \phi^{(-)}(x_\mu)] = [\phi^{(+)}(x'_\mu), \tilde{\phi}^{(-)}(x_\mu)] = (i\hbar/c)D^{(+)}_{(\kappa)}(x'_\mu - x_\mu);$$

† We substitute $\phi(x_\mu)$ or $\tilde{\phi}(x_\mu)$ for f, and then use the frequency splitting ($\mathbf{P}$ is independent of time).

‡ The first step follows because $[\tilde{\phi}(x'_\mu), \phi(x_\mu)]$ is a function of $(x'_\mu - x_\mu)$; the second step, because the projection operator $P(+)$ which gives the positive frequency part, obeys $\{P(+)\}^2 = P(+)$.

§ From (26), $D(-x_\mu) = -D(x_\mu)$; hence $D^{(+)}(-x_\mu) = -D^{(-)}(x_\mu)$.

the argument which led from (41) to (47) now proves that

$$[A(\mathbf{k}'), \tilde{A}(\mathbf{k})] = [B(\mathbf{k}'), \tilde{B}(\mathbf{k})] = \frac{4\pi\hbar\omega_k}{c^2}\delta^3(\mathbf{k}-\mathbf{k}'). \tag{120}$$

Dimensionless operators $a(\mathbf{k})$, $\tilde{a}(\mathbf{k})$, $b(\mathbf{k})$, $\tilde{b}(\mathbf{k})$ are defined by (cf. (49))

$$A(\mathbf{k}) = \left(\frac{4\pi\hbar\omega_k}{c^2}\rho_{\mathbf{k}}\right)^{\frac{1}{2}} a(\mathbf{k}), \qquad B(\mathbf{k}) = \left(\frac{4\pi\hbar\omega_k}{c^2}\rho_{\mathbf{k}}\right)^{\frac{1}{2}} b(\mathbf{k}),$$

together with the Hermitian conjugates of these relations.

The only non-zero commutators between pairs of these operators are (cf. (50))

$$[a(\mathbf{k}), \tilde{a}(\mathbf{k}')] = \delta_{\mathbf{k},\mathbf{k}'}, \qquad [b(\mathbf{k}), \tilde{b}(\mathbf{k}')] = \delta_{\mathbf{k},\mathbf{k}'}. \tag{121}$$

The Hermitian operators

$$n(\mathbf{k}, +) = \tilde{a}(\mathbf{k})a(\mathbf{k}), \qquad n(\mathbf{k}, -) = \tilde{b}(\mathbf{k})b(\mathbf{k})$$

obey the relations

$$\left.\begin{aligned} [n(\mathbf{k}, +), a(\mathbf{k}')] &= -a(\mathbf{k})\delta_{\mathbf{k},\mathbf{k}'}, & [n(\mathbf{k}, +), \tilde{a}(\mathbf{k}')] &= \tilde{a}(\mathbf{k})\delta_{\mathbf{k},\mathbf{k}'} \\ [n(\mathbf{k}, -), b(\mathbf{k}')] &= -b(\mathbf{k})\delta_{\mathbf{k},\mathbf{k}'}, & [n(\mathbf{k}, -), \tilde{b}(\mathbf{k}')] &= \tilde{b}(\mathbf{k})\delta_{\mathbf{k},\mathbf{k}'} \end{aligned}\right\}. \tag{122}$$

Also $n(\mathbf{k}, +)$ commutes with $b(\mathbf{k}')$ and $\tilde{b}(\mathbf{k}')$ while $n(\mathbf{k}, -)$ commutes with $a(\mathbf{k}')$ and $\tilde{a}(\mathbf{k}')$.

The operators $n(\mathbf{k}, +)$ and $n(\mathbf{k}, -)$ can be made diagonal simultaneously; the arguments used in § 4 show that both sets of operators have the eigenvalues 0, 1, 2,.... The commutators of $\mathbf{H}$, Q, and $\mathbf{P}$ with any function of the field variables can be derived directly from (115), (116), and (118). Comparing these relations with (122) it follows that, apart from additive constant numbers,† we can write

$$\mathbf{H} = \sum_{\mathbf{k}} \hbar\omega_k\{n(\mathbf{k}, +)+n(\mathbf{k}, -)\}, \tag{123}$$

$$Q = \sum_{\mathbf{k}} e\{n(\mathbf{k}, +)-n(\mathbf{k}, -)\}, \tag{124}$$

$$\mathbf{P} = \sum_{\mathbf{k}} \hbar\mathbf{k}\{n(\mathbf{k}, +)+n(\mathbf{k}, -)\}. \tag{125}$$

Obviously the eigenvalues of $n(\mathbf{k}, +)$ and $n(\mathbf{k}, -)$ give the number of positive and negative pions respectively.

Eqns. (122) show that $a(\mathbf{k})$, $b(\mathbf{k})$ destroy a positive or a negative pion respectively. The vacuum state $|0\rangle$ is defined by

$$a(\mathbf{k})|0\rangle = 0; \quad b(\mathbf{k})|0\rangle = 0; \quad (\text{all } \mathbf{k}). \tag{126}$$

Using (123), (124), and (125), the vacuum has zero eigenvalue of energy, charge, and momentum. There is therefore no need to add any con-

† These arbitrary constants can appear in the transition from the classical to the quantum theory; for example in choosing the order of the operators in (111).

stants to expressions (123), (124), or (125). The vacuum state can be defined in an invariant way on using (114) and (126):

$$\phi^{(+)}(x_\mu)|0\rangle = 0, \quad \tilde{\phi}^{(+)}(x_\mu)|0\rangle = 0 \quad (\text{all } x_\mu). \tag{127}$$

This definition has the advantage of being independent of any particular representation.

The total current $\mathbf{J}$ (which is not a constant of motion) is given by

$$\mathbf{J} = \int d^3\mathbf{x}\, \mathbf{j}(\mathbf{x},t).$$

It is easy to find the time-independent component, or time average, $\langle \mathbf{J}\rangle_{\text{av}}$ of this operator. From (110) and integration by parts

$$\mathbf{J} = 2iec^2/\hbar \int d^3\mathbf{x}\, \{\text{grad}\, \tilde{\phi}(\mathbf{x},t)\}\phi(\mathbf{x},t).$$

The contribution to the time average can be written

$$\langle \mathbf{J}\rangle_{\text{av}} = 2iec^2/\hbar \int d^3\mathbf{x}\, \overline{\{[\text{grad}\, \tilde{\phi}^{(+)}(\mathbf{x},t)]\phi^{(-)}(\mathbf{x},t) + [\text{grad}\, \tilde{\phi}^{(-)}(\mathbf{x},t)]\phi^{(+)}(\mathbf{x},t)\}}.$$

Substituting (114) gives

$$\langle \mathbf{J}\rangle_{\text{av}} = (ec^4/4\pi\hbar) \int \frac{d^3\mathbf{k}}{\omega_k^2} \mathbf{k}\{\tilde{A}(\mathbf{k})A(\mathbf{k}) - B(\mathbf{k})\tilde{B}(\mathbf{k})\},$$

hence†

$$\langle \mathbf{J}\rangle_{\text{av}} = e \int d^3\mathbf{k}\, \rho_{\mathbf{k}} \left(\frac{c^2\mathbf{k}}{\omega_k}\right) \{n(\mathbf{k},+) - n(\mathbf{k},-)\}, \tag{128}$$

where $\rho_{\mathbf{k}}$ is the density of states (cf. (48)). The meaning of (128) becomes clear on noticing that

$$c^2\mathbf{k}/\omega_k = \mathbf{v},$$

where $\mathbf{v}$ is the velocity of the pion; an average current of $e\mathbf{v}$ and $-e\mathbf{v}$ is produced by each positive and negative pion respectively.

8. The isotopic spin of pions

The expression (124) for the total charge operator Q, which has been chosen to give zero charge in the vacuum state, is given by

$$Q = \frac{ie}{\hbar} \int d^3\mathbf{x}\, \{\tilde{\pi}(\mathbf{x},t)\tilde{\phi}(\mathbf{x},t) - \pi(\mathbf{x},t)\phi(\mathbf{x},t)\} \tag{129}$$

rather than (111).‡ This assertion is proved by noticing that because Q is independent of time, only terms of the form $\pi^{(+)}\phi^{(-)}$, $\tilde{\pi}^{(+)}\tilde{\phi}^{(-)}$, $\pi^{(-)}\phi^{(+)}$, $\tilde{\pi}^{(-)}\tilde{\phi}^{(+)}$ can contribute to (129); acting on the vacuum state $|0\rangle$, the

† The order of $B(\mathbf{k})\tilde{B}(\mathbf{k})$ can be reversed because the integral extends over all directions of $\mathbf{k}$.

‡ The operators (111) and (129) differ by a constant number; the arbitrariness arises from the ambiguity in the order of operators in the transition from classical theory.

latter two vanish by (127). Remembering (107), the operator (129) gives†

$$Q|0\rangle = \frac{ie}{\hbar}\int d^3\mathbf{x}\,\{\tilde{\pi}^{(+)}(\mathbf{x},t)\tilde{\phi}^{(-)}(\mathbf{x},t)-\pi^{(+)}(\mathbf{x},t)\phi^{(-)}(\mathbf{x},t)\}|0\rangle$$

$$= (ec^2/8\pi\hbar)\int \frac{d^3\mathbf{k}}{\omega_k}\{A(\mathbf{k})\tilde{A}(\mathbf{k})-B(\mathbf{k})\tilde{B}(\mathbf{k})\}|0\rangle. \tag{130}$$

Changing the order of both pairs of operators in the integrand of (130), we have

$$Q|0\rangle = 0.$$

When the operator (129) is written in terms of the Hermitian field amplitudes $\phi_1(x_\mu)$, $\phi_2(x_\mu)$ and their conjugate canonical momenta, it takes the particularly simple form

$$Q = (e/\hbar)\int d^3\mathbf{x}\,\{\pi_2(\mathbf{x},t)\phi_1(\mathbf{x},t)-\pi_1(\mathbf{x},t)\phi_2(\mathbf{x},t)\}. \tag{131}$$

The integrand of (131) is suggestive of an angular momentum, if the (ϕ_i) are regarded as coordinates and the (π_i) as momenta. This idea can be developed if we remember that there are neutral as well as charged pions. Denoting the neutral pion amplitude and canonical momentum density by $\phi_3(x)$, $\pi_3(x)$, the three field amplitudes at each point x_μ may be regarded as forming a vector

$$\boldsymbol{\varphi}(x_\mu) = \{\phi_1(x_\mu), \phi_2(x_\mu), \phi_3(x_\mu)\}.$$

This vector is in a new three-dimensional space which we call the *isotopic space*.‡

Now we consider rotations of the isotopic space, assuming that the same isotopic rotation is used at each point $\mathbf{x}$ of ordinary coordinate space. The generator§ for an infinitesimal isotopic rotation about the O_3 isotopic axis at the point $\mathbf{x}$ is, by Chapter I, § 9,

$$\frac{1}{\hbar}d^3\mathbf{x}\,\{\pi_2(\mathbf{x},t)\phi_1(\mathbf{x},t)-\pi_1(\mathbf{x},t)\phi_2(\mathbf{x},t\}; \tag{132}$$

the infinitesimal volume element $d^3\mathbf{x}$ has to be introduced here, because the variable which is conjugate to $\phi_i(\mathbf{x},t)$ $(i = 1,2,3)$ is $d^3\mathbf{x}\,\pi_i(\mathbf{x},t)$. The generator which gives the same rotation for all points $\mathbf{x}$ is the sum of the generators (132) taken over all coordinate space, i.e.

$$T_3 = \frac{1}{\hbar}\int d^3\mathbf{x}\,\{\pi_2(\mathbf{x},t)\phi_1(\mathbf{x},t)-\pi_1(\mathbf{x},t)\phi_2(\mathbf{x},t)\}. \tag{133}$$

† The second step uses (114) and a simple calculation.

‡ The idea was first used by N. Kemmer (*Proc. Camb. Phil. Soc.* **34** (1938) 354) in deriving charge-independent nucleon-nucleon forces; for pion-nucleon scattering it was used by W. Heitler, *Proc. Roy. Irish Acad.* **51** (1946) 33.

§ The Hermitian generator is used here; it is analogous to $(1/\hbar)\mathbf{L}$ rather than $\mathbf{I}$, in the notation of Chapter I, § 9.

Similarly the generators of infinitesimal rotations about the isotopic axes O_1 and O_2 are T_1 and T_2 respectively; together with T_3 they can be written in the concise form

$$\mathbf{T} = (1/\hbar)\int d^3\mathbf{x}\,\{\boldsymbol{\varphi}(\mathbf{x},t)\times\boldsymbol{\pi}(\mathbf{x},t)\}. \tag{134}$$

Here $\boldsymbol{\pi}(\mathbf{x},t) = \{\pi_1(\mathbf{x},t), \pi_2(\mathbf{x},t), \pi_3(\mathbf{x},t)\}$ and $\mathbf{T} = (T_1, T_2, T_3)$ are vectors in the isotopic space, and $\times$ denotes the vector product operation in this space. These operators $\mathbf{T}$ are in many ways analogous to the orbital angular momentum operator $\mathbf{L}$ which was discussed in Chapter I, § 9.

Using the commutation relations (21) and (106), the commutators of the rotation generators are

$$[T_1, T_2] = iT_3, \quad \text{etc.} \tag{135}$$

The Hamiltonian for the three free fields is

$$\mathsf{H} = \mathsf{H}^{(\text{charge})}+\mathsf{H}^{(\text{neutral})},$$

where $\mathsf{H}^{(\text{charge})}$ and $\mathsf{H}^{(\text{neutral})}$ are given by (108) and (20). Assuming for the present that charged and neutral pions have the same mass, the total Hamiltonian may be written

$$\mathsf{H} = \tfrac{1}{2}\int d^3\mathbf{x}\,\{\boldsymbol{\pi}(\mathbf{x},t).\boldsymbol{\pi}(\mathbf{x},t)+c^2\kappa^2\boldsymbol{\varphi}(\mathbf{x},t).\boldsymbol{\varphi}(\mathbf{x},t)+ +c^2\operatorname{grad}\boldsymbol{\varphi}(\mathbf{x},t).\operatorname{grad}\boldsymbol{\varphi}(\mathbf{x},t)\}. \tag{136}$$

Here the notation of scalar products of vectors in isotopic space has been used, and in the last term in the integrand a scalar product both in isotopic space and in coordinate space is implied. Because H is a sum of scalar products in isotopic space, it is a scalar in isotopic space; thus it is unaltered by rotations of isotopic space, so

$$[\mathsf{H}, \mathbf{T}] = 0. \tag{137}$$

From (135) and (137) it follows that the eigenstates of H can be specified by their eigenvalues of $\mathbf{T}^2$ and of one component T_3. The states thus specified are said to have definite *isotopic spin*.

It is found that for processes in which electromagnetic effects are negligible, pion-nucleon and nucleon-nucleon interactions conserve isotopic spin,† just as they conserve the total angular momentum; the isotopic spin quantum numbers $\mathbf{T}^2$ and T_3 are therefore of fundamental importance in elementary particle physics. This conservation law implies that the Hamiltonians for the free particles and for their strongest

† See Chapter IV, § 12. The isotopic spin formation for nucleons is given in Chapter IV, § 11.

interactions are invariant under the rotations of the isotopic group;† such interactions are called *charge independent*.

Neglecting electromagnetic effects means neglecting Coulomb and magnetic moment effects in nucleon-nucleon and pion-nucleon interactions; it also means that the mass difference between the neutron and proton and the mass difference between charged and neutral pions‡ is to be neglected. These mass differences are thought to be due to electromagnetic effects, although it has not yet been possible to give any satisfactory method for calculating them.

In phenomena where these mass differences or the electromagnetic effects are not negligible, the total isotopic spin $\mathbf{T}^2$ is no longer a good quantum number.§ However, the component T_3 is always related directly to the charge, e.g. for pions (131) and (133) give

$$Q = eT_3. \tag{138}$$

This means that T_3 is always a good quantum number because its conservation is equivalent to the conservation of charge. It is worth noticing that the gauge transformation of the first kind (which replaces the non-Hermitian pion amplitudes ϕ, $\tilde{\phi}$ by $\phi e^{i\alpha}$, $\tilde{\phi}e^{-i\alpha}$) is equivalent to a rotation of the isotopic space about its O_3 axis. The pion Lagrangian $\mathscr{L}$ is therefore strictly invariant under such rotations; the same must be true for any interacting charged fields.

Eigenstates of isotopic spin

It remains to set up the pion state vectors which are eigenstates of $\mathbf{T}^2$ and T_3. By (138) it follows that

$$T_3\,|0\rangle = 0,$$

and it is easy to see that‖

$$\mathbf{T}\,|0\rangle = 0. \tag{139}$$

The vacuum state therefore has zero isotopic spin. State vectors giving single-pion states are (by (35) and (114))

$$\phi_i^{(-)}(x_\mu)|0\rangle \quad (i = 1, 2, 3).$$

† As will be shown in Chapter IV, the isotopic group has half-integral representations in the nucleon case.

‡ $m_{\pi^\mp} - m_{\pi^0} = 8{\cdot}8m_e$; cf. W. Chinowsky and J. Steinberger, *Phys. Rev.* **93** (1954) 586.

§ It is possible to give simple selection rules for the change in $\mathbf{T}^2$ which can occur during nuclear photo-processes, cf. Chapter IV, § 13.

‖ Because T_j ($j = 1, 2$) is a constant of the motion, the only non-zero contribution to eqn. (134) for T_j comes from

$$\int d^3\mathbf{x}\,\{\pi_k^{(+)}\phi_l^{(-)} + \pi_k^{(-)}\phi_l^{(+)} - \pi_l^{(+)}\phi_k^{(-)} - \pi_l^{(-)}\phi_k^{(+)}\} \quad (l \neq k).$$

The order of the operators in the integrand can be altered, and (139) follows on using $\pi_k = \dot{\phi}_k$, etc., and eqns. (59) and (127).

These state vectors are not eigenstates of T_3 (except for $i = 3$), but comparing them with the coordinate components (x_1, x_2, x_3) and looking at eqn. (1.48) for the spherical harmonics $Y_1^{(m)}$ ($|m| \leqslant 1$), it follows that the eigenstates of T_3 are

$$-\tilde{\phi}^{(-)}(x_\mu)|0\rangle, \quad \phi_3^{(-)}(x_\mu)|0\rangle, \quad \phi^{(-)}(x_\mu)|0\rangle. \tag{140}$$

These have eigenvalues $T_3' = 1,\ 0,\ -1$ respectively; they form the set of three states which have unit total isotopic spin ($\mathbf{T}^2 = 2$). The minus sign in the first term in (140) is introduced to agree with the standard notation of Chapter I, § 9.

Two-pion states are given by the nine state vectors

$$\tilde{\phi}^{(-)}(x_\mu)\tilde{\phi}^{(-)}(x'_\mu)|0\rangle, \quad \tilde{\phi}^{(-)}(x_\mu)\phi_3^{(-)}(x'_\mu)|0\rangle, \quad ..., \quad \phi^{(-)}(x_\mu)\phi^{(-)}(x'_\mu)|0\rangle.$$

These nine state vectors can be combined into eigenstates of $\mathbf{T}^2$ using the vector addition law of Chapter I, § 9. There are five states ($-2 \leqslant T_3' \leqslant 2$) having total isotopic spin 2 (i.e. $\mathbf{T}^2 = 6$), three states ($-1 \leqslant T_3' \leqslant 1$) with unit total isotopic spin ($\mathbf{T}^2 = 2$), and one state with zero isotopic spin ($\mathbf{T}^2 = 0$). The details of the analysis have been given in Chapter I, § 11. Three-pion states or many-pion states may be similarly combined to give eigenstates of $\mathbf{T}^2$ and T_3.

9. The free electromagnetic field

In Chapter I, § 4, the classical equations for this field are shown. The field strengths are given by a tensor $f_{\mu\nu}$:

$$\left.\begin{aligned} E_k &= if_{k4} \\ H_k &= \tfrac{1}{2}\epsilon_{klm}f_{lm} \end{aligned}\right\}. \tag{141}$$

All field variables can be expressed as functions of the 4-vector potential $A_\mu(x_\nu)$ on using

$$f_{\mu\nu} = \partial_\mu A_\nu - \partial_\nu A_\mu. \tag{142}$$

It is possible to regard the components $A_\mu(x_\nu)$ as the independent variables, but it will be necessary subsequently to reduce the number of degrees of freedom by imposing subsidiary conditions.†

The Lagrangian density for the free electromagnetic field is‡

$$\mathscr{L} = -\tfrac{1}{4}f_{\mu\nu}f_{\mu\nu} - \tfrac{1}{2}(\partial_\mu A_\mu)^2, \tag{143}$$

where $f_{\mu\nu}$ is expressed by (142); the Lagrangian equations of motion are

$$\partial_\mu^2 A_\nu = 0 \quad (\nu = 1, 2, 3, 4). \tag{144}$$

† For each propagation vector $\mathbf{k}$ there are two independent photon states, while for each $\mathbf{k}$ there are four components of the potential A_μ.

‡ E. Fermi, *R.C. Accad. Lincei*, **9** (1929) 881, and *Rev Mod. Phys.* **4** (1932) 87.

The canonical momentum density $\pi^{(\mu)}$ which is conjugate to A_μ is

$$\pi^{(\mu)} = \frac{i}{c}\{f_{4\mu}+\delta_{4\mu}(\partial_\lambda A_\lambda)\}, \tag{145}$$

and the Hamiltonian is

$$\mathsf{H} = \int d^3\mathbf{x}\,[\tfrac{1}{2}c^2\{\boldsymbol{\pi}^2+(\pi^{(4)})^2\}+\tfrac{1}{2}(\mathrm{curl}\,\mathbf{A})^2-ic(\pi^{(4)}\mathrm{div}\,\mathbf{A}+A_4\,\mathrm{div}\,\boldsymbol{\pi})], \tag{146}$$

where we have used the vector notation

$$\mathbf{A} = (A_1, A_2, A_3); \qquad \boldsymbol{\pi} = (\pi^{(1)}, \pi^{(2)}, \pi^{(3)}).$$

In classical wave theory the expression (146) does not give the usual energy expression for the electromagnetic field,†

$$W = \tfrac{1}{2}\int d^3\mathbf{x}\,(\mathbf{E}^2+\mathbf{H}^2).$$

Agreement between the Hamiltonian and W is obtained if we consider only those classical solutions which satisfy the initial conditions‡ (at some arbitrary time t)

$$\left.\begin{aligned} \partial_\mu A_\mu(\mathbf{x},t) &= 0 \\ \partial_4\{\partial_\mu A_\mu(\mathbf{x},t)\} &= 0 \end{aligned}\right\}. \tag{147}$$

In quantum electrodynamics it is necessary to be particularly careful in finding conditions to replace (147).§

By eqns. (10) and (13), the field operators in quantum electrodynamics obey the commutation rules||

$$\left.\begin{aligned} [A_\mu(\mathbf{x},t),\, A_\nu(\mathbf{x}',t)] &= 0 \\ [\pi^{(\mu)}(\mathbf{x},t),\, \pi^{(\nu)}(\mathbf{x}',t)] &= 0 \end{aligned}\right\}, \tag{148}$$

$$[\pi^{(\mu)}(\mathbf{x},t),\, A_\nu(\mathbf{x}',t)] = \left(\frac{\hbar}{i}\right)\delta_{\mu\nu}\,\delta^3(\mathbf{x}-\mathbf{x}'). \tag{149}$$

From (145) we see that

$$\pi^{(\mu)}(\mathbf{x},t) = \frac{1}{c^2}\frac{\partial}{\partial t}A_\mu(\mathbf{x},t)+(\text{spatial derivatives of } A_\nu(\mathbf{x},t));$$

therefore, using (148), the commutator (149) can be written

$$\left[\frac{\partial}{\partial t}A_\mu(\mathbf{x},t),\, A_\nu(\mathbf{x}',t)\right] = (\hbar c^2/i)\delta_{\mu\nu}\,\delta^3(\mathbf{x}-\mathbf{x}'). \tag{150}$$

The quantum field amplitudes again obey the propagation eqns. (144); therefore using (148) and (150) as initial conditions on the plane

† In this chapter, Heaviside–Lorentz units are used in agreement with the usual field theory notation. In these units $\mathrm{div}\,\mathbf{E} = \rho$, $\mathrm{curl}\,\mathbf{H} = \mathbf{j}+(1/c)\dot{\mathbf{E}}$; the field of a point charge e is $\mathbf{E} = e\mathbf{r}/4\pi|\mathbf{r}|^3$, and $e^2/4\pi\hbar c \simeq 1/137$.

‡ Conditions (147) ensure that $\partial_\mu A_\mu = 0$ for all time.

§ Classical initial conditions are in general replaced by a restriction on the state vectors in quantum theory.

|| As usual, $\delta_{\mu\nu} = \begin{cases} 1, \text{ if } \mu = \nu \ (\mu, \nu = 1, 2, 3, 4) \\ 0, \text{ otherwise.} \end{cases}$

$t = \text{const.}$, and integrating by (25) or (A.70), the general commutator is (cf. (27))

$$[A_\mu(x_\lambda), A_\nu(x'_\lambda)] = i\hbar c\delta_{\mu\nu} D(x_\lambda - x'_\lambda). \tag{151}$$

Here $D(x)$ is an invariant solution of the homogeneous wave equation for particles of zero rest mass; it obeys (26) and

$$\partial_\mu^2 D(x_\nu) = 0.$$

The right-hand side of (151) is a second-rank symmetric tensor, as is required by general considerations of Lorentz invariance;† this justifies the use‡ of $\delta_{\mu\nu}$ in (149). The operators $A_k(x_\mu)$ $(k = 1, 2, 3)$ are required to be Hermitian. Also $A_4(x_\mu) = iA_0(x_\mu)$, where $A_0(x_\mu)$ (which is the scalar potential) has to be Hermitian; thus $\tilde{A}_4(x_\mu) = -A_4(x_\mu)$.

The particle aspect

The particle aspect of the field may be seen by expanding the field operators in terms of the plane wave solutions of the wave equation; viz.

$$A_\mu(x_\nu) = \frac{1}{(2\pi)^2} \int d^4k\, \delta(k_\nu^2) A_\mu(k_\nu) e^{ik_\nu x_\nu}. \tag{152}$$

The constant operators $A_\mu(k_\nu)$ are 4-vectors; because $A_l(x_\mu)$ is Hermitian and $A_4(x_\mu)$ is anti-Hermitian these operator coefficients obey

$$\left.\begin{aligned} \tilde{A}_l(k_\mu) &= A_l(-k_\mu) \quad (l = 1, 2, 3) \\ \tilde{A}_4(k_\mu) &= -A_4(-k_\mu) \end{aligned}\right\}. \tag{153}$$

It is convenient to write $A_4(k_\mu) = iA_0(k_\mu)$, where $\tilde{A}_0(k_\mu) = A_0(-k_\mu)$. Separation into positive and negative frequency parts

$$A_\mu(x_\nu) = A_\mu^{(+)}(x_\nu) + A_\mu^{(-)}(x_\nu)$$

is carried out by an analysis similar to that for free neutral pions (§ 4). Defining

$$\left.\begin{aligned} A_l(\mathbf{k}) &= A_l(\mathbf{k}, k_0 = |\mathbf{k}|) \quad (l = 1, 2, 3) \\ A_0(\mathbf{k}) &= A_0(\mathbf{k}, k_0 = |\mathbf{k}|) \end{aligned}\right\}$$

gives§

$$\left.\begin{aligned} A_l^{(+)}(x_\mu) &= \frac{1}{8\pi^2} \int \frac{d^3\mathbf{k}}{|\mathbf{k}|} A_l(\mathbf{k}) e^{i(\mathbf{k}.\mathbf{x} - |\mathbf{k}|x_0)} \\ A_l^{(-)}(x_\mu) &= \frac{1}{8\pi^2} \int \frac{d^3\mathbf{k}}{|\mathbf{k}|} \tilde{A}_l(\mathbf{k}) e^{-i(\mathbf{k}.\mathbf{x} - |\mathbf{k}|x_0)} \\ A_0^{(+)}(x_\mu) &= \frac{1}{8\pi^2} \int \frac{d^3\mathbf{k}}{|\mathbf{k}|} A_0(\mathbf{k}) e^{i(\mathbf{k}.\mathbf{x} - |\mathbf{k}|x_0)} \\ A_0^{(-)}(x_\mu) &= \frac{1}{8\pi^2} \int \frac{d^3\mathbf{k}}{|\mathbf{k}|} \tilde{A}_0(\mathbf{k}) e^{-i(\mathbf{k}.\mathbf{x} - |\mathbf{k}|x_0)} \end{aligned}\right\}. \tag{154}$$

† A direct derivation of (151) from the Lagrangian (143) is given by Peierls's method (R. E. Peierls, *Proc. Roy. Soc.* A, **214** (1952) 143).

‡ Because $A_4(x_\lambda)$ is not Hermitian, it is not obvious that the form of (149) for $\mu = \nu = 4$ is a direct extension of (13).

§ The notation is $k_4 = ik_0$, $x_4 = ix_0 = ict$.

The commutation relations for the operator coefficients follow on comparing (151) with (27). All the operators $A_l(\mathbf{k})$, $A_0(\mathbf{k})$ commute with each other, and all the operators $\tilde{A}_l(\mathbf{k})$, $\tilde{A}_0(\mathbf{k})$ commute with each other; also

$$[A_0(\mathbf{k}), \tilde{A}_l(\mathbf{k}')] = [A_l(\mathbf{k}), \tilde{A}_0(\mathbf{k}')] = 0.$$

The remaining commutators are (cf. (47))

$$\left.\begin{aligned} [A_l(\mathbf{k}), \tilde{A}_m(\mathbf{k}')] &= 4\pi\hbar c|\mathbf{k}|\delta_{lm}\,\delta^3(\mathbf{k}-\mathbf{k}') \\ [A_0(\mathbf{k}), \tilde{A}_0(\mathbf{k}')] &= -4\pi\hbar c|\mathbf{k}|\,\delta^3(\mathbf{k}-\mathbf{k}') \end{aligned}\right\}. \tag{155}$$

The difference of sign in the last expression arises on replacing $A_4(x_\mu)$ by $A_0(x_\mu)$ in (151). The dimensionless operators $a_\alpha(\mathbf{k})$, $\tilde{a}_\alpha(\mathbf{k})$ ($\alpha = 0, 1, 2, 3$) are defined by

$$A_\alpha(\mathbf{k}) = (4\pi\hbar c|\mathbf{k}|\rho_\mathbf{k})^{\frac{1}{2}}a_\alpha(\mathbf{k}); \qquad \tilde{A}_\alpha(\mathbf{k}) = (4\pi\hbar c|\mathbf{k}|\rho_\mathbf{k})^{\frac{1}{2}}\tilde{a}_\alpha(\mathbf{k}), \tag{156}$$

where $\rho_\mathbf{k}$ is the density of states (as in § 4). The only non-zero commutators between these dimensionless operators are

$$\left.\begin{aligned} [a_l(\mathbf{k}), \tilde{a}_m(\mathbf{k}')] &= \delta_{lm}\,\delta_{\mathbf{k},\mathbf{k}'} \\ [a_0(\mathbf{k}), \tilde{a}_0(\mathbf{k}')] &= -\delta_{\mathbf{k},\mathbf{k}'} \end{aligned}\right\}. \tag{157}$$

The number operators $n_l(\mathbf{k})$, $n_0(\mathbf{k})$, which have eigenvalues 0, 1, 2,..., are

$$\left.\begin{aligned} n_l(\mathbf{k}) &= \tilde{a}_l(\mathbf{k})a_l(\mathbf{k}) \quad (l = 1, 2, 3) \\ n_0(\mathbf{k}) &= \tilde{a}_0(\mathbf{k})a_0(\mathbf{k}) \end{aligned}\right\}.$$

From (157) it follows that $\tilde{a}_l(\mathbf{k})$ and $a_l(\mathbf{k})$ respectively increase and decrease the eigenvalue $n_l'(\mathbf{k})$ by unity; however, $\tilde{a}_0(\mathbf{k})$, $a_0(\mathbf{k})$ respectively *decrease* and *increase* the eigenvalue $n_0'(\mathbf{k})$ by unity.

From Heisenberg's equation of motion (14) and (154) it follows that

$$\left.\begin{aligned} [\mathbf{H}, a_\alpha(\mathbf{k})] &= -\hbar c|\mathbf{k}|a_\alpha(\mathbf{k}) \\ [\mathbf{H}, \tilde{a}_\alpha(\mathbf{k})] &= +\hbar c|\mathbf{k}|\tilde{a}_\alpha(\mathbf{k}) \end{aligned}\right\} \quad (\alpha = 0, 1, 2, 3). \tag{158}$$

Using (157) we see that, apart from an additive constant number,

$$\left.\begin{aligned} \mathbf{H} &= \sum_\mathbf{k} c\hbar|\mathbf{k}|\Big\{\sum_{l=1}^{3} n_l(\mathbf{k}) - n_0(\mathbf{k})\Big\} \\ &= \int d^3\mathbf{k}\,\rho_\mathbf{k} c\hbar|\mathbf{k}|\Big\{\sum_{l=1}^{3} n_l(\mathbf{k}) - n_0(\mathbf{k})\Big\} \end{aligned}\right\}. \tag{159}$$

As it stands here, $\mathbf{H}$ can have negative eigenvalues because of the negative energy contribution $-c\hbar|\mathbf{k}|$ arising from the modes of vibration of $A_0(x_\mu)$. It should, however, be remembered that because it was desirable to use the four amplitudes $A_\mu(x_\nu)$ as independent variables, there must be *redundant* variables in our description of the field. This means that not all eigenstates of $\mathbf{H}$ are physical states; it is shown below that on limiting the eigenstates to the *physical states*, **H** no longer has undesirable properties.

10. The vacuum and the supplementary condition

It is clearly not possible to interpret all the operators $n_l(\mathbf{k})$, $n_0(\mathbf{k})$ as giving the numbers of real photons of various types. In order to find the physical interpretation of the quantized theory we start by defining vacuum states $|0\rangle$. For pions the vacuum state was defined by (59) or (127); thus it is natural in the electromagnetic case to use

$$E_l^{(+)}(x_\mu)|0\rangle = 0, \quad H_l^{(+)}(x_\mu)|0\rangle = 0 \quad (l = 1,2,3;\ \text{all}\ x_\mu). \tag{160}$$

Conditions (160) are preferable to a definition which is explicit in the potentials $A_\mu(x_\nu)$, because the former conditions refer to actual physical quantities, the field strengths. Using (141) and (154), the magnetic field condition becomes

$$\mathbf{k}\times\mathbf{A}(\mathbf{k})|0\rangle = 0 \quad (\text{all}\ \mathbf{k}), \tag{161}$$

where $\mathbf{A}(\mathbf{k}) = \{A_1(\mathbf{k}), A_2(\mathbf{k}), A_3(\mathbf{k})\}$. Eqn. (161) may be written

$$\mathbf{A}_{\mathrm{tr}}(\mathbf{k})|0\rangle = 0, \tag{162}$$

where $\mathbf{A}_{\mathrm{tr}}(\mathbf{k})$ is the component of the operator $\mathbf{A}(\mathbf{k})$ which is *transverse* to $\mathbf{k}$. The electric field condition similarly gives

$$\{\mathbf{k}A_0(\mathbf{k}) - |\mathbf{k}|\mathbf{A}(\mathbf{k})\}|0\rangle = 0. \tag{163}$$

The component of this equation which is perpendicular to $\mathbf{k}$ again gives (162), hence the conditions (160) are self-consistent. The component of (163) parallel to $\mathbf{k}$ is

$$\{|\mathbf{k}|A_0(\mathbf{k}) - \mathbf{k}.\mathbf{A}(\mathbf{k})\}|0\rangle = 0. \tag{164}$$

This can be written in the invariant form

$$\partial_\mu A_\mu^{(+)}(x_\nu)|0\rangle = 0 \quad (\text{all}\ x_\mu). \tag{165}$$

The equations which have been used in this section are invariant under gauge transformations of the second kind (cf. Chapter I, § 4); that is, they are unaltered by the replacement

$$A_\mu(x_\nu) \to A_\mu(x_\nu) + \partial_\mu \Lambda(x_\nu), \tag{166}$$

where $\Lambda(x_\nu)$ is an arbitrary real invariant number which obeys the wave equation

$$\partial_\mu^2 \Lambda(x_\nu) = 0. \tag{167}$$

This last equation implies that $\Lambda(x_\nu)$ can be divided into positive and negative frequency parts in an invariant way:

$$\Lambda(x_\nu) = \Lambda^{(+)}(x_\nu) + \Lambda^{(-)}(x_\nu).$$

The Fourier transform of $\Lambda(x_\nu)$ is $\Lambda(k_\nu)$ which is defined by an equation analogous to (152). It is necessary that $\Lambda^*(k_\mu) = \Lambda(-k_\mu)$, and, defining $\Lambda(\mathbf{k}) \equiv \Lambda(\mathbf{k}, k_0 = |\mathbf{k}|)$, the gauge transformation becomes

$$\left.\begin{aligned} \mathbf{A}(\mathbf{k}) &\to \mathbf{A}(\mathbf{k})+i\mathbf{k}\Lambda(\mathbf{k}) \\ A_0(\mathbf{k}) &\to A_0(\mathbf{k})+i|\mathbf{k}|\Lambda(\mathbf{k}) \end{aligned}\right\} \tag{168}$$

together with the Hermitian conjugates of these equations.†

The operator $\mathbf{A}_{\mathrm{tr}}(\mathbf{k})$ is gauge invariant, so (162) is a gauge invariant condition; similarly, (164) is gauge invariant. It is convenient to choose a different coordinate axes system for each distinct direction of the propagation vector $\mathbf{k}$. For each $\mathbf{k}$ the axes O_1, O_2 are chosen orthogonal to $\mathbf{k}$ and O_3 is along $\mathbf{k}$. The dimensionless operators $a_l(\mathbf{k})$ of (156) are the components of a vector; we denote the dimensionless operators in the new coordinate system by $a^{(l)}(\mathbf{k})$ ($l = 1, 2, 3$) and $a_0(\mathbf{k})$. The Hamiltonian (159) can now be written

$$\mathsf{H} = \sum_{\mathbf{k}} c\hbar|\mathbf{k}|\{n^{(1)}(\mathbf{k})+n^{(2)}(\mathbf{k})+n^{(3)}(\mathbf{k})-n^{(0)}(\mathbf{k})\}, \tag{169}$$

where

$$n^{(l)}(\mathbf{k}) = \tilde{a}^{(l)}(\mathbf{k})a^{(l)}(\mathbf{k}), \qquad n_0(\mathbf{k}) = \tilde{a}_0(\mathbf{k})a_0(\mathbf{k}).$$

The operators $n^{(1)}(\mathbf{k})$ and $n^{(2)}(\mathbf{k})$ are gauge invariant, therefore they can be given a definite physical meaning. They are the number operators for photons of momentum‡ $\hbar\mathbf{k}$ whose polarizations are respectively along the O_1 and O_2 axes. The eigenstate for n_1 photons having polarization along O_1 and n_2 photons having polarization along O_2 (all having momentum $\hbar\mathbf{k}$) is (cf. (53))

$$\frac{1}{(n_1!\,n_2!)^{\frac{1}{2}}}\{\tilde{a}^{(1)}(\mathbf{k})\}^{n_1}\{\tilde{a}^{(2)}(\mathbf{k})\}^{n_2}|0\rangle; \tag{170}$$

this is a gauge invariant state vector.

Physical states

From the gauge transformation (168) it follows that besides $\tilde{a}^{(1)}(\mathbf{k})$, $a^{(1)}(\mathbf{k})$, $\tilde{a}^{(2)}(\mathbf{k})$, $a^{(2)}(\mathbf{k})$, the only other gauge invariant creation and annihilation operators are $\{\tilde{a}^{(3)}(\mathbf{k})-\tilde{a}_0(\mathbf{k})\}$ and $\{a^{(3)}(\mathbf{k})-a_0(\mathbf{k})\}$. The commutation relations (157) show that

$$[\tilde{a}^{(3)}(\mathbf{k})-\tilde{a}_0(\mathbf{k}),\, a^{(3)}(\mathbf{k}')-a_0(\mathbf{k}')] = 0. \tag{171}$$

† The gauge transformation (168) is given by the unitary transformation

$$A'_\alpha(\mathbf{k}) = e^{iK}A_\alpha(\mathbf{k})e^{-iK}$$

with $$K = -\frac{1}{4\pi\hbar c}\int \frac{d^3\mathbf{k}}{|\mathbf{k}|}\{\Lambda(\mathbf{k})[\mathbf{k}.\tilde{\mathbf{A}}(\mathbf{k})-|\mathbf{k}|\tilde{A}_0(\mathbf{k})]+\Lambda^*(\mathbf{k})[\mathbf{k}.\mathbf{A}(\mathbf{k})-|\mathbf{k}|A_0(\mathbf{k})]\}.$$

‡ The commutation relations between the total field momentum $\mathbf{P}$ and the operators $\tilde{a}^{(l)}(\mathbf{k})$, $a^{(l)}(\mathbf{k})$ are easily seen to be

$$[\mathbf{P}, \tilde{a}^{(l)}(\mathbf{k})] = \hbar\mathbf{k}\tilde{a}^{(l)}(\mathbf{k}), \qquad [\mathbf{P}, a^{(l)}(\mathbf{k})] = -\hbar\mathbf{k}a^{(l)}(\mathbf{k})$$

(cf. eqn. (40)). This shows the momentum of the eigenstates of $n^{(1)}(\mathbf{k})$, $n^{(2)}(\mathbf{k})$.

A *physical state* is defined as a state which is obtained by acting on a vacuum state vector $|0\rangle$ with a gauge invariant operator. The only physical states, other than vacuum, are formed (like the state (170)) by acting on $|0\rangle$ with the *transverse* creation operators $\tilde{a}^{(1)}(\mathbf{k})$ and $\tilde{a}^{(2)}(\mathbf{k}')$. This is because the state vector

$$\{\tilde{a}^{(3)}(\mathbf{k})-\tilde{a}_0(\mathbf{k})\}^m|0\rangle \quad (m = \text{arbitrary integer}),$$

by (171) and (157), obeys both the vacuum-state definitions (162) and (164); it is therefore a vacuum state.

Remembering that $\tilde{a}^{(1)}(\mathbf{k})$ and $\tilde{a}^{(2)}(\mathbf{k})$ commute with $A_0(\mathbf{k})$ and $\mathbf{k}.\mathbf{A}(\mathbf{k})$ it follows that

$$\{|\mathbf{k}|A_0(\mathbf{k})-\mathbf{k}.\mathbf{A}(\mathbf{k})\}\,|\,\rangle = 0 \quad (\text{all } \mathbf{k}), \tag{172}$$

where $|\,\rangle$ is any physical state. This can be written in the covariant form†

$$\partial_\mu A_\mu^{(+)}(x_\nu)\,|\,\rangle = 0. \tag{173}$$

This relation (172) or (173) is the *supplementary condition* which has to be obeyed by any physical state vector; it is analogous to the initial conditions (147) of the classical theory. The Hermitian conjugate of the supplementary condition is

$$\left.\begin{aligned} \langle\,|\{|\mathbf{k}|\tilde{A}_0(\mathbf{k})-\mathbf{k}.\tilde{\mathbf{A}}(\mathbf{k})\} &= 0 \quad (\text{all } \mathbf{k}) \\ \text{or} \qquad \langle\,|\,\partial_\mu A_\mu^{(-)}(x_\nu) &= 0 \end{aligned}\right\}, \tag{174}$$

where $\langle\,|$ is any physical state. The supplementary condition in the form (173) is derived from (172) by using eqns. (154) which give the space-time propagation of $A_\mu^{(+)}(x_\nu)$. Eqn. (173) holds for all time t, and in this sense we say that the supplementary condition is consistent with the equations of motion for the field.

The operator $\{n^{(3)}(\mathbf{k})-n_0(\mathbf{k})\}$, which occurs in **H**, is not gauge invariant,‡ therefore this operator cannot be given a physical meaning. Using the identity

$$n^{(3)}(\mathbf{k})-n_0(\mathbf{k}) = \tfrac{1}{2}\{\tilde{a}^{(3)}(\mathbf{k})-\tilde{a}_0(\mathbf{k})\}\{a^{(3)}(\mathbf{k})+a_0(\mathbf{k})\}+ \\ +\tfrac{1}{2}\{\tilde{a}^{(3)}(\mathbf{k})+\tilde{a}_0(\mathbf{k})\}\{a^{(3)}(\mathbf{k})-a_0(\mathbf{k})\}$$

and the supplementary conditions (172), (174), we see that the matrix

† This condition was first used by S. N. Gupta, *Proc. Phys. Soc.* **63** (1950) 681; **64** (1951) 850. Gupta applied Dirac's indefinite metric quantization (*Proc. Roy. Soc.* A, **180** (1942) 1) to discuss the operator $\{n^{(3)}(\mathbf{k})-n_0(\mathbf{k})\}$. The method has been extended by K. Bleuler, *Helv. phys. Acta*, **23** (1950) 567, and by K. Bleuler and W. Heitler, *Prog. Theor. Phys.* **5** (1950) 600. See also F. J. Belinfante, *Phys. Rev.* **76** (1949) 226.

‡ The gauge transformation (168) increases the operator

$$\{\mathbf{k}.\tilde{\mathbf{A}}(\mathbf{k})\}\{\mathbf{k}.\mathbf{A}(\mathbf{k})\}-\mathbf{k}^2\tilde{A}_0(\mathbf{k})A_0(\mathbf{k})$$

by $$i\mathbf{k}^2\Lambda^*(\mathbf{k})\{|\mathbf{k}|A_0(\mathbf{k})-\mathbf{k}.\mathbf{A}(\mathbf{k})\}-i\mathbf{k}^2\Lambda(\mathbf{k})\{|\mathbf{k}|\tilde{A}_0(\mathbf{k})-\mathbf{k}.\tilde{\mathbf{A}}(\mathbf{k})\}.$$

element of $\{n^{(3)}(\mathbf{k})-n_0(\mathbf{k})\}$ between any pair of physical states will vanish; i.e.

$$\langle\,|\{n^{(3)}(\mathbf{k})-n_0(\mathbf{k})\}|\,\rangle = 0, \tag{175}$$

where any physical states occur to left and right.

The Hamiltonian (169) acting on any vacuum state gives another vacuum state. This is because $n^{(1)}(\mathbf{k})$, $n^{(2)}(\mathbf{k})$ commute with the operator $\{a^{(3)}(\mathbf{k})-a_0(\mathbf{k})\}$ which occurs in (164); also, by the commutation relations (157):

$$[n^{(3)}(\mathbf{k})-n_0(\mathbf{k}),\, a^{(3)}(\mathbf{k})-a_0(\mathbf{k})] = -\{a^{(3)}(\mathbf{k})-a_0(\mathbf{k})\}.$$

Therefore, if $|\,\rangle$ is any physical state, i.e. it is of the form

$$|\,\rangle = \tilde{a}^{(1)}(\mathbf{k})\,....\,\tilde{a}^{(2)}(\mathbf{k}')\,....\,|\,0\rangle,$$

then $\mathsf{H}\,|\,\rangle$ is also a physical state. It follows that if we consider only physical states, the Hamiltonian (169) can be replaced by

$$\mathsf{H} = \sum_{\mathbf{k}} c\hbar|\mathbf{k}|\{n^{(1)}(\mathbf{k})+n^{(2)}(\mathbf{k})\}. \tag{176}$$

In the representation which has been used, the particle aspect is therefore described by photons of momentum $\hbar\mathbf{k}$ having transverse polarization in the directions O_1 and O_2. The longitudinal oscillations (given by $\mathbf{k}.\mathbf{A}(\mathbf{k})$) and the scalar potential oscillations (given by $A_0(\mathbf{k})$) are not associated with any quanta.

From the definition of $\mathbf{E}$ and $\mathbf{H}$ in terms of the potential $A_\mu(x_\nu)$ (eqns. (141) and (142)), it follows that the field operators obey

$$\operatorname{div}\mathbf{H} = 0, \quad \operatorname{curl}\mathbf{E}+\frac{1}{c}\dot{\mathbf{H}} = 0. \tag{177}$$

Differentiating the supplementary condition (165) with respect to time gives

$$\operatorname{div}\mathbf{E}^{(+)}(x_\nu)\,|\,\rangle = 0. \tag{178}$$

From the Hamiltonian in the form (146), the equation for $\dot{\boldsymbol{\pi}}(\mathbf{x},t)$ can be derived; on using the supplementary condition (and the definition of $\pi^{(\mu)}$ given by (145)) we have

$$\left\{\operatorname{curl}\mathbf{H}^{(+)}(x_\nu)-\frac{1}{c}\dot{\mathbf{E}}^{(+)}(x_\nu)\right\}|\,\rangle = 0. \tag{179}$$

Taking the Hermitian conjugates of (178) and (179), it follows that for matrix elements between any pair of *physical states* we have

$$\left.\begin{aligned}\langle\,|\operatorname{div}\mathbf{E}(x_\nu)\,|\,\rangle &= 0\\ \langle\,|\left\{\operatorname{curl}\mathbf{H}(x_\nu)-\frac{1}{c}\dot{\mathbf{E}}(x)\right\}|\,\rangle &= 0\end{aligned}\right\}. \tag{180}$$

Eqns. (180) show, as a particular case, that the expectation values of these operators in any physical state will vanish. These equations with (177) give the quantum form of Maxwell's *free* field equations.

11. The electromagnetic field propagators

In solving general collision problems which involve the scattering, creation, and absorption of photons, it is necessary to know the causal solution of the inhomogeneous equation†

$$\partial_\mu^2 A'_\nu(x_\lambda) = -\frac{1}{c} j_\nu(x_\lambda), \tag{181}$$

where $j_\nu(x_\lambda)$ is in general an operator source function. In § 5 it was shown that for the neutral pion field the causal Green's function was given by the vacuum expectation value $\langle 0|T\{\phi(x_\mu)\phi(x'_\mu)\}|0\rangle$ of the chronological product of a pair of *free* field amplitudes $\phi(x_\mu)$, $\phi(x'_\mu)$. We now discuss the corresponding problem in quantum electrodynamics.

Because the free field operators $A_\mu(x_\nu)$ obey the homogeneous wave equation (144), on using the general commutation relations (151) the analysis at the end of § 5 shows that‡

$$\partial_{x_\mu}^2 T\{A_\nu(x_\lambda)A_{\nu'}(x'_\lambda)\} = i\hbar c\delta_{\nu\nu'}\delta^4(x_\lambda - x'_\lambda), \tag{182}$$

where $T\{A_\nu(x_\lambda)A_{\nu'}(x'_\lambda)\}$ is the chronologically ordered operator product.§ On account of the more complicated definition of the vacuum state in electrodynamics, we have to be particularly careful in deriving the field propagator from (182). The vacuum expectation value $\langle 0|T\{A_\nu(x_\lambda)A_{\nu'}(x'_\lambda)\}|0\rangle$ is a Green's function (by (182)), but it is not possible, using the gauge invariant definitions of the vacuum given above, to show that it is a causal Green's function (a causal Green's function‖ $G(x)$ equals $f^{(+)}(x)$ for $x_0 > 0$ and $-f^{(-)}(x)$ for $x_0 < 0$, where $f(x)$ is some function having unique frequency splitting.) The difficulty arises because $\langle 0|T\{A_\nu(x_\lambda)A_{\nu'}(x'_\lambda)\}|0\rangle$ is not gauge invariant, so it is possible by a gauge transformation to add arbitrary positive and negative frequency parts.

It would be possible to use a gauge invariant Green's function such as††

$$\langle 0|T\{A_\nu(x_\lambda)A_{\nu'}(x'_\lambda)\}|0\rangle - \langle 0|A_\nu(x_\lambda)|0\rangle\langle 0|A_{\nu'}(x'_\lambda)|0\rangle,$$

† Cf. Chapter I, eqn. (25); in the present chapter Heaviside units are used and the factor 4π does not occur in (181). The notation $A'_\nu(x_\lambda)$ is used to distinguish the solution $A'_\nu(x_\lambda)$ of (181) from the free field operator $A_\nu(x_\lambda)$ which obeys the homogeneous equation (144).

‡ Eqn. (62) holds for the chronological product as well as for its vacuum expectation value.

§ Because the field variables commute outside each other's light cones the definition of the chronological product is consistent with special relativity.

‖ A full discussion of causal Green's functions is given in the Appendix.

†† F. J. Dyson, *Phys. Rev.* **77** (1950) 421, shows that if $\langle 0|T\{A_\nu(x_\lambda)A_{\nu'}(x'_\lambda)\}|0\rangle$ is used as a causal Green's function with the gauge invariant definition of vacuum (160), the errors which are thereby introduced cannot give any contribution to any gauge invariant quantity.

but for practical purposes it is more convenient to choose a particular gauge. Because we are dealing with free field operators, the solenoidal gauge may be used. In classical theory this gauge is given by the condition

$$\operatorname{div} \mathbf{A}(x_\mu) = 0;$$

in quantum theory the vacuum-state definition (160) is replaced by the stronger definition†

$$A_\mu^{(+)}(x_\nu)|0\rangle = 0 \quad (\mu = 1,2,3,4). \tag{183}$$

This definition of the vacuum‡ is not gauge invariant but it is consistent with the equations of motion; with this definition, $|0\rangle$ is an eigenstate of the Hamiltonian $\mathbf{H}$ (eqn. (159)) and of the total momentum operator $\mathbf{P}$, and it has zero eigenvalues for both of these operators.

Using (183) and the Hermitian conjugate condition

$$\langle 0|A_\mu^{(-)}(x_\nu) = 0,$$

it is clear that $\langle 0|T\{A_\nu(x_\lambda)A_{\nu'}(x'_\lambda)\}|0\rangle$ is a causal Green's function. Comparing (182) with (A.52) we have§

$$\langle 0|T\{A_\nu(x_\lambda)A_{\nu'}(x'_\lambda)\}|0\rangle = \tfrac{1}{2}\hbar c\delta_{\nu\nu'} D_F(x_\lambda - x'_\lambda) \tag{184}$$

in this gauge. The causal solutions of the inhomogeneous eqn. (181) (in which, of course, the operators $A'_\mu(x_\lambda)$ are not in general free-field operators) can now be written, with the help of (184), in terms of expectation values of free-field operators:

$$A'_\nu(x_\lambda) = \frac{i}{\hbar c^2}\int d^4x'_\lambda \langle 0|T\{A_\nu(x_\lambda)A_{\nu'}(x'_\lambda)\}|0\rangle j_{\nu'}(x'_\lambda).$$

Provided we only wish to calculate gauge invariant quantities, the causal Green's function (184) is suitable for solving collision problems in quantum electrodynamics.

12. Example: The electromagnetic field interacting with charges and currents

Maxwell's equations

If charges and currents are present they act as sources of the electromagnetic field, and the field operators obey the propagation equations (181). The total Lagrangian density for the system is

$$\mathscr{L} = \mathscr{L}_0 + \mathscr{L}_1 + \mathscr{L}\text{ (particles)},$$

† We call this the solenoidal gauge because states $|\,\rangle$ which have real quanta are got from $|0\rangle$ by operating with $\mathbf{A}_{\text{tr}}^{(-)}$. Therefore $A_{\text{long}}^{(+)}|\,\rangle = 0$, where $\mathbf{A}_{\text{long}}$ is the longitudinal part of $\mathbf{A}$; this means that $\operatorname{div} \mathbf{A}^{(+)}|\,\rangle = 0$.

‡ The condition (183) was used by S. N. Gupta and K. Bleuler (cf. p. 95, n. ‡).

§ The expression vanishes for $\nu \neq \nu'$ because there is no similar solution of the homogeneous wave equation (details are given in the Appendix).

where $\mathscr{L}_0$ is the Lagrangian density for the free electromagnetic field (143); $\mathscr{L}_1$ is the interaction term†

$$\mathscr{L}_1 = \frac{1}{c} j_\mu(x_\nu) A'_\mu(x_\nu) \tag{185}$$

(which is obviously invariant), and $\mathscr{L}$ (particles) is the Lagrangian density for the free particles which give rise to the charge and current (e.g. electrons, pions, or nucleons).

For the present we do not wish to discuss the quantization of the particle field; consequently the analysis cannot be quite complete. By the usual quantization method of § 2 the electromagnetic field variables $A'_\mu(x_\nu)$ and their canonical momentum densities $\pi'^{(\mu)}(x_\nu)$ have to obey the commutation relations (cf. (10) and (13) of § 2)

$$\left.\begin{aligned} [A'_\mu(\mathbf{x},t),\, A'_\nu(\mathbf{x}',t)] = 0, \qquad [\pi'^{(\mu)}(\mathbf{x},t),\, \pi'^{(\nu)}(\mathbf{x}',t)] = 0 \\ [\pi'^{(\mu)}(\mathbf{x},t),\, A'_\nu(\mathbf{x}',t)] = (\hbar/i)\delta_{\mu\nu}\,\delta^3(\mathbf{x}'-\mathbf{x}) \end{aligned}\right\}. \tag{186}$$

The $\pi'^{(\mu)}(x_\nu)$ are expressed in terms of the $A'_\mu(x_\nu)$ by the same formulae as before (eqn. (145)), because the interaction term $\mathscr{L}_1$ does not contain derivatives of $A'_\mu(x_\nu)$. The equations of motion for the electromagnetic field operators are deduced from the Hamiltonian

$$\mathbf{H} = \mathbf{H}_0(A',\pi') + \mathbf{H}_1(A'), \tag{187}$$

where $\mathbf{H}_0(A',\pi')$ is the Hamiltonian for the free radiation field (146), written in terms of the new variables A'_μ, $\pi'^{(\mu)}$. By (185),

$$\mathbf{H}_1(A') = \int d^3\mathbf{x} \left\{ \rho(\mathbf{x},t) A'_0(\mathbf{x},t) - \frac{1}{c} \mathbf{j}(\mathbf{x},t) . \mathbf{A}'(\mathbf{x},t) \right\}. \tag{188}$$

Using (187) the equations of motion for the electromagnetic field are

$$\left.\begin{aligned} \dot{\mathbf{A}}' &= c^2 \boldsymbol{\pi}' + ic\,\mathrm{grad}\, A'_4, \qquad \dot{A}'_4 = c^2 \pi'^{(4)} - ic\,\mathrm{div}\,\mathbf{A}' \\ \dot{\boldsymbol{\pi}}' &= -\mathrm{curl}\,\mathrm{curl}\,\mathbf{A}' - ic\,\mathrm{grad}\,\pi'^{(4)} + \frac{1}{c}\mathbf{j} \\ \dot{\pi}'^{(4)} &= ic\left(\mathrm{div}\,\boldsymbol{\pi}' + \frac{1}{c}\rho\right) \\ \text{where} \quad \mathbf{A}' &= (A'_1, A'_2, A'_3), \qquad \boldsymbol{\pi}' = (\pi'^{(1)}, \pi'^{(2)}, \pi'^{(3)}) \end{aligned}\right\}. \tag{189}$$

From (189), the propagation equations (181) for the potentials follow

† The field operators are written $A'_\mu(x_\nu)$ to indicate that they differ from the free field operators $A_\mu(x_\nu)$.

directly. Also, assuming that the charge density and current operators ρ, $\mathbf{j}$ obey the charge continuity equation (cf. (1.19))

$$\frac{\partial \rho}{\partial t}+\operatorname{div}\mathbf{j} = 0,$$

we have

$$\partial_\mu^2\{\partial_\nu A'_\nu(x_\lambda)\} = 0. \tag{190}$$

It follows that $\pi'^{(4)}(x_\lambda)$ can be divided into positive and negative frequency parts in a Lorentz invariant fashion. This shows that it is possible to impose the supplementary condition for any *physical state vector* $|\rangle$:

$$\pi'^{(4)}(x_\nu)^{(+)}|\rangle = 0 \quad (\text{all } x_\nu). \tag{191}$$

The last two equations in (189) now give

$$\left.\begin{aligned}\left\{\operatorname{curl}\mathbf{H}'(\mathbf{x},t)-\frac{1}{c}\dot{\mathbf{E}}'(\mathbf{x},t)-\frac{1}{c}\mathbf{j}(\mathbf{x},t)\right\}^{(+)}|\rangle &= 0\\ \{\operatorname{div}\mathbf{E}'(\mathbf{x},t)-\rho(\mathbf{x},t)\}^{(+)}|\rangle &= 0\end{aligned}\right\}. \tag{192}$$

Using these conditions and their Hermitian conjugates,† we find, as in § 10, that on taking matrix elements between any pair of physical states,

$$\left.\begin{aligned}\langle|\left\{\operatorname{curl}\mathbf{H}'(\mathbf{x},t)-\frac{1}{c}\dot{\mathbf{E}}'(\mathbf{x},t)-\frac{1}{c}\mathbf{j}(\mathbf{x},t)\right\}|\rangle &= 0\\ \langle|\{\operatorname{div}\mathbf{E}'(\mathbf{x},t)-\rho(\mathbf{x},t)\}|\rangle &= 0\end{aligned}\right\}. \tag{193}$$

These are the quantum forms of two of Maxwell's equations when charge and current are present; in particular when the state vectors to left and right are identical, they show that the expectation values of these quantities vanish in any physical state. The other pair of Maxwell's equations,‡

$$\operatorname{div}\mathbf{H}' = 0, \qquad \operatorname{curl}\mathbf{E}'+\frac{1}{c}\dot{\mathbf{H}}' = 0, \tag{194}$$

are operator identities; they result from the definition of the field-strength operators

$$f'_{\mu\nu} = \partial_\mu A'_\nu-\partial_\nu A'_\mu.$$

The transverse components

At any time the field-strength operators can be analysed into Fourier components in space:

$$\left.\begin{aligned}\mathbf{E}'(\mathbf{x},t) &= \int\limits_{-\infty}^{\infty} d^3\mathbf{k}\,\{\mathbf{E}'(\mathbf{k},t)e^{i\mathbf{k}.\mathbf{x}}+\tilde{\mathbf{E}}'(\mathbf{k},t)e^{-i\mathbf{k}.\mathbf{x}}\}\\ \mathbf{H}'(\mathbf{x},t) &= \int\limits_{-\infty}^{\infty} d^3\mathbf{k}\,\{\mathbf{H}'(\mathbf{k},t)e^{i\mathbf{k}.\mathbf{x}}+\tilde{\mathbf{H}}'(\mathbf{k},t)e^{-i\mathbf{k}.\mathbf{x}}\}\end{aligned}\right\}, \tag{195}$$

† It is assumed that ρ, $\mathbf{j}$ are Hermitian operators.

‡ In this treatment it is assumed that all magnetic moments can be described by currents $\mathbf{j}$; to extend the treatment to other magnetic moments $\mathbf{M}$, a term curl $\mathbf{M}$ may be added to $\mathbf{j}$ (cf. eqn. (1.18)).

where $\mathbf{E}'(\mathbf{k},t)$, $\mathbf{H}'(\mathbf{k},t)$, etc., are time-dependent operators. The first equation of (194) gives

$$\mathbf{k}.\mathbf{H}'(\mathbf{k},t) = 0, \quad \mathbf{k}.\tilde{\mathbf{H}}'(\mathbf{k},t) = 0 \quad (\text{all } \mathbf{k}); \tag{196}$$

therefore $\mathbf{H}'(\mathbf{x},t)$ consists entirely of *transverse* components.† We now check that this statement is true for all time t. Operating on the third equation of motion (189) with *curl* and using (194) gives

$$\partial_\mu^2 \mathbf{H}'(\mathbf{x},t) = -\frac{1}{c}\operatorname{curl}\mathbf{j}(\mathbf{x},t). \tag{197}$$

Expanding the operator $\mathbf{j}(\mathbf{x},t)$ in plane Fourier components,

$$\mathbf{j}(\mathbf{x},t) = \int_{-\infty}^{\infty} d^3\mathbf{k}\,\{\mathbf{j}(\mathbf{k},t)e^{i\mathbf{k}.\mathbf{x}}+\tilde{\mathbf{j}}(\mathbf{k},t)e^{-i\mathbf{k}.\mathbf{x}}\},$$

eqn. (197) becomes

$$\left.\begin{aligned} \frac{1}{c^2}\ddot{\mathbf{H}}'(\mathbf{k},t)+\mathbf{k}^2\mathbf{H}'(\mathbf{k},t) &= \frac{i}{c}\mathbf{k}\times\mathbf{j}(\mathbf{k},t) \\ \frac{1}{c^2}\ddot{\tilde{\mathbf{H}}}'(\mathbf{k},t)+\mathbf{k}^2\tilde{\mathbf{H}}'(\mathbf{k},t) &= -\frac{i}{c}\mathbf{k}\times\tilde{\mathbf{j}}(\mathbf{k},t) \end{aligned}\right\}; \tag{198}$$

also, by (194),

$$\dot{\mathbf{H}}'(\mathbf{k},t) = -ic\mathbf{k}\times\mathbf{E}'(\mathbf{k},t), \qquad \dot{\tilde{\mathbf{H}}}'(\mathbf{k},t) = ic\mathbf{k}\times\tilde{\mathbf{E}}'(\mathbf{k},t). \tag{199}$$

Eqns. (198) and (199) show that (196) always holds, whatever the source of the field. Further, (198) and (199) are operator equations which show how the source produces (or absorbs) quanta with transverse polarization (i.e. photons). Using them it is possible to calculate the expectation values of the field—and hence justify the classical equations which we used to calculate multipole emission in Chapter I—or we can directly evaluate the energy or momentum density of the photons which are emitted in a specified direction.

The second equation of (193) shows that $\mathbf{E}'(\mathbf{x},t)$ is not entirely transverse. It is possible to perform a unitary transformation on the field variables which will reduce $\mathbf{E}'(x_\nu)$ to a transverse operator $\mathbf{E}(x_\nu)$, and at the same time exhibit the Coulomb interaction of the particles. The reader is referred to the literature for the details of this method;‡ here it is only briefly outlined.

† That is, the vibrations are transverse to the propagation vector **k**.

‡ P. A. M. Dirac, *Proc. Roy. Soc.* A, **114** (1927) 243, 710, and *Quantum Mechanics* (Clarendon Press, 3rd edn., 1947), ch. 12; W. Heitler, *Quantum Theory of Radiation* (Clarendon Press, 3rd edn., 1954), ch. 3 and app. 3. The *covariant* separation of the Coulomb field is due to Z. Koba, T. Tati, and S. Tomonaga, *Prog. Theor. Phys.* **2** (1947) 198; Z. Koba, Y. Oisa, and M. Sasaki, ibid. **3** (1948) 141, 229. See also J. Schwinger, *Phys. Rev.* **74** (1948) 1439, and J. M. Jauch and F. Rohrlich, *Photons and Electrons* (Addison-Wesley, Cambridge, Mass., 1955), ch. 6.

Separation of the Coulomb interaction

It is possible, without altering the commutation relations (186), to add ordinary functions to the field potentials, or to the field-strength operators. Such a substitution is equivalent to a unitary transformation. In deriving the equations of motion it is necessary to remember that these added functions may depend on time; modified equations of motion then hold.† So far as the electromagnetic field operators are concerned, the charge density $\rho(\mathbf{x},t)$ behaves like an ordinary function, because it commutes with all the electromagnetic field operators.‡ We define a new potential operator $A_4(\mathbf{x},t)$ by

$$A'_4(\mathbf{x},t) = A_4(\mathbf{x},t)+\frac{i}{4\pi}\int \frac{\rho(\mathbf{x}',t)}{|\mathbf{x}-\mathbf{x}'|}\,d^3\mathbf{x}'. \tag{200}$$

The other components of the potential $\mathbf{A}'(\mathbf{x},t)$ are to remain unaltered. The commutation relation

$$[A_4(\mathbf{x},t),\, A_4(\mathbf{x}',t)] = 0 \quad (\text{all } \mathbf{x},\, \mathbf{x}')$$

holds, provided we make the reasonable assumption that

$$[\rho(\mathbf{x},t),\, \rho(\mathbf{x}',t)] = 0 \quad (\text{all } \mathbf{x},\, \mathbf{x}'). \tag{200 a}$$

It is unnecessary to modify the canonical momentum density

$$\pi'^{(4)} = (i/c)(\partial_\lambda A'_\lambda);$$

the canonical commutation relations (186) are then valid with $A_4(\mathbf{x},t)$ replacing $A'_4(\mathbf{x},t)$.

The substitution (200) leaves unaltered the magnetic field operator $\mathbf{H}'(\mathbf{x},t)$, but the electric field operator $\mathbf{E}'(\mathbf{x},t)$ is replaced by a new operator $\mathbf{E}(\mathbf{x},t)$, where

$$\mathbf{E}'(\mathbf{x},t) = \mathbf{E}(\mathbf{x},t)-\operatorname{grad}_x\frac{1}{4\pi}\int \frac{\rho(\mathbf{x}'t)}{|\mathbf{x}-\mathbf{x}'|}\,d^3\mathbf{x}'. \tag{201}$$

The vector operator $\mathbf{E}'(\mathbf{x},t)$ can be split into a transverse part $\mathbf{E}'_{\mathrm{tr}}(\mathbf{x},t)$ (defined by $\operatorname{div}\mathbf{E}'_{\mathrm{tr}} = 0$) and a longitudinal part $\mathbf{E}'_{\mathrm{long}}(\mathbf{x},t)$ (defined by $\operatorname{curl}\mathbf{E}'_{\mathrm{long}} = 0$). The substitution (201) gives a new longitudinal component $\mathbf{E}_{\mathrm{long}}$:

$$\mathbf{E}'_{\mathrm{long}}(\mathbf{x},t) = \mathbf{E}_{\mathrm{long}}(\mathbf{x},t)-\operatorname{grad}_x\frac{1}{4\pi}\int \frac{\rho(\mathbf{x}',t)}{|\mathbf{x}-\mathbf{x}'|}\,d^3\mathbf{x}'; \tag{202}$$

eqn. (201) leaves unaltered the transverse component $\mathbf{E}'_{\mathrm{tr}}$. It should be emphasized that so long as the terms which are subtracted from the

† If f depends explicitly on time, then

$$\frac{df}{dt} = \frac{\partial f}{\partial t}+\frac{i}{\hbar}[H,f].$$

‡ Also, $\rho(x_\nu)$ obeys eqn. (200 a).

field amplitudes can be treated as ordinary functions, they cannot alter any of the essentially quantum properties of the field.†

The significance of the operator $\mathbf{E}(\mathbf{x}, t)$ is that it is obtained from the actual electric field $\mathbf{E}'(\mathbf{x}, t)$ by subtracting the (classical) Coulomb field (eqn. (201)). We now show an important property of the longitudinal part $\mathbf{E}_{\text{long}}(\mathbf{x}, t)$, namely, that it obeys the homogeneous wave equation. By eqn. (190), viz.
$$\partial_\mu^2 \pi'^{(4)}(x_\nu) = 0,$$
and the third equation of motion (189), we have
$$\partial_\mu^2 \mathbf{C}(x_\nu) = 0, \tag{203}$$
where
$$\mathbf{C}(x_\nu) \equiv \operatorname{curl} \mathbf{H}'(\mathbf{x}, t) - \frac{1}{c}\dot{\mathbf{E}}'(\mathbf{x}, t) - \frac{1}{c}\mathbf{j}(\mathbf{x}, t).$$

From (203) it follows that $\mathbf{C}(x_\nu)$ can be expanded in the form
$$\mathbf{C}(\mathbf{x}, t) = \int d^3\mathbf{k}\,\{\mathbf{C}(\mathbf{k})e^{i(\mathbf{k}.\mathbf{x}-|\mathbf{k}|x_0)} + \tilde{\mathbf{C}}(\mathbf{k})e^{-i(\mathbf{k}.\mathbf{x}-|\mathbf{k}|x_0)}\}, \tag{204}$$
where $\mathbf{C}(\mathbf{k})$, $\tilde{\mathbf{C}}(\mathbf{k})$ are constant operator coefficients. Using (204) we can split $\mathbf{C}(x_\nu)$ into positive and negative frequency parts
$$\mathbf{C}(x_\nu) = \mathbf{C}^{(+)}(x_\nu) + \mathbf{C}^{(-)}(x_\nu),$$
where the first and second terms in the integrand give $\mathbf{C}^{(+)}$ and $\mathbf{C}^{(-)}$ respectively. Also, $\mathbf{C}$, $\mathbf{C}^{(+)}$, or $\mathbf{C}^{(-)}$ can be divided into longitudinal and transverse parts; for example
$$\mathbf{C}_{\text{long}}^{(+)}(\mathbf{x}, t) = \int \frac{d^3\mathbf{k}}{\mathbf{k}^2}\mathbf{k}\{\mathbf{k}.\mathbf{C}(\mathbf{k})\}e^{i(\mathbf{k}.\mathbf{x}-|\mathbf{k}|x_0)},$$
$$\mathbf{C}_{\text{tr}}^{(+)}(\mathbf{x}, t) = \mathbf{C}^{(+)}(\mathbf{x}, t) - \mathbf{C}_{\text{long}}^{(+)}(\mathbf{x}, t).$$
The current vector $\mathbf{j}(\mathbf{x}, t)$ is split into longitudinal and transverse parts by using the identity‡
$$4\pi\mathbf{j}(\mathbf{x}, t) = \operatorname{curl}\int \frac{\operatorname{curl}\mathbf{j}(\mathbf{x}', t)}{|\mathbf{x}-\mathbf{x}'|}\,d^3\mathbf{x}' - \operatorname{grad}\int \frac{\operatorname{div}\mathbf{j}(\mathbf{x}', t)}{|\mathbf{x}-\mathbf{x}'|}\,d^3\mathbf{x}'. \tag{205}$$
Therefore
$$\mathbf{C}_{\text{tr}}(\mathbf{x}, t) = \operatorname{curl}\mathbf{H}'(\mathbf{x}, t) - \frac{1}{c}\dot{\mathbf{E}}'_{\text{tr}}(\mathbf{x}, t) - \frac{1}{4\pi c}\operatorname{curl}\int \frac{\operatorname{curl}\mathbf{j}(\mathbf{x}', t)}{|\mathbf{x}-\mathbf{x}'|}\,d^3\mathbf{x}'.$$

From (202), (205), and the charge conservation equation we get
$$\mathbf{C}_{\text{long}}(\mathbf{x}, t) = -\frac{1}{c}\dot{\mathbf{E}}_{\text{long}}(\mathbf{x}, t). \tag{206}$$

† The general commutation relations $[\mathbf{E}(x_\nu), \mathbf{E}(x_\nu)]$ are altered by the subtraction for $(x_\nu - x'_\nu)^2 \leqslant 0$; these general commutators have not been used above in discussing the electromagnetic field with sources present.

‡ This follows from $\mathbf{j}(\mathbf{x}, t) = -\nabla_{\mathbf{x}}^2 \frac{1}{4\pi}\int \frac{\mathbf{j}(\mathbf{x}'t)}{|\mathbf{x}-\mathbf{x}'|}\,d^3\mathbf{x}'$
and the identity $\nabla^2 = \operatorname{grad}\operatorname{div} - \operatorname{curl}\operatorname{curl}$, on integrating by parts.

By (203),
$$\partial_\mu^2\,\dot{\mathbf{E}}_{\text{long}}(\mathbf{x},t) = 0, \tag{207}$$
and on integrating this with respect to time,
$$\partial_\mu^2\,\mathbf{E}_{\text{long}}(\mathbf{x},t) = \mathbf{f}(\mathbf{x})$$
where $\mathbf{f}(\mathbf{x})$ is independent of time. From the fourth equation of motion (189), (202), and (190),
$$\partial_\mu^2(\operatorname{div}\mathbf{E}_{\text{long}}) = 0.$$
Remembering the identity $\operatorname{curl}\mathbf{E}_{\text{long}} = 0$, it follows that $\mathbf{f}(\mathbf{x})$ must be a constant $\mathbf{f}$. Restricting the operators $\mathbf{E}_{\text{long}}(\mathbf{x},t)$ to a set which is finite (or zero) for infinite $|\mathbf{x}|$ and infinite t, requires that $\mathbf{f}$ be zero. Hence the physically permissible solutions of (207) obey
$$\partial_\mu^2\,\mathbf{E}_{\text{long}}(\mathbf{x},t) = 0. \tag{208}$$
The behaviour of the operator $\mathbf{E}_{\text{long}}(\mathbf{x},t)$ is therefore not related to the particular charge or current density which is present.

The supplementary condition and the Hamiltonian

The first of Maxwell's equations (192) may now be divided into a transverse and a longitudinal part.

The transverse part
$$\left(\operatorname{curl}\mathbf{H}'(x,t)-\frac{1}{c}\dot{\mathbf{E}}'_{\text{tr}}(\mathbf{x},t)-\frac{1}{4\pi c}\operatorname{curl}\int\frac{\operatorname{curl}\mathbf{j}(\mathbf{x}',t)}{|\mathbf{x}-\mathbf{x}'|}\,d^3\mathbf{x}'\right)^{(+)}|\rangle = 0 \tag{209}$$
together with Maxwell's equations (194) and the identity
$$\operatorname{div}\mathbf{E}'_{\text{tr}}(\mathbf{x},t) = 0$$
describe the creation, destruction, and scattering of real photons by the charge-current distribution. The propagation of the transverse component is given by eqn. (197) above.

The longitudinal component of the first equation of (192) is
$$\dot{\mathbf{E}}_{\text{long}}(\mathbf{x},t)^{(+)}\,|\rangle = 0, \tag{210}$$
also the second equation (192) becomes
$$\operatorname{div}\mathbf{E}^{(+)}_{\text{long}}(\mathbf{x},t)\,|\rangle = 0. \tag{211}$$
From (208) we deduce that $\mathbf{E}_{\text{long}}(\mathbf{x},t)$ itself can be expanded in the form (204). Therefore (210) can be integrated to give
$$\mathbf{E}_{\text{long}}(\mathbf{x},t)^{(+)}\,|\rangle = 0. \tag{212}$$
This equation is consistent with (211); it holds for any physical state vector. Eqn. (212) has the same form as the condition (172) which enabled us to show that the longitudinal component of the field $\mathbf{E}$ could be ignored in the case of free electromagnetic radiation. The same deduction can be made here, namely that having subtracted the classical

Coulomb field, the remainder of the longitudinal field operator can be ignored; the details of this deduction will not be repeated.

There are two other simple consequences of (212). Taking matrix elements between any two physical states, (212) and its Hermitian conjugate give

$$\langle \,|\, \mathbf{E}_{\text{long}}(\mathbf{x},t) \,|\, \rangle = 0,$$

in particular, $\mathbf{E}_{\text{long}}$ always has zero expectation value. The other consequence is the form of the matrix elements $\langle \,|\, \mathbf{H} \,|\, \rangle$ between any pair of physical states, where $\mathbf{H}$ is the Hamiltonian (187),

$$\mathbf{H} = \mathbf{H}_0 + \mathbf{H}_1.$$

Using the commutators (186), the last equation of (189) and the propagation equation (190) for $\pi'^{(4)}(x_\nu)$ we deduce†

$$[\pi'^{(4)}(x_\nu), \pi'^{(4)}(x'_\nu)] = 0 \quad (\text{all } x_\nu,\, x'_\nu). \tag{213}$$

It follows from the supplementary condition (191) that‡

$$\langle \,|\, \pi'^{(4)}(x_\nu)\pi'^{(4)}(x'_\nu) \,|\, \rangle = 0. \tag{214}$$

From the third equation of (189) for $\dot{\boldsymbol{\pi}}'$ we pick out the longitudinal component, using (205), the charge conservation equation, and (202); this gives

$$\dot{\mathbf{E}}_{\text{long}}(\mathbf{x},t) = ic^2 \operatorname{grad} \pi'^{(4)}(\mathbf{x},t).$$

Therefore the commutator $[\dot{\mathbf{E}}_{\text{long}}(\mathbf{x},t), \mathbf{E}_{\text{long}}(\mathbf{x}',t)]$ vanishes for $\mathbf{x} \neq \mathbf{x}'$; for $\mathbf{x} = \mathbf{x}'$ the commutator is a constant number. Also, assuming $\rho(\mathbf{x},t)$, $\rho(\mathbf{x}',t)$ commute, it follows that $\mathbf{E}_{\text{long}}(\mathbf{x},t)$, $\mathbf{E}_{\text{long}}(\mathbf{x}',t)$ commute. From the propagation equation (208) we therefore deduce that

$$[\mathbf{E}_{\text{long}}(\mathbf{x},t)^{(+)}, \mathbf{E}_{\text{long}}(\mathbf{x},t)^{(-)}]$$

is a constant (infinite) number.§ Consequently,‖ all matrix elements (between physical states) of the form

$$\langle \,|\, \int d^3\mathbf{x}\, \{\mathbf{E}_{\text{long}}(\mathbf{x},t)\}^2 \,|\, \rangle$$

can be replaced by $\langle \,|\, h \,|\, \rangle$, where h is a constant (infinite) number. This constant gives no physical effect, and it may be ignored.

Splitting the total electric field into longitudinal and transverse parts, $\mathbf{E}' = \mathbf{E}'_{\text{tr}} + \mathbf{E}'_{\text{long}}$, using the relation††

$$\int d^3\mathbf{x}\, (\mathbf{E}'_{\text{tr}} \cdot \mathbf{E}'_{\text{long}}) = 0,$$

† Because $[\pi'^{(4)}(\mathbf{x},t), \pi'^{(4)}(\mathbf{x}',t)] = 0$, and $[\dot{\pi}'^{(4)}(\mathbf{x},t), \pi'^{(4)}(\mathbf{x}',t)] = 0$, eqn. (190) gives (213) on using (25).

‡ Because, by (213), $[\pi'^{(4)}(x_\nu)^{(+)}, \pi'^{(4)}(x'_\nu)^{(-)}] = 0$.

§ This can be seen by expanding $\mathbf{E}_{\text{long}}(\mathbf{x},t)$ in plane waves with operator coefficients.

‖ Using the supplementary condition (212).

†† Cf. W. Pauli, *Handbuch der Physik* (J. Springer, Berlin, 1933), vol. xxiv/1, p. 265. Substituting $\mathbf{E}'_{\text{long}} = \operatorname{grad} \Lambda$ (where Λ is an operator) and integrating by parts gives the relation.

and eqns. (202), (212), (214), gives

$$\langle|\mathbf{H}|\rangle = \langle|\int d^3\mathbf{x}\left\{\tfrac{1}{2}\{\mathbf{E}'^2_{\mathrm{tr}}(\mathbf{x},t)+\mathbf{H}'^2(\mathbf{x},t)\}-\frac{1}{c}\mathbf{j}(\mathbf{x},t).\mathbf{A}'_{\mathrm{tr}}(\mathbf{x},t)\right\}|\rangle+$$
$$+\frac{1}{8\pi}\langle|\iint\frac{\rho(\mathbf{x},t)\rho(\mathbf{x}',t)}{|\mathbf{x}-\mathbf{x}'|}\,d^3\mathbf{x}d^3\mathbf{x}'|\rangle. \quad (215)$$

The last term† is the Coulomb energy of the charge distribution.

Eqn. (215) gives the matrix elements of $\mathbf{H}$ between *any* physical states, hence this form of $\mathbf{H}$ can be used for any practical calculations. It should be noted that in the electromagnetic terms only transverse field operators appear. Further, in calculating the emission, absorption, or scattering of radiation, only the transverse component $\mathbf{A}'_{\mathrm{tr}}(\mathbf{x},t)$ is to be used in the interaction term $-(1/c)(\mathbf{j}.\mathbf{A}'_{\mathrm{tr}})$. This is because in such problems we are only concerned with initial and final physical states which have definite eigenvalues for the number of *transverse* quanta, or photons. Thus in (215) all the quantum field effects are in the transverse components.

13. Example: Emission of low-frequency photons

The emission of low-frequency photons by a charged particle is an important physical effect which can be discussed by a method which is much more accurate than perturbation theory. This method will provide a good illustration of the distinction between the *bare* particle which does not interact with the electromagnetic field, and the *real* particle which interacts all the time with the (quantized) electromagnetic field. The real particle carries around with it a disturbance in the electromagnetic field.

Classical theory

The correspondence principle suggests that classical electrodynamics is a good approximation in the case of low-frequency photons, because the individual quantum of energy is so small. In the limit of zero frequency quantum effects disappear. First we examine the classical result.

The radiation in the wave zone at a distance $\mathbf{R}$ from a charged particle is given by‡

$$\mathbf{H}(t) = \frac{1}{4\pi c^2}\frac{1}{R^2}(\mathbf{R}\times\ddot{\mathbf{Z}})\Big|_{(t-R/c)}, \qquad \mathbf{E}(t) = \frac{1}{R}\{\mathbf{R}\times\mathbf{H}(t)\}, \quad (216)$$

where $\mathbf{Z} = e\mathbf{x}$ is the dipole moment of the particle measured from a

† This term is obtained by integration by parts, and putting $\langle|\pi'_4|\rangle = 0$.

‡ Cf. W. Heitler, *Quantum Theory of Radiation* (Clarendon Press, 3rd edn., 1954), ch. 1, § 3.

fixed origin; $\ddot{\mathbf{Z}}$ is evaluated at the retarded time $(t-R/c)$. Heaviside units are used. If the velocity of the particle is much less than c, the retardation is not strongly dependent on the direction of $\mathbf{R}$, and (216) readily gives the angular distribution of the radiation.†

Consider a charged particle which moves with uniform velocities $\mathbf{v}$ and $\mathbf{w}$ before and after a collision (see Fig. 4). The collision is confined to a finite region of space‡ (d is a measure of the linear dimension of this region). The nature of the force producing the deflexion $(\mathbf{w}-\mathbf{v})$ is

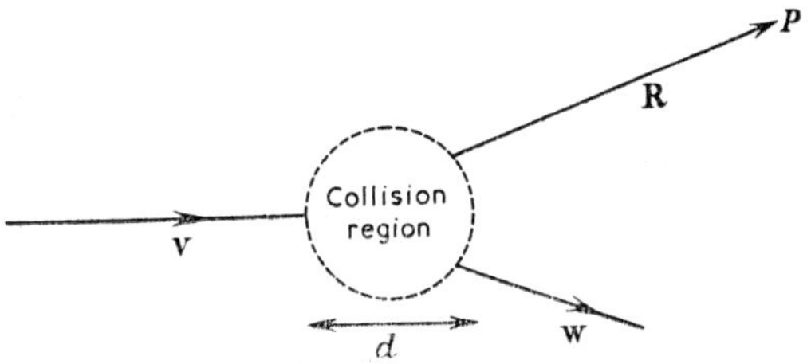

FIG. 4. Emission of radiation in the direction $\mathbf{R}$ when the velocity of a charged particle is deflected from $\mathbf{v}$ to $\mathbf{w}$.

unimportant. The emitted radiation is examined at a point P which is so far away that d/R is small. The *total energy* flowing in the direction $\mathbf{R}$ across unit area at P is

$$I(P) = c\int\limits_{-\infty}^{\infty} dt\,|\mathbf{E}(t)\times\mathbf{H}(t)| = c\int\limits_{-\infty}^{\infty} dt\,|\mathbf{E}(t)|^2. \tag{217}$$

Expanding the electric field $\mathbf{E}(t)$ at P in frequency components gives

$$\mathbf{E}(t) = \int\limits_{-\infty}^{\infty} d\nu\,\mathbf{E}(\nu)e^{2\pi i\nu t}, \tag{218}$$

where $\mathbf{E}^*(\nu) = \mathbf{E}(-\nu)$. If $I(\nu, P)\,d\nu$ is the contribution to the energy $I(P)$ from the frequency interval ν, $\nu+d\nu$, then (217) and (218) give

$$I(\nu, P) = 2c\left|\int\limits_{-\infty}^{\infty} \mathbf{E}(t)e^{-2\pi i\nu t}\,dt\right|^2. \tag{219}$$

We define a *low frequency* by $\nu < \nu_0$ where ν_0 is the inverse of the duration of the collision. For low frequencies, (219) may be written

$$I(\nu, P) = 2c\left|\int\limits_{-\infty}^{\infty} \mathbf{E}(t)\,dt\right|^2, \tag{220}$$

because (νt) alters little during the time that $\mathbf{E}(t)$ is appreciable. If the

† If the velocity is close to c, the retardation effect gives strong radiation along the direction of motion.

‡ The collision of an electron with a neutral atom is in this category; the collision of two unscreened charged particles is not.

velocity of the charged particle is not relativistic, the integral over t in (220) can be replaced by an integral over the retarded time $(t-R/c)$; by (216) we get

$$\int_{-\infty}^{\infty} \mathbf{E}(t)\,dt = \frac{e}{4\pi c^2}\frac{1}{R^3}[\mathbf{R}\times\{\mathbf{R}\times(\mathbf{w}-\mathbf{v})\}].$$

If θ is the angle between $\mathbf{R}$ and $(\mathbf{w}-\mathbf{v})$, the total intensity in the range ν, $\nu+d\nu$ which is emitted in the solid angle $d\Omega$ about $\mathbf{R}$ is

$$I(\nu,\theta)\,d\nu d\Omega = \frac{e^2}{8\pi^2c^3}(\mathbf{w}-\mathbf{v})^2\sin^2\theta\,d\nu d\Omega. \tag{221}$$

Integrating over all directions gives

$$I(\nu)\,d\nu = \frac{e^2}{3\pi c^3}(\mathbf{w}-\mathbf{v})^2\,d\nu. \tag{222}$$

Hence we expect that $n(\nu)\,d\nu$, the number of photons with frequency between ν and $\nu+d\nu$, is†

$$n(\nu)\,d\nu = \frac{e^2}{4\pi\hbar c}\frac{2}{3\pi}\frac{(\mathbf{w}-\mathbf{v})^2}{c^2}\frac{d\nu}{\nu}. \tag{223}$$

As $\nu \to 0$ the number of photons emitted becomes infinite; this is the so-called *infra-red* divergence. Obviously the quantum theory of this emission process cannot be evaluated by perturbation theory.

Quantum theory

The emission of l.f.p.‡ was first discussed by Bloch and Nordsieck;§ here we follow the method of Jost.|| Consider a single spin-$\frac{1}{2}$ fermion of mass m and charge e which suffers a collision during which its potential energy is $V(\mathbf{x})$.†† $V(\mathbf{x})$ will include the electrostatic interaction with other particles. Inserting the current density $\mathbf{j}(\mathbf{x}') = ec\boldsymbol{\alpha}\,\delta^3(\mathbf{x}-\mathbf{x}')$ into (215), the total Hamiltonian becomes

$$\mathbf{H} = c(\mathbf{p}.\boldsymbol{\alpha})+\beta mc^2+V(\mathbf{x})-e\{\boldsymbol{\alpha}.\mathbf{A}'(\mathbf{x})\}+\tfrac{1}{2}\int d^3\mathbf{x}'\,[\{\mathbf{E}_{\mathrm{tr}}(\mathbf{x}')\}^2+\{\mathbf{H}'(\mathbf{x}')\}^2]. \tag{224}$$

$\mathbf{A}'(\mathbf{x})$ is the transverse potential operator at the position of the electron; $\boldsymbol{\alpha}$, β are 4×4 matrices which are defined in Chapter III, § 1.

† $\dfrac{e^2}{4\pi\hbar c} \simeq \dfrac{1}{137}$.

‡ l.f.p. = low-frequency photon, h.f.p. = high-frequency photon.

§ F. Bloch and A. Nordsieck, *Phys. Rev.* **52** (1937) 54; other early papers are W. Pauli and M. Fiertz, *Nuovo Cim.* **15** (1938) 167; S. Dancoff, *Phys. Rev.* **55** (1939) 959.

|| R. Jost, *Phys. Rev.* **72** (1947) 815, used a similar method for investigating the low-frequency photon emission accompanying Compton scattering.

†† The equations of motion of a fermion are given in Chapter III.

The electromagnetic field operator $\mathbf{A}'(\mathbf{x})$ can be expanded in terms of photon creation and destruction operators $\tilde{a}_\lambda(\mathbf{k})$, $a_\lambda(\mathbf{k})$ by (cf. (156))

$$\mathbf{A}'(\mathbf{x}) = V^{-\frac{1}{2}} \sum_{\mathbf{k}} \sum_{\lambda=1}^{2} \left(\frac{\hbar c}{2|\mathbf{k}|}\right)^{\frac{1}{2}} \{a_\lambda(\mathbf{k})\mathbf{e}_\lambda(\mathbf{k})e^{i\mathbf{k}.\mathbf{x}} + \tilde{a}_\lambda(\mathbf{k})\mathbf{e}_\lambda(\mathbf{k})e^{-i\mathbf{k}.\mathbf{x}}\}, \tag{225}$$

where V is the volume of space and $\mathbf{e}_\lambda(\mathbf{k})$ ($\lambda = 1, 2$) are a pair of unit polarization vectors which, together with $\mathbf{k}$, form an orthogonal triad. The operator coefficients obey

$$[a_\lambda(\mathbf{k}), \tilde{a}_{\lambda'}(\mathbf{k}')] = \delta_{\lambda\lambda'}\delta_{\mathbf{k},\mathbf{k}'} \quad (\lambda, \lambda' = 1, 2),$$

all other pairs commute. Substituting (225) into (224) gives

$$\mathbf{H} = c(\mathbf{p}.\boldsymbol{\alpha}) + \beta mc^2 + V(\mathbf{x}) - \sum_{\mathbf{k},\lambda} \{\boldsymbol{\alpha}.\mathbf{b}_\lambda(\mathbf{k})\}\{a_\lambda(\mathbf{k})e^{i\mathbf{k}.\mathbf{x}} + \tilde{a}_\lambda(\mathbf{k})e^{-i\mathbf{k}.\mathbf{x}}\} + \\ + \sum_{\mathbf{k},\lambda} n_\lambda(\mathbf{k})c\hbar|\mathbf{k}|, \tag{226}$$

where $n_\lambda(\mathbf{k})$ is the number operator for the photons. Also,

$$\mathbf{b}_\lambda(\mathbf{k}) = \mathbf{e}_\lambda(\mathbf{k})\left(\frac{\hbar c}{2|\mathbf{k}|V}\right)^{\frac{1}{2}} e.$$

In the quantum case we define high-frequency and low-frequency photons by $|\mathbf{k}| > K$ and $|\mathbf{k}| < K$, where for the present we only require $\hbar K$ to be small compared with the initial and final momentum of the fermion (also $\hbar K$ has to be small compared with mc).†

The approximation for $\boldsymbol{\alpha}$

A simple approximation is used for the matrix element

$$\langle \tilde{u}(\mathbf{p}')(\boldsymbol{\alpha}.\mathbf{b})u(\mathbf{p})\rangle$$

for the emission or absorption of a low-frequency photon. Here $u(\mathbf{p})$, $u(\mathbf{p}')$ are the four-component state vectors for an electron of momentum $\mathbf{p}$, $\mathbf{p}'$ respectively. The normalization used is

$$\tilde{u}(\mathbf{p}).u(\mathbf{p}) = 1,$$

and with the notation of Chapter III (eqn. (3.3)) these state vectors obey Dirac's equation

$$(i\gamma^\mu p_\mu + mc)u(\mathbf{p}) = 0,$$

where $\gamma^k = -i\beta\alpha_k$ ($k = 1, 2, 3$), $\gamma^4 = \beta$, $p_4 = i(\mathbf{p}^2 + m^2c^2)^{\frac{1}{2}}$. Only positive energy solutions (electron solutions) are considered.

It is easy to show that any matrix element

$$M_\mu \equiv \bar{u}(\mathbf{p}')\gamma^\mu u(\mathbf{p}) = \tilde{u}(\mathbf{p}')\gamma^4\gamma^\mu u(\mathbf{p})$$

† When the scatterer is not fixed, for example when it is another particle, the division into high and low frequencies is to be made in the centre of mass system.

can be written†

$$iM_\mu = \frac{(p_\mu+p'_\mu)}{2mc}\bar{u}(\mathbf{p}')u(\mathbf{p})+i\sum_{\nu=1}^{4}\frac{(p_\nu-p'_\nu)}{2mc}\bar{u}(\mathbf{p}')\sigma^{\mu\nu}u(\mathbf{p}),$$

where $\sigma^{\mu\nu} = (\gamma^\mu\gamma^\nu-\gamma^\nu\gamma^\mu)/2i$ is the electron spin operator which has eigenvalues ± 1 (cf. eqn. (3.10)). Hence

$$\bar{u}(\mathbf{p}')\alpha_k u(\mathbf{p}) = \frac{1}{2mc}(p_k+p'_k)\bar{u}(\mathbf{p}')u(\mathbf{p})+\frac{i}{2mc}\sum_\nu (p_\nu-p'_\nu)\bar{u}(\mathbf{p}')\sigma^{k\nu}u(\mathbf{p}). \tag{227}$$

Assuming that the momentum of the emitted photon is small, so that $|\mathbf{p}-\mathbf{p}'| \ll mc$, the second term on the right of (227) will be negligible compared with the first.‡ The first term is evaluated by neglecting the difference between **p** and **p**′, and using the relation§

$$\bar{u}(\mathbf{p})u(\mathbf{p}) = mc^2/T, \quad \text{where } T = c(\mathbf{p}^2+m^2c^2)^{\frac{1}{2}};$$

hence for the emission of low-frequency photons we may write

$$\boldsymbol{\alpha} = c\mathbf{p}/T+\boldsymbol{\alpha}_1, \tag{228}$$

where $\boldsymbol{\alpha}_1$ is a small 4×4 matrix. The result holds for slow or relativistic electrons. The contribution from $\boldsymbol{\alpha}_1$ vanishes as $\mathbf{p}'\to\mathbf{p}$, so $\boldsymbol{\alpha}_1$ does *not* contribute to the infra-red divergence. For l.f.p. we now replace $\{\boldsymbol{\alpha}.\mathbf{b}_\lambda(\mathbf{k})\}$ by $c\{\mathbf{p}.\mathbf{b}_\lambda(\mathbf{k})\}/T$.

The first unitary transformation

The eigenstates of **H** are found by making two unitary transformations. The first of these removes the spatial dependence from the l.f.p. interaction term. Any operator F is replaced by $F' = S^{-1}FS$, where

$$S = \exp(iL) = \exp\Big[i\sum_{\mathbf{k}_l}\sum_\lambda n_\lambda(\mathbf{k})(\mathbf{k}.\mathbf{x})\Big].$$

$\sum_{\mathbf{k}_l}$ indicates that the summation is only over the low-frequency range ($|\mathbf{k}_l| < K$). Using the relation

$$F' = F+(-i)[L,F]+(-i)^2[L,[L,F]]+...$$

† Using the equation of motion we write $2imcM_\mu = \bar{u}(\mathbf{p}')(\gamma^\nu p'_\nu\gamma^\mu+\gamma^\mu\gamma^\nu p_\nu)u(\mathbf{p})$. The commutation relation (3.4) gives $\gamma^\mu\gamma^\nu = \delta_{\mu\nu}+i\sigma^{\mu\nu}$.

‡ For $\nu\neq 4$, $\bar{u}(\mathbf{p}')\sigma^{k\nu}u(\mathbf{p})$ is of the same order as $\bar{u}(\mathbf{p}')u(\mathbf{p})$; for $\nu = 4$,

$$|p_4-p'_4| \simeq |\mathbf{p}-\mathbf{p}'|.|\mathbf{p}|/|p_4|,$$

and $|\bar{u}\gamma^k u|$ cannot be greater than unity.

§ This is proved in Chapter IV, § 3.

we see that the only variables which are altered by this transformation are

$$\left.\begin{aligned}\mathbf{p}' &= \mathbf{p}+\sum_{\mathbf{k}_l}\sum_{\lambda} n_\lambda(\mathbf{k})\hbar\mathbf{k}\\ a'_\lambda(\mathbf{k}_l) &= a_\lambda(\mathbf{k}_l)e^{i(\mathbf{k}_l.\mathbf{x})}\\ \tilde{a}'_\lambda(\mathbf{k}_l) &= \tilde{a}_\lambda(\mathbf{k}_l)e^{-i(\mathbf{k}_l.\mathbf{x})}\end{aligned}\right\}. \tag{229}$$

Clearly $\mathbf{p}'$ is the total momentum of the bare particle and the l.f. photons. The Hamiltonian (226) can now be written†

$$\mathsf{H} = c(\boldsymbol{\alpha}.\mathbf{p}')+\beta mc^2+V(\mathbf{x}')+\mathsf{H}(\text{h.f.p.})+\sum_{\mathbf{k}_l,\lambda} n'_\lambda(\mathbf{k})\{\mathbf{p}',\hbar\mathbf{k}_l\}/T'- \\ -\sum_{\mathbf{k}_l,\lambda}\{a'_\lambda(\mathbf{k})+\tilde{a}'_\lambda(\mathbf{k})\}c(\mathbf{p}'.\mathbf{b}_\lambda(\mathbf{k}))/T'+g, \tag{230}$$

where‡

$$\{\mathbf{p}',\hbar\mathbf{k}\} = c\hbar|\mathbf{k}|T'-c^2\hbar(\mathbf{k}.\mathbf{p}') \qquad (T' = c(\mathbf{p}'^2+m^2c^2)^{\frac{1}{2}})$$

and

$$g = -\sum_{\mathbf{k}_l,\lambda}\{a'_\lambda(\mathbf{k})+\tilde{a}'_\lambda(\mathbf{k})\}(\boldsymbol{\alpha}_1.\mathbf{b}_\lambda(\mathbf{k}))-\sum_{\mathbf{k}_l,\lambda} n_\lambda(\mathbf{k})(\boldsymbol{\alpha}_1.\mathbf{k})\hbar.$$

H(h.f.p.) is the high-frequency photon part of (226). The operator g only makes a small contribution to the low-frequency part of the interaction, and it will be ignored.

The Bloch–Nordsieck transformation§

This unitary transformation removes the low-frequency part of the interaction. It gives $F'' = S^{-1}F'S$, where $S = \exp(U)$ and

$$U = \sum_{\mathbf{k}_l,\lambda}\eta_{\mathbf{k}\lambda}(\mathbf{p}')\{a'_\lambda(\mathbf{k})-\tilde{a}'_\lambda(\mathbf{k})\}, \quad \eta_{\mathbf{k}\lambda}(\mathbf{p}') = c(\mathbf{p}'.\mathbf{b}_\lambda(\mathbf{k}))/\{\mathbf{p}',\hbar\mathbf{k}\}. \tag{231}$$

The h.f.p. operators are unaltered, while the l.f.p. operators become

$$\left.\begin{aligned}a''_\lambda(\mathbf{k}) &= a'_\lambda(\mathbf{k})-\eta_{\mathbf{k}\lambda}(\mathbf{p}')\\ \tilde{a}''_\lambda(\mathbf{k}) &= \tilde{a}'_\lambda(\mathbf{k})-\eta_{\mathbf{k}\lambda}(\mathbf{p}')\\ n''_\lambda(\mathbf{k}) &= n'_\lambda(\mathbf{k})-\eta_{\mathbf{k}\lambda}(\mathbf{p}')\{a'_\lambda(\mathbf{k})+\tilde{a}'_\lambda(\mathbf{k})\}+\{\eta_{\mathbf{k}\lambda}(\mathbf{p}')\}^2\end{aligned}\right\}. \tag{232}$$

This transformation does not change the particle's momentum ($\mathbf{p}'' = \mathbf{p}'$), but it changes its position to $\mathbf{x}'' = e^{-U}\mathbf{x}'e^{U}$. We substitute in (230), and (for the present) leave the terms in $\mathbf{x}'$ as they stand; thus||

$$\mathsf{H} = c(\boldsymbol{\alpha}.\mathbf{p}'')+\beta mc^2+V(\mathbf{x}')-\sum_{\mathbf{k}_h,\lambda}(\boldsymbol{\alpha}.\mathbf{b}_\lambda(\mathbf{k}))\{a''_\lambda(\mathbf{k})e^{i\mathbf{k}.\mathbf{x}'}+\tilde{a}''_\lambda(\mathbf{k})e^{-i\mathbf{k}.\mathbf{x}'}\}+ \\ +\sum_{\mathbf{k}_h,\lambda} n''_\lambda(\mathbf{k})c\hbar|\mathbf{k}|+\sum_{\mathbf{k}_l,\lambda} n''_\lambda(\mathbf{k})\{\mathbf{p}'',\hbar\mathbf{k}\}/T''-\frac{c^2}{T''}\sum_{\mathbf{k}_l,\lambda}\frac{(\mathbf{p}''.\mathbf{b}_\lambda(\mathbf{k}))^2}{\{\mathbf{p}'',\hbar\mathbf{k}\}}. \tag{233}$$

The only l.f.p. operator in (233) is $n''_\lambda(\mathbf{k}_l)$; there is no interaction between the l.f.p. and the charged particle other than via the terms which

† $\mathbf{x}' = \mathbf{x}$ is the position of the fermion.

‡ Eqn. (228) is used in the form $\boldsymbol{\alpha} = \boldsymbol{\alpha}_1+c\mathbf{p}'/T'$; this is because we find that $\mathbf{p}'$ is the momentum of the *real* charged particle.

§ See p. 108, nn. §, ||.

|| $\mathbf{k}_h$ refers to h.f.p.; $\mathbf{k}_l$ refers to l.f.p.; $T'' = c(\mathbf{p}''^2+m^2c^2)^{\frac{1}{2}}$.

contain $\mathbf{x}'$. These terms are $V(\mathbf{x}')$ and the h.f.p. interaction; we denote their sum by $\mathbf{H}_1$, and we assume that perturbation theory can be used to calculate transitions caused by $\mathbf{H}_1$.

Apart from $\mathbf{H}_1$, eqn. (233) is *separable* into particle and l.f.p. terms without any interaction. We may say that (ignoring $\mathbf{H}_1$) the Hamiltonian (233) describes a *real* fermion and *real* l.f. photons; the last term in (233) is the fermion self-energy due to the l.f.p. field. This is of the order $(e^2/\hbar c)c\hbar K$, and will be neglected. The presence of the fermion alters the energy of each real l.f.p. from $c\hbar|\mathbf{k}|$ to $\{\mathbf{p}'', \hbar\mathbf{k}\}/T''$.

Now we find the eigenstates of the photon part of (233). For any $\mathbf{k}$, λ we introduce new operators

$$Q''_\lambda(\mathbf{k}) = \frac{1}{\sqrt{2}}\{a''_\lambda(\mathbf{k})+\tilde{a}''_\lambda(\mathbf{k})\}, \qquad P''_\lambda(\mathbf{k}) = \frac{i}{\sqrt{2}}\{a''_\lambda(\mathbf{k})-\tilde{a}''_\lambda(\mathbf{k})\}.$$

The only non-zero commutators between these new variables are

$$[P''_\lambda(\mathbf{k}), Q''_{\lambda'}(\mathbf{k}')] = i\delta_{\lambda\lambda'}\delta_{\mathbf{k},\mathbf{k}'}. \tag{234}$$

Taking $Q''_\lambda(\mathbf{k})$ diagonal, (234) is satisfied by $P''_\lambda(\mathbf{k}) = i\partial/\partial Q''_\lambda(\mathbf{k})$. Also

$$n''_\lambda(\mathbf{k}) = \tilde{a}''_\lambda(\mathbf{k})a''_\lambda(\mathbf{k}) = \tfrac{1}{2}[\{P''_\lambda(\mathbf{k})\}^2+\{Q''_\lambda(\mathbf{k})\}^2-1];$$

therefore the eigenstates of $n''_\lambda(\mathbf{k})$ are the Hermite functions $h_n\{Q''_\lambda(\mathbf{k})\}$ $(n = 0, 1, 2,...)$ which satisfy†

$$\tfrac{1}{2}(-\partial^2/\partial Q''^2+Q''^2)h_n(Q'') = (n+\tfrac{1}{2})h_n(Q''). \tag{235}$$

These eigenfunctions obey

$$\int_{-\infty}^{\infty} dQ'' h_n(Q'')h_m(Q'') = \delta_{nm}, \tag{236}$$

and they are related to Hermite's polynomials $H_n(Q'')$ by‡

$$h_n(Q'') = \{2^n n!\sqrt{\pi}\}^{-\frac{1}{2}} e^{-\frac{1}{2}Q''^2} H_n(Q'').$$

Ignoring $\mathbf{H}_1$, the eigenstates of (233) are of the form

$$\psi(\mathbf{p}'', s; n_{\mathbf{k}h\lambda}; n_{\mathbf{k}l\lambda}) = \phi(\mathbf{p}'', s) \prod_{\mathbf{k},\lambda} h_{n_{\mathbf{k}h\lambda}}\{Q''_\lambda(\mathbf{k})\} h_{n_{\mathbf{k}l\lambda}}\{Q''_\lambda(\mathbf{k})\}, \tag{237}$$

where $\phi(\mathbf{p}'', s)$ is the eigenstate for a free fermion of momentum $\mathbf{p}''$ and spin s. Different sets of integers $(n_{\mathbf{k}\lambda})$ give different photon configurations.

The emitted radiation

We examine the change in the l.f.p. field when the fermion's velocity is altered by a collision with the scatterer (i.e. by $V(\mathbf{x})$), by scattering a h.f. photon, or by bremsstrahlung involving a h.f. photon. These

† We also require $h_n(Q'') \to 0$ for $|Q''| \to \infty$.

‡ E. Madelung, *Mathematische Hilfsmittel des Physikers* (Dover, New York, 1943), p. 200.

processes are described by $\mathbf{H}_1$.† It is convenient to carry out the perturbation theory calculation in the F' representation. In this representation the fermion, h.f.p., and l.f.p. eigenstates are, respectively,‡

$$\phi(\mathbf{p}',s);\quad h_{n_{\mathbf{k}}\lambda}\{Q'_\lambda(\mathbf{k}_h)\};\quad h_{n_{\mathbf{k}}\lambda}\{Q'_\lambda(\mathbf{k}_l)-\sqrt{2}\,\eta_{\mathbf{k}_l\lambda}(\mathbf{p}')\}.$$

We can regard the l.f.p. field as a set of *biased* simple harmonic oscillators; the bias $(\sqrt{2}\,\eta_{\mathbf{k}_l\lambda}(\mathbf{p}'))$ depends on the photon and the fermion momenta.

We calculate the matrix element of $\mathbf{H}_1$ for a transition in which the fermion momentum changes from $\mathbf{p}'$ to $\mathbf{q}'$, the h.f.p. occupation numbers change from a set a to a set b, and the l.f.p. occupation numbers change from $n_{\mathbf{k}\lambda}$ to $m_{\mathbf{k}\lambda}$. It is

$$\langle\mathbf{q}',b|\,\mathbf{H}_1\,|\mathbf{p}',a\rangle\prod_{\mathbf{k}_l\lambda}\int\limits_{-\infty}^{\infty}dQ_{\mathbf{k}\lambda}\,h_{m_{\mathbf{k}}\lambda}\{Q'_{\mathbf{k}\lambda}-\sqrt{2}\,\eta_{\mathbf{k}\lambda}(\mathbf{q}')\}h_{n_{\mathbf{k}}\lambda}\{Q'_{\mathbf{k}\lambda}-\sqrt{2}\,\eta_{\mathbf{k}\lambda}(\mathbf{p}')\}. \tag{238}$$

Here $\langle\mathbf{q}',b|\,\mathbf{H}_1\,|\mathbf{p}',a\rangle$ is the matrix element which is obtained by ignoring all l.f.p.; it can be evaluated directly from the original Hamiltonian (226).

Writing§

$$\langle m,\mathbf{q}|n,\mathbf{p}\rangle = \int\limits_{-\infty}^{\infty}dQ'\,h_m\{Q'-\sqrt{2}\,\eta(\mathbf{q})\}h_n\{Q'-\sqrt{2}\,\eta(\mathbf{p})\}, \tag{239}$$

we have‖

$$\langle m,\mathbf{q}|n,\mathbf{p}\rangle = (i)^{m-n}(m!\,n!)^{\frac{1}{2}}\exp(-\tfrac{1}{2}w^2)\sum_{\mu=0}^{\infty}\frac{(-iw)^{m-n+2\mu}}{(n-\mu)!\,\mu!\,(m-n+\mu)!}, \tag{240}$$

where $\quad w = \eta(\mathbf{q})-\eta(\mathbf{p}),\quad$ and $\quad 1/\sigma! = 0\quad$ if $\sigma < 0$.

It follows from (236) and the definition (239) (because the functions $h_n(Q)$ form a complete set in $-\infty \leqslant Q \leqslant \infty$) that

$$\sum_{m=0}^{\infty}\langle n_1\mathbf{p}_1|m,\mathbf{q}\rangle\langle m,\mathbf{q}|n_2\mathbf{p}_2\rangle = \langle n_1\mathbf{p}_1|n_2\mathbf{p}_2\rangle \tag{241}$$

for any integers n_1, n_2 and any momenta $\mathbf{p}_1$, $\mathbf{p}_2$, $\mathbf{q}$; in particular

$$\sum_{m=0}^{\infty}\langle n_1\mathbf{p}|m,\mathbf{q}\rangle\langle m,\mathbf{q}|n_2,\mathbf{p}\rangle = \delta_{n_1n_2}. \tag{242}$$

The transition probability for scattering of the fermion by a centre of force is obtained directly from the matrix element (238) by the usual methods of perturbation theory. For scattering by a h.f.p. or for

† $\mathbf{H}_1 = V(\mathbf{x}')+$(the h.f.p. interaction).

‡ We have $\mathbf{p}'' = \mathbf{p}'$, $Q''_\lambda(\mathbf{k}_h) = Q'_\lambda(\mathbf{k}_h)$, $Q''_\lambda(\mathbf{k}_l) = Q'_\lambda(\mathbf{k}_l)-\sqrt{2}\,\eta$.

§ Obviously $\langle n\mathbf{p}|m\mathbf{q}\rangle = \langle m\mathbf{q}|n\mathbf{p}\rangle$, and all $\langle m\mathbf{q}|n\mathbf{p}\rangle$ are real.

‖ The integral has been evaluated by W. Pauli and M. Fiertz, *Nuovo Cim.* **15** (1938) 167.

bremsstrahlung involving a h.f.p. it is necessary to form the *compound* matrix element (which allows for intermediate virtual states).† If the dividing frequency cK is very small we can ignore the variation in the energy and momentum of the intermediate state with the number of l.f. quanta in that state.‡ Using (241), it follows that any matrix element is of the form

$$\langle \mathbf{q}',b|\,M\,|\mathbf{p}',a\rangle \prod_{\mathbf{k}_l\lambda} \langle m_{\mathbf{k}\lambda},\mathbf{q}'|n_{\mathbf{k}\lambda},\mathbf{p}'\rangle, \tag{243}$$

where $\langle \mathbf{q}',b|\,M\,|\mathbf{p}',a\rangle$ is either the compound matrix element, or the scattering matrix element of Chapter V, and is calculated from $\mathbf{H}_1$ by ignoring the l.f.p.

Discussion of the results

The transition probability deduced from (243) is

$$\Gamma = \frac{2\pi}{\hbar}\rho(E)|\langle \mathbf{q}',b|\,M\,|\mathbf{p}',a\rangle|^2 \prod_{\mathbf{k}_l\lambda} |\langle m_{\mathbf{k}\lambda},\mathbf{q}'|n_{\mathbf{k}\lambda},\mathbf{p}'\rangle|^2, \tag{244}$$

where $\rho(E)$ is the density (in energy) of the final states. Ignoring the restriction imposed by energy and momentum conservation on the number $m_{\mathbf{k}\lambda}$ of l.f.p. in the final state, we can sum the transition probability Γ over all values of $m_{\mathbf{k}\lambda}$ using (242):

$$\sum_{m_{\mathbf{k}\lambda}} \Gamma = 2\pi\rho(E)/\hbar\,.\,|\langle \mathbf{q}',b|\,M\,|\mathbf{p}',a\rangle|^2. \tag{245}$$

This shows that the usual perturbation theory calculation for scattering or for processes involving h.f. photons is correct,§ provided the results are interpreted as giving the total transition probability for *all* numbers of l.f. photons in the final state.||

For $n = 0$, (240) gives

$$\langle m,\mathbf{q}|0,\mathbf{p}\rangle = \frac{w^m}{(m!)^{\frac{1}{2}}}e^{-w^2/2}.$$

If there are initially no l.f. photons, (244) gives

$$\Gamma = 2\pi\rho(E)/\hbar\,.\,|\langle \mathbf{q}',b|\,M\,|\mathbf{p}',a\rangle|^2 \prod_{\mathbf{k}_l\lambda} \frac{(w_{\mathbf{k}\lambda}^2)^{m_{\mathbf{k}\lambda}}}{m_{\mathbf{k}\lambda}!}e^{-w_{\mathbf{k}\lambda}^2}. \tag{246}$$

Thus the l.f.p. are emitted with a Poisson distribution. It is a general

† Cf. W. Heitler, *Quantum Theory of Radiation* (Clarendon Press, 3rd edn., 1954), ch. iv.

‡ The expectation values of the energy and momentum of the l.f. quanta can be made as small as we like by choosing K small (see below).

§ We do not discuss here whether perturbation theory is valid for the high-frequency processes themselves.

|| The interpretation of (245) without using the Bloch–Nordsieck transformation is that the l.f.p. configurations in the initial and final states are identical.

property that on account of being indistinguishable and obeying Bose statistics, photons are emitted with a Poisson distribution.† The mean number of photons of type $(\mathbf{k},\lambda)$ is

$$\bar{m}_{\mathbf{k},\lambda} = w_{\mathbf{k}\lambda}^2 = \{\eta_{\mathbf{k}\lambda}(\mathbf{q}')-\eta_{\mathbf{k}\lambda}(\mathbf{p}')\}^2. \tag{247}$$

For non-relativistic values of $\mathbf{p}'$, by (231),

$$\eta_{\mathbf{k}\lambda}(\mathbf{p}') \simeq \left(\frac{e^2}{4\pi\hbar c}\right)^{\frac{1}{2}} \frac{(\mathbf{p}'.\mathbf{e}_\lambda)}{mc}(4\pi^2\rho_{\mathbf{k}}|\mathbf{k}|^3)^{-\frac{1}{2}}. \tag{248}$$

Assuming the initial and final velocities of the fermion are $\mathbf{v}$ and $\mathbf{w}$ respectively, (247) and (248) give the average number of photons with polarization $\mathbf{e}_\lambda$ and propagation vector $\mathbf{k}$ lying in the solid angle $d\Omega$ and in $d|\mathbf{k}|$:

$$\bar{m}_{\mathbf{k}\lambda}\rho_{\mathbf{k}}|\mathbf{k}|^2\,d\Omega\,d|\mathbf{k}| = \frac{e^2}{4\pi\hbar c}[((\mathbf{w}-\mathbf{v}).\mathbf{e}_\lambda)^2/c^2].\frac{d\Omega}{4\pi^2|\mathbf{k}|}.d|\mathbf{k}|.$$

Summing over the two polarizations $\mathbf{e}_\lambda$, and over the direction of $\mathbf{k}$ gives the same result (223) as the classical theory.

We notice that if the propagation vectors $\mathbf{k}$ are selected by the periodicity condition in a cubic box, the product $\rho_{\mathbf{k}}|\mathbf{k}|^3$ occurring in (248) can never be less than unity; therefore, the expectation value $\bar{m}_{\mathbf{k}\lambda}$ for a single value of $(\mathbf{k},\lambda)$ is always less than unity, even when the periodicity box becomes infinite. The expectation values for the total energy and momentum of the l.f.p. emitted in any deflexion of the fermion are

$$\epsilon = \sum_{\mathbf{k}_l\lambda} c\hbar|\mathbf{k}|w_{\mathbf{k}\lambda}^2, \qquad \boldsymbol{\pi} = \sum_{\mathbf{k}_l\lambda} \hbar\mathbf{k}w_{\mathbf{k}\lambda}^2,$$

respectively. Using (247) it can be shown‡ that $\epsilon < B.c\hbar K$. Here $B = (\text{const}).\log(p/mc)$, where p is of the order of the fermion's momentum in the centre of mass system. B is small for $p \simeq 2\,mc$, but in all cases, the total energy ϵ can be made as small as we wish by choosing a small value of K. A similar result‡ holds for $|\boldsymbol{\pi}|$.

The probability for the emission of no l.f.p. is, by (246),

$$\Gamma = 2\pi\rho(E)/\hbar.|\langle\mathbf{q}',b|M|\mathbf{p}',a\rangle|^2\exp\Big(-\sum_{\mathbf{k}_l\lambda} w_{\mathbf{k}\lambda}^2\Big). \tag{249}$$

From (248) it follows that as the lower limit of integration for $|\mathbf{k}|$ tends to zero, $\Big(\sum_{\mathbf{k}\lambda} w_{\mathbf{k}\lambda}^2\Big)$ becomes infinite. Hence by (249), if we could detect photons of indefinitely small energy, the probability of finding that no photons were emitted during a deflexion of the fermion would be zero. A somewhat more striking result is that, in the same circumstances, the probability of finding that a *finite* number of photons was emitted

† See, for example, W. Thirring and B. F. Touschek, *Phil. Mag.* **62** (1951) 244.
‡ R. Jost, *Phys. Rev.* **72** (1947) 815.

is also zero.† This is because the introduction of a *finite* number of factors $(w_{\mathbf{k}\lambda}^2)^m/m!$ cannot prevent the exponential sum in (249) from vanishing. In practice, of course, we cannot detect photons of indefinitely small energy.

The Bloch–Nordsieck method‡ for discussing the emission of l.f. photons is incomplete. This is because, so far as the low-frequency interaction is concerned, we deal with real photons and a real fermion, but for the h.f. photons we still use the bare particle description. The incompleteness shows up in the appearance of the upper limit cK of the low-frequency range in the answers to certain questions.§ This difficulty will be removed if we can work with real particles in the high-frequency range as well as in the low-frequency range; unfortunately this cannot be done with simple perturbation theory. It can be shown|| that the renormalization technique may be used to complete the discussion so as to prevent K from appearing in the answer to physical questions (cf. also Chapter V, § 10).

† An infinite number of photons must be emitted.

‡ R. Ascoli and G. Bussetti, *Nuovo Cim.* **3** (1956) 189, have applied the Bloch–Nordsieck method to study the polarization in bremsstrahlung.

§ For example, cK appears in the probability that on being scattered an electron does not emit any photon having $|\mathbf{k}| > k_1$, where $k_1 < K$.

|| J. Hamilton, *Proc. Phys. Soc.* A, **62** (1949) 749; E. L. Lomon, *Nucl. Phys.* **1** (1956) 101.

III

DIRAC'S WAVE EQUATION

1. Introduction

As a preliminary to fermion field theory it is necessary to give some account of the single particle approximation for spin-$\frac{1}{2}$ particles which is given by Dirac's equation.† Although this equation cannot adequately describe such important phenomena as the Lamb shift and the vacuum polarization, it is an essential foundation for the quantized field theory. In this chapter some of the important properties of Dirac's equation and its solutions are discussed, in particular those properties which are useful in investigating the nature of elementary particles. We do not attempt to discuss the quantitative application of Dirac's equation to the theory of atomic spectra, or the theory of scattering; these topics are adequately treated in the standard textbooks.

Because fundamental particles, if charged, may carry either sign of charge, Dirac's wave function has four components $\psi_\rho(x_\mu)$ $(\rho = 1, 2, 3, 4)$ so as to be sufficiently general to describe states with either positive or negative charge, and spin up or down (with respect to any given direction).‡ The momentum, or the spatial distribution of the particle, is given in the usual way by the dependence of $\psi_\rho(x_\mu)$ on $\mathbf{x}$. Electrons and positrons were the first particles to be described by such wave functions; protons and anti-protons and positive and negative muons or μ-mesons are described in the same way. An anti-neutron is believed to differ from a neutron by virtue of having a magnetic moment which is parallel to the spin, rather than opposite to the spin as for the neutron; this pair is also described by a four-component Dirac wave function. It appears that the neutrino and the anti-neutrino are distinct particles; they are to be described by a special type of Dirac wave function having only two independent components. This will be discussed later (§ 16 below).

The basic relativistic wave equation for a free fermion is

$$i\hbar\frac{\partial\psi}{\partial t} = \{c(\boldsymbol{\alpha}.\mathbf{p})+\beta mc^2\}\psi, \tag{1}$$

where $\mathbf{p}$ and m are the momentum and mass of the particle, ψ is the

† P. A. M. Dirac, *Quantum Mechanics* (Clarendon Press, 3rd edn., 1947), ch. 12.

‡ We only discuss fermions with spin $\frac{1}{2}$.

four-component column vector (ψ_ρ), and $\boldsymbol{\alpha}$, β are 4×4 matrices obeying

$$\alpha_k\alpha_j+\alpha_j\alpha_k = 2\delta_{kj}, \quad \alpha_k\beta+\beta\alpha_k = 0, \quad \beta^2 = 1 \quad (k,j = 1,2,3). \tag{2}$$

Using the covariant notation $x_\mu = (\mathbf{x}, x_4)$, where $x_4 = ix_0 = ict$, and defining matrices γ^μ by $\gamma^k = -i\beta\alpha_k$, $\gamma^4 = \beta$, it is easy to see that (1) may be written†

$$\gamma^\mu\partial_\mu\psi+\kappa\psi = 0, \tag{3}$$

where $\kappa = mc/\hbar$ is the reciprocal Compton wavelength for the particle. The matrices γ^μ obey

$$\gamma^\mu\gamma^\nu+\gamma^\nu\gamma^\mu = 2\delta_{\mu\nu} \quad (\mu,\nu = 1,2,3,4). \tag{4}$$

Eqns. (4) can only be satisfied by using 4×4 matrices for γ^μ, and the only ambiguity possible is the replacement of each γ^μ by $S\gamma^\mu S^{-1}$, where S is any non-singular‡ 4×4 matrix.§ This replacement gives a new solution ψ' of (3) such that $\psi' = S\psi$; thus the solutions ψ'_ρ of the new equation are (constant) linear combinations of the original ψ_ρ. Physically this means that the same phenomena are analysed in a different way (for example, the component of the spin may be measured in a different direction, or the particle may be observed from a different Lorentz reference frame). The various forms which can in this way be chosen for γ^μ, give what are called *equivalent* representations of the particle's properties and behaviour; two of these representations which are of particular importance will be mentioned below.

In classical mechanics the motion of a particle of charge e in an electromagnetic field is described by replacing the energy momentum 4-vector $p_\mu = (p, iE/c)$ by $p_\mu+(e/c)A_\mu$, where A_μ is the four-potential $(\mathbf{A}, i\phi)$. In quantum mechanics the corresponding replacement is‖

$$\partial_\mu \to \partial_\mu+\frac{ie}{\hbar c}A_\mu, \tag{5}$$

and in the presence of a given (un-quantized) electromagnetic field—the so-called *external* field—eqn. (3) is replaced by

$$\gamma^\mu\left(\partial_\mu+\frac{ie}{\hbar c}A_\mu(x)\right)\psi+\kappa\psi = 0. \tag{6}$$

This equation can be used to describe, with considerable accuracy, the motion of electrons in atoms and the scattering of electrons; here we

† Summation over repeated indices is implied throughout. $\partial_\mu \equiv \partial/\partial x_\mu$.

‡ We restrict the γ^μ to be Hermitian.

§ For the proof of this statement see B. L. van der Waerden, *Gruppentheoretische Methode in der Quantenmechanik* (Edwards, Ann Arbor, 1944), p. 54.

‖ In Chapter III the particle has charge e and potential energy $-e\phi$.

use it to discuss the general electromagnetic properties of spin-$\frac{1}{2}$ particles. We define a new operator

$$\pi_\mu = p_\mu + \frac{e}{c} A_\mu,$$

so that (6) may be written

$$(\gamma^\mu \pi_\mu - imc)\psi = 0. \tag{7}$$

The π_μ do not in general commute; their commutator is

$$[\pi_\mu, \pi_\nu] = (\hbar e/ic) f_{\mu\nu}, \tag{8}$$

where $f_{\mu\nu} = \partial_\mu A_\nu - \partial_\nu A_\mu$ is the electromagnetic field-strength tensor (cf. eqn. (1.23)). Operating on (7) with $(\gamma^\nu \pi_\nu + imc)$ gives, by (4) and (8),

$$\left\{\pi_\mu^2 + m^2c^2 + \frac{\hbar e}{2c} \sigma^{\mu\nu} f_{\mu\nu}\right\}\psi = 0, \tag{9}$$

where the anti-symmetric matrix $\sigma^{\mu\nu}$ is defined by

$$\sigma^{\mu\nu} = \frac{1}{2i}[\gamma^\mu, \gamma^\nu]. \tag{10}$$

In (9) the term containing $f_{\mu\nu}$ represents electromagnetic effects; further examination of these has to be left until the spin properties of the fermion have been discussed.

2. Transformation properties and spin

Eqn. (1), or (3), describes the relativistic behaviour of a spin-$\frac{1}{2}$ particle, and it is necessary that these equations give an equivalent description from *any* two Lorentz frames of reference. Assume a new frame of reference (x'_μ) given by

$$x'_\mu = a_{\mu\nu} x_\nu \qquad \begin{pmatrix} a_{\nu\mu} a_{\nu\lambda} = \delta_{\mu\lambda} \\ a_{\mu\nu} a_{\lambda\nu} = \delta_{\mu\lambda} \end{pmatrix}, \tag{11}$$

where $a_{\mu\nu}$ are constant parameters describing either a rotation or reflection of spatial coordinates,† or a uniform motion relative to the (x_μ) frame. We expect the fermion to be described in the new (x'_μ) frame by a four-component wave function ψ', such that

$$\psi'(x'_\mu) = \Lambda\psi(x_\mu), \tag{12}$$

where Λ is a non-singular 4×4 matrix which is a function of $a_{\mu\nu}$ alone. The Dirac equation (3) in the new frame is

$$\gamma^\mu \partial_{x'_\mu} \psi' + \kappa\psi' = 0. \tag{13}$$

† Here we give the reflection-invariant form of the theory; in § 16 the two-component neutrino theory is given—it is not reflection invariant.

By (11), $\partial_{x'_\mu} = a_{\mu\lambda}\partial_{x_\lambda}$, and a little manipulation shows that (13) is identical with (3) provided Λ obeys

$$\Lambda^{-1}\gamma^\nu\Lambda = a_{\nu\lambda}\gamma^\lambda \quad (\nu = 1,2,3,4). \tag{14}$$

(The same argument holds for eqn. (6).) It is easy to verify that matrices Λ with such properties do exist.† For the typical rotation

$$\left.\begin{aligned} x'_1 &= x_1, & x'_2 &= x_2\cos\theta+x_3\sin\theta \\ x'_4 &= x_4, & x'_3 &= -x_2\sin\theta+x_3\cos\theta \end{aligned}\right\} \tag{15}$$

a suitable operator is

$$\Lambda(\theta) = \{\cos(\tfrac{1}{2}\theta)+\gamma^2\gamma^3\sin(\tfrac{1}{2}\theta)\} = \exp(\tfrac{1}{2}\gamma^2\gamma^3\theta). \tag{16}$$

For the spatial reflection P,

$$\mathbf{x}' = -\mathbf{x}, \qquad x'_4 = x_4,$$

we can use

$$\Lambda = \gamma^4. \tag{17}$$

A typical uniform velocity transformation is

$$\left.\begin{aligned} x'_1 &= \eta\{x_1+i(v/c)x_4\}, & x'_2 &= x_2, \\ x'_4 &= \eta\{x_4-i(v/c)x_1\}, & x'_3 &= x_3, \end{aligned} \quad \eta = (1-v^2/c^2)^{-\frac{1}{2}} \right\} \tag{18}$$

and a suitable Λ is

$$\Lambda(v) = \frac{1}{\surd 2}\left\{(1+\eta)^{\frac{1}{2}}+\frac{iv\eta}{c(1+\eta)^{\frac{1}{2}}}\gamma^1\gamma^4\right\} = \exp(\tfrac{1}{2}i\gamma^1\gamma^4\phi), \tag{19}$$

where $\sinh\phi = v\eta/c$. Using (4) it is easy to verify that (16), (17), and (19) satisfy (14), and it is also easy to see that $\Lambda(-\theta) = \{\Lambda(\theta)\}^{-1}$, $\Lambda(-v) = \{\Lambda(v)\}^{-1}$. $\Lambda(\theta)$ and $\Lambda(v)$ are chosen so that they tend to unity as θ or v go to zero.

From (12) and (16) it is clear that the wave function $\psi(x_\mu)$ at any point x_μ is two valued; rotating the spatial axes through an angle 2π about any direction changes the sign of $\psi(x_\mu)$. It is an essential property of fermion wave functions that they are two valued in sign, but no ambiguity occurs in any physical result, because all physical observables contain an even number of fermion wave functions.

The spin

The operator $\Lambda(\theta)$ given by (16) is only one solution of (14); it describes the effect of a rotation θ about the O_1 axis on a fermion in a state of zero orbital angular momentum. The operator $\exp(im\theta)\Lambda(\theta)$, where m is any integer, describes the change in the wave function of a fermion having the component of orbital angular momentum $m\hbar$ about the O_1 direction.

† See W. Pauli, *Handbuch der Physik* (J. Springer, Berlin, 1933), vol. xxiv/1.

As we saw in Chapter I, the operator L_1 for the component of angular momentum about the axis O_1 is given by $L_1 = (\hbar/i)I_1$ where the operator $(1+I_1\,\delta\theta)$ describes the effect on the wave function of rotating the axes through the infinitesimal angle $\delta\theta$ about axis O_1.† Replacing θ in (16) by $\delta\theta$ gives

$$\Lambda(\delta\theta) = 1+\tfrac{1}{2}i\sigma^{23}\,\delta\theta \tag{20}$$

(where (10) and (4) have been used), so $S_1 = \frac{1}{2}\hbar\sigma^{23}$, where $\mathbf{S} = (S_1, S_2, S_3)$ is the spin or intrinsic angular momentum operator. Using (4) it is easy to show that $(\sigma^{23})^2 = 1$, so the eigenvalues of σ^{23} are ± 1; hence the eigenvalues of the spin component in any direction are $\pm\frac{1}{2}\hbar$. The total angular momentum of a fermion is the vector sum of the orbital angular momentum and the spin. Further details of how these two components are combined are given below (§ 7).

The magnetic moment

It is now easy to see that one part of the extra term appearing in (9) describes a magnetic moment. On dividing by $2m$ eqn. (9) may be written

$$\frac{E+e\phi+mc^2}{2mc^2}(E+e\phi-mc^2)\psi = \left\{\frac{1}{2m}\left(\mathbf{p}+\frac{e}{c}\mathbf{A}\right)^2+\frac{e}{2mc}\tfrac{1}{2}\hbar\sigma^{\mu\nu}f_{\mu\nu}\right\}\psi. \tag{21}$$

If $E-mc^2+e\phi$ is small—as it is for a slowly moving particle in a weak electric field—the factor $(E+mc^2+e\phi)/2mc^2$ on the left of (21) may be replaced by unity. (In the limit $\phi = 0$ and zero velocity, this substitution is exact.) Eqn. (21), apart from the term

$$\frac{e}{2mc}\tfrac{1}{2}\hbar\sigma^{\mu\nu}f_{\mu\nu}, \tag{22}$$

is now just the Schrödinger equation for a spinless particle in an electromagnetic field. The components $\mu = 4$, $\nu = 1, 2, 3$ of (22) give an effect which, on choosing a representation, can be shown to vanish for particles of low velocity; the components $\mu, \nu = 1, 2, 3$, give $(e/mc)(\mathbf{S}.\mathbf{H})$, which is the energy of a magnetic dipole of moment $-(e/mc)\mathbf{S}$ in the external magnetic field $\mathbf{H}$. The intrinsic magnetic moment of the particle is $e\hbar/2mc$.

It was pointed out by Pauli‡ that it is possible to add a term $iK\gamma^\mu\gamma^\nu f_{\mu\nu}\psi$ to the left-hand side of (6), where K is any real constant. On making the same low-velocity approximation, this gives an *arbitrary* additional magnetic moment. The magnetic moments of the proton and the neutron are $2{\cdot}79$ and $-1{\cdot}91$ times the nuclear magneton $e\hbar/2Mc$

† See p. 118, n. §, B. L. van der Waerden (in particular § 6).

‡ W. Pauli, *Rev. Mod. Phys.* **13** (1941) 203–32.

(where M is the proton mass); the difference between these values and 1 and 0, respectively, arises from magnetic fields associated with charged mesons in virtual states which surround the proton or the neutron. Pauli's extra term may be used to describe the electromagnetic properties of the proton and neutron in a phenomenological way.

Exact measurements of the magnetic moment of the electron give a value which is greater than the Bohr magneton $e\hbar/2m_e c$ (m_e = electron mass) by about one part in 1,000. This discrepancy has been explained as a quantum field effect (see Chapter V, § 13).

The adjoint wave function

When we try to derive Dirac's equation (3) from a Lagrangian or when we go over to quantized field theory, it is necessary to have, as well as (3), the equation for $\tilde{\psi}$, the Hermitian conjugate to ψ. For the present $\tilde{\psi}$ is a four-component row vector (ψ_ρ^*) $(\rho = 1,2,3,4)$; taking the Hermitian conjugate of (3) gives the equation for $\tilde{\psi}$,

$$\sum_{k=1}^{3} \partial_k \tilde{\psi}\gamma^k - \partial_4 \tilde{\psi}\gamma^4 + \kappa\tilde{\psi} = 0.$$

Here, as usual, it is assumed that the γ^μ are Hermitian matrices, as is necessary in order to make $\boldsymbol{\alpha}$, β Hermitian. The ∂_4 term has the opposite sign to the ∂_k terms, because $x_4 = ix_0$; a more symmetric equation results if we write† $\bar{\psi} = \tilde{\psi}\gamma^4$. Then

$$\partial_\mu \bar{\psi}\gamma^\mu - \kappa\bar{\psi} = 0 \tag{23}$$

and if an external electromagnetic field is present, (6) gives

$$\left(\partial_\mu - \frac{ie}{\hbar c} A_\mu\right)\bar{\psi}\gamma^\mu - \kappa\bar{\psi} = 0. \tag{24}$$

3. The Lagrangian and the current

A Lorentz invariant Lagrangian density which gives both (3) and (23) is

$$\mathscr{L} = -\hbar c\{\bar{\psi}\gamma^\mu \partial_\mu \psi + \kappa\bar{\psi}\psi\}. \tag{25}$$

Treating ψ_ρ and $\bar{\psi}_\rho$ $(\rho = 1,2,3,4)$ as independent variables, by using

$$\partial_\mu\left(\frac{\partial\mathscr{L}}{\partial(\partial_\mu \psi)}\right) = \frac{\partial\mathscr{L}}{\partial\psi},$$

we get (23), while the equation

$$\frac{\partial\mathscr{L}}{\partial\bar{\psi}} = 0$$

† $\bar{\psi}$ is the *adjoint* wave function.

gives (3). It is characteristic of fermion theory that ∂_μ appears only linearly in (25). A more symmetric form of Lagrangian is (cf. (9.63))

$$\mathscr{L} = -\tfrac{1}{2}\hbar c\{\bar{\psi}\gamma^\mu\partial_\mu\psi+\kappa\bar{\psi}\psi\}+\tfrac{1}{2}\hbar c\{(\partial_\mu\bar{\psi})\gamma^\mu\psi-\kappa\bar{\psi}\psi\}. \tag{26}$$

The significance of this symmetric form of $\mathscr{L}$ is only made clear on using charge conjugation in the quantized field theory. On integrating the action integral by parts, (26) goes over to (25).

From (25) the canonical momentum conjugate to ψ is $\pi = -(\hbar/i)\tilde{\psi}$, and there is no canonical momentum conjugate to $\bar{\psi}$ (or $\tilde{\psi}$). The Hamiltonian density† of field theory is

$$H_f = \pi\dot{\psi}-\mathscr{L} = \hbar c\tilde{\psi}\left\{\frac{1}{i}(\alpha\,.\,\text{grad})\psi+\kappa\beta\psi\right\}. \tag{27}$$

The function $\mathscr{L}$ has to be real, so the invariance of $\mathscr{L}$ under the gauge transformation

$$\psi(x) \to \psi(x)e^{i\alpha}, \quad \bar{\psi}(x) \to \bar{\psi}(x)e^{-i\alpha} \quad (\alpha \text{ is a constant})$$

gives the 4-vector current (cf. Chapter IX, § 2)

$$j_\mu = \frac{ie}{\hbar}\left\{\bar{\psi}\frac{\partial\mathscr{L}}{\partial(\partial_\mu\bar{\psi})}-\frac{\partial\mathscr{L}}{\partial(\partial_\mu\psi)}\psi\right\} = iec\bar{\psi}\gamma^\mu\psi. \tag{28}$$

The charge density is thus $\rho = e\tilde{\psi}\psi$.

4. Lorentz covariant quantities

It is easy to verify that (23) and (24) go over into the corresponding equation in a new Lorentz reference frame (11) provided that (14) holds, and that $\bar{\psi}$ is replaced by $\bar{\psi}'$, where

$$\bar{\psi}' = \bar{\psi}\Lambda^{-1}. \tag{29}$$

It is not obvious that the new $\bar{\psi}'$ will be the adjoint of ψ' given by (12); the condition

$$\widetilde{\psi'} = (\bar{\psi}')\gamma^4$$

requires‡

$$\gamma^4\tilde{\Lambda}\gamma^4 = \Lambda^{-1}. \tag{30}$$

This condition is satisfied by the matrices Λ given by (16), (17), and (19); it means, however, that in general Λ is not unitary. The charge density in the field $e\psi_\rho^*\psi_\rho$ is not invariant under a Lorentz transformation like (18), so we do not expect $\Lambda(v)$ to be unitary. We would expect $\Lambda(\theta)$ given by (16) to be unitary and it is easy to verify that this is so.

The matrix Λ determined by (14) and (30) is arbitrary to a multiplicative constant of modulus unity, and we may, for example, multiply any of the explicit expressions given above by ± 1, $\pm i$. Eqn. (91)

† For further discussion see G. Wentzel, *Quantum Theory of Fields* (Interscience, New York, 1949), ch. v.

‡ $\tilde{\Lambda}$ is the Hermitian conjugate of Λ.

below provides a possible method for distinguishing between the pair ± 1 and the pair $\pm i$.

Using (12), (14), and (29) the following Lorentz covariant quantities can be formed from expressions bilinear in the wave function:

$$\left.\begin{aligned} J &= \bar{\psi}\psi, \text{ invariant}; \qquad L_\mu = \bar{\psi}\gamma^\mu\psi, \text{ 4-vector} \\ M_{\mu\nu} &= \bar{\psi}\sigma^{\mu\nu}\psi, \text{ anti-symmetric tensor} \\ K_\mu &= \bar{\psi}\gamma^5\gamma^\mu\psi, \text{ pseudo-vector};\dagger \qquad N = \bar{\psi}\gamma^5\psi, \text{ pseudo-scalar}\ddagger \end{aligned}\right\}, \tag{31}$$

where $\gamma^5 = \gamma^1\gamma^2\gamma^3\gamma^4$. This matrix obeys (cf. (4))

$$(\gamma^5)^2 = 1, \qquad \gamma^5\gamma^\mu + \gamma^\mu\gamma^5 = 0. \tag{32}$$

These sixteen functions may be used to construct the interaction Lagrangian between a fermion field and other fields; the pseudo-vector and pseudo-scalar are particular useful in constructing interactions between nucleons and pions. To get an invariant interaction between a pion field ϕ and a nucleon field ψ we must use a Lagrangian interaction term containing $\bar{\psi}\gamma^5\psi\phi$ or $\bar{\psi}\gamma^5\gamma^\mu\psi\partial_\mu\phi$.

5. The low-velocity representation

It is necessary, before giving further general arguments, to exhibit representations for the γ^μ matrices. The most commonly used representation (which is very suitable for treating low-velocity phenomena) is

$$\boldsymbol{\alpha} = \begin{pmatrix} 0 & \boldsymbol{\sigma} \\ \boldsymbol{\sigma} & 0 \end{pmatrix}, \qquad \beta = \begin{pmatrix} I & 0 \\ 0 & -I \end{pmatrix}, \tag{33}$$

where 0 and I are the 2×2 zero and unit matrices respectively, and $\boldsymbol{\sigma} = (\sigma_1, \sigma_2, \sigma_3)$ are the Pauli spin matrices

$$\sigma_1 = \begin{pmatrix} 0 & 1 \\ 1 & 0 \end{pmatrix}, \qquad \sigma_2 = \begin{pmatrix} 0 & -i \\ i & 0 \end{pmatrix}, \qquad \sigma_3 = \begin{pmatrix} 1 & 0 \\ 0 & -1 \end{pmatrix}. \tag{34}$$

These obey $\sigma_1\sigma_2 = -\sigma_2\sigma_1 = i\sigma_3$; $\sigma_1^2 = I$, and the cyclic permutations of these relations. In this representation

$$\gamma^5 = \begin{pmatrix} 0 & -I \\ -I & 0 \end{pmatrix}, \quad \text{and} \quad \sigma^{23} = \begin{pmatrix} \sigma_1 & 0 \\ 0 & \sigma_1 \end{pmatrix}, \quad \text{etc.} \tag{35}$$

We substitute
$$\psi(x_\mu) = e^{-iEt/\hbar}U(\mathbf{x}), \tag{36}$$
where $U(\mathbf{x}) = \begin{pmatrix} u_1 \\ u_2 \end{pmatrix}$, u_1 and u_2 being a pair of two-component vectors, or spinors. Eqn. (1), for a free particle of momentum $\mathbf{p}$, becomes

$$\left.\begin{aligned} (E - mc^2)u_1 &= c(\mathbf{p}.\boldsymbol{\sigma})u_2 \\ (E + mc^2)u_2 &= c(\mathbf{p}.\boldsymbol{\sigma})u_1 \end{aligned}\right\}. \tag{37}$$

† Or axial vector. ‡ The transform of N is $N' = \det(a_{\mu\nu}).N$ (cf. (1.7)).

Eliminating either u_1 or u_2, we see (37) gives the energy eigenvalues

$$E = \pm c(\mathbf{p}^2+m^2c^2)^{\frac{1}{2}}.$$

Dirac interpreted the solution of (37) having positive E as describing fermions (electrons) and the solution having negative E as describing anti-fermions (positrons). He used the exclusion principle to make it possible in a many-particle theory to describe vacuum as the state in which all energy levels with negative values of E are filled and those with positive values of E are empty. An electron is described by a filled positive energy state, and a positron is interpreted as an empty negative energy state.†

Although this interpretation of the solutions of (1) gives the correct answers, it is unsatisfactory in two respects; it is undesirable and confusing to have to talk of negative energies of free particles, and the description is not symmetric between fermions and anti-fermions. It is not sufficient to say that we could equally well associate the fermions with negative values of E and anti-fermions with positive values of E; the interpretation itself should be symmetric. The quantized field description of Chapter IV avoids these difficulties.

For non-relativistic motion (i.e. $p \leqslant mc$) the solution of (37) with positive energy E has u_2 small (of order (p/mc)) compared with u_1, while for negative E, the small component is u_1. The expectation value of the operator $\boldsymbol{\alpha}$ for any state involves the inner product of the vectors u_1 and u_2, so for low-velocity fermion states, this operator has small expectation values of order (p/mc) (cf. (2.228)).

The commutator of the spin component $S_1 = \frac{1}{2}\hbar\sigma^{23}$ and the *single particle* Hamiltonian

$$H = c(\boldsymbol{\alpha}.\mathbf{p})+\beta mc^2$$

is (in any representation)

$$[S_1, H] = i\hbar c(\alpha_3 p_2-\alpha_2 p_3). \tag{38}$$

It follows that for eigenstates of a free fermion having plane wave (or rectilinear) motion, we can specify the spin eigenvalue $(\pm\frac{1}{2}\hbar)$ only in the direction of motion (in that case $p_2 = p_3 = 0$ and $[S_1, H] = 0$). If the fermion is at rest, $\mathbf{p} = 0$ and we can find solutions in which the spin is specified in an arbitrary direction. For non-relativistic fermions, remembering that the expectation value of $\boldsymbol{\alpha}$ is small, (38) shows that $[\mathbf{S}, H]$ is small, and it is a reasonable approximation to take $[\mathbf{S}, H] = 0$, so that the spin can take the values $\pm\frac{1}{2}\hbar$ in an arbitrary direction. This approximation is no longer good when (p/mc) is not small.

† This is the 'hole theory'.

Spin expectation values

Using the solutions of (37) for a fermion having momentum $p = \hbar k$ in the direction O_3 and energy $E = c(p^2+m^2c^2)^{\frac{1}{2}}$ (the solutions are given in (66) below), we can compute the *expectation value* of the spin **S** for any eigenstate having this momentum. Denoting the four-component wave functions for states having spin $+\frac{1}{2}\hbar$ and $-\frac{1}{2}\hbar$ in the O_3 direction by $\psi(+\frac{1}{2})$, $\psi(-\frac{1}{2})$ respectively, we consider the eigenstate (having momentum p along O_3)

$$\psi = a\psi(+\tfrac{1}{2})+b\psi(-\tfrac{1}{2}), \tag{39}$$

where the complex numbers a, b satisfy

$$|a|^2+|b|^2 = 1.$$

The expectation value of S_3 for this state is obviously

$$(\tilde{\psi}S_3\psi) = \tfrac{1}{2}\hbar(a^*a-b^*b). \tag{40}$$

By (46) and (66), the expectation value of S_1 is seen to be

$$(\tilde{\psi}S_1\psi) = \tfrac{1}{2}\hbar(a^*b+ab^*)\frac{mc^2}{E}, \tag{41 a}$$

and a similar expression can be given for the expectation value of S_2,

$$(\tilde{\psi}S_2\psi) = \tfrac{1}{2}\hbar i(ab^*-a^*b)\frac{mc^2}{E}. \tag{41 b}$$

For eigenstates ψ having $a = 2^{-\frac{1}{2}}$, $b = \pm 2^{-\frac{1}{2}}$, the expectation value of S_3 is zero. S_2 has zero expectation value and in the case of non-relativistic motion, S_1 has expectation values of approximately $\pm\frac{1}{2}\hbar$. Choosing $a = 2^{-\frac{1}{2}}$, $b = \pm 2^{-\frac{1}{2}}i$ interchanges the values of S_1 and S_2. For non-relativistic motion it is in this way possible to make the spin expectation value (approximately) $\pm\frac{1}{2}\hbar$ in an arbitrary direction. For very relativistic motion the expectation values of S_1 and S_2 are necessarily small (being zero in the extreme relativistic limit), and the spin expectation value is only appreciable along the direction of motion.

Let ψ_p be any fermion eigenstate with the momentum and energy eigenvalues **p** and $E = cp_4/i$. There is a covariant projection operator $P_{\mathbf{t}}$ such that the spin expectation value $\tilde{\psi}'\mathbf{S}\psi'$ ($\mathbf{S} = (S_1, S_2, S_3)$) of the projected state $\psi' = P_{\mathbf{t}}\psi$ is parallel to a given vector **t**. This operator is†

$$\begin{aligned} P_{\mathbf{t}} &= \tfrac{1}{2}\left\{1+i\gamma^5\gamma^\mu t_\mu \frac{E}{|E|}\right\} \\ &= \tfrac{1}{2}\left\{1+\{i\gamma^5(\boldsymbol{\gamma}.\mathbf{t})-\gamma^5\gamma^4 t_0\}\frac{E}{|E|}\right\}, \end{aligned} \tag{42}$$

† L. Michel and A. S. Wightman, *Phys. Rev.* **98** (1955) 1190.

where t_μ is a 4-vector. For a given direction $\mathbf{t}$, the magnitude $|\mathbf{t}|$ and the fourth component t_4 ($t_4 = it_0$) are chosen, so that

$$t_\mu^2 = 1, \qquad t_\mu p_\mu = 0.$$

If θ is the angle between $\mathbf{t}$ and $\mathbf{p}$, this requires

$$\mathbf{t}^2 = \frac{\mathbf{p}^2+m^2c^2}{\mathbf{p}^2\sin^2\theta+m^2c^2} \geqslant 1, \qquad t_0^2 = \frac{\mathbf{p}^2\cos^2\theta}{\mathbf{p}^2\sin^2\theta+m^2c^2} \leqslant \frac{\mathbf{p}^2}{m^2c^2}.$$

Obviously $P_\mathbf{t}$ is dependent on the eigenvalues p_μ.

It is easy to verify that

$$(P_\mathbf{t})^2 = P_\mathbf{t}, \qquad [P_\mathbf{t}, \gamma^\mu p_\mu] = 0;$$

these show that $P_\mathbf{t}$ is a projection operator, and that it transforms eigenstates ψ_p into eigenstates with the same energy-momentum eigenvalue p_μ.

In examining the spin properties of $P_\mathbf{t}$ we first consider the case that $\mathbf{t}$ is parallel or anti-parallel to the momentum $\mathbf{p}$. The Dirac equation then gives

$$(E/c)(\boldsymbol{\gamma}.\mathbf{t})\psi_p + i\gamma^4(\mathbf{t}.\mathbf{p})\psi_p = -mc\gamma^4(\boldsymbol{\gamma}.\mathbf{t})\psi_p.$$

Therefore, by (42),†

$$P_\mathbf{t}\psi_p = \frac{1}{2}\left\{1 - i\gamma^5\gamma^4(\boldsymbol{\gamma}.\mathbf{t})\frac{mc^2}{|E|}\right\}\psi_p.$$

In this case $|\mathbf{t}| = |E|/mc^2$, so†

$$P_\mathbf{t}\psi_p = \tfrac{1}{2}\{1+(\boldsymbol{\sigma}'.\mathbf{t})/|\mathbf{t}|\}\psi_p,$$

where‡ $\boldsymbol{\sigma}' \equiv (\sigma^{23}, \sigma^{31}, \sigma^{12})$. Hence $P_\mathbf{t}$ respectively leaves unaltered or annihilates the eigenstates for which $(\boldsymbol{\sigma}'.\mathbf{t})\psi_p$ equals $|\mathbf{t}|\psi_p$ or $-|\mathbf{t}|\psi_p$.

If $\mathbf{t}$ is not in the direction of $\mathbf{p}$, we consider the expectation value

$$\tilde{\psi}'\boldsymbol{\sigma}'\psi' = \tilde{\psi}_p\tilde{P}_\mathbf{t}\boldsymbol{\sigma}'P_\mathbf{t}\psi_p = \tilde{\psi}_p\gamma^4P_\mathbf{t}\gamma^4\boldsymbol{\sigma}'P_\mathbf{t}\psi_p.$$

Let $\mathbf{t}'$ be any vector such that $\mathbf{t}.\mathbf{t}' = 0$. Then, by (42),

$$\gamma^4P_\mathbf{t}\gamma^4(\boldsymbol{\sigma}'.\mathbf{t}')P_\mathbf{t} = \gamma^4P_\mathbf{t}\gamma^4\frac{1}{2}\left\{1-(i\gamma^5\boldsymbol{\gamma}.\mathbf{t}+\gamma^5\gamma^4t_0)\frac{E}{|E|}\right\}(\boldsymbol{\sigma}'.\mathbf{t}')$$
$$= \gamma^4P_\mathbf{t}(1-P_\mathbf{t})\gamma^4(\boldsymbol{\sigma}'.\mathbf{t}') = 0.$$

Hence $\tilde{\psi}'(\boldsymbol{\sigma}'.\mathbf{t}')\psi'$ vanishes. This completes the proof of the properties of $P_\mathbf{t}$. (These properties can also be proved by making a Lorentz transformation to the frame of reference in which the particle is at rest.)

In practice, we work with beams of particles in which there is a statistical alignment of spins. A method for dealing with this alignment, or *polarization*, is discussed in Chapter VIII.

† We remember $t_0E = c(\mathbf{t}.\mathbf{p})$.

‡ $\mathbf{S} = \frac{1}{2}\hbar\boldsymbol{\sigma}'$.

In general (removing the restriction to rectilinear motion) because the total angular momentum $\mathbf{L}+\mathbf{S}$ commutes with H and is a constant of motion, it is possible to specify an eigenvalue of the component S_1 provided the state ψ is an eigenstate of the orbital angular momentum component L_1. For such ψ,

$$[S_1, H]\psi = -[L_1, H]\psi = 0.$$

This property is used in setting up the angular momentum eigenstates (§ 7 below).

The spin interaction

Now we use (33) to complete the investigation of the spin interaction (22). We have seen above that it contains the magnetic moment term; the remainder of (22) may now be written

$$(-i)\frac{e\hbar}{2mc}\begin{pmatrix} 0 & (\boldsymbol{\sigma}.\mathbf{E}) \\ (\boldsymbol{\sigma}.\mathbf{E}) & 0 \end{pmatrix}. \tag{43}$$

Substituting this into the non-relativistic approximation obtained from (21) leads to an interaction tending to alter the spin of the fermion as it passes through any electric field. This produces a *polarization* of the fermion in collisions with charged particles. The spins of a beam of fermions suffering such collisions will be orientated more frequently up than down.† For slowly moving (non-relativistic) particles the effect will be small; on substituting (43) into (21) (and putting $E \simeq mc^2$) the equation for u_1 becomes

$$(E-mc^2+e\phi)u_1 = \left[\frac{1}{2m}\left(\mathbf{p}+\frac{e}{c}\mathbf{A}\right)^2+\frac{e\hbar}{2mc}(\boldsymbol{\sigma}.\mathbf{H})\right]u_1+\frac{1}{i}\frac{e\hbar}{2mc}(\boldsymbol{\sigma}.\mathbf{E})u_2.$$

A rough estimate given by (37)‡ is $u_2 \simeq (\boldsymbol{\sigma}.\mathbf{p})u_1/2mc$; thus by (21) the effect of (43) is to add to the Hamiltonian of the non-relativistic particle a term§

$$\frac{1}{i}\frac{e\hbar}{4m^2c^2}(\boldsymbol{\sigma}.\mathbf{E})(\boldsymbol{\sigma}.\mathbf{p}).$$

This gives rise to two terms, one of which, in a radial electric field with potential $\varphi(r)$, is the 'spin-orbital interaction'

$$-\frac{e\hbar}{4m^2c^2}\frac{1}{r}\frac{d\varphi}{dr}(\boldsymbol{\sigma}.\mathbf{L}),$$

where $\mathbf{L}$ is the orbital angular momentum of the fermion.

The pseudo-scalar interaction between nucleons and pions is $\bar{\psi}\gamma^5\psi\phi$,

† With reference to the collision plane. See § 8 below for further details.

‡ The relation between u_2 and u_1 cannot be obtained from (21).

§ Notice $(\boldsymbol{\sigma}.\mathbf{a})(\boldsymbol{\sigma}.\mathbf{b}) = (\mathbf{a}.\mathbf{b})+i(\boldsymbol{\sigma}.\mathbf{a}\times\mathbf{b})$.

where ϕ is the pion field. By (33) and (35) the matrix $\gamma^4\gamma^5$ only gives terms in $\tilde{u}_1 u_2$ and $\tilde{u}_2 u_1$, and therefore the interaction between a pion and a slowly moving nucleon is small. The pseudo-vector interaction $\bar{\psi}\gamma^5\gamma^\mu\psi\partial_\mu\phi$, however, does not become small as the nucleon's momentum is decreased.

6. Relative parity of fermion and anti-fermion

Because $\boldsymbol{\sigma}$ is a spin, or angular momentum, it is an axial vector (pseudo-vector), and does not change sign on reflection of the spatial coordinates. (It can be verified from (14) and (17) that $(\sigma^{23}, \sigma^{31}, \sigma^{12})$ of eqn. (10) is an axial vector.) The momentum $\mathbf{p}$ is a polar vector, so by (37) u_1 and u_2 must have opposite parities under the inversion P $(\mathbf{x}' \rightarrow -\mathbf{x},\ x_4' \rightarrow x_4)$. This is also true if the fermion moves in a potential energy $V(\mathbf{x})$ such that $V(-\mathbf{x}) = V(\mathbf{x})$, because (37) is then replaced by

$$\left.\begin{aligned} \{E - V(\mathbf{x}) - mc^2\}u_1 &= c(\boldsymbol{\sigma}.\mathbf{p})u_2 \\ \{E - V(\mathbf{x}) + mc^2\}u_2 &= c(\boldsymbol{\sigma}.\mathbf{p})u_1 \end{aligned}\right\}. \tag{44}$$

Again u_1 and u_2 must have opposite parities. We write the four-component wave function $U(\mathbf{x})$ of (36)

$$U(\mathbf{x}) = u_1 v_1 + u_2 v_2, \tag{45}$$

where u_1 and u_2 are given by (44), and

$$v_1 = \begin{pmatrix} 1 \\ 0 \end{pmatrix}, \qquad v_2 = \begin{pmatrix} 0 \\ 1 \end{pmatrix}$$

in the representation (33).

By (17) (which gives P) both v_1 and v_2 are transformed into themselves under spatial inversion P. Also, it is always possible to find wave functions $U(\mathbf{x})$ which have definite parity, hence v_1 and v_2 must have opposite parity under P. For slowly moving fermions, u_1 is the large component, and by (21) it is approximately the same as the Schrödinger wave function. Choosing (as we may) the parity of v_1 to be $+1$ (so that of v_2 is -1), a slowly moving fermion has the same parity as the related Schrödinger wave function. For the slow anti-fermion, u_2 is large and approximately the same as the Schrödinger wave function. Thus an electron in an S state has parity $(+1)$ while a positron in an S state has parity (-1). Because v_1 and v_2 have opposite parities, we say a (spin-$\frac{1}{2}$) fermion and an anti-fermion (of the same kind) have opposite intrinsic parities. Because the Hamiltonian which we have used is invariant under P, we can, if we wish, find fermion wave functions of definite parity, whether or not the fermions are moving slowly.

7. Angular momentum eigenstates

If the potential $V(\mathbf{x})$ occurring in (44) is spherically symmetric, it may be convenient to solve (44) in terms of spherical polar coordinates, obtaining eigenfunctions which are eigenstates of the angular momentum. We first discuss the spherical harmonic solutions for the free (spin-$\frac{1}{2}$) fermion equation (37), i.e. for the case $V(\mathbf{x}) = 0$. These solutions are useful for analysing a variety of problems; they are valid in the relativistic case.

The angular momentum $\mathbf{J}$ of a free fermion about an arbitrary origin O is constant. It is the vector sum of the spin $\mathbf{S}$ and the orbital angular momentum $\mathbf{L}$, and its component about an arbitrary axis O_3 can take the $(2j+1)$ values $m\hbar$, where $m = j, j-1,..., -j$, and j is half an odd integer. Let $s_{\frac{1}{2}}$, $s_{-\frac{1}{2}}$ be the normalized spin space eigenvectors obeying (cf. (34))†

$$\sigma_3 s_{\frac{1}{2}} = s_{\frac{1}{2}}, \qquad \sigma_3 s_{-\frac{1}{2}} = -s_{-\frac{1}{2}}. \tag{46}$$

The normal-orthogonal property of these two-component vectors may be written‡

$$\tilde{s}_m . s_{m'} = \delta_{mm'} \quad (m, m' = \pm\tfrac{1}{2}). \tag{47}$$

The orbital angular momentum is described by the normalized spherical harmonics $Y_l^{(m)}(\theta, \phi)$, where θ, ϕ are spherical polar angles measured about the origin O. These functions, defined in Chapter I, § 10, obey the normal-orthogonal relation

$$\int d\Omega\, Y_{l'}^{(m')*}(\theta,\phi) Y_l^{(m)}(\theta,\phi) = \delta_{ll'}\,\delta_{mm'}, \tag{48}$$

where $d\Omega$ is the element of solid angle, and the integration extends over the surface of a sphere of unit radius centred on O.

Eigenstates of total angular momentum $W_{l,j}^{(m)}$ having total angular momentum j, with component $m\hbar$ about O_3, can arise from two values of orbital angular momentum $l = j\pm\frac{1}{2}$. These eigenfunctions are written down with the help of the Clebsch–Gordan coefficients (cf. Chapter I, § 10) $(l\,\frac{1}{2}\,m'm''\,|\,jm)$, where $m' = l, l-1,..., -l$; $m'' = \pm\frac{1}{2}$, and $m = j, m-1,..., -j$. We have (cf. (1.52))

$$W_{l,j}^{(m)} = \sum_{m',m''} (l\,\tfrac{1}{2}\,m'm''\,|\,jm) Y_l^{(m')}(\theta,\phi) s_{m''}. \tag{49}$$

The Clebsch–Gordan coefficients are zero except for $m'+m'' = m$, so for each value of m, the two values $m' = m\pm\frac{1}{2}$ occur. The values of

† We are, of course, using the representation of § 5.
‡ $\tilde{s}_m$ is the Hermitian transpose of s_m, and is a row vector.

the coefficients are given in Table 2.† The functions $W_{l,j}^{(m)}$ are normal and are orthogonal for different values of the set (l, j, m); in verifying these properties, the angles (θ, ϕ) are to be integrated over the unit sphere, as in (48), and the inner product of the spin vectors is taken, as in (47).

TABLE 2

Values of Clebsch–Gordan Coefficients $(l\,\tfrac{1}{2}\,m'm''|\,jm)$

	$m'' = \tfrac{1}{2}$	$m'' = -\tfrac{1}{2}$
$j = l+\tfrac{1}{2}$	$\left(\dfrac{j+m}{2j}\right)^{\frac{1}{2}}$	$\left(\dfrac{j-m}{2j}\right)^{\frac{1}{2}}$
$j = l-\tfrac{1}{2}$	$-\left(\dfrac{j-m+1}{2(j+1)}\right)^{\frac{1}{2}}$	$\left(\dfrac{j+m+1}{2(j+1)}\right)^{\frac{1}{2}}$

Two frequently used examples are the two sets of functions formed from unit orbital angular momentum:

(*a*) $j = \tfrac{1}{2}$, $l = 1$:

$$\left.\begin{aligned} W_{1,\frac{1}{2}}^{(\frac{1}{2})} &= -\frac{1}{\sqrt{3}}Y_1^{(0)}s_{\frac{1}{2}}+\sqrt{\frac{2}{3}}Y_1^{(1)}s_{-\frac{1}{2}} \\ W_{1,\frac{1}{2}}^{(-\frac{1}{2})} &= -\sqrt{\frac{2}{3}}Y_1^{(-1)}s_{\frac{1}{2}}+\frac{1}{\sqrt{3}}Y_1^{(0)}s_{-\frac{1}{2}} \end{aligned}\right\}; \tag{50}$$

(*b*) $j = \tfrac{3}{2}$, $l = 1$:

$$\left.\begin{aligned} W_{1,\frac{3}{2}}^{(\frac{3}{2})} &= Y_1^{(1)}s_{\frac{1}{2}}, \qquad W_{1,\frac{3}{2}}^{(-\frac{3}{2})} = Y_1^{(-1)}s_{-\frac{1}{2}} \\ W_{1,\frac{3}{2}}^{(\frac{1}{2})} &= \sqrt{\frac{2}{3}}Y_1^{(0)}s_{\frac{1}{2}}+\frac{1}{\sqrt{3}}Y_1^{(1)}s_{-\frac{1}{2}}, \\ W_{1,\frac{3}{2}}^{(-\frac{1}{2})} &= \frac{1}{\sqrt{3}}Y_1^{(-1)}s_{\frac{1}{2}}+\sqrt{\frac{2}{3}}Y^{(0)}s_{-\frac{1}{2}} \end{aligned}\right\}; \tag{51}$$

where (by (1.48))

$$Y_1^{(1)} = -\sqrt{\left(\frac{3}{8\pi}\right)}\sin\theta\, e^{i\phi}, \quad Y_1^{(-1)} = \sqrt{\left(\frac{3}{8\pi}\right)}\sin\theta\, e^{-i\phi}, \quad Y_1^{(0)} = \sqrt{\left(\frac{3}{4\pi}\right)}\cos\theta.$$

Eqns. (37) are solved by noticing that the operator $(\mathbf{p}.\boldsymbol{\sigma}) = (\hbar/i)(\boldsymbol{\sigma}.\text{grad})$ is a pseudo-scalar with respect to rotations and inversions in three-dimensional space. Hence $(\mathbf{p}.\boldsymbol{\sigma})$ applied to $W_{l,j}^{(m)}$ leaves j and m unaltered, but it changes the value of l from $l' = j\pm\tfrac{1}{2}$, to $l'' = j\mp\tfrac{1}{2}$; this change is necessary because the parity of $W_{l,j}^{(m)}$ is determined by the spherical harmonics and equals $(-1)^l$. A straightforward

† E. P. Wigner, *Anwendungen der Gruppentheorie* (Vieweg, 1931), or J. M. Blatt and V. F. Weisskopf, *Theoretical Nuclear Physics* (Wiley, New York, 1952), app. A.

calculation shows that†

$$\left.\begin{aligned}(\mathbf{p}.\boldsymbol{\sigma})W^{(m)}_{j-\frac{1}{2},j} &= -(j-\tfrac{1}{2})\frac{\hbar i}{r}W^{(m)}_{j+\frac{1}{2},j}\\ (\mathbf{p}.\boldsymbol{\sigma})W^{(m)}_{j+\frac{1}{2},j} &= (j+\tfrac{3}{2})\frac{\hbar i}{r}W^{(m)}_{j-\frac{1}{2},j}\end{aligned}\right\}. \tag{52}$$

Here r is the distance from the origin or centre of symmetry.

The radial functions

It is now easy to see that if u_1 (in (37) or (44)) contains $W^{(m)}_{l',j}$ then u_2 must contain $W^{(m)}_{l'',j}$. We try a solution of (37) of the form

$$u_1 = a(r)W^{(m)}_{l',j}, \qquad u_2 = b(r)W^{(m)}_{l'',j}, \tag{53}$$

where $a(r)$, $b(r)$ are scalar functions of r. Then†

$$(\mathbf{p}.\boldsymbol{\sigma})a(r)W^{(m)}_{l',j} = a(r)(\mathbf{p}.\boldsymbol{\sigma})W^{(m)}_{l',j}+\frac{\hbar}{i}a'(r)\epsilon W^{(m)}_{l',j}, \tag{54}$$

where $\epsilon = (\mathbf{x}.\boldsymbol{\sigma})/r$. ϵ is a dimensionless pseudo-scalar, and it is easy to verify that

$$\epsilon W^{(m)}_{l',j} = -W^{(m)}_{l'',j}, \tag{55}$$

where $l' = j\pm\frac{1}{2}$ and $l'' = j\mp\frac{1}{2}$, the upper or lower signs being taken together.‡

From (37) it follows that if $V(\mathbf{x}) = 0$, both u_1 and u_2 (given by (53)) must satisfy the d'Alembert equation

$$(E^2/c^2-m^2c^2-\mathbf{p}^2)u_{1,2} = 0. \tag{56}$$

Remembering (49) it is clear that the angular part of the operator $\mathbf{p}^2$ acts only on the spherical harmonic functions $Y^{(m')}_l(\theta,\phi)$; therefore in (53) the radial functions $a(r)$ and $b(r)$ must be multiples of the normalized spherical Bessel functions $g_{l'k}(r)$ and $g_{l''k}(r)$ respectively, where

$$g_{lk}(r) = \left(\frac{\pi k}{\mathscr{R}r}\right)^{\frac{1}{2}}J_{l+\frac{1}{2}}(kr). \tag{57}$$

These functions, which are defined in Chapter I, §§ 14 and 15, are normalized in a sphere of radius $\mathscr{R}$ (large), so that

$$\int\limits_0^{\mathscr{R}} g_{lk}(r)g_{lk'}(r)r^2\,dr = \delta_{kk'}.$$

The eigenvalues of the radial wave number k are approximately equally spaced with an interval $(\pi/\mathscr{R})$ between successive values (cf. Chapter II, § 6). It follows from (56) that the eigenvalues of E for spherical

† Cf. B. L. van der Waerden, *Gruppentheoretische Methode in der Quantenmechanik* (Edwards, Ann Arbor, 1944), p. 101. Slightly different definitions give the opposite signs to (52).

‡ We always use l', l'' in this sense during the present argument.

fermion waves are
$$E/c = \pm(m^2c^2+\hbar^2k^2)^{\frac{1}{2}}. \tag{58}$$

Using elementary properties of Bessel functions† it can be seen that the functions $g_{lk}(r)$ obey the equations (cf. (1.93))

$$\left.\begin{aligned} \frac{d}{dr}\{g_{lk}(r)\}+\frac{l+1}{r}g_{lk}(r) &= kg_{l-1,k}(r) \\ \frac{d}{dr}\{g_{lk}(r)\}-\frac{l}{r}g_{lk}(r) &= -kg_{l+1,k}(r) \end{aligned}\right\}. \tag{59}$$

Using (52), (54), (55), and (59) we can show that the normalized positive energy solution of (37) ($E > mc^2$) is

$$u_1^{(+)} = w_{l'jk}^{(m)}, \qquad u_2^{(+)} = (-1)^{(l'-j+\frac{1}{2})}\frac{\hbar ck}{i(|E|+mc^2)}w_{l''jk}^{(m)} \tag{60}$$

and the negative energy solution ($E < -mc^2$) is

$$u_2^{(-)} = w_{l'jk}^{(m)}, \qquad u_1^{(-)} = (-1)^{(l'-j+\frac{1}{2})}\frac{\hbar ck}{i(|E|+mc^2)}w_{l''jk}^{(m)}, \tag{61}$$

where
$$w_{ljk} = \left(\frac{|E|+mc^2}{2|E|}\right)^{\frac{1}{2}}g_{lk}(r)W_{l,j}^{(m)}. \tag{62}$$

It should be noted that, taking v_1 and v_2 in (45) to have parity $(+1)$ and (-1) respectively, the solution (60) has parity $(-1)^{l'}$ while (61) has parity $(-1)^{l''}$. In the low-velocity limit $w_{l'jk}^{(m)} \to g_{l'k}(r)W_{l'j}^{(m)}$, and the components $u_2^{(+)}$ and $u_1^{(-)}$ are of order $(\hbar k/mc)$ and may be ignored. $u_1^{(+)}$ and $u_2^{(-)}$ now become the non-relativistic wave functions (including spin) for fermions and anti-fermions respectively.

8. Scattering of spin-$\frac{1}{2}$ particles

The separation of angular and spin components given by (49) and (53) is valid for eqns. (44) provided $V(\mathbf{x})$ is a spherically symmetric potential. The form of the radial functions $a(r)$ and $b(r)$ is no longer given by (57), but on using (53) the equations for $a(r)$ and $b(r)$ become

$$\left.\begin{aligned} \{E-V(r)-mc^2\}a(r)+\frac{\hbar c}{i}\left\{\frac{db(r)}{dr}-\frac{\alpha-1}{r}b(r)\right\} &= 0 \\ \{E-V(r)+mc^2\}b(r)+\frac{\hbar c}{i}\left\{\frac{da(r)}{dr}+\frac{\alpha+1}{r}a(r)\right\} &= 0 \end{aligned}\right\}, \tag{63}$$

where
$$\alpha = \begin{cases} l' & \text{for } l' = j+\frac{1}{2}, \\ -(l'+1) & \text{for } l' = j-\frac{1}{2}. \end{cases}$$

Dirac‡ solved (63) for the H-atom case, and Darwin§ has considered the general solution of (63).

† See, for example, E. T. Whittaker and G. N. Watson, *Modern Analysis* (Cambridge, 4th edn., 1940), ch. 17.

‡ P. A. M. Dirac, *Quantum Mechanics* (Clarendon Press, 1947), ch. 12.

§ C. G. Darwin, *Proc. Roy. Soc.* A, **118** (1928) 654.

The asymptotic form of $g_{lk}(r)$ for large values of kr is

$$g_{lk}(r) \to \left(\frac{2}{\mathscr{R}}\right)^{\frac{1}{2}} \frac{1}{r} \sin(kr - \tfrac{1}{2}l\pi). \tag{64}$$

For a force of finite range, the effect of $V(r)$ in (63) is negligible for large values of r, and the radial wave functions for a scattering problem will have the same asymptotic form as (64) apart from a constant phase change.† Thus for large r we see that, for $E > mc^2$, (63) is satisfied by

$$\left.\begin{aligned} a_{l'j}(r) &\sim \frac{A}{r}\sin(kr - \tfrac{1}{2}l'\pi + \eta_{l'j}) \\ b_{l'j}(r) &\sim \frac{\hbar ck}{i(E+mc^2)}(-1)^{(l'-j+\frac{1}{2})}\frac{A}{r}\sin(kr - \tfrac{1}{2}l''\pi + \eta_{l'j}) \end{aligned}\right\}, \tag{65}$$

where A is an arbitrary constant. The similarity of these radial functions to the solutions (60) is obvious.

Eqns. (44) may be used to describe the scattering of an electron in a spherically symmetric electric field, for example, the field of an atom or a nucleus. (At present we make no attempt to calculate the radiative corrections.) Using a similar equation we can also study the scattering of a fermion by a spin zero target, including a spin-orbital interaction of the form $f(r)(\mathbf{S}.\mathbf{L})$, where $f(r)$ is an arbitrary function of the distance r from the centre of the scatterer, and $\mathbf{S}$, $\mathbf{L}$ are the spin and orbital angular momentum of the fermion respectively. The spin-orbital interaction commutes‡ with $\mathbf{L}^2$ as well as with the total angular momentum $(\mathbf{L}+\mathbf{S})$. Hence the angular and spin components of the wave function in the spherical harmonic representation are of the form $W_{l,j}^{(m)}$, and at large distances from the scatterer the radial components $a(r)$, $b(r)$ are of the form (65).

The incident wave giving rise to the scattering will be described by a positive energy solution of (37) having linear momentum $p = \hbar k$ along the O_3 direction and having spin $m'\hbar = \pm\frac{1}{2}\hbar$ in the same direction. The solution of (37) may be written (using (46))

$$\left.\begin{aligned} u_1(m') &= \left(\frac{E+mc^2}{2E}\right)^{\frac{1}{2}} s_{m'}\, e^{ikx_3} \\ u_2(m') &= \frac{c\hbar k}{E+mc^2}\left(\frac{E+mc^2}{2E}\right)^{\frac{1}{2}} (\sigma_3\, s_{m'})e^{ikx_3} \end{aligned}\right\}, \tag{66}$$

where $E = +c(p^2+m^2c^2)^{\frac{1}{2}}$.

We expand the plane-wave solution (66) in terms of the spherical

† The boundary conditions at $r = 0$ are such that the charge density at that point is finite.

‡ This is because $2(\mathbf{L}.\mathbf{S}) = (\mathbf{L}+\mathbf{S})^2 - \mathbf{L}^2 - \mathbf{S}^2$.

harmonic fermion eigenfunctions (62). First, $\exp(ikx_3)$ is written in terms of spherical harmonics,† thus

$$e^{ikx_3} = \frac{(2\pi\mathscr{R})^{\frac{1}{2}}}{k} \sum_{l=0}^{\infty} i^l(2l+1)^{\frac{1}{2}} Y_l^{(0)}(\theta,\phi) g_{lk}(r). \tag{67}$$

The relation (49) is merely a unitary transformation from one normalized set of angular momentum eigenstates $Y_l^{(m')} s_{m''}$ to another similar set $W_{l,j}^{(m)}$, and it is easy to see that the relation may be reversed to give

$$Y_l^{(m)}(\theta,\phi)s_{m'} = \sum_{j=|l-\frac{1}{2}|}^{l+\frac{1}{2}} (l\,\tfrac{1}{2}\,mm'\,|\,j\,m+m')\,W_{l,j}^{(m+m')}. \tag{68}$$

Using Table 2 (p. 131), this gives

$$Y_l^{(0)}(\theta,\phi)s_{\pm\frac{1}{2}} = (2l+1)^{-\frac{1}{2}}\{(l+1)^{\frac{1}{2}} W_{l,l+\frac{1}{2}}^{(\pm\frac{1}{2})} \mp l^{\frac{1}{2}} W_{l,l-\frac{1}{2}}^{(\pm\frac{1}{2})}\}, \tag{69}$$

where either the upper or the lower signs are to be taken throughout. The positive energy solutions (66) may now be written (using (62), (67), and (68))

$$\left.\begin{aligned} u_1(m' &= \pm\tfrac{1}{2}) \\ &= N\frac{(2\pi\mathscr{R})^{\frac{1}{2}}}{k}\sum_{l=0}^{\infty} i^l\{(l+1)^{\frac{1}{2}} w_{l,l+\frac{1}{2},k}^{(\pm\frac{1}{2})} \mp l^{\frac{1}{2}} w_{l,l-\frac{1}{2},k}^{(\pm\frac{1}{2})}\} \\ u_2(m' &= \pm\tfrac{1}{2}) \\ &= \frac{1}{i}\,\frac{c\hbar k}{E+mc^2}N\frac{(2\pi\mathscr{R})^{\frac{1}{2}}}{k}\sum_{l=0}^{\infty} i^l\{(l+1)^{\frac{1}{2}} w_{l+1,l+\frac{1}{2},k}^{(\pm\frac{1}{2})} \pm l^{\frac{1}{2}} w_{l-1,l-\frac{1}{2},k}^{(\pm\frac{1}{2})}\} \end{aligned}\right\}, \tag{70}$$

where $N = \left(\dfrac{E+mc^2}{2E}\right)^{\frac{1}{2}}$.

The scattering state wave function

The wave which describes the incident and the scattered fermions is determined by the condition that for large r the time-dependent wave function (36) contains only outgoing waves $e^{i(kr-Et)}$ $(E > 0)$. This wave function is found by adding solutions of (63) (or the equivalent equation including a spin-orbital interaction) to the incident plane wave (70) so that all terms which have the asymptotic form e^{-ikr} are cancelled. Let this wave function be

$$\left.\begin{aligned} u_1'(m') &= u_1(m') + \sum_{l'=|j-\frac{1}{2}|}^{j+\frac{1}{2}} \sum_{j=\frac{1}{2}}^{\infty} A_{l'j}\, a_{l'j}(r)\, W_{l',j}^{(m')} \\ u_2'(m') &= u_2(m') + \sum_{l'=|j-\frac{1}{2}|}^{j+\frac{1}{2}} \sum_{j=\frac{1}{2}}^{\infty} A_{l'j}\, b_{l'j}(r)\, W_{l',j}^{(m')} \end{aligned}\right\}, \tag{71}$$

† Cf. eqn. (1.77).

where $u_1(m')$, $u_2(m')$ are the incident wave (70), and $A_{l'j}$ are constants. The radial functions $a_{l'j}(r)$, $b_{l'j}(r)$ have the asymptotic form (65). Using (64) it follows that the required (outgoing) asymptotic form is

$$\left.\begin{aligned} u_1'(m' = \pm\tfrac{1}{2}) &= \frac{e^{ikr}}{r}\frac{1}{2ik}(4\pi)^{\frac{1}{2}}N\times \\ &\quad\times\sum_{l=0}^{\infty}\{(l+1)^{\frac{1}{2}}W^{(\pm\frac{1}{2})}_{l,l+\frac{1}{2}}e^{2i\eta_{l,l+\frac{1}{2}}}\mp l^{\frac{1}{2}}W^{(\pm\frac{1}{2})}_{l,l-\frac{1}{2}}e^{2i\eta_{l,l-\frac{1}{2}}}\} \\ u_2'(m' = \pm\tfrac{1}{2}) &= \frac{e^{ikr}}{r}\frac{1}{2ik}(4\pi)^{\frac{1}{2}}N\frac{1}{i}\frac{\hbar ck}{E+mc^2}\times \\ &\quad\times\sum_{l=0}^{\infty}\{(l+1)^{\frac{1}{2}}W^{(\pm\frac{1}{2})}_{l+1,l+\frac{1}{2}}e^{2i\eta_{l,l+\frac{1}{2}}}\pm l^{\frac{1}{2}}W^{(\pm\frac{1}{2})}_{l-1,l-\frac{1}{2}}e^{2i\eta_{l,l-\frac{1}{2}}}\} \end{aligned}\right\}. \tag{72}$$

Because relation (65) between $a_{l'j}(r)$ and $b_{l'j}(r)$ is similar to that between u_1 and u_2 in (60),† the proper choice of $A_{l'j}$ for u_1' reduces *both* u_1' and u_2' to outgoing waves. The solutions (72) still contain part of the incident wave, namely the terms whose asymptotic form is e^{ikr}/r. Subtracting these terms leaves the asymptotic form of the scattered wave itself. This gives‡ (we assume the phases $\eta_{l,j}$ are finite, i.e. we do not discuss infinite range (Coulomb) forces)

$$\begin{aligned} u_1''(m' = \pm\tfrac{1}{2}) & \\ = N\frac{e^{ikr}}{r}\frac{1}{2ik}\sum_{l=0}^{\infty}[s_{\pm\frac{1}{2}}P_l(\cos\theta)\{(l+1)(e^{2i\eta_{l,l+\frac{1}{2}}}-1)+l(e^{2i\eta_{l,l-\frac{1}{2}}}-1)\}\mp & \\ \mp s_{\mp\frac{1}{2}}P_l^1(\cos\theta)e^{\pm i\phi}\{e^{2i\eta_{l,l+\frac{1}{2}}}-e^{2i\eta_{l,l-\frac{1}{2}}}\}] & \end{aligned} \tag{73}$$

together with a somewhat more complicated expression for u_2''. Here $u''(m' = \frac{1}{2})$ is the scattered wave arising from the incident wave $u(m' = \frac{1}{2})$. We have used the relations (cf. (1.45))

$$\left.\begin{aligned} Y_l^{(0)}(\theta,\phi) &= \left(\frac{2l+1}{4\pi}\right)^{\frac{1}{2}}P_l(\cos\theta) \\ Y_l^{(1)}(\theta,\phi) &= -\left(\frac{2l+1}{4\pi l(l+1)}\right)^{\frac{1}{2}}P_l^1(\cos\theta)e^{i\phi} \\ Y_l^{(-1)}(\theta,\phi) &= -Y_l^{(1)}(\theta,\phi)^* \end{aligned}\right\}.$$

Eqn. (73) has been given by Mott.§ He points out that the total elastic differential cross-section can be evaluated using u_1'' alone. A single scattering experiment (as distinct from a double scattering experiment or a correlation experiment) will not distinguish between the spin

† The first term in each of the brackets in (72) is of the form $l' = j-\frac{1}{2}$, $l'' = j+\frac{1}{2}$; the second term is $l' = j+\frac{1}{2}$, $l'' = j-\frac{1}{2}$.

‡ It is worth noticing that this result could be written down directly from (70).

§ N. F. Mott, *Proc. Roy. Soc.* A, **124** (1929) 425; **135** (1932) 429. See also N. F. Mott and H. S. W. Massey, *Atomic Collisions* (Clarendon Press, 2nd edn., 1949), pp. 74–77.

orientations of the scattered particles; also the differential cross-section has to be summed over both values of m'. At large distances from the scatterer the outgoing wave (73) behaves like a linear combination of plane waves, so in any scattering direction **t** the scattered wave is a multiple of the plane-wave solution (66), where x_3 is measured in the direction **t** and $s_{m'}$ are spin eigenstates relating to this direction. The scattering probability is given by $\tilde{u}_1''.u_1''+\tilde{u}_2''.u_2''$. The spin summation can be referred to the new direction **t**, and by (66)

$$(\tilde{u}_2''.u_2'')/(\tilde{u}_1''.u_1'') = \left(\frac{c\hbar k}{E+mc^2}\right)^2$$

for either of the new spin directions. It follows that the ratio of the term $\tilde{u}_2.u_2$ to $\tilde{u}_1.u_1$ is the same for the incident and the scattered waves, so the differential cross-section may be obtained by comparing $\tilde{u}_1''.u_1''$ with $\tilde{u}_1.u_1$. For a double scattering experiment, the individual spin directions will be important and it is no longer exact to calculate cross-sections using the u_1'' component only. The error introduced by doing so is, however, only large when $(|E|/mc^2)$ is of order unity. (For large $(|E|/mc^2)$ there is little polarization.)

9. The polarization effect

Eqn. (73) also shows that polarization may be produced in scattering. Assuming for simplicity that the fermions are not moving so fast that the components u_2'' need be considered, the differential cross-section $Q\,d\Omega$ for fermions being scattered into an element of solid angle $d\Omega$ in the direction (θ, ϕ) may be written down in simple form. For scattering so that the fermion spin is left pointing in its original direction we have†

$$Q_u(\theta)\,d\Omega = \frac{d\Omega}{4k^2}\left|\sum_{l=0}^{\infty}\{(l+1)(e^{2i\eta_{l,l+\frac{1}{2}}}-1)+l(e^{2i\eta_{l,l-\frac{1}{2}}}-1)\}P_l(\cos\theta)\right|^2. \quad (74)$$

For scattering in which the spin direction is reversed, the differential cross-section is

$$Q_c(\theta)\,d\Omega = \frac{d\Omega}{4k^2}\left|\sum_{l=1}^{\infty}\{e^{2i\eta_{l,l+\frac{1}{2}}}-e^{2i\eta_{l,l-\frac{1}{2}}}\}P_l^1(\cos\theta)\right|^2. \quad (75)$$

The total differential cross-section is given by

$$Q(\theta)\,d\Omega = \{Q_u(\theta)+Q_c(\theta)\}\,d\Omega.$$

† When the scattered wave produced by an incident wave of unit density is of the form $f(\theta, \phi)(e^{ikr}/r)$, the differential cross-section is $Q\,d\Omega = |f(\theta, \phi)|^2\,d\Omega$ (cf. Chapter VIII). If the velocities v_f and v_i of the outgoing and incident particles are different, we have $Q\,d\Omega = (v_f/v_i)|f|^2\,d\Omega$.

$Q_c(\theta)$ vanishes unless $\eta_{l,l+\frac{1}{2}}$ and $\eta_{l,l-\frac{1}{2}}$ are different; this is because an interaction which only depends on the orbital angular momentum of the fermion relative to the scatterer cannot change the spin direction. For electrons the spin orbital interaction discussed in § 5 above can give rise to such a spin transition (sometimes called 'spin-flip'). The function $P_l^1(\cos\theta)$ contains a factor $\sin\theta$, so spin transitions will not occur in scattering through a small angle.

In § 5 above we considered eigenstates of momentum (39) which are mixtures of the two spin eigenstates $\psi(m' = +\frac{1}{2})$ and $\psi(m' = -\frac{1}{2})$, such that their spin expectation value is perpendicular to the momentum. With initial states of this type, the differential cross-section (summed over both final state spin values) may depend on the azimuthal angle ϕ measured about the incident momentum. It is clear by rotation symmetry that it is only possible to have a scattering cross-section which depends on the azimuthal angle ϕ, if the expectation value of the spin of the incident state lies at an angle to the incident momentum. It also requires a non-zero spin-flip term.

When the scattering cross-section can depend appreciably on the azimuthal angle ϕ, an incident beam of fermions whose spin expectation values are randomly distributed (an *unpolarized* beam) can be scattered into a given direction so that there is a preferential spin direction in the scattered beam (we say it is partially polarized). A second scattering,† or some other experiment, may now be used to detect this polarization.‡ Polarization experiments are of considerable importance in showing up spin dependent forces in nucleon-nucleon scattering; they are discussed in Chapter VIII.

10. The extreme relativistic representation

Another important representation is that in which§

$$\boldsymbol{\alpha} = \begin{pmatrix} \boldsymbol{\sigma} & 0 \\ 0 & -\boldsymbol{\sigma} \end{pmatrix}, \quad \beta = \begin{pmatrix} 0 & I \\ I & 0 \end{pmatrix}, \quad \gamma^5 = \begin{pmatrix} -I & 0 \\ 0 & +I \end{pmatrix}, \tag{76}$$

where $\boldsymbol{\sigma}$ is again given by (34). In this representation

$$\sigma^{23} = \begin{pmatrix} \sigma_1 & 0 \\ 0 & \sigma_1 \end{pmatrix}, \quad \text{etc.} \tag{77}$$

† This idea was first investigated by N. F. Mott, *Proc. Roy. Soc.* A, **124** (1929) 425.

‡ For a survey of the theory and experimental results of electron polarization in scattering see H. A. Tolhoek, *Rev. Mod. Phys.* **28** (1956) 277.

§ W. Pauli, *Handbuch der Physik* (J. Springer, Berlin, 1933), vol. xxiv/1, p. 225.

If we again write $\psi(x_\mu) = e^{-iEt/\hbar}U(\mathbf{x})$, where $U(\mathbf{x}) = \begin{pmatrix} u_1 \\ u_2 \end{pmatrix}$,† it is clear that $\Lambda(\theta)$ of (16) and $\Lambda(v)$ of (19) both transform u_1 into a multiple of u_1, and transform u_2 into a multiple of u_2. This representation would thus be reducible if we did not have to include the reflection operator (17) (i.e. β) which exchanges u_1 and u_2. For zero-mass particles we can have the two-component neutrino representation (§ 16 below).

In representation (76) the eqn. (6) for a fermion moving in a given electrostatic potential ϕ becomes

$$\left.\begin{aligned} \{E+e\phi-c(\boldsymbol{\sigma}.\mathbf{p})\}u_1 &= mc^2u_2 \\ \{E+e\phi+c(\boldsymbol{\sigma}.\mathbf{p})\}u_2 &= mc^2u_1 \end{aligned}\right\}. \tag{78}$$

These equations are useful in the extreme relativistic case in which, as an approximation, the rest-mass term mc^2 is neglected, giving

$$\left.\begin{aligned} \{E+e\phi-c(\boldsymbol{\sigma}.\mathbf{p})\}u_1 &= 0 \\ \{E+e\phi+c(\boldsymbol{\sigma}.\mathbf{p})\}u_2 &= 0 \end{aligned}\right\}. \tag{79}$$

This approximation has been used in studying the scattering of electrons of about 100 MeV in nuclei;‡ such scattering gives information about the distribution of electric charge in the nucleus. First we consider the free particle case $\phi = 0$; the eigenvalues of E are then $\pm c|\mathbf{p}|$ for both u_1 and u_2. Choosing the O_3 direction along the momentum $\mathbf{p}$, we have the following eigenstates:

$$\begin{aligned} &u_1 = \begin{pmatrix} 1 \\ 0 \end{pmatrix},\ u_2 = 0 \quad \text{has spin parallel to } \mathbf{p} \text{ and } E = c|\mathbf{p}|, \\ &u_1 = \begin{pmatrix} 0 \\ 1 \end{pmatrix},\ u_2 = 0 \quad \text{,,} \quad \text{,,} \quad \text{anti-parallel to } \mathbf{p} \text{ and } E = -c|\mathbf{p}|, \\ &u_2 = \begin{pmatrix} 1 \\ 0 \end{pmatrix},\ u_1 = 0 \quad \text{,,} \quad \text{,,} \quad \text{parallel to } \mathbf{p} \text{ and } E = -c|\mathbf{p}|, \\ &u_2 = \begin{pmatrix} 0 \\ 1 \end{pmatrix},\ u_1 = 0 \quad \text{,,} \quad \text{,,} \quad \text{anti-parallel to } \mathbf{p} \text{ and } E = +c|\mathbf{p}|. \end{aligned} \tag{80}$$

The positive and negative values of E describe fermions and anti-fermions respectively. In the extreme relativistic case we do not have any states having momentum $\mathbf{p}$ whose spin expectation values lie at an angle to $\mathbf{p}$. This is also obvious from (41 a) and (41 b).

Scattering of extremely relativistic electrons

Using the approximation (79) to describe the elastic scattering of extremely relativistic electrons by the electric field of a nucleus, we

† Of course these vectors u_1, u_2 are not identical with those in § 5 above.

‡ For details see D. R. Yennie, D. G. Ravenhall, and R. N. Wilson, *Phys. Rev.* **95** (1954) 500–12.

see that there is no mixing of the u_1 and u_2 solutions due to the presence of the potential ϕ. Therefore, if the incident beam contains only electrons whose spin is parallel (anti-parallel) to their momentum, the scattered electrons also must have their spin parallel (anti-parallel) to their momentum.†

If the scattering potential $\phi(\mathbf{x})$ obeys‡ $\phi(\mathbf{x}) = \phi(-\mathbf{x})$ (for example, if the electric field of the scatterer is symmetric about its centre), then the solutions of the *exact* eqn. (78) are unaltered on replacing $u_1(\mathbf{x})$ and $u_2(\mathbf{x})$ by $u_2(-\mathbf{x})$ and $u_1(-\mathbf{x})$ respectively. Now if an incident beam of slow or relativistic fermions strikes a spherically symmetric scatterer, we can examine whether fermions having their spin parallel to their momentum are more readily scattered into a given direction than fermions with their spin anti-parallel to the momentum. This is done by comparing the solutions $u_1(\mathbf{x})$ and $u_2(\mathbf{x})$ of (78). Using the relation $u_1(\mathbf{x}) = u_2(-\mathbf{x})$ and rotating the axis system through 180° about a line perpendicular to the incident beam, it is clear that the angular dependence of the scattered parts of $u_1(\mathbf{x})$ and $u_2(\mathbf{x})$ is the same (provided the scatterer has spherical symmetry). Also, reversing the sign of the spin $\boldsymbol{\sigma}$ in (78) will exchange u_1 and u_2. This means that electrons having their spins parallel to the initial momentum have the same differential scattering cross-section as electrons having their spins anti-parallel to the initial momentum (for slow electrons this can also be seen from (73)). As extremely relativistic fermions can only have such *longitudinal* spin alignment, we deduce that their polarization can only be detected by some more ingenious method (e.g. by the polarization of the bremsstrahlung radiated in a collision).§||

11. Charge conjugation

So far the anti-particle states have been distinguished by having negative energy eigenvalues E. We now show that the complex conjugate of each solution for a fermion of charge e moving in an external electromagnetic field is linearly related to a solution of the equation for a fermion of charge $(-e)$ moving in the same external field. On

† Away from the nucleus ϕ can be ignored, and a positive value of E must give a u_1 solution in which the spin $\mathbf{s}$ is parallel to $\mathbf{p}$, or a u_2 solution in which $\mathbf{s}$ and $\mathbf{p}$ are anti-parallel.

‡ Under spatial inversion P the transform ϕ' of ϕ is $\phi'(\mathbf{x}) = +\phi(-\mathbf{x})$; in the present case $\phi'(\mathbf{x}) = \phi(\mathbf{x})$ is assumed. The general considerations leading to (14) also hold for (6) on replacing ϕ by ϕ' and $A_k(\mathbf{x}, t)$ by $A'_k(\mathbf{x}, t) = -A_k(\mathbf{x}, t)$.

§ A similar argument shows that there can be no detection by randomly orientated asymmetric nuclei (Yennie *et al.*, loc. cit).

|| K. W. McVoy and F. J. Dyson, *Phys. Rev.* **106** (1957) 1360.

taking the complex conjugate ψ^* of ψ, the sign of E in the exponent $e^{-iEt/\hbar}$ changes; thus positive and negative values of E may be associated respectively with particles of charge $+e$ and $-e$, that is with fermions and anti-fermions.

Charge conjugation† is the operation of changing the sign of the charge of all particles, and for fermions it is the operation of exchanging particles and anti-particles. The charge conjugate wave function ψ_c obeys the equation derived from (6) on replacing e by $-e$:

$$\gamma^\mu\left(\partial_\mu - \frac{ie}{\hbar c}A_\mu(x)\right)\psi_c + \kappa\psi_c = 0, \tag{81}$$

and the charge conjugate adjoint wave function $\bar{\psi}_c$ obeys

$$\left(\partial_\mu + \frac{ie}{\hbar c}A_\mu(x)\right)\bar{\psi}_c\gamma^\mu - \kappa\bar{\psi}_c = 0. \tag{82}$$

We keep strictly to the notation that ψ, ψ_c are column vectors and $\bar{\psi}$, $\bar{\psi}_c$ are row vectors.‡ ψ_T denotes ψ written as a row vector, and $\bar{\psi}_T$ denotes $\bar{\psi}$ written as a column vector, and in general B_T is the transpose of the 4×4 matrix B. The transpose of eqn. (24) is

$$\left(\partial_\mu - \frac{ie}{\hbar c}A_\mu\right)\gamma^\mu_T\bar{\psi}_T - \kappa\bar{\psi}_T = 0.$$

It is easy to see that the charge conjugate wave function ψ_c, defined by

$$\psi_c = C\bar{\psi}_T = C\gamma^4_T\psi^*, \tag{83}$$

satisfies (81) provided the 4×4 non-singular matrix C obeys

$$C^{-1}\gamma^\mu C = -\gamma^\mu_T \quad (\mu = 1,2,3,4). \tag{84}$$

The matrices $(-\gamma^\mu_T)$ obey the relations (4) which define γ^μ, and by the theorem quoted in § 1, $(-\gamma^\mu_T)$ and γ^μ must therefore be related as required in (84) (i.e. $-\gamma^\mu_T$ and γ^μ are equivalent matrices).§ Further, because both γ^μ and $(-\gamma^\mu_T)$ are Hermitian, C can be chosen to be unitary ($C\tilde{C} = 1$). Because of (84) C has the further important property $C = -C_T$.‖

† H. A. Kramers, *Proc. Amst. Akad. Sci.* **40** (1937) 814.

‡ ψ^* the complex conjugate of ψ is a four-component column vector. On quantizing the field, ψ^* is to be replaced by the Hermitian conjugate $(\tilde{\psi})$.

§ This argument is due to W. Pauli, *Ann. Inst. Poincaré*, **6** (1936) 109. The notation is similar to that of J. Schwinger, *Phys. Rev.* **74** (1948) 1439.

‖ Applying (84) twice gives $CC_T^{-1}\gamma^\mu C_T C^{-1} = \gamma^\mu$, hence CC_T^{-1} commutes with all γ^μ, $\sigma^{\mu\nu}$, $\gamma^5\gamma^\mu$, γ^5, and by Schur's lemma, $CC_T^{-1} = kI$, where k is a number. Clearly $k^2 = 1$. Also, C, $\gamma^5 C$, $\gamma^5\gamma^\mu C$ equal their transposes multiplied by k, while $\gamma^\mu C$, $\sigma^{\mu\nu}C$ equal their transposes multiplied by $(-k)$; there are ten linearly independent symmetric 4×4 matrices and six skew symmetric 4×4 matrices. Hence $k = -1$. This argument, due to Haantjes, is quoted by Pauli (loc. cit.).

Taking the adjoint of ψ_c, it is easy to see that

$$\bar{\psi}_c = -\psi_T C^{-1} = (C^{-1}\psi)_T, \tag{85}$$

and substituting into (6) gives (82).† Eqns. (83) and (85) show that the four components of the wave function ψ describe a fermion and its charge conjugate, each particle having two spin components. In the representation (33) the matrix C can be written in terms of 2×2 matrices

$$C = \begin{pmatrix} C_{11} & C_{12} \\ C_{21} & C_{22} \end{pmatrix}.$$

The relations $C^{-1}\gamma^4 C = -\gamma_T^4$, and $C = -C_T$, show that C must be of the form

$$C = \begin{pmatrix} 0 & C_{12} \\ C_{21} & 0 \end{pmatrix}, \tag{86}$$

where C_{12}, C_{21} are unitary 2×2 matrices, and $C_{12}+(C_{21})_T = 0$. It is easy to verify that in this representation suitable expressions are $C_{12} = C_{21} = i\sigma_2$. Writing $(u_1)_c$, $(u_2)_c$ for the components of ψ_c in the representation (33), (83) and (86) give

$$\left.\begin{aligned} (u_1)_c &= -C_{12}\, u_2^* \\ (u_2)_c &= C_{21}\, u_1^* \end{aligned}\right\}. \tag{87}$$

Because $(u_1)_c$ and $(u_2)_c$ are related to the complex conjugates of u_2 and u_1, they satisfy equations like (37) and (44) with the sign of E reversed (and e replaced by $-e$ in the potential energy V in (44)). Those solutions of (33) or (44) for which $E \simeq -mc^2$ and u_2 is large, are properly to be thought of as solutions of the ψ_c equation (81) for which $E \simeq mc^2$ and $(u_1)_c$ is large; that is they are anti-particle solutions.

For the representation (76) we use the conditions‡ $C^{-1}\gamma^5 C = \gamma_T^5$, $C = -C_T$, to show that C is of the form

$$C = \begin{pmatrix} C_{11} & 0 \\ 0 & C_{22} \end{pmatrix}.$$

The unitary 2×2 matrices C_{11}, C_{22} here obey

$$C_{11}+(C_{11})_T = 0, \qquad C_{22}+(C_{22})_T = 0.$$

Therefore the binary components u_1 and u_2 which satisfy (78) each contain a solution and its charge conjugate.

The charge conjugate expression for the fermion current $j_\mu = iec\bar{\psi}\gamma^\mu\psi$ is

$$iec\bar{\psi}_c\gamma^\mu\psi_c = iec\psi_T\gamma_T^\mu\bar{\psi}_T = iec\bar{\psi}\gamma^\mu\psi \tag{88}$$

† It is easy to verify that charge conjugation applied twice gives the identity, i.e. $(\psi_c)_c = \psi$, etc. If K is the operator giving the complex conjugate (K is not a linear operator), then $\psi_c = C\gamma_T^4 K\psi$, and $(C\gamma_T^4 K)^2 = C\gamma_T^4 C^*\gamma^4 = I$.

‡ The condition $C^{-1}\gamma^5 C = \gamma_T^5$ is derived directly from (84).

by (83), (84), and (85). The last step in (88) would involve a change of sign in the quantized field theory in which ψ, $\bar{\psi}$ are operators; this would give the charge density and current density of anti-fermions opposite in sign to that for fermions. This change of sign in (88) is necessary for a satisfactory physical interpretation, and we will therefore leave the discussion of the charge conjugate form of charge, current, etc., until the quantized field theory has been introduced in Chapter IV.

By (84), $$C^{-1}\sigma^{\mu\nu}C = -\sigma^{\mu\nu}_T.$$

If ψ is an eigenstate of spin such that $\sigma^{kl}\psi = \epsilon\psi$, where $\epsilon = \pm 1$, it follows from (83) that ψ_c satisfies $\sigma^{kl}\psi_c = -\epsilon\psi_c$. This reversal of sign of the spin eigenvalue under charge conjugation is just what we would expect according to 'hole theory'. Similarly, the complex conjugation in (83) shows that if ψ has the momentum eigenvalue $\mathbf{p}$, then ψ_c has the eigenvalue $-\mathbf{p}$.

12. Charge conjugation and Lorentz transformations

The proper Lorentz transformations consist of the rotations (15) and the velocity transformations (18). Spatial reflection P, or time reversal T ($\mathbf{x}' = \mathbf{x}$, $t' = -t$) are not included in the proper Lorentz transformations. The operation of charge conjugation should be invariant under proper Lorentz transformations, because it would be unreasonable for such a transformation to change the role of particle and anti-particle. Denoting the Lorentz transformed wave function by ψ' as in (12), this requires $(\psi')_c = e^{i\alpha}(\psi_c)'$, where c indicates the charge conjugate, and α is real. The matrix C (cf. (62)) is a constant, so for the proper Lorentz transformations which go over continuously to the identity ($\theta \to 0$, or $v \to 0$), we require $(\psi')_c = (\psi_c)'$. The condition $(\Lambda\psi)_c = \Lambda(C\bar{\psi}_T)$ must hold for any ψ, and, using (84), this imposes the condition on Λ†

$$\gamma^4 C\Lambda^* = \Lambda\gamma^4 C.$$

In the form $$\Lambda^* = C^{-1}\gamma^4\Lambda\gamma^4 C \tag{89}$$

this relation is easy to use. Remembering that the γ^μ are Hermitian, it is straightforward to verify that $\Lambda(\theta)$ of (16) and $\Lambda(v)$ of (19) satisfy (89).

Racah also assumed† that under the spatial inversion P ($\mathbf{x}' = -\mathbf{x}$, $t' = t$), the relation (89) has to be satisfied, and instead of (17), he suggested that the inversion transformation should be

$$\Lambda = \pm i\gamma^4. \tag{90}$$

† Relation (89) is due to G. Racah, *Nuovo Cim.* **14** (1937) 322; Λ^* is the complex conjugate of Λ.

This, however, is not a physical requirement, and it is no objection to (17) that it gives $(\psi')_c = -(\psi_c)'$.

The Yang–Tiomno classification

The four values of Λ which may be used to transform the wave function under the spatial inversion P have been used by Yang and Tiomno† to provide a possible classification of fermion fields and new selection rules. Their rules are only valid for interactions which obey parity conservation. They suggest that fermion fields may be classified into four types‡ ψ_A, ψ_B, ψ_C, ψ_D by their transformation properties under the inversion P. We have

$$\left.\begin{aligned} \psi'_A &= \pm\gamma^4\psi_A, & \psi'_B &= \mp\gamma^4\psi_B \\ \psi'_C &= \pm i\gamma^4\psi_C, & \psi'_D &= \mp i\gamma^4\psi_D \end{aligned}\right\}, \tag{91}$$

where all the upper, or all the lower, signs should be taken together. A and B are only *relative* types, i.e. we can say that two fields, both of which are known to be either A or B, are the *same* type or *different* types. Because of the double-valued character of fermion fields we cannot assert that any field is definitely one of the types A or B. Similarly, C and D are relative types.

Bosons have scalar, pseudo-scalar, vector, etc., wave functions and can only have parity (± 1); hence if two fermion fields interact directly with a boson field, the fermion fields must belong either to types A, B or to types C, D. Because nucleons interact with pions, the proton and the neutron must both be either of types A, B or of types C, D. (These arguments only apply to parity-conserving interactions.)

Types C and D have the Racah transformation (90), therefore the charge conjugates of fields of types C and D are of types C and D respectively. Using (83) and (84) we can find the charge conjugates of types A and B. We have by (91)

$$(\psi'_A)_c = C\gamma^4_T(\psi'_A)^* = \pm C\psi^*_A;$$

exchanging the order of inversion and charge conjugation gives a change in sign because

$$(\psi_{Ac})' = (C\gamma^4_T\psi^*_A)' = \mp C\psi^*_A.$$

Hence the charge conjugate of a field of type A is of type B and vice versa. It is essential to remember that for a single field, fermion and

† C. N. Yang and J. Tiomno, *Phys. Rev.* **79** (1950) 495.

‡ No confusion should arise between the field type ψ_C and the charge conjugate notation ψ_c.

anti-fermion have opposite intrinsic parity. In the notation of (33) and (37) the spatial inversion P changes u_1, u_2 to u'_1, u'_2, where

$$u'_1(\mathbf{x}') = \alpha u_1(-\mathbf{x}), \quad u'_2(\mathbf{x}') = -\alpha u_2(-\mathbf{x}) \quad (\mathbf{x}' = -\mathbf{x}). \tag{92}$$

The types A, B, C, D are distinguished by the values $(\pm 1, \pm i)$ of α. The opposite intrinsic parity of fermion and anti-fermion arises from the minus sign in the second equation of (92).

Wick, Wightman, and Wigner† have given a careful examination of the circumstances in which it may not be possible to determine the relative phase of fermion fields, for example, of ψ_A and ψ_C.

13. The Majorana representations

We have assumed that the spin-$\frac{1}{2}$ fermion wave function consists of a set of four complex components ψ_ρ and we have seen that a charge-current density j_μ (eqn. (28)) can be determined. Majorana‡ showed that there are solutions of Dirac's equation for which $\psi(x_\mu)$ is real; such solutions cannot give a charge-current, and they must correspond to fermions which have no electric charge (or magnetic moment). Because the wave function is real, the corresponding quantum field operator has to be Hermitian. Half of the degrees of freedom of the field are thus lost, and the distinction between fermion and anti-fermion disappears. A particle of this type would be identical with its anti-particle.§

The Majorana solutions are not readily determined in either of the representations given above, and we have to derive new representations for this purpose. The complex conjugate of eqn. (3) is

$$\Big(\sum_{k=1}^{3} \gamma_T^k \partial_k - \gamma_T^4 \partial_4 + \kappa\Big)\psi^*(x_\nu) = 0, \tag{93}$$

where (as always) we assume γ^μ are Hermitian. Choosing

$$\psi^*(\mathbf{x}, t_0) = \psi(\mathbf{x}, t_0)$$

for all $\mathbf{x}$ at some time t_0, we shall have $\psi^*(x_\mu) = \psi(x_\mu)$ in general, provided we can find a representation for γ^μ such that‖

$$\gamma_T^k = \gamma^k, \quad \gamma_T^4 = -\gamma^4 \quad (k = 1, 2, 3), \tag{94}$$

i.e. γ^k have to be real and γ^4 pure imaginary. Any representation satisfying (94) will be called a Majorana representation. If γ^μ is such a

† G. C. Wick, A. S. Wightman, and E. P. Wigner, *Phys. Rev.* **88** (1952) 101.

‡ E. Majorana, *Nuovo Cim.* **14** (1937) 171.

§ No known particle is of this type.

‖ For zero-mass particles we might try to find a representation such that $\gamma_T^k = -\gamma^k$, $\gamma_T^4 = \gamma^4$; this requires ten anti-symmetric 4×4 matrices and is impossible.

representation, so is $S\gamma^\mu S^{-1}$, where S is a *real* 4×4 matrix satisfying $S_T S = 1$. We shall show below how a Majorana representation can be set up.

The condition (94) defining a Majorana representation may be written

$$\gamma_T^\mu = \gamma^5\gamma^4\gamma^\mu\gamma^4\gamma^5 \quad (\mu = 1,2,3,4) \tag{95}$$

and with the help of the charge conjugation matrix C and eqn. (84) this may be written

$$(C\gamma^5\gamma^4)\gamma^\mu+\gamma^\mu(C\gamma^5\gamma^4) = 0 \quad (\mu = 1,2,3,4). \tag{96}$$

Therefore in any Majorana representation the charge conjugation matrix C must be of the form†

$$C = e^{i\lambda}\gamma^4 \quad (\lambda \text{ real}). \tag{97}$$

Considering any wave function ψ in this representation (not necessarily a real wave function) we have by (83) and (85)

$$\left.\begin{aligned}\psi_c &= C\gamma_T^4\psi^* = -e^{i\lambda}\psi^* \\ \bar\psi_c &= -\psi_T C^{-1} = e^{-i\lambda}(\bar\psi)^* = -e^{-i\lambda}\overline{(\psi^*)}\end{aligned}\right\}. \tag{98}$$

This simple relation between the charge conjugate of ψ and its complex conjugate is of considerable importance. Because charge conjugation is invariant under Lorentz transformations, (98) provides us with a Lorentz invariant method of splitting any wave function ψ in this representation into a real and an imaginary part. Taking $C = -\gamma^4$ (i.e. $\lambda = \pi$), we can write‡

$$\left.\begin{aligned}\psi &= \frac{1}{\sqrt{2}}(v+iw) \\ v &= \frac{1}{\sqrt{2}}(\psi+\psi^*) = \frac{1}{\sqrt{2}}(\psi+\psi_c) \\ w &= \frac{1}{i\sqrt{2}}(\psi-\psi^*) = \frac{1}{i\sqrt{2}}(\psi-\psi_c)\end{aligned}\right\}. \tag{99}$$

v and w are real, and under charge conjugation $v_c = v$, $w_c = -w$.

A real solution of Dirac's equation satisfies ($\lambda = 0$ or π)

$$\psi_c = \pm\psi \tag{100}$$

and is its own charge conjugate. This shows that the solution is independent of charge, and that there are only two independent components in ψ. These components are associated with the spin properties.§

† Eqn. (96) can only be satisfied by $C\gamma^4\gamma^5 = (\text{const.})\gamma^5$.

‡ Cf. W. Pauli, *Rev. Mod. Phys.* **13** (1941) 203 (particularly § 3).

§ Using (100) it is obvious that σ^{kl} cannot have real eigenstates $\psi(x)$. The situation is similar to classical electrodynamics in which the real potential $A_k(x)$ cannot be an eigenstate of the orbital angular momentum operator $L_3 = (\hbar/i)\partial/\partial\phi$. In quantized theory ψ and A_k are replaced by Hermitian operators and the difficulty vanishes.

Relation (100) also shows that real fermion fields can only belong to Yang and Tiomno's type C or D, because the spatial reflection properties of fields types A and B are opposite to those of their charge conjugates.

Explicit Majorana representation

Finally, we set up a Majorana representation. The spin matrices σ^{kl} (defined by (10)) obey

$$\sigma^{kl}+\sigma^{kl}_T = 0 \quad (k,l = 1,2,3).$$

This suggests using a representation in which

$$\sigma^{31} = \begin{pmatrix} \sigma_2 & 0 \\ 0 & \sigma_2 \end{pmatrix}, \quad \sigma^{12} = \begin{pmatrix} 0 & i\sigma_3 \\ -i\sigma_3 & 0 \end{pmatrix}, \quad \sigma^{23} = \begin{pmatrix} 0 & i\sigma_1 \\ -i\sigma_1 & 0 \end{pmatrix},$$

where σ_1, σ_2, σ_3 are Pauli's 2×2 matrices given by (34). It is easy to see that suitable γ^μ are

$$\gamma^1 = \begin{pmatrix} \sigma_1 & 0 \\ 0 & \sigma_1 \end{pmatrix}, \quad \gamma^2 = \begin{pmatrix} 0 & i\sigma_2 \\ -i\sigma_2 & 0 \end{pmatrix}, \quad \gamma^3 = \begin{pmatrix} \sigma_3 & 0 \\ 0 & \sigma_3 \end{pmatrix}, \quad \gamma^4 = \begin{pmatrix} 0 & \sigma_2 \\ \sigma_2 & 0 \end{pmatrix}.$$

Eigensolutions can readily be written down.

14. The neutrino and β-decay

The neutron cannot be described by a real field because it has a magnetic moment and because a distinct anti-neutron exists.† It was suggested by Majorana‡ that the neutrino might be its own anti-particle; this is not so. At present we do not know of any particle which is described by a *real* fermion field.

The neutrino is closely related to β-decay and allied phenomena. The fundamental β^--decay process is

$$\mathrm{N} \rightarrow \mathrm{P}+e^-+\bar{\nu}, \tag{101}$$

where N, P, e^-, $\bar{\nu}$ are neutron, proton, electron, and anti-neutrino respectively.§ The free neutron decays in this way with a mean life‖ of 17·5 minutes.

For this process the most general relativistic invariant interaction

† B. Cork, G. R. Lamberton, O. Piccioni, and W. A. Wenzel, *Phys. Rev.* **104** (1956) 1193.

‡ E. Majorana, loc. cit.; see also W. H. Furry, *Phys. Rev.* **56** (1939) 1184.

§ It is the usual convention to call the particle in process (101) the anti-neutrino.

‖ J. M. Robson, *Phys. Rev.* **83** (1951) 349.

(without gradient coupling) which can be formed from the covariants in (31) is†

$$\begin{aligned} H_{\text{int}} = {} & (\bar{\psi}_P \psi_N)\{C_S(\bar{\psi}_e \psi_\nu) + C'_S(\bar{\psi}_e \gamma^5 \psi_\nu)\} + (\bar{\psi}_P \gamma^\mu \psi_N)\{C_V(\bar{\psi}_e \gamma^\mu \psi_\nu) + \\ & + C'_V(\bar{\psi}_e \gamma^\mu \gamma^5 \psi_\nu)\} + \tfrac{1}{2}(\bar{\psi}_P \sigma^{\mu\nu} \psi_N)\{C_T(\bar{\psi}_e \sigma^{\mu\nu} \psi_\nu) + C'_T(\bar{\psi}_e \sigma^{\mu\nu} \gamma^5 \psi_\nu)\} - \\ & - (\bar{\psi}_P \gamma^\mu \gamma^5 \psi_N)\{C_A(\bar{\psi}_e \gamma^\mu \gamma^5 \psi_\nu) + C'_A(\bar{\psi}_e \gamma^\mu \psi_\nu)\} + \\ & + (\bar{\psi}_P \gamma^5 \psi_N)\{C_P(\bar{\psi}_e \gamma^5 \psi_\nu) + C'_P(\bar{\psi}_e \psi_\nu)\} + \\ & + (\text{Hermitian conjugate}). \end{aligned} \tag{102}$$

$\psi_P, \psi_N, \psi_e, \psi_\nu$ are respectively the proton, neutron, electron, and neutrino fields. The subscripts S, V, T, A, P on the constant coefficients C_S, C'_S, etc., indicate the scalar, vector, tensor, axial vector, and pseudoscalar interactions; we use the notation of β-decay theory.‡ The interaction (102) is invariant under proper Lorentz transformations, but it is not invariant under spatial inversion (unless all coefficients C' vanish); the terms C' are included to allow for the known left-right asymmetry in β-decay processes. It is shown in Chapter VII, § 4, that if H_{int} is invariant under Wigner's time reversal, all the coefficients C, C' must be real. We do not assume such invariance; the relation between left-right asymmetry and time reversal is discussed in Chapter VII, § 5.

Neutrino and anti-neutrino

In quantum theory the positive frequency parts of the operators ψ_e, $\bar{\psi}_e$ destroy electrons and positrons respectively; the negative frequency parts of ψ_e, $\bar{\psi}_e$ create positrons and electrons respectively. Hence H_{int} (eqn. (102)) gives the process (101), and it also gives the other important (virtual) β^+-decay process

$$\mathrm{P} \rightarrow \mathrm{N} + e^+ + \nu. \tag{103}$$

The process

$$\bar{\nu} + \mathrm{N} \rightarrow \mathrm{P} + e^- \tag{104}$$

is not possible§ if the neutrino ν and the anti-neutrino $\bar{\nu}$ are not identical.

When a heavy nucleus undergoes fission the nuclear particles produced contain more neutrons than do stable nuclei of the same mass. These fragments decay radioactively to stable nuclei, emitting electrons according to the β-decay process (101). Therefore, we may expect any

† T. D. Lee and C. N. Yang, *Phys. Rev.* **104** (1956) 254; the usual notation of β-decay theory is used.

‡ See, for example, M. E. Rose in *Beta and Gamma-Ray Spectroscopy* (Interscience, New York, 1955), pp. 271–91.

§ Process (104) would require $\bar{\psi}_e$, $\bar{\psi}_\nu$ in the same term of H_{int}.

nuclear pile to emit large numbers of anti-neutrinos. Stars derive energy by a process (for example the carbon-oxygen cycle†) which in effect combines four protons to give an α-particle. In each cycle two protons have to be changed to neutrons, so the positron process (103) occurs. Hence we expect a star to emit large numbers of neutrinos.

Using a high intensity thermal neutron reactor it was demonstrated directly that the induced process

$$\bar{\nu}+\mathrm{P} \rightarrow \mathrm{N}+e^{+} \tag{105}$$

occurs. Anti-neutrinos from the reactor pass through a large liquid scintillation detector. An anti-neutrino striking a proton in the scintillator induces reaction (105); the positron is detected by the two annihilation γ-rays which it produces, and the neutron is detected by the later γ-ray burst occurring when it is captured in cadmium contained in the scintillator.‡

In an experiment under similar conditions it was shown that the reaction

$$\bar{\nu}+\mathrm{Cl}^{37} \rightarrow \mathrm{A}^{37}+e^{-}$$

does not take place.§ This implies that (104) does not occur, therefore ν and $\bar{\nu}$ must be distinct. Supporting evidence comes from the failure to observe double β-decay, that is, the simultaneous emission of two electrons in a nuclear transition. If ν and $\bar{\nu}$ are distinct this process is

$$2\mathrm{N} \rightarrow 2\mathrm{P}+2e^{-}+2\bar{\nu}; \tag{106}$$

if $\nu \equiv \bar{\nu}$, then (104) can be an intermediate step and we get

$$2\mathrm{N} \rightarrow 2\mathrm{P}+2e^{-}. \tag{107}$$

If (107) can occur it should be about 10^{6} faster than (106), due to the greater importance of intermediate states. Also, (107) is characterized by the almost constant total energy of the two electrons. Both reactions (106) and (107) are very slow, but comparatively favourable conditions for observing (107) occur in several nuclei. Cowan *et al.*‖ using Nd^{150} have failed to detect process (107) in conditions in which it is estimated that it should have been observed if it existed.

† H. A. Bethe, *Phys. Rev.* **55** (1939) 434. For the direct reaction $\mathrm{P}+\mathrm{P} \rightarrow \mathrm{D}+e^{+}$ see E. E. Salpeter, *Phys. Rev.* **88** (1952) 547.

‡ C. L. Cowan, F. Reines, F. B. Harrison, H. W. Kruse, and A. D. McGuire, *Science*, **124** (1956) 103. A diagram of the process appears in a Los Alamos Scientific Laboratory advertisement in *Physics Today*, **9** (1956) No. 11, 35.

§ R. Davis, *Bull. Amer. Phys. Soc.* **1** (1956) 219. See also C. O. Meuhlhause and S. Oleska, *Phys. Rev.* **105** (1957) 1332.

‖ C. L. Cowan, F. B. Harrison, L. M. Langer, and F. Reines, *Nuovo Cim.* **3** (1956) 649; C. L. Cowan and F. Reines, *Phys. Rev.* **106** (1957) 825.

15. Non-conservation of parity

It was suggested by Lee and Yang† that parity conservation might be violated in the weak decay processes. Parity violation has been found by Wu *et al.* in the β^--decay of oriented Co^{60} nuclei‡ and by Garwin, Lederman, and Weinrich§ in both of the $\pi^+ \rightarrow \mu^+ \rightarrow e^+$ decay processes. There is no evidence of parity violation in the strong nucleon-nucleon and pion-nucleon interactions, or in electromagnetic interactions, and we assume that any parity mixing appearing in these interactions is very small, and can be neglected.

It follows that to a high order of accuracy the energy levels of nuclei are states‖ of definite parity.†† Thus in the β-disintegration of Co^{60} the initial and final nuclear states have definite parities, but the electron-neutrino part of the final state does not have a definite parity. If θ is the angle between the momentum $\mathbf{p}$ of the emitted electron and the initial spin $\mathbf{J}$ of the Co^{60} nucleus, the angular distribution of the emitted electrons is of the form

$$I(\theta)\,d\theta = (\text{const.})(1+\alpha\cos\theta)\sin\theta\,d\theta, \tag{108}$$

where α is a constant. For electron velocity $v \simeq 0{\cdot}6c$, $\alpha \simeq -0{\cdot}4$. Hence the angular distribution depends markedly on $(\mathbf{p}.\mathbf{J})$; this necessarily violates parity conservation, since under space inversion $\mathbf{p} \rightarrow -\mathbf{p}$, $\mathbf{J} \rightarrow \mathbf{J}$, and $(\mathbf{p}.\mathbf{J}) \rightarrow -(\mathbf{p}.\mathbf{J})$. As is seen in Fig. 5 the Co^{60} nucleus differs from its mirror image due to this weak decay process. The value of the asymmetry constant α which is expected from the interaction (102) is given by eqn. (117) below. Here we merely remark that the large observed value of α appears to be consistent with the maximum parity violation in (102);‡‡ this is obtained by putting $C' = C$, or $C' = -C$, in all terms in (102).

Schopper§§ has examined the *circular* polarization P of the γ-ray which is emitted after the β-decay of randomly oriented Co^{60}. The

† See p. 148, n. †.

‡ C. S. Wu, E. Ambler, R. W. Hayward, D. D. Hoppes, and R. P. Hudson, *Phys. Rev.* **105** (1957) 1413.

§ R. L. Garwin, L. M. Lederman, and M. Weinrich, *Phys. Rev.* **105** (1957) 1415; see also C. Castagnoli, C. Franzinetti, and A. Manfredini, *Nuovo Cim.* **5** (1957) 684; G. B. Chadwick *et al.*, *Phil. Mag.* **2** (1957) 684; J. I. Friedman and V. L. Telegdi, *Phys. Rev.* **105** (1957) 1681.

‖ The weak parity-violating β-decay process has a very small effect on nuclear wave functions.

†† The same is true for atomic states.

‡‡ T. D. Lee and C. N. Yang, *Phys. Rev.* **105** (1957) 1671.

§§ H. Schopper, *Phil. Mag.* **2** (1957) 710. This experiment detects $(\mathbf{p}.\mathbf{J}')$, where $\mathbf{J}'$ is the nuclear spin after β-emission.

polarization P is proportional to $\cos\phi$ where ϕ is the angle between the β- and γ-rays. Again this shows that parity is not conserved in β-decay; the magnitude of P indicates that there is considerable parity violation in the interaction (102).† A similar experiment with the positron emitter Na^{22} gives the opposite sign of polarization P of the γ-ray.

Charged pion decay and charged muon decay are weak processes,

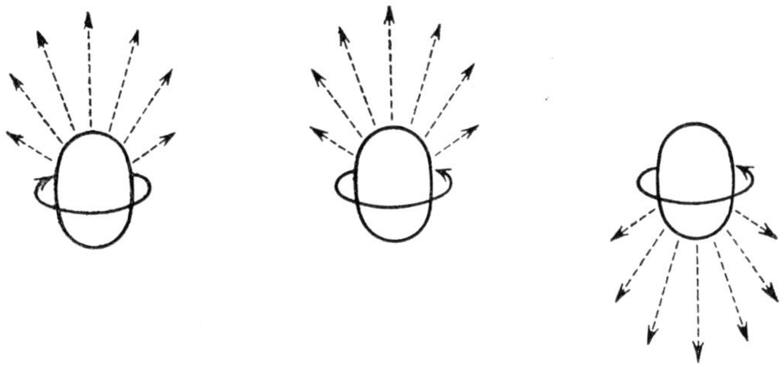

(a) (b) (c)

FIG. 5. The β-decay of Co^{60}: (*a*) emission of electrons from the oriented nucleus; (*b*) is the mirror image of the nucleus shown in (*a*); (*c*) is the result of rotating (*a*) through 180°. The spin of (*b*) and (*c*) is the same, but the electron distributions differ.

the mean lives being $2{\cdot}5\times10^{-8}$ sec and $2{\cdot}2\times10^{-6}$ sec respectively. When the muon coming from the decay

$$\pi^+ \rightarrow \mu^+ + \nu \tag{109}$$

is stopped in carbon‡ the angular distribution of the positrons from the subsequent μ-decay

$$\mu^+ \rightarrow e^+ + \nu + \bar{\nu} \tag{110}$$

shows asymmetry. The mean angular distribution for all the positrons is of the form $(1+a\cos\theta)$, where $a \simeq -\frac{1}{3}$ and θ is the angle between the positron velocity and the direction in which the muon was moving. This asymmetry in the positron distribution proves that parity is violated in both of the decays (109) and (110). The stopped muon can only 'remember' its direction of motion if it was polarized along that direction.§ This polarization implies that in the probability distribution

† H. Frauenfelder *et al.*, *Phys. Rev.* **106** (1957) 386, find that the electrons emitted by Co^{60} are polarized in their direction of motion. This polarization is $P \simeq -(v/c)$, which is the value given by the 2-component theory (§ 16 below).

‡ Garwin *et al.*, loc. cit.

§ There appears to be little depolarization of the muons stopped in C.

for the decay (109), the term $(\boldsymbol{\sigma}_\mu . \mathbf{p}_\mu)$ occurs, where $\boldsymbol{\sigma}_\mu$, $\mathbf{p}_\mu$ are the spin and momentum of the muon; hence parity is violated in (109). The asymmetry in the positron distribution in the decay of these polarized muons proves that parity is violated in (110); this is a process similar to the β-decay of oriented Co^{60}. The large asymmetry in (110) implies a large degree of parity violation in both (109) and (110). When the process (110) is observed in photographic emulsion† the asymmetry is appreciably less. This is believed to be due to a depolarization subsequent to the capture of an electron by the μ^+ stopped in the emulsion.

Backward asymmetry also occurs in the distribution of decay positrons from muons in $K_{\mu 2}$ decay (cf. Chapter VII, § 1).

16. The two-component neutrino theory

It is possible to explain these left-right asymmetry phenomena by a two-component neutrino theory. There is much evidence that the weak decays are to be explained by this two-component theory together with the universal interaction of Chapter VII, § 7.

For spin-$\frac{1}{2}$ particles of *zero mass*‡ it is possible to factorize the expression $E^2 - c^2\mathbf{p}^2$ with the help of three anti-commuting matrices; thus we get the Hamiltonian

$$H = c(\boldsymbol{\sigma}.\mathbf{p}), \tag{111}$$

where $\boldsymbol{\sigma}$ are the 2×2 Pauli matrices. The existence of a two-component theory using (111) was pointed out by Pauli.§ Obviously the Hamiltonian (111) is not invariant under space inversion. The invariance of this theory under Lorentz transformations can be seen by writing Dirac's equation in the extreme relativistic representation of § 10 above. Let ψ_ν be a four-component neutrino wave function; we restrict this wave function by the condition

$$\gamma^5 \psi_\nu = -\psi_\nu. \tag{112}$$

This condition is invariant under the proper Lorentz transformations (15) and (18), and it is consistent with the Hamiltonian (111). It follows from (76) that

$$c(\boldsymbol{\alpha}.\mathbf{p})\psi_\nu = \tfrac{1}{2}c(\boldsymbol{\alpha}.\mathbf{p})(1-\gamma^5)\psi_\nu = c(\boldsymbol{\sigma}.\mathbf{p})\phi_1,$$

† See the second and subsequent references in note §, p.150

‡ The neutrino mass is known to be $< 0{\cdot}0005 m_e$.

§ W. Pauli, *Handbuch der Physik* (Springer, Berlin, 1933), vol. xxiv/1, pp. 226–7.

where we write ψ_ν as a pair of two-component state vectors†

$$\psi_\nu = \begin{pmatrix}\phi_1\\ \phi_2\end{pmatrix}. \qquad (112\,\text{a})$$

Thus the two-component theory is Lorentz invariant.‡

The physical consequences of this two-component theory are easily deduced.§ By (77) the spin operator is $\frac{1}{2}\hbar\boldsymbol{\sigma}$; it follows, as in § 10, that the eigensolutions of (111) are

$$\left.\begin{aligned} E &= c|\mathbf{p}|, && \boldsymbol{\sigma}\text{ parallel to }\mathbf{p}\\ E &= -c|\mathbf{p}|, && \boldsymbol{\sigma}\text{ anti-parallel to }\mathbf{p}\end{aligned}\right\}. \qquad (113)$$

Thus the spin of the neutrino is always parallel to its momentum, and the spin of the anti-neutrino is anti-parallel to its momentum. The neutrino and the anti-neutrino therefore have right-handed and left-handed screw character respectively.‖ It is easy to see from 'hole theory' that similar properties hold in quantized field theory.††

The two-component theory imposes a severe restriction on the neutrino's interactions. The theory is only consistent with the interaction (102) provided $C'_S = -C_S$, $C'_V = -C_V$,..., etc.; that is, the neutrino field always occurs in the form $(1-\gamma^5)\psi_\nu$, which is equivalent to ϕ_1 (by 112 a)). The two-component theory therefore implies the maximum amount of parity mixing in the interactions. By (112), $\bar{\psi}_\nu \boldsymbol{\sigma} \psi_\nu$ vanishes, therefore the neutrino cannot have a magnetic or electric dipole moment.

Instead of (112) we could have imposed the condition

$$\gamma^5\psi_\nu = \psi_\nu. \qquad (114)$$

This is equivalent to putting $C'_S = C_S$, $C'_V = C_V$, etc., in (102) and using ϕ_2 in (112 a). Now the neutrino and anti-neutrino are left-handed and right-handed screws respectively. Whether we must use (112) or (114) depends upon the experimental evidence. The experiment of Wu *et al.* on Co^{60} shows that $\alpha < 0$; the nuclear transition is $5^+ \to 4^+$, so using (117) and ignoring the small Coulomb effect term, we see that (112) is the correct choice for the neutrino if $|C_T|^2$ is the predominant term.‡‡

† This method has been used by A. Salam, *Nuovo Cim.* **5** (1957) 299. Condition (112) or (114) implies that the renormalized neutrino mass is zero.

‡ Alternatively, we notice that in any representation $(\boldsymbol{\alpha}.\mathbf{p}) = -\gamma^5(\boldsymbol{\sigma}.\mathbf{p})$.

§ T. D. Lee and C. N. Yang, *Phys. Rev.* **105** (1957) 1671; A. Landau, *Nuclear Phys.* **3** (1957) 127.

‖ Hence the name 'screwon' and the term *helicity*.

†† We do not consider the case in which the neutrino is its own anti-particle; then eqn. (113) does *not* give asymmetry.

‡‡ See for example J. M. Blatt and V. F. Weisskopf, *Theoretical Nuclear Physics* (J. Wiley, New York, 1952), ch. 13, § 7.

If it turns out that the axial interaction is predominant, then (114) is the correct choice.

The β-decay interaction and longitudinal polarization

Valuable information about the β-decay process is obtained by examining the polarization of the emitted electron (or positron) along the direction of its momentum **p**. The two-component neutrino theory (in the form (112)) requires that the electron-neutrino part of any term in the β-decay interaction (102) be written $\{\bar{\psi}_e O(1-\gamma^5)\psi_\nu\}$, where O is some product of γ-matrices. This equals $\{\bar{\psi}_e(1\pm\gamma^5)\gamma^4 O\psi_\nu\}$, where (+) holds for S, T, and P interactions, and (—) for V and A. The argument in § 10 shows that, for extremely relativistic electrons, the matrices $(1+\gamma^5)$ and $(1-\gamma^5)$ select electron states which are polarized so that $(\boldsymbol{\sigma}.\mathbf{p}) = -|\mathbf{p}|$ and $(\boldsymbol{\sigma}.\mathbf{p}) = +|\mathbf{p}|$ respectively. Hence if a β-decay process involves only one of the interactions S, T, V, or A, and if we assume the two-component neutrino theory in the form (112), all electrons which are emitted with relativistic energies will have longitudinal polarization $P = -1$ for the interactions S and T, and $P = +1$ for V and A. The opposite polarizations occur for relativistic positrons. The signs of all these polarizations would be reversed if we used the two-component theory in the form (114).

The longitudinal polarization of electrons in allowed β-transitions, averaged over nuclear orientations and neutrino directions, can readily be evaluated† for the general interaction (102). In the notation of § 17 it is

$$P = G\frac{v_e}{c}\Big/\left(1\pm\frac{bm}{W}\right),$$

where v_e is the electron's velocity and

$$G\xi = \pm 2\mathrm{Re}\{|M_F|^2(C_S C_S'^* - C_V C_V'^*) + |M_{GT}|^2(C_T C_T'^* - C_A C_A'^*)\}.$$

The upper and lower signs refer to electron and positron emitters respectively. (Coulomb effects are omitted here.)

Using the values of ξ and b given below, we see that in a pure transition (where only one of S, T, V, or A occurs) the electron polarization is $(-v_e/c)$ for S, T, and $(+v_e/c)$ for V, A, provided (112) holds. Positrons have the opposite polarization. If the Fierz interference term b is assumed to be small,‡ the magnitudes of these longitudinal polariza-

† R. B. Curtis and R. R. Lewis, *Phys. Rev.* **107** (1957) 543; J. D. Jackson, S. B. Treiman, and H. W. Wyld, ibid. **106** (1957) 517; K. Alder, B. Steck, and A. Winther, ibid. **107** (1957) 728, give comprehensive polarization formulae.

‡ See pp. 155 and 157 for the justification.

tions are the maximum which can be achieved for any value of the coefficients C, C' in (102).

The longitudinal polarization of electrons can be measured by two methods.† Electrostatic deflexion of the electrons converts the longitudinal polarization into transverse polarization; this can then be measured by scattering the electrons in material of high atomic number (Mott scattering). As was seen in § 9 above, the scattered electrons will have a marked left-right asymmetry. Alternately, the longitudinally polarized electrons can be scattered by polarized electrons (Møller scattering); the cross-section for this process depends strongly on the relative orientation of the spins of the incident and target electrons.† The second method can also be used to detect the longitudinal polarization of positrons.

Experiments show that the electrons emitted by Co^{60} and P^{32} (Gamow–Teller transitions) have longitudinal polarization $(-v_e/c)$ to within 20 per cent.† Similar results have been obtained for the mixed transition Au^{198} and for various other β^- emitters.‡ Emitted positrons are found to have the opposite polarization, for example§ in Na^{22} (Gamow–Teller). Pure Fermi transitions are given by the positron emitters Ga^{66} and Cl^{34} $(0 \rightarrow 0)$; the positrons have longitudinal polarization|| $(+v_e/c)$. (For the selection rules see § 17.)

The large longitudinal polarization of β-particles shows that the constant G in the preceding formula must be close to (-1) for electrons. These polarization results, the result (118) below, and the value of Miss Wu's parameter α are simply explained by either of the alternative assumptions:

(i) condition (112) and $|C_S|^2 = |C_T|^2$ with C_V and C_A much smaller.

(ii) condition (114) and $|C_V|^2 = |C_A|^2$ with C_S and C_T much smaller.

The helicity of the neutrino determines whether the pair of interactions $(S,\ T)$ or the pair (V, A) is predominant. The nucleus Eu^{152} decays by capturing a K-electron and emitting a neutrino. The resulting excited state of Sm^{152} emits a γ-ray. By measuring†† the circular polarization of the γ-ray it is seen that the neutrino has negative helicity (i.e. $\boldsymbol{\sigma}.\mathbf{p}_\nu = -|\mathbf{p}_\nu|$). Hence alternative (ii) is correct. Confirmation

† H. Frauenfelder *et al.*, *Phys. Rev.* **106** (1957) 386; **107** (1957) 643.

‡ C. S. Wu *et al.*, *Phys. Rev.* **109** (1958) 85.

§ L. A. Page and M. Heinberg, *Phys. Rev.* **106** (1957) 1220.

|| M. Deutsch *et al.*, *Phys. Rev.* **107** (1957) 1733. They measure the polarization of γ-rays produced by annihilation of the positron.

†† M. Goldhaber, L. Grodzins, and A. W. Sunyar, *Phys. Rev.* **109** (1958) 1015.

comes from the observed correlation† between the neutrino momentum and the neutron spin in neutron decay (101); this favours (V, A).

Finally we notice that if Wigner time reversal holds, C_V/C_A is real, so we can only have $C_V \simeq \pm C_A$. The observed asymmetry† of the electrons in neutron decay suggests $C_V \simeq -C_A$.‡

The muon and lepton conservation

There is evidence from the value of the Michel parameter§ that (110) is the correct process for muon decay|| (rather than $\mu^+ \to e^+ + 2\nu$ or $\mu^+ \to e^+ + 2\bar{\nu}$). The two-component theory gives a value of the asymmetry parameter a in process (110) which agrees with the results of Garwin *et al.*††

If we *assume* lepton conservation (i.e. the conservation of the total number of muons, electrons, and neutrinos—apart from pair production), it follows from (110) that μ^+ is an anti-lepton. Then the pion decay must be

$$\pi^+ \to \mu^+ + \nu, \qquad \pi^- \to \mu^- + \bar{\nu}. \tag{115}$$

As (114) is the correct choice for the neutrino field, the negative muon in (115) is completely polarized along its direction of motion $(\boldsymbol{\sigma}.\mathbf{p}_\mu = +|\mathbf{p}_\mu|)$ and the positive muon is polarized in the opposite direction. This spin alignment has been observed,‡‡ but its sign has yet to be determined. However the following observations on μ^+ decay are together consistent with the above sign, (1) the positive helicity of e^+,§§ (2) the backward asymmetry of e^+, (3) the predominance of high-energy e^+ (i.e. the large Michel parameter).

17. β-decay formulae

The selection rules for the *allowed β-transitions* are obtained from the interaction (102) on neglecting relativistic effects in the nucleon motion and taking the long wavelength limit for the light particle wave function.|||| The electron and neutrino, in this case, can only take away

† V. L. Telegdi *et al.*, *Phys. Rev.* **110** (1958) 1214.

‡ The electron-neutrino angular correlation also indicates the type of interaction. W. B. Hermannsfeld *et al.*, *Phys. Rev.* **107** (1957) 641; *Phys. Rev. Letters*, **1** (1958) 61, have found that A^{35} is V and He^6 is A (cf. eqn. (116) below).

§ T. D. Lee and C. N. Yang, *Phys. Rev.* **105** (1957) 1671.

|| L. Michel, *Proc. Phys. Soc.* A **63** (1950) 514.

†† See p. 150, n. §.

‡‡ After passing through a magnetic field, the muon is still polarized in the direction of its momentum (Garwin *et al.*, loc. cit.). Therefore the cyclotron frequency equals the Larmor precession frequency; hence the magnetic moment is close to $(e\hbar/2m_\mu c)$ as is the case for a spin-$\frac{1}{2}$ particle.

§§ G. Culligan *et al.*, *Nature* **180** (1957) 757.

|||| For a survey see the article by M. E. Rose in *Beta- and Gamma-Ray Spectroscopy* (North Holland, Amsterdam, 1955).

angular momentum by their spins. The nuclear matrix elements are therefore (cf. p. 196)

$$M_F = \int \Psi_f^* \Big(\sum_k \tau_2^{(k)}\Big) \Psi_i \, d^3\mathbf{x}_k \quad \text{(the Fermi term)}$$

for the interactions S, V; and

$$M_{GT} = \sum_k \int \Psi_f^* \tau_2^{(k)} \boldsymbol{\sigma}^{(k)} \Psi_i \, d^3\mathbf{x}_k \quad \text{(the Gamow–Teller term)}$$

for the interactions T, A. Ψ_i, Ψ_f are the initial and final nuclear states and the summation (k) is over all nucleons.† Thus the selection rules for the nuclear states between which *allowed* transitions can occur are

$$\left.\begin{array}{ll} \Delta J = 0, & \text{for } S,\, V \\ \Delta J = 0,\ \pm 1 \quad (\text{not } 0 \to 0), & \text{for } T,\, A \end{array}\right\}.$$

In all these cases there is *no change* in parity of the nuclear states.‡

Two important quantities are evaluated by standard methods. The probability that the β-particle of momentum p and total energy W is emitted at angle θ to the anti-neutrino (or neutrino) whose energy is $(W_0 - W)$, is given by

$$N_{\mp}(W,\theta)\, dW \sin\theta\, d\theta$$
$$= F(\pm Z, W) p W (W_0 - W)^2 \frac{\xi}{4\pi^3}\left(1 \pm \frac{b}{W} + \frac{ap}{W}\cos\theta\right) dW \sin\theta\, d\theta, \quad (116)$$

where the upper (lower) sign refers to the electron (positron) case. Energy is measured in units of $m_e c^2$, and time in $\hbar/m_e c^2 = 1{\cdot}3 \times 10^{-21}$ sec. Also,§

$$\xi = (D_S + D_V)|M_F|^2 + (D_T + D_A)|M_{GT}|^2,$$
$$a\xi = (D_V - D_S)|M_F|^2 + \tfrac{1}{3}(D_T - D_A)|M_{GT}|^2 +$$
$$+ 2\,\mathrm{Re}\left\{ i \frac{Ze^2}{\hbar c p} [(C_S C_V^* + C_S' C_V'^*)|M_F|^2 - \tfrac{1}{3}(C_T C_A^* + C_T' C_A'^*)|M_{GT}|^2] \right\}$$
$$b\xi = 2\gamma\, \mathrm{Re}\,(C_S^* C_V + C_S'^* C_V')|M_F|^2 + 2\gamma\, \mathrm{Re}(C_T^* C_A + C_T'^* C_A')|M_{GT}|^2,$$

where $\gamma = (1 - \alpha^2 Z^2)^{\frac{1}{2}}$ ($\alpha \simeq \frac{1}{137}$, and Z is the atomic number) and

$$D_k = |C_k|^2 + |C_k'|^2 \quad \text{for } k = S,\, V,\, T,\, A.$$

$F(\pm Z, W)$ is the Coulomb field factor; it essentially gives the density of β-particles at the nucleus relative to the density at infinity. This factor appreciably reduces the number of slow positrons and increases the number of slow electrons (also $F(0, W) = 1$). The Fierz interference terms‖ $b\xi$ are clearly small.†† The symmetry of ξ, $a\xi$, $b\xi$ in

† The interaction P does not give allowed transitions.

‡ The isotopic spin T (Chapter IV, § 11) cannot change in M_F (i.e. $\Delta T = 0$); in M_{GT} we can have $\Delta T = 0, \pm 1$.

§ T. D. Lee and C. N. Yang, *Phys. Rev.* **104** (1956) 254; ibid. **106** (1957) 1371.

‖ M. Fierz, *Z. Phys.* **104** (1937) 553.

†† See § 16 above.

the coefficients C, C' is due to the fact (which is readily verified) that without measuring the spin of the neutrino the interactions with C and C' cannot be distinguished, unless parity interference occurs.†

The asymmetry coefficient α for $\beta^{\mp}$-emission by an oriented nucleus (eqn. (108)) is given by $\beta^{\mp}\langle J_3\rangle/J$ for an allowed transition $J \to J-1$, and $-\beta^{\mp}\langle J_3\rangle/(J+1)$ for $J \to (J+1)$. $\langle J_3\rangle$ is the initial nuclear spin average. Also,‡

$$\beta^{\mp} = \pm\left(\frac{v_e}{c}\right)\frac{\text{re}(C_T C_T'^{*}-C_A C_A'^{*})-(Ze^2/\hbar cp)\text{im}(C_A C_T'^{*}+C_A' C_T^{*})}{\frac{1}{2}(D_T+D_A)+(\gamma/W)\text{re}(C_T^{*} C_A+C_T'^{*} C_A')}. \tag{117}$$

v_e and p are the final velocity and momentum of the electron. It is shown in Chapter VII, § 5, that the term $\text{Re}(C_T C_T'^{*}-C_A C_A'^{*})$ vanishes if H_{int} is invariant under charge conjugation; the term $\text{Im}(C_A C_T'^{*}+C_A' C_T'^{*})$ vanishes if H_{int} is invariant under Wigner time reversal.

The absolute values D_k of the β-decay coupling constants are determined from the lifetime for the 1·83 MeV β^+ emission by O^{14} and the lifetime of the neutron. In both cases the nuclear matrix elements ($|M_F|^2$, $|M_{GT}|^2$) are accurately known. The former is a pure Fermi transition from an 0^+ state of O^{14} to an 0^+ state of N^{14}. These states are members of an isotopic spin triplet ($T = 1$, $T_3 = +1, 0, -1$) in the nuclei O^{14}, N^{14}, C^{14} (cf. Chapter IV, § 12); it follows that the matrix element is $|M_F|^2 = T(T+1)-T_3 T_3' = 2$. Using (116) we deduce from the observed lifetime that§

$$D_S+D_V = (1{\cdot}374\pm0{\cdot}016)10^{-49}\text{ erg cm}^3.$$

The neutron's decay involves both the Fermi and the Gamow–Teller interactions. From the observed lifetime|| (mean life = 17·5 min), and with the above value of (D_S+D_V) we deduce§

$$\frac{D_T+D_A}{D_S+D_V} = 1{\cdot}36, \tag{118}$$

with an error of about 30 per cent. The arguments of § 16 show that D_V and D_A are predominant; therefore $C_A \simeq -1{\cdot}15C_V$.

† For the theory of the *forbidden* β-decay the reader should consult the article by E. Konopinski in *Beta- and Gamma-Ray Spectroscopy*.

‡ Detailed calculations of the polarizations and angular distributions in nuclear β-decays have been made by J. D. Jackson, S. B. Treiman, and H. W. Wyld, *Phys. Rev.* **106** (1957) 517.

§ J. B. Gerhart, *Phys. Rev.* **95** (1954) 288; **109** (1958) 897; M. T. Burgy *et al.*, ibid. **107** (1957) 1731; O. Kofoed-Hansen and A. Winther, *K. danske vidensk. Selsk.* **30** (1956) No. 20.

|| J. M. Robson, *Phys. Rev.* **83** (1951) 349.

IV

QUANTIZATION OF FERMION FIELDS AND THE INTERACTION OF FIELDS: ISOTOPIC SPIN

1. Quantization rules for spin-$\frac{1}{2}$ fermion fields

DIRAC's equation for a spin-$\frac{1}{2}$ fermion which has been discussed in the preceding chapter, only deals with strictly single-particle problems. It cannot be used to investigate a variety of important phenomena. For example, without extension Dirac's theory does not describe the fermion vacuum; a correct description of the fermion vacuum is necessary if we are to investigate the polarization of the vacuum which occurs close to a nucleus.† Also, the interaction of a fermion with its own (electromagnetic or pion) field cannot be discussed with any precision without having a quantized theory of the fermion field.

In Maxwell's theory, as given in Chapter I, the field potentials $A_\mu(x)$ were ordinary functions; they were sufficient to describe the classical theory. The quantized electromagnetic field (given in Chapter II) is expressed in terms of field potential operators $A_\mu(x)$; this operator theory accounts for both the particle (photon) properties and the wave properties of the field. The Dirac theory, as given in Chapter III, is expressed in terms of the four ordinary functions (ψ_ρ) $(\rho = 1,2,3,4)$ which make up the spinor wave function ψ, this is sometimes called the classical fermion theory. The fermion field has particle properties which are not given by the classical fermion theory (such as: the charge in the fermion field is $\pm ne$, where n is an integer). In order to describe these particle properties as well as the wave properties (such as electron diffraction) it is necessary to replace the functions (ψ_ρ) by four operators. State vectors on which the operators ψ_ρ act are used to describe the states of the field; it will be shown that in this way we can give a satisfactory description of the vacuum and of the many-fermion states.

The quantization of a fermion field is deduced by a method similar to the quantization of a boson field, as given in Chapter II, § 2. We assume that at a fixed time t the independent classical field variables are $\phi^{(\alpha)}(\mathbf{x}, t)$ $(\alpha = 1, 2,..., N)$. From the Lagrangian density $\mathscr{L}$ which

† The electric field produced by the nuclear charge causes a separation of charge to appear in the vacuum. This polarization, due to the separation of positrons and electrons, is analogous to the polarization of a dielectric by an electric field.

gives the classical equations of motion, the canonical conjugate momentum density is deduced:

$$\pi^{(\alpha)}(\mathbf{x},t) = \partial\mathscr{L}/\partial\dot{\phi}^{(\alpha)}(\mathbf{x},t).$$

The functions $\phi^{(\alpha)}(\mathbf{x},t)$, $\pi^{(\alpha)}(\mathbf{x},t)$ are now replaced by operators, and we must write down their commutation relations.

It is clear that it would be incorrect to use the quantization rules (2.10) and (2.13) for a fermion field; this is because the fermions must obey the exclusion principle. Let us consider what happens in the boson case. In neutral pion theory, by (2.53), the state vector for the 1st, 2nd,..., rth pions having momenta $\hbar\mathbf{k}_1$, $\hbar\mathbf{k}_2$,..., $\hbar\mathbf{k}_r$ is

$$|\mathbf{k}_1,\mathbf{k}_2,...,\mathbf{k}_r\rangle = \tilde{a}(\mathbf{k}_1)\tilde{a}(\mathbf{k}_2)...\,\tilde{a}(\mathbf{k}_r)|0\rangle, \tag{1}$$

where $|0\rangle$ is the vacuum state vector. Any pair of pions may be exchanged; for example, exchanging the pions which have momenta $\hbar\mathbf{k}_1$, $\hbar\mathbf{k}_2$ gives $|\mathbf{k}_2,\mathbf{k}_1,...,\mathbf{k}_r\rangle$. Because the creation operators $\tilde{a}$ commute with each other,

$$|\mathbf{k}_2,\mathbf{k}_1,\mathbf{k}_3,...,\mathbf{k}_r\rangle = |\mathbf{k}_1,\mathbf{k}_2,\mathbf{k}_3,...,\mathbf{k}_r\rangle. \tag{2}$$

Hence the state vector is unaltered by any permutation of the particles; this result ensures that the particles obey Bose–Einstein statistics.

It is assumed that spin-$\frac{1}{2}$ particles obey Fermi–Dirac statistics;† that is the particles are indistinguishable and they obey the exclusion principle. Because the particles are indistinguishable, the state vectors must have simple properties when subjected to a permutation of the particles. It can be shown‡—just as in the theory of electrons in an atom or a metal—that the state vectors should be anti-symmetric with respect to the exchange of any pair of particles. Thus if r fermions have properties described by λ_1, λ_2,..., λ_r, their state vector must obey

$$|\lambda_{s_1},\lambda_{s_2},...,\lambda_{s_r}\rangle = (-1)^P|\lambda_1,\lambda_2,...,\lambda_r\rangle, \tag{3}$$

where the set $(\lambda_{s_1},\lambda_{s_2},...,\lambda_{s_r})$ is obtained from the set $(\lambda_1, \lambda_2,..., \lambda_r)$ by any permutation. P is even or odd according as this permutation is obtained by an even or an odd number of exchanges of pairs. Each symbol stands for the momentum, the component of spin (in a given direction), and the sign of the charge of a single fermion§ (or any

† The relation between spin and statistics (integral spin having *B–E* statistics and half-integral spin having *F–D* statistics) is mentioned in Chapter VII, § 4; see also the article by W. Pauli in *Niels Bohr and the Development of Physics* (Pergamon, London, 1955).

‡ For a discussion of the invariance of quantum systems under the permutation group see H. Weyl, *Theory of Groups and Quantum Mechanics* (Methuen, London, 1931), ch. 4c; or W. Pauli, *Handbuch der Physik* (Springer, Berlin, 1933), vol. xxiv/1, § 14.

§ Notice that the state vector changes sign on exchanging a fermion and an anti-fermion. For the neutron λ_i stands for momentum, spin component, and the sign of the magnetic moment relative to the spin.

equivalent description, such as the angular momentum classification). If the state vector $|\lambda_1,...,\lambda_r\rangle$ is to be obtained from a vacuum state vector by the application of creation operators as in (1), it is necessary that all pairs of creation operators $\tilde{a}(\lambda_i)$ anti-commute,† i.e.

$$\tilde{a}(\lambda_i)\tilde{a}(\lambda_j)+\tilde{a}(\lambda_j)\tilde{a}(\lambda_i) = 0 \quad (\text{all } \lambda_i,\ \lambda_j). \tag{4}$$

The Hermitian conjugate of (4) is

$$a(\lambda_i)a(\lambda_j)+a(\lambda_j)a(\lambda_i) = 0 \quad (\text{all } \lambda_i,\ \lambda_j). \tag{5}$$

It is convenient to use the notation

$$[A, B]_+ = AB+BA$$

for the anti-commutator of A and B.

It was pointed out by Jordan and Wigner‡ that the only simple way of obtaining a quantum field theory in which the creation and annihilation operators obeyed the anti-commutation relations (4) and (5), was to change the sign before one of the products of operators in each of the basic commutation relations (2.10) and (2.13). Thus for any fermion field we assume

$$\left.\begin{aligned}[\phi^{(\alpha)}(\mathbf{x},t),\ \phi^{(\alpha')}(\mathbf{x}',t)]_+ &= 0\\ [\pi^{(\alpha)}(\mathbf{x},t),\ \pi^{(\alpha')}(\mathbf{x}',t)]_+ &= 0\end{aligned}\right\}. \tag{6}$$

On replacing the commutator $[\pi^{(\alpha)}, \phi^{(\alpha')}]$ of (2.13) by an anti-commutator, it is not clear from the above arguments which of the terms ($\pi^{(\alpha)}\phi^{(\alpha)}$ or $-\phi^{(\alpha)}\pi^{(\alpha)}$) should have its sign reversed.§ As will be seen in the next section, for the Dirac field there can only be one possibility; this, when written in general notation is

$$[\pi^{(\alpha)}(\mathbf{x},t),\ \phi^{(\alpha')}(\mathbf{x}',t)]_+ = -(\hbar/i)\delta_{\alpha\alpha'}\delta^3(\mathbf{x}-\mathbf{x}'). \tag{7}$$

We can adopt the viewpoint that the method of Jordan and Wigner is only a guide to enable us to set up a quantized fermion theory. The theory must then be shown to be self-consistent. The more powerful quantization method, according to Schwinger's variation principle, shows directly that (7) is in all cases the correct form (cf. Chapter IX, § 2).

† In particular, $\tilde{a}(\lambda_i)\tilde{a}(\lambda_i) = 0$ ensures that two particles cannot be in the same state λ_i. This by itself would give the exclusion principle; however, eqn. (3) (and hence (4)) is necessary if the particles are indistinguishable.

‡ P. Jordan and E. Wigner, *Z. Phys.* **47** (1928) 231. These authors also show how operators $\tilde{a}$, a obeying (4) and (5) may be set up. Further details on this point are given by G. Wentzel, *Quantum Theory of Fields* (Interscience, New York, 1949), ch. 5.

§ The ambiguity in sign is related to the ambiguity in the sign of $\pi^{(\alpha)}(x)$ in the fermion case. The latter arises because when $\mathscr{L}$ is written in terms of operators, a change in order of a pair of operators changes the sign of the term; hence $\partial\mathscr{L}/\partial\phi^{(\alpha)}$ is ambiguous in sign, unless we use *right* and *left derivatives*. Cf. Chapter IX for further details.

2. The free Dirac field

Only particles with spin $\frac{1}{2}$ will be considered. The Dirac equation for electrons, protons, neutrons, etc., is given by (3.3):

$$\gamma^\mu \partial_\mu \psi + \kappa\psi = 0, \tag{8}$$

where $\psi = (\psi_\rho)$ ($\rho = 1, 2, 3, 4$), and $\kappa = (mc/\hbar)$ is the reciprocal Compton wavelength for the particle. The properties of the 4×4 matrices γ^μ have been discussed in Chapter III. Eqn. (8) is given by the Lagrangian density (cf. Chapter III, eqn. (25))

$$\mathscr{L} = -\hbar c\bar{\psi}(\gamma^\mu \partial_\mu \psi + \kappa\psi),$$

where† $\bar{\psi} = \psi_T^* \gamma^4 = \tilde{\psi}\gamma^4$. The canonical momentum density conjugate to $\psi_\rho(x_\mu)$ is $\pi_\rho(x_\mu) = i\hbar\tilde{\psi}_\rho(x_\mu)$.

On quantizing, the operator $\tilde{\psi}_\rho(\mathbf{x}, t)$ denotes the Hermitian conjugate of the operator $\psi_\rho(\mathbf{x}, t)$. We combine the four operators $\psi_\rho(\mathbf{x}, t)$ to give a column vector $\psi(\mathbf{x}, t)$, and the four operators $\tilde{\psi}_\rho(\mathbf{x}, t)$ to give a row vector $\tilde{\psi}(\mathbf{x}, t)$. We define $\bar{\psi}(\mathbf{x}, t) = \tilde{\psi}(\mathbf{x}, t)\gamma^4$. The field commutators (6) and (7) give

$$\left.\begin{array}{c} [\psi_\rho(\mathbf{x}, t), \psi_{\rho'}(\mathbf{x}', t)]_+ = 0, \qquad [\tilde{\psi}_\rho(\mathbf{x}, t), \tilde{\psi}_{\rho'}(\mathbf{x}', t)]_+ = 0 \\ [\tilde{\psi}_\rho(\mathbf{x}, t), \psi_{\rho'}(\mathbf{x}', t)]_+ = \delta_{\rho\rho'}\delta^3(\mathbf{x}-\mathbf{x}') \end{array}\right\}. \tag{9}$$

(It is impossible for the last equation to have a negative sign on the right-hand side, because $\tilde{\psi}_\rho(\mathbf{x}, t)\psi_\rho(\mathbf{x}, t)$ and $\psi_\rho(\mathbf{x}, t)\tilde{\psi}_\rho(\mathbf{x}, t)$ both must have positive expectation values.‡ This gives the sign shown in (7).)

It should be noted that physical quantities associated with the fermion field must be bilinear (or quadrilinear) in the field operators $\bar{\psi}(x)$, $\psi(x)$. There are two reasons for this requirement: (*a*) physical quantities measured at a space-like separation must commute, (*b*) the spinors which give the four-component character of ψ, $\bar{\psi}$ are two valued under rotations of the spatial axes; eqn. (3.16) shows that a rotation through 2π changes the sign of ψ, $\bar{\psi}$. Physical quantities cannot change sign under this rotation. The energy, momentum, charge, etc., which are discussed below are all bilinear in ψ, $\bar{\psi}$.

The Hamiltonian operator, formed in the usual way, is (cf. (3.27))

$$\mathbf{H} = \hbar c \int d^3\mathbf{x}\, \{\bar{\psi}(\mathbf{x}, t)(\boldsymbol{\gamma}.\mathrm{grad})\psi(\mathbf{x}, t) + \kappa\bar{\psi}(\mathbf{x}, t)\psi(\mathbf{x}, t)\}, \tag{10}$$

where $\boldsymbol{\gamma} = (\gamma^1, \gamma^2, \gamma^3)$. Using the Heisenberg representation so that the

† T denotes the transpose.

‡ If $|\alpha\rangle$ is any state, then $\langle\alpha|\tilde{A}A|\alpha\rangle = \sum_\lambda \langle\alpha|\tilde{A}|\lambda\rangle\langle\lambda|A|\alpha\rangle$, where $|\lambda\rangle$ is a complete set. Hence $\langle\alpha|\tilde{A}A|\alpha\rangle = \sum_\lambda |\langle\lambda|A|\alpha\rangle|^2 \geqslant 0$ for any operator A.

state vectors are constant, the rate of change of any operator f (which is not explicitly dependent on the time) is

$$\frac{\partial f}{\partial t} = (i/\hbar)[\mathbf{H}, f]. \tag{11}$$

From the anti-commutators (9) and the identity

$$[BC, A] = B[C, A]_+ - [B, A]_+ C,$$

it is easy to verify that the operator ψ obeys the equation of motion (8), and the operator $\bar{\psi}$ obeys the adjoint equation (cf. (3.23))

$$\partial_\mu \bar{\psi}\gamma^\mu - \kappa\bar{\psi} = 0. \tag{12}$$

Also, it is easy to show that the anti-commutators (9) hold for all time t if they are true for one value t_0.†

The general field commutators can be deduced from (9) using the equation of motion (8).‡ As shown in the Appendix, the form of a function (or operator) which obeys Dirac's equation (8) is expressed in terms of its values at a fixed time t by (eqn. (A.97))§

$$\psi(\mathbf{x}', t') = \frac{1}{i}\int_{-\infty}^{\infty} d^3\mathbf{x}\, S(\mathbf{x}'-\mathbf{x}, t'-t)\gamma^4\psi(\mathbf{x}, t), \tag{13}$$

where $S(x_\mu)$ is a Lorentz invariant 4×4 matrix which satisfies the homogeneous equation (A.93)

$$(\gamma^\mu\partial_\mu + \kappa)S(x_\nu) = 0 \tag{14}$$

and obeys the conditions (A.94), (A.92), and (A.57):

$$S(x_\nu) = 0 \quad (x_\nu^2 > 0); \qquad S(\mathbf{x}, 0) = i\gamma^4\,\delta^3(\mathbf{x}). \tag{15}$$

This function is related to the solution $D_{(\kappa)}(x_\nu)$ of the homogeneous Klein–Gordon equation by

$$S(x_\nu) = (\gamma^\mu\partial_\mu - \kappa)D_{(\kappa)}(x_\nu).$$

Using (13) and (9), it follows that

$$[\psi_\rho(x_\nu), \psi_{\rho'}(x'_\nu)]_+ = 0, \qquad [\bar{\psi}_\rho(x_\nu), \bar{\psi}_{\rho'}(x'_\nu)]_+ = 0 \quad (\text{all } x_\nu,\, x'_\nu). \tag{16}$$

The third anti-commutator in (9) gives

$$[\tilde{\psi}_\rho(\mathbf{x}, t), \psi_{\rho'}(\mathbf{x}', t')]_+ = -i\{S(\mathbf{x}'-\mathbf{x}, t'-t)\gamma^4\}_{\rho'\rho}.$$

† $\partial/\partial t[\psi(\mathbf{x}, t), \psi(\mathbf{x}', t)]_+ = 0$ and its Hermitian conjugate equation are easy to see. Also $\partial/\partial t[\tilde{\psi}_\rho(\mathbf{x}, t), \psi_{\rho'}(\mathbf{x}', t)]_+ = ic\{(\boldsymbol{\gamma}\gamma^4)_{\rho'\rho}\cdot\text{grad}_{\mathbf{x}}\,\delta^3(\mathbf{x}-\mathbf{x}') - (\gamma^4\boldsymbol{\gamma})_{\rho'\rho}\cdot\text{grad}_{\mathbf{x}'}\delta^3(\mathbf{x}-\mathbf{x}')\} = 0.$

‡ The derivation given here is similar to that for the general commutators of boson fields given in Chapter II, § 3.

§ In the notation of the Appendix, $d\sigma_\mu = (0, 0, 0, -i\,d^3\mathbf{x})$ for a flat σ-surface $t =$ constant.

This can be written in the more convenient form

$$[\psi_{\rho'}(x'_\nu), \bar{\psi}_\rho(x_\nu)]_+ = -iS_{\rho'\rho}(x'_\nu - x_\nu). \tag{17}$$

Eqns. (16) and (17) give the free field anti-commutators in Lorentz invariant form.†

3. The particle aspect

The particle aspect of the spin-$\frac{1}{2}$ fermion field can be found by expanding the field operators in terms of plane wave solutions or spherical harmonic solutions of Dirac's equation (3.3);‡ here the plane wave expansion is used.§ For each plane wave $\exp(ik_\mu x_\mu)$ having

$$k_0 = +(\mathbf{k}^2 + \kappa^2)^{\frac{1}{2}}$$

there are two independent solutions of Dirac's equation, corresponding to the two spin values; similarly, for each plane wave having

$$k_0 = -(\mathbf{k}^2 + \kappa^2)^{\frac{1}{2}}$$

there are two solutions. These solutions can be combined into the form $w(k_\mu)\exp(ik_\mu x_\mu)$, where $w(k_\mu)$ is a four-component column vector, satisfying (cf. (3.3))

$$(i\gamma^\mu k_\mu + \kappa)w(k_\mu) = 0. \tag{18}$$

The four independent solutions of (18) are written

$$\left.\begin{aligned} u^{(s)}(\mathbf{k}) &= w^{(s)}\{\mathbf{k}, k_0 = +(\mathbf{k}^2+\kappa^2)^{\frac{1}{2}}\} \\ v^{(s)}(\mathbf{k}) &= w^{(s)}\{-\mathbf{k}, k_0 = -(\mathbf{k}^2+\kappa^2)^{\frac{1}{2}}\} \end{aligned} \quad (s = \pm\tfrac{1}{2}) \right\}, \tag{19}$$

where $u^{(s)}(\mathbf{k})$ is Dirac's wave function for a fermion of momentum $\hbar\mathbf{k}$ having spin $s\hbar$ about the direction $\mathbf{k}$ $(s = \pm\frac{1}{2})$; and $v^{(s)}(\mathbf{k})$ is the wave function for an anti-fermion state of momentum $-\hbar\mathbf{k}$ having spin $-s\hbar$ about the direction $\mathbf{k}$ $(s = \pm\frac{1}{2})$.‖

The expansion of the operator $\psi(x_\mu)$ in terms of these independent solutions may be written

$$\psi(x_\mu) = \frac{1}{(2\pi)^2} \sum_{s=-\frac{1}{2}}^{\frac{1}{2}} \int d^4k\, \delta(k_\mu^2 + \kappa^2) e^{ik_\mu x_\mu} w^{(s)}(k_\mu) C^{(s)}(k_\mu), \tag{20}$$

† The only case which is not obvious is (17). Multiply both sides of (17) by η_ρ $(\rho = 1, 2, 3, 4)$, where (η_ρ) transforms like a Dirac (spinor) wave function. Summation over ρ now shows the Lorentz transformation property.

‡ The spherical harmonic solutions are given in Chapter III, § 7 (especially eqns. (3.60) and (3.61)). The particle aspect can be developed in terms of these angular momentum eigenstates in much the same way as for bosons (Chapter II, § 6).

§ In Chapter V, § 14, the electron field is expanded in terms of the Dirac solutions in a Coulomb field.

‖ The momenta of these spinors are the values of $\mathbf{p}$ occurring in eqn. (3.1). The justification for reversing the sign of $\mathbf{k}$ for $v^{(s)}(\mathbf{k})$ lies in the form of the momentum operator and the spin operator for the field (eqns. (50) and (52) below). From hole theory it is clear that the reversal must occur, because the hole has the opposite properties to the filled state.

where $C^{(s)}(k_\mu)$ is a constant operator coefficient. By (2.32) the δ-function in (20) is rewritten so as to give

$$\psi(x_\mu) = \frac{c}{8\pi^2}\sum_{s=-\frac{1}{2}}^{\frac{1}{2}}\int\frac{d^3\mathbf{k}}{\omega_k}\{C^{(s)}(\mathbf{k})u^{(s)}(\mathbf{k})e^{i(\mathbf{k}.\mathbf{x}-\omega_k t)}+\tilde{D}^{(s)}(\mathbf{k})v^{(s)}(\mathbf{k})e^{-i(\mathbf{k}.\mathbf{x}-\omega_k t)}\}, \tag{21}$$

where $\omega_k = c(\mathbf{k}^2+\kappa^2)^{\frac{1}{2}}$, and the constant operator coefficients $C^{(s)}(\mathbf{k})$, $D^{(s)}(\mathbf{k})$ are defined in a manner similar to those of the charged pion field (cf. p. 82):

$$\left.\begin{aligned} C^{(s)}(\mathbf{k}) &= C^{(s)}\{\mathbf{k},\, k_0 = (\mathbf{k}^2+\kappa^2)^{\frac{1}{2}}\} \\ D^{(s)}(\mathbf{k}) &= \tilde{C}^{(s)}\{-\mathbf{k},\, k_0 = -(\mathbf{k}^2+\kappa^2)^{\frac{1}{2}}\} \end{aligned}\right\}. \tag{22}$$

The similarity of definitions (19) and (22) should be noted. The equation adjoint to (21) is

$$\bar{\psi}(x_\mu) = \frac{c}{8\pi^2}\sum_{s=-\frac{1}{2}}^{\frac{1}{2}}\int\frac{d^3\mathbf{k}}{\omega_k}\{\tilde{C}^{(s)}(\mathbf{k})\bar{u}^{(s)}(\mathbf{k})e^{-i(\mathbf{k}.\mathbf{x}-\omega_k t)}+D^{(s)}(\mathbf{k})\bar{v}^{(s)}(\mathbf{k})e^{i(\mathbf{k}.\mathbf{x}-\omega_k t)}\}, \tag{23}$$

where $\bar{u}^{(s)}(\mathbf{k}) = \tilde{u}^{(s)}(\mathbf{k})\gamma^4$, $\bar{v}^{(s)}(\mathbf{k}) = \tilde{v}^{(s)}(\mathbf{k})\gamma^4$ are the row vectors which are adjoint to $u^{(s)}(\mathbf{k})$, $v^{(s)}(\mathbf{k})$ respectively.

Spinor normalization

The operator coefficients are not completely determined by (21) and (23) until the normalization of the spinors, $w^{(s)}(k_\mu)$, is specified. There are two simple conventions for normalization, and two corresponding ways of *stating* the orthogonality relation. The first is the obvious scheme:

$$\text{(i)}\qquad \left\{\begin{aligned} \tilde{w}^{(s)}\{\mathbf{k}, k_0 = \pm(\mathbf{k}^2+\kappa^2)^{\frac{1}{2}}\}.w^{(s')}\{\mathbf{k}, k_0 = \pm(\mathbf{k}^2+\kappa^2)^{\frac{1}{2}}\} &= \delta_{ss'} \\ \tilde{w}^{(s)}\{\mathbf{k}, k_0 = \pm(\mathbf{k}^2+\kappa^2)^{\frac{1}{2}}\}.w^{(s')}\{\mathbf{k}, k_0 = \mp(\mathbf{k}^2+\kappa^2)^{\frac{1}{2}}\} &= 0 \end{aligned}\right\}$$

$$(s, s' = \pm\tfrac{1}{2}).$$

In each equation either the two upper or the two lower signs are to be taken. The orthogonality relations are deduced from Dirac's equation (18).† The normalization in (i) ensures that each of the four states ($s = \pm\frac{1}{2}$, $k_0 = \pm(\mathbf{k}^2+\kappa^2)^{\frac{1}{2}}$) for a given $\mathbf{k}$ has unit weight; therefore the number of states having one value of spin and one sign of charge (or magnetic moment) whose propagation vectors $\mathbf{k}$ end in the element of volume

† When it is only the spin values s which are different, we remember that the component of spin $\boldsymbol{\sigma}'$ in the direction of the momentum $\mathbf{p} = \hbar\mathbf{k}$ can be specified in addition to eqn. (18).

$d^3\mathbf{k}$ is $\rho_{\mathbf{k}}\, d^3\mathbf{k}$, where $\rho_{\mathbf{k}}$ is a constant. For unit volume of configuration space there are $d^3\mathbf{k}/(2\pi)^3$ such states (i.e. $\rho_{\mathbf{k}} = (2\pi)^{-3}$).

The second normalization convention is†

$$\text{(ii)} \quad \left.\begin{cases} \bar{u}^{(s)}(\mathbf{k}).u^{(s')}(\mathbf{k}) = \delta_{ss'}, & \bar{v}^{(s)}(\mathbf{k}).v^{(s')}(\mathbf{k}') = -\delta_{ss'} \\ \bar{u}^{(s)}(\mathbf{k}).v^{(s')}(\mathbf{k}) = 0, & \bar{v}^{(s)}(\mathbf{k}).u^{(s')}(\mathbf{k}') = 0 \end{cases}\right\} \quad (s, s' = \pm\tfrac{1}{2}).$$

The last two orthogonality relations follow from (18) and (19).‡ The first two relations can be written

$$\bar{w}^{(s)}(k_\mu).w^{(s')}(k_\mu) = \delta_{ss'}(k_0/|k_0|) \quad (\text{for } k_0 = \pm(\mathbf{k}^2+\kappa^2)^{\frac{1}{2}}). \tag{24}$$

Here the same value of k_0 is used in both spinors. Whatever the normalization, we have§

$$k_0\, \bar{w}^{(s)}(k_\mu).w^{(s')}(k_\mu) = \kappa \tilde{w}^{(s)}(k_\mu).w^{(s')}(k_\mu); \tag{25}$$

therefore scheme (ii) gives||

$$\tilde{w}^{(s)}(k_\mu).w^{(s')}(k_\mu) = \left(\frac{\hbar\omega_k}{mc^2}\right)\delta_{ss'}.$$

From this relation it follows that each of the four states for a given $\mathbf{k}$ must have the weight $mc^2/\hbar\omega_k$; therefore the total weight of the states with one spin and charge whose propagation vectors $\mathbf{k}$ end in $d^3\mathbf{k}$ is (in scheme (ii))

$$\rho'_{\mathbf{k}}\, d^3\mathbf{k} = \rho_{\mathbf{k}} \frac{mc^2}{\hbar\omega_k}\, d^3\mathbf{k}.$$

An advantage of scheme (ii) is that $\rho'_{\mathbf{k}}\, d^3\mathbf{k}$ is Lorentz invariant,†† so it is easy to see the effect of a Lorentz transformation on any transition probability.

Scheme (i) has the advantage that expressions for the field energy, momentum, etc., can be written down in an obvious way without any complication arising from using the somewhat artificial density $\rho'_{\mathbf{k}}$. For this reason *scheme* (i) *will be used throughout.*

† The orthogonality relations between positive and negative energy states (i.e. the second line in both schemes) are equivalent.

‡ We use $2\hbar c k_0\, \bar{w}(k_\mu)w(-k_\mu) = \tilde{w}(k_\mu)\{[c(\boldsymbol{\alpha}.\mathbf{p})+\beta mc^2]\beta - \beta[-c(\boldsymbol{\alpha}.\mathbf{p})+\beta mc^2]\}w(-k_\mu)$. By the relation $[\beta, \boldsymbol{\alpha}]_+ = 0$, this vanishes. ($\mathbf{p} = \hbar\mathbf{k}$.)

§ $2\hbar c k_0\, \bar{w}(k_\mu).w(k_\mu) = \tilde{w}(k_\mu)[c(\boldsymbol{\alpha}.\mathbf{p})+\beta mc^2, \beta]_+\, w(k_\mu) = 2mc^2\tilde{w}w$.

|| Clearly this scheme cannot be used for fermions of zero mass.

†† Because $d^3\mathbf{k}/w_k = (2/c)\int_{k_0=0}^{\infty} dk_0\, \delta(k_\mu^2+\kappa^2)\, d^3\mathbf{k}$ is invariant (by 2.33).

Frequency splitting in the free field

The expansions (21) and (22) divide $\psi(x_\mu)$ and $\tilde{\psi}(x_\mu)$ into positive and negative frequency parts as follows:†

$$\left.\begin{aligned}
\psi^{(+)}(x_\mu) &= \frac{c}{8\pi^2}\sum_{s=-\frac{1}{2}}^{\frac{1}{2}}\int\frac{d^3\mathbf{k}}{\omega_k}C^{(s)}(\mathbf{k})u^{(s)}(\mathbf{k})e^{i(\mathbf{k}.\mathbf{x}-\omega_k t)}\\
\tilde{\psi}^{(+)}(x_\mu) &= \frac{c}{8\pi^2}\sum_{s=-\frac{1}{2}}^{\frac{1}{2}}\int\frac{d^3\mathbf{k}}{\omega_k}D^{(s)}(\mathbf{k})\bar{v}^{(s)}(\mathbf{k})e^{i(\mathbf{k}.\mathbf{x}-\omega_k t)}\\
\psi^{(-)}(x_\mu) &= \frac{c}{8\pi^2}\sum_{s=-\frac{1}{2}}^{\frac{1}{2}}\int\frac{d^3\mathbf{k}}{\omega_k}\tilde{D}^{(s)}(\mathbf{k})v^{(s)}(\mathbf{k})e^{-i(\mathbf{k}.\mathbf{x}-\omega_k t)}\\
\tilde{\psi}^{(-)}(x_\mu) &= \frac{c}{8\pi^2}\sum_{s=-\frac{1}{2}}^{\frac{1}{2}}\int\frac{d^3\mathbf{k}}{\omega_k}\tilde{C}^{(s)}(\mathbf{k})\bar{u}^{(s)}(\mathbf{k})e^{-i(\mathbf{k}.\mathbf{x}-\omega_k t)}
\end{aligned}\right\}. \tag{26}$$

The time dependence of all field variables is given by the Heisenberg equation of motion (11) using the Hamiltonian (10). Substituting the expressions (26) in (11) and comparing the coefficients of independent terms gives‡

$$\left.\begin{aligned}
[\mathsf{H}, C^{(s)}(\mathbf{k})] &= -\hbar\omega_k C^{(s)}(\mathbf{k}), & [\mathsf{H}, D^{(s)}(\mathbf{k})] &= -\hbar\omega_k D^{(s)}(\mathbf{k})\\
[\mathsf{H}, \tilde{C}^{(s)}(\mathbf{k})] &= \hbar\omega_k \tilde{C}^{(s)}(\mathbf{k}), & [\mathsf{H}, \tilde{D}^{(s)}(\mathbf{k})] &= \hbar\omega_k \tilde{D}^{(s)}(\mathbf{k})
\end{aligned}\right\}. \tag{27}$$

As for boson fields, it is possible to find a total field momentum operator $\mathbf{P}$ such that any function f of the field operators obeys§

$$(\hbar/i)\text{grad} f = [f, \mathbf{P}]. \tag{28}$$

The operator $\mathbf{P}$ can be obtained from the general formulae for any field (9.36) and (9.37), if we use the Lagrangian $\mathscr{L}$ given in § 2 above and the Lorentz transformation relations (3.16) and (3.19) for the fermion field. The result is (eqn. (9.65))

$$\mathbf{P} = (\hbar/2i)\int d^3\mathbf{x}\,[\tilde{\psi}(\mathbf{x},t)\text{grad}\,\psi(\mathbf{x},t)-\{\text{grad}\,\tilde{\psi}(\mathbf{x},t)\}\psi(\mathbf{x},t)]. \tag{29}$$

Using the anti-commutators (9) it is easy to verify directly that (28) is satisfied if f is replaced by $\psi(\mathbf{x},t)$ or $\tilde{\psi}(\mathbf{x},t)$. Hence it holds for any f. It is also easy to verify, using the equations of motion (8) and (12) that $\dot{\mathbf{P}} = 0$, so $\mathbf{P}$ commutes with H. The operator (29) therefore has the properties required of the field momentum operator.

† As for charged pions, it is necessary to distinguish carefully between $(\tilde{\psi})^{(+)}$ and $\widetilde{\psi^{(+)}}$. In fact, $\tilde{\psi}^{(+)} = \widetilde{\psi^{(-)}}$ or $\tilde{\psi}^{(+)} = \overline{\psi^{(-)}}$.

‡ Cf. eqns. (2.115) for charged pions. As for pions, we write down Heisenberg's equation of motion (11) for $\psi(x_\mu)$ or $\tilde{\psi}(x_\mu)$ and then split the frequency (remembering H is independent of time). This gives $\partial\psi^{(+)}/\partial t = (i/\hbar)[\mathsf{H}, \psi^{(+)}]$, etc.

§ f should not depend *explicitly* on $\mathbf{x}$.

Applying (28) to $\psi(x_\mu)$, $\bar{\psi}(x_\mu)$ and splitting the resultant equations into positive and negative frequency parts (remembering $\dot{\mathbf{P}} = 0$) we have

$$(\hbar/i)\mathrm{grad}\,\psi^{(\pm)}(x_\mu) = [\psi^{(\pm)}(x_\mu), \mathbf{P}],$$

and similar equations for $\bar{\psi}(x_\mu)$. Substituting (26) gives

$$\left.\begin{aligned} [\mathbf{P}, C^{(s)}(\mathbf{k})] &= -\hbar\mathbf{k}C^{(s)}(\mathbf{k}), & [\mathbf{P}, D^{(s)}(\mathbf{k})] &= -\hbar\mathbf{k}D^{(s)}(\mathbf{k}) \\ [\mathbf{P}, \tilde{C}^{(s)}(\mathbf{k})] &= \hbar\mathbf{k}\tilde{C}^{(s)}(\mathbf{k}), & [\mathbf{P}, \tilde{D}^{(s)}(\mathbf{k})] &= \hbar\mathbf{k}\tilde{D}^{(s)}(\mathbf{k}) \end{aligned}\right\}. \tag{30}$$

The physical interpretation

The final step in deducing the physical interpretation of the operators $C^{(s)}$, $D^{(s)}$, $\tilde{C}^{(s)}$, $\tilde{D}^{(s)}$ requires their commutation relations with the total charge operator Q. By (3.28) (or by the general theory of Chapter IX),

$$Q = e\int d^3\mathbf{x}\,\bar{\psi}(\mathbf{x},t)\psi(\mathbf{x},t). \tag{31}$$

Using the equations of motion (8) and (12) (and integrating by parts) it is easy to see that $\dot{Q} = 0$. Thus $[Q, \mathbf{H}] = 0$. Similarly, using (28) it follows that $[Q, \mathbf{P}] = 0$. Eigenstates of the field can therefore be described by eigenvalues E, $\mathbf{P}'$, Q' of energy, momentum, and charge.

The anti-commutation relations (9) show that†

$$\left.\begin{aligned} [Q, \psi(\mathbf{x},t)] &= -e\psi(\mathbf{x},t) \\ [Q, \bar{\psi}(\mathbf{x},t)] &= e\bar{\psi}(\mathbf{x},t) \end{aligned}\right\}. \tag{32}$$

Splitting (32) into positive and negative frequency parts (both sides of (32) obey the Klein–Gordon eqn.) and substituting (26) gives

$$\left.\begin{aligned} [Q, C^{(s)}(\mathbf{k})] &= -eC^{(s)}(\mathbf{k}), & [Q, D^{(s)}(\mathbf{k})] &= eD^{(s)}(\mathbf{k}) \\ [Q, \tilde{C}^{(s)}(\mathbf{k})] &= e\tilde{C}^{(s)}(\mathbf{k}), & [Q, \tilde{D}^{(s)}(\mathbf{k})] &= -e\tilde{D}^{(s)}(\mathbf{k}) \end{aligned}\right\}. \tag{33}$$

We adopt the convention of calling a particle of charge e a fermion and one of charge $(-e)$ an anti-fermion. From the commutators of the operator coefficients, etc., with $\mathbf{H}$, with the total momentum $\mathbf{P}$, and with the total charge Q (eqns. (27), (30), (33)) we deduce that $C^{(s)}(\mathbf{k})$, $D^{(s)}(\mathbf{k})$ respectively destroy a fermion and an anti-fermion of momentum $\hbar\mathbf{k}$, while $\tilde{C}^{(s)}(\mathbf{k})$, $\tilde{D}^{(s)}(\mathbf{k})$ respectively create a fermion and an anti-fermion of momentum $\hbar\mathbf{k}$.‡ Because of the spin properties§ of the spinors $u^{(s)}(\mathbf{k})$, $v^{(s)}(\mathbf{k})$, it is to be expected that $C^{(s)}(\mathbf{k})$, $D^{(s)}(\mathbf{k})$ destroy

† The same relation holds if $\bar{\psi}$ is replaced by ψ.

‡ For neutrons, we get the physical interpretation of the operators by using $N = (Q/e)$ (given by (31)) which is interpreted as the number of neutrons minus the number of anti-neutrons. It is a constant.

§ Notice footnote ‖, p. 164.

particles having spin $s\hbar$ in the direction $\mathbf{k}$ ($s = \pm\frac{1}{2}$), and $\tilde{C}^{(s)}(\mathbf{k})$, $\tilde{D}^{(s)}(\mathbf{k})$ create particles with this spin. This conjecture is proved by eqn. (44) below.

The commutation properties

It is now necessary to discuss the commutation properties of the operator coefficients which occur in (26). From (16) it follows that

$$[\psi^{(+)}(x_\nu), \psi^{(+)}(x'_\nu)]_+ = [\psi^{(+)}(x_\nu), \psi^{(-)}(x'_\nu)]_+ = [\psi^{(-)}(x_\nu), \psi^{(-)}(x'_\nu)]_+ = 0;$$

identical relations hold for $\bar{\psi}^{(+)}$, $\bar{\psi}^{(-)}$. Therefore

$$\left.\begin{aligned} [C^{(s)}(\mathbf{k}), C^{(s')}(\mathbf{k}')]_+ &= [D^{(s)}(\mathbf{k}), D^{(s')}(\mathbf{k}')]_+ = 0 \\ [C^{(s)}(\mathbf{k}), \tilde{D}^{(s')}(\mathbf{k}')]_+ &= [\tilde{C}^{(s)}(\mathbf{k}), D^{(s')}(\mathbf{k}')]_+ = 0 \\ [\tilde{C}^{(s)}(\mathbf{k}), \tilde{C}^{(s')}(\mathbf{k}')]_+ &= [\tilde{D}^{(s)}(\mathbf{k}), \tilde{D}^{(s')}(\mathbf{k}')]_+ = 0 \end{aligned}\right\} \quad (\text{all } s,\, s',\, \mathbf{k},\, \mathbf{k}'). \tag{34}$$

Because (17) is a function of $(x'_\nu - x_\nu)$ it follows that†

$$[\psi^{(+)}_{\rho'}(x'_\nu), \bar{\psi}_\rho(x_\nu)]_+ = [\psi^{(+)}_{\rho'}(x'_\nu), \bar{\psi}^{(-)}_\rho(x_\nu)]_+,$$

therefore $$[\psi^{(+)}_{\rho'}(x'_\nu), \bar{\psi}^{(+)}_\rho(x_\nu)]_+ = 0;$$

similarly, $$[\psi^{(-)}_{\rho'}(x'_\nu), \bar{\psi}^{(-)}_\rho(x_\nu)]_+ = 0.$$

These relations give

$$[C^{(s)}(\mathbf{k}), D^{(s')}(\mathbf{k}')]_+ = [\tilde{C}^{(s)}(\mathbf{k}), \tilde{D}^{(s')}(\mathbf{k}')]_+ = 0 \quad (\text{all } s, s', \mathbf{k}, \mathbf{k}'). \tag{35}$$

The final relations are deduced from

$$\left.\begin{aligned} [\psi^{(+)}_{\rho'}(x'_\nu), \bar{\psi}^{(-)}_\rho(x_\nu)]_+ &= -iS^{(+)}_{\rho'\rho}(x'_\nu - x_\nu) \\ [\psi^{(-)}_{\rho'}(x'_\nu), \bar{\psi}^{(+)}_\rho(x_\nu)]_+ &= -iS^{(-)}_{\rho'\rho}(x'_\nu - x_\nu) \end{aligned}\right\}. \tag{36}$$

As is shown in the Appendix, eqn. (A.92),

$$\left.\begin{aligned} S^{(\pm)}(x_\nu) &= (\gamma^\mu \partial_\mu - \kappa) D^{(\pm)}_{(\kappa)}(x_\nu) \\ &\text{also, by eqn. (A.55),} \\ D^{(+)}_{(\kappa)}(\mathbf{x}, x_0) &= -D^{(-)}_{(\kappa)}(\mathbf{x}, -x_0) \end{aligned}\right\}. \tag{37}$$

Reversing (26) gives (with normalization scheme (i))

$$\left.\begin{aligned} C^{(s)}(\mathbf{k}) &= \frac{1}{\pi\kappa}\left(\frac{\omega_k}{c}\right)^2 \int d^3\mathbf{x}\, \bar{u}^{(s)}(\mathbf{k}) \psi^{(+)}(\mathbf{x}, 0) e^{-i\mathbf{k}.\mathbf{x}} \\ D^{(s)}(\mathbf{k}) &= -\frac{1}{\pi\kappa}\left(\frac{\omega_k}{c}\right)^2 \int d^3\mathbf{x}\, \bar{\psi}^{(+)}(\mathbf{x}, 0) v^{(s)}(\mathbf{k}) e^{-i\mathbf{k}.\mathbf{x}} \\ \tilde{C}^{(s)}(\mathbf{k}) &= \frac{1}{\pi\kappa}\left(\frac{\omega_k}{c}\right)^2 \int d^3\mathbf{x}\, \bar{\psi}^{(-)}(\mathbf{x}, 0) u^{(s)}(\mathbf{k}) e^{i\mathbf{k}.\mathbf{x}} \\ \tilde{D}^{(s)}(\mathbf{k}) &= -\frac{1}{\pi\kappa}\left(\frac{\omega_k}{c}\right)^2 \int d^3\mathbf{x}\, \bar{v}^{(s)}(\mathbf{k}) \psi^{(-)}(\mathbf{x}, 0) e^{i\mathbf{k}.\mathbf{x}} \end{aligned}\right\}. \tag{38}$$

† Both sides of (17) obey the homogeneous Klein–Gordon equation.

Now using (36), (37), (A.66), and (2.33), we have

$$\left.\begin{aligned}[C^{(s)}(\mathbf{k}), \tilde{C}^{(s')}(\mathbf{k}')]_+ &= 8\pi(\omega_k/c)^2\,\delta_{ss'}\,\delta^3(\mathbf{k}-\mathbf{k}')\\ [D^{(s)}(\mathbf{k}), \tilde{D}^{(s')}(\mathbf{k}')]_+ &= 8\pi(\omega_k/c)^2\,\delta_{ss'}\,\delta^3(\mathbf{k}-\mathbf{k}')\end{aligned}\right\}. \tag{39}$$

Eqns. (34), (35), and (39) give the complete set of anti-commutators for the operator coefficients.

The spin operator

As an example of the use of these anti-commutators we now prove that the operators $C^{(s)}(\mathbf{k})$, $D^{(s)}(\mathbf{k})$, etc., are associated with particles having spin $s\hbar$ in the direction $\mathbf{k}$. Using the general formalism of Chapter IX, it is shown in eqns. (9.66) and (9.67) that the angular momentum operator $\mathbf{M}$ for the quantized Dirac field can be written in the form

$$\mathbf{M} = \mathbf{M}^{\mathrm{o}}+\mathbf{M}^{\mathrm{sp}},$$

where $\mathbf{M}^{\mathrm{o}}$ is the orbital angular momentum and $\mathbf{M}^{\mathrm{sp}}$ is the spin contribution. The latter operator is

$$\mathbf{M}^{\mathrm{sp}} = \tfrac{1}{4}\hbar \int d^3\mathbf{x}\,\mathbf{x}\times\operatorname{curl}\{\tilde{\psi}(\mathbf{x},t)\boldsymbol{\sigma}'\psi(\mathbf{x},t)\}, \tag{40}$$

where $\boldsymbol{\sigma}' = (\sigma^{23}, \sigma^{31}, \sigma^{12})$ is the 4×4 matrix defined by eqn. (3.10).† On integration by parts over configuration space, (40) becomes

$$\mathbf{M}^{\mathrm{sp}} = \tfrac{1}{2}\hbar \int d^3\mathbf{x}\,\tilde{\psi}(\mathbf{x},t)\boldsymbol{\sigma}'\psi(\mathbf{x},t). \tag{41}$$

Using the anti-commutation relations (9) it is easy to show that the operator $\mathbf{M}^{\mathrm{sp}}$ commutes with the total momentum operator $\mathbf{P}$ (eqn. (29)); however, $\mathbf{M}^{\mathrm{sp}}$ is *not* a constant of motion. It was shown in Chapter III, § 5, that for a plane-wave solution of Dirac's equation, the component of spin in the direction of the momentum could be made diagonal. This suggests that we examine the longitudinal part $\mathbf{M}^{\mathrm{sp}}_{\mathrm{long}}$ of $\mathbf{M}^{\mathrm{sp}}$, i.e. the component of $\mathbf{M}^{\mathrm{sp}}$ in the direction of the propagation vector $\mathbf{k}$ of the plane waves occurring in the expansion (26). It follows from the definition of $u^{(s)}(\mathbf{k})$, $v^{(s)}(\mathbf{k})$ (eqn. (19)) that

$$\left.\begin{aligned}\tfrac{1}{2}\hbar(\boldsymbol{\sigma}'.\mathbf{k})u^{(s)}(\mathbf{k}) &= s\hbar|\mathbf{k}|u^{(s)}(\mathbf{k})\\ \tfrac{1}{2}\hbar(\boldsymbol{\sigma}'.\mathbf{k})v^{(s)}(\mathbf{k}) &= -s\hbar|\mathbf{k}|v^{(s)}(\mathbf{k})\end{aligned}\right\}. \tag{42}$$

Substituting (26) in the integral (41) for $\mathbf{M}^{\mathrm{sp}}$, and using (42) and the normalization condition (i), we get

$$\mathbf{M}^{\mathrm{sp}}_{\mathrm{long}} = \frac{c^2}{8\pi}\sum_{s=-\frac{1}{2}}^{\frac{1}{2}}\int\frac{d^3\mathbf{k}}{\omega_k^2}\,\frac{\mathbf{k}}{|\mathbf{k}|}\,s\hbar\{\tilde{C}^{(s)}(\mathbf{k})C^{(s)}(\mathbf{k})-D^{(s)}(\mathbf{k})\tilde{D}^{(s)}(\mathbf{k})\}. \tag{43}$$

† In the unquantized Dirac theory the spin matrix is $\mathbf{S} = \tfrac{1}{2}\hbar\boldsymbol{\sigma}'$.

The anti-commutators (34), (35), and (39) now show that

$$\left.\begin{aligned}[\mathbf{M}^{\mathrm{sp}}_{\mathrm{long}}, C^{(s)}(\mathbf{k})] &= -C^{(s)}(\mathbf{k})s\hbar\mathbf{k}/|\mathbf{k}| \\ [\mathbf{M}^{\mathrm{sp}}_{\mathrm{long}}, D^{(s)}(\mathbf{k})] &= -D^{(s)}(\mathbf{k})s\hbar\mathbf{k}/|\mathbf{k}|\end{aligned}\right\} \tag{44}$$

together with the Hermitian conjugate relations. Hence $C^{(s)}(\mathbf{k})$, $D^{(s)}(\mathbf{k})$ annihilate particles having spin $s\hbar$ ($s = \pm\frac{1}{2}$) along the direction $\mathbf{k}$, etc.

The number operators

In order to derive the number operators for fermions and anti-fermions, we first introduce dimensionless operator coefficients $c^{(s)}(\mathbf{k})$, $\tilde{c}^{(s)}(\mathbf{k})$, $d^{(s)}(\mathbf{k})$, $\tilde{d}^{(s)}(\mathbf{k})$. In (39) the δ-function is replaced by the density of states as in (2.48); here

$$\delta^3(\mathbf{k}-\mathbf{k}') = \rho_{\mathbf{k}}\, \delta_{\mathbf{k},\mathbf{k}'}, \tag{45}$$

where $\rho_{\mathbf{k}}$ is the density of the states according to the normalization scheme (i).† The discrete values of $\mathbf{k}$ appearing in $\delta_{\mathbf{k},\mathbf{k}'}$ are so distributed that the summation

$$\sum_{s=-\frac{1}{2}}^{\frac{1}{2}} \sum_{\mathbf{k}}$$

gives the sum over all fermion (or all anti-fermion) states. The dimensionless operators are given by

$$\left.\begin{aligned}C^{(s)}(\mathbf{k}) &= (8\pi\omega_k^2\rho_{\mathbf{k}}/c^2)^{\frac{1}{2}}c^{(s)}(\mathbf{k}) \\ D^{(s)}(\mathbf{k}) &= (8\pi\omega_k^2\rho_{\mathbf{k}}/c^2)^{\frac{1}{2}}d^{(s)}(\mathbf{k})\end{aligned}\right\} \tag{46}$$

together with the Hermitian conjugate relations.

All the dimensionless operator coefficients anti-commute with each other (by eqns. (34) and (35)), except for the cases (eqn. (39))

$$\left.\begin{aligned}[c^{(s)}(\mathbf{k}), \tilde{c}^{(s')}(\mathbf{k}')]_+ &= \delta_{ss'}\,\delta_{\mathbf{k},\mathbf{k}'} \\ [d^{(s)}(\mathbf{k}), \tilde{d}^{(s')}(\mathbf{k}')]_+ &= \delta_{ss'}\,\delta_{\mathbf{k},\mathbf{k}'}\end{aligned}\right\}. \tag{47}$$

Now we define operators

$$n^{(s)}(\mathbf{k},+) = \tilde{c}^{(s)}(\mathbf{k})c^{(s)}(\mathbf{k}), \qquad n^{(s)}(\mathbf{k},-) = \tilde{d}^{(s)}(\mathbf{k})d^{(s)}(\mathbf{k}).$$

It is easy to show (as for charged pions) that these operators have zero or integral eigenvalues. This follows from the commutators‡

$$\left.\begin{aligned}[n^{(s)}(\mathbf{k},+), c^{(s')}(\mathbf{k}')] &= -\delta_{ss'}\,\delta_{\mathbf{k},\mathbf{k}'}\,c^{(s')}(\mathbf{k}') \\ [n^{(s)}(\mathbf{k},-), d^{(s')}(\mathbf{k}')] &= -\delta_{ss'}\,\delta_{\mathbf{k},\mathbf{k}'}\,d^{(s')}(\mathbf{k}')\end{aligned}\right\} \tag{48}$$

and their Hermitian conjugates. We interpret $n^{(s)}(\mathbf{k},+)$, $n^{(s)}(\mathbf{k},-)$ as the number operators for fermions and anti-fermions of momentum $\hbar\mathbf{k}$

† $\rho_{\mathbf{k}} = (L/2\pi)^3$ for a periodic cube of edge L.

‡ In deriving these commutators it is convenient to use the identity

$$[BC, A] = B[C, A]_+ - [B, A]_+ C.$$

and spin $s\hbar$ (in the direction $\mathbf{k}$). From the anti-commutators (34) and (47) it follows that†

$$\{n^{(s)}(\mathbf{k},\pm)\}^2-n^{(s)}(\mathbf{k},\pm) = 0 \quad (\text{all } s,\, \mathbf{k}).$$

This shows that each of the number operators can only have eigenvalues zero or unity. It is of course a consequence of quantizing according to Fermi–Dirac statistics that each state can be empty or, at the most, occupied by one particle. From the basic anti-commutators and (48) it can be shown that all pairs of the operators $n^{(s)}(\mathbf{k},\pm)$ commute; therefore the number of fermions and anti-fermions of all types can be specified independently.

Relations (48) show that the commutation relations (27) are satisfied if H is replaced by $\hbar\omega_k\{n^{(s)}(\mathbf{k},+)+n^{(s)}(\mathbf{k},-)\}$. Thus, apart from an additive constant number (which cannot affect the quantum equations) eqns. (27) show that

$$\mathsf{H} = \sum_{s=-\frac{1}{2}}^{\frac{1}{2}} \sum_{\mathbf{k}} \hbar\omega_k\{n^{(s)}(\mathbf{k},+)+n^{(s)}(\mathbf{k},-)\}. \tag{49}$$

Similarly eqns. (30) give

$$\mathbf{P} = \sum_{s=-\frac{1}{2}}^{\frac{1}{2}} \sum_{\mathbf{k}} \hbar\mathbf{k}\{n^{(s)}(\mathbf{k},+)+n^{(s)}(\mathbf{k},-)\}, \tag{50}$$

and, by (33), the charge operator is

$$Q = \sum_{s=-\frac{1}{2}}^{\frac{1}{2}} \sum_{\mathbf{k}} e\{n^{(s)}(\mathbf{k},+)-n^{(s)}(\mathbf{k},-)\}. \tag{51}$$

By substituting (46) into (43), and using (47) we get

$$\mathbf{M}^{\mathrm{sp}}_{\mathrm{long}} = \sum_{s=-\frac{1}{2}}^{\frac{1}{2}} \sum_{\mathbf{k}} s\hbar(\mathbf{k}/|\mathbf{k}|)\{n^{(s)}(\mathbf{k},+)+n^{(s)}(\mathbf{k},-)\}; \tag{52}$$

in writing this expression an infinite constant number has been omitted. The physical interpretation of the energy, momentum, charge, and spin operators in the forms (49) to (52) is obvious. It should be noticed that the form of quantization which has been used avoids any difficulty with negative energy values; there is no need to consider holes in a sea of negative energy particles.‡

4. The vacuum and the propagators

The vacuum state $|0\rangle$ of the free fermion field is determined by the condition that there are no fermions or anti-fermions present. The

† $n^2 = \tilde{c}c\tilde{c}c = \tilde{c}(-\tilde{c}c+1)c = \tilde{c}c = n.$

‡ The important step is writing (26) in a form similar to that used for charged pions (eqn. (2.114)). The method is essentially based on the work of W. Heisenberg (*Z. Phys.* **90** (1934) 209).

definition can be written†

$$c^{(s)}(\mathbf{k})|0\rangle = 0, \quad d^{(s)}(\mathbf{k})|0\rangle = 0 \quad (\text{all } s, \mathbf{k}). \tag{53}$$

Using (26) the definition of $|0\rangle$ can be written in the equivalent Lorentz covariant form

$$\psi^{(+)}(x_\mu)|0\rangle = 0, \qquad \bar{\psi}^{(+)}(x_\mu)|0\rangle = 0 \ (\text{all } x_\mu); \tag{54}$$

this shows that $|0\rangle$ is independent of any particular Lorentz frame. The Hermitian conjugates of (54) can be written‡

$$0 = \langle 0|\bar{\psi}^{(-)}(x_\mu), \qquad 0 = \langle 0|\psi^{(-)}(x_\mu). \tag{55}$$

The normalized single fermion and single anti-fermion state vectors are§ $\tilde{c}^{(s)}(\mathbf{k})|0\rangle$, $\tilde{d}^{(s)}(\mathbf{k})|0\rangle$. The general state vector for N fermions and N' anti-fermions is

$$\tilde{c}^{(s_1)}(\mathbf{k}_1)\ldots\tilde{c}^{(s_N)}(\mathbf{k}_N)\tilde{d}^{(s_1')}(\mathbf{k}_1')\ldots\tilde{d}^{(s_{N'}')}(\mathbf{k}_{N'}')|0\rangle. \tag{56}$$

Obviously (56) is anti-symmetric with respect to any exchange of a pair of particles. From (26) it is seen that the state vectors $\bar{\psi}_\rho^{(-)}(x_\mu)|0\rangle$, $\psi_\rho^{(-)}(x_\mu)|0\rangle$ ($\rho = 1, 2, 3, 4$) are linear combinations of the single fermion and single anti-fermion state vectors respectively. Linear combinations of the two-particle states are given by

$$\bar{\psi}_\rho^{(-)}(x_\mu)\bar{\psi}_{\rho'}^{(-)}(x_\mu')|0\rangle, \quad \bar{\psi}_\rho^{(-)}(x_\mu)\psi_{\rho'}^{(-)}(x_\mu')|0\rangle, \quad \psi_\rho^{(-)}(x_\mu)\psi_{\rho'}^{(-)}(x_\mu')|0\rangle,$$

and so on.

As in the case of bosons we expect that the vacuum expectation values of the pairs of operators

$$\psi_\rho^{(+)}(x_\mu)\psi_{\rho'}^{(-)}(x_\mu'), \quad \psi_\rho^{(+)}(x_\mu)\bar{\psi}_{\rho'}^{(-)}(x_\mu'), \quad \bar{\psi}_\rho^{(+)}(x_\mu)\psi_{\rho'}^{(-)}(x_\mu'), \quad \bar{\psi}_\rho^{(+)}(x_\mu)\bar{\psi}_{\rho'}^{(-)}(x_\mu') \quad (\text{for } x_0 > x_0')$$

are related to the *causal* propagation of the field. However, it follows from the anti-commutators (34) and from eqn. (54) that both

$$\psi^{(+)}(x_\mu)\psi^{(-)}(x_\mu')|0\rangle \quad \text{and} \quad \bar{\psi}^{(+)}(x_\mu)\bar{\psi}^{(-)}(x_\mu')|0\rangle$$

vanish; these pairs of operators cannot form propagators, because they describe the creation of a fermion and the subsequent destruction of an anti-fermion, or vice versa. We are left with $\langle 0|\bar{\psi}_\rho^{(+)}(x_\mu)\psi_{\rho'}^{(-)}(x_\mu')|0\rangle$ and $\langle 0|\psi_\rho^{(+)}(x_\mu)\bar{\psi}_{\rho'}^{(-)}(x_\mu')|0\rangle$ where $x_0 > x_0'$. Both of these functions can be obtained from a chronological product.

† Definition (53) follows from $n^{(s)}(\mathbf{k}, \pm)|0\rangle = 0$, because

$$\langle 0|n^{(s)}(\mathbf{k}, +)|0\rangle = |c^{(s)}(\mathbf{k})|0\rangle|^2, \quad \text{etc.}$$

‡ In each case the property $\det(\gamma^4) = \pm 1$ is used to rewrite the equations in the form (55).

§ $\tilde{c}|0\rangle$ is normalized because $\langle 0|c\tilde{c}|0\rangle = \langle 0|1-\tilde{c}c|0\rangle = \langle 0|0\rangle$. Similarly, $\tilde{d}|0\rangle$ and the general state vector (56) are normalized.

The chronological product

For the fermion field operators the chronological product
$$T\{A(x_\mu)B(x'_\mu)\}$$
is defined by
$$T\{A(x_\mu)B(x'_\mu)\} = \begin{cases} A(x_\mu)B(x'_\mu) & (x_0 > x'_0) \\ -B(x'_\mu)A(x_\mu) & (x_0 < x'_0) \end{cases}, \tag{57}$$
where $A(x_\mu)$ denotes $\psi_\rho(x_\mu)$ or $\bar{\psi}_\rho(x_\mu)$ and $B(x'_\mu)$ denotes $\psi_{\rho'}(x'_\mu)$ or $\bar{\psi}_{\rho'}(x'_\mu)$. It is necessary to have the change of sign on the right of (57) for $x_0 < x'_0$, if the chronological product is to be uniquely defined for any Lorentz frame of reference. In the region of space-like separation $(x_\mu - x'_\mu)^2 > 0$, the anti-commutators (16) and (17) show that
$$A(x_\mu)B(x'_\mu) = -B(x'_\mu)A(x_\mu).$$
Clearly $T\{A(x_\mu)B(x'_\mu)\} = -T\{B(x'_\mu)A(x_\mu)\}$ (any x_μ, x'_μ). (58)

Using (54) and (55) we get
$$\langle 0|T\{\psi_\rho(x_\mu)\bar{\psi}_{\rho'}(x'_\mu)\}|0\rangle = \begin{cases} \langle 0|\psi_\rho^{(+)}(x_\mu)\bar{\psi}_{\rho'}^{(-)}(x'_\mu)|0\rangle & (x_0 > x'_0) \\ -\langle 0|\bar{\psi}_{\rho'}^{(+)}(x'_\mu)\psi_\rho^{(-)}(x_\mu)|0\rangle & (x_0 < x'_0). \end{cases} \tag{59}$$

It will now be proved that the expectation value (59) is a causal Green's function for the solution of the inhomogeneous Dirac equation. It obeys†
$$(\gamma^\mu \partial_{x\mu} + \kappa)_{\rho''\rho} \langle 0|T\{\psi_\rho(x_\mu)\bar{\psi}_{\rho'}(x'_\mu)\}|0\rangle = -i\delta_{\rho''\rho'}\delta^4(x_\mu - x'_\mu), \tag{60}$$
where summation over the repeated suffix ρ is understood. This inhomogeneous Dirac equation will describe the propagation of the Dirac field from the sources where it is created (in (60) the source is concentrated at the space-time point x'_μ). This equation and its solutions are discussed in the Appendix.

By eqn. (8),
$$(\gamma^\mu \partial_{x\mu} + \kappa)_{\rho''\rho} T\{\psi_\rho(x_\mu)\bar{\psi}_{\rho'}(x'_\mu)\} = 0 \quad \text{for } x'_\mu \neq x_\mu. \tag{61}$$
The value for $x_\mu = x'_\mu$ is found by integrating the left-hand side of (61) over the small space-time region between the planes $t = t' \pm \epsilon$, where ϵ is positive and small. The only contribution to this integral which does not vanish as ϵ tends to zero is (by (17) and (15))
$$\begin{aligned} \int d^4x_\mu\, \gamma^4_{\rho''\rho}\partial_4\, T\{\psi_\rho(x_\mu)\bar{\psi}_{\rho'}(x'_\mu)\} &= -i \int d^3\mathbf{x}\, \gamma^4_{\rho''\rho}\{\psi_\rho(\mathbf{x}, t'+\epsilon)\bar{\psi}_{\rho'}(\mathbf{x}', t') + \\ &\qquad + \bar{\psi}_{\rho'}(\mathbf{x}', t')\psi_\rho(\mathbf{x}, t'-\epsilon)\} \\ &= -i \int d^3\mathbf{x}\, \delta_{\rho''\rho'}\delta^3(\mathbf{x}-\mathbf{x}') \\ &= -i\delta_{\rho''\rho'}. \end{aligned}$$
Eqn. (60) follows.

† $\delta^4(x_\mu) = \delta(x_0)\delta(x_1)\delta(x_2)\delta(x_3)$, where $x_0 = ct$.

The function $\langle 0|T\{\psi_\rho(x_\mu)\bar{\psi}_{\rho'}(x'_\mu)\}|0\rangle$ is a causal function because, for $x_0 > x'_0$ it equals the positive frequency function $(-i)S^{(+)}_{\rho\rho'}(x-x')$, and for $x_0 < x'_0$ it equals $iS^{(-)}_{\rho\rho'}(x-x')$. Eqn. (59) shows that these statements are true. This causal property determines the Green's function, and comparing with (A.89), (A.98) we see that

$$\langle 0|T\{\psi_\rho(x_\mu)\bar{\psi}_{\rho'}(x'_\mu)\}|0\rangle = -\tfrac{1}{2}\{S_F(x_\mu-x'_\mu)\}_{\rho\rho'}, \tag{62}$$

where
$$S_F(x_\nu) = (\gamma^\mu\partial_\mu-\kappa)D_{F(\kappa)}(x_\nu) \tag{63}$$

and $D_{F(\kappa)}(x_\nu)$ is the causal Green's function for pions which is given in (2.63) and in the Appendix.

Using (58) the function $\langle 0|T\{\bar{\psi}_\rho(x_\mu)\psi_{\rho'}(x'_\mu)\}|0\rangle$ is seen to be a Green's function; however, it is more naturally related (as a function of x_μ) to the adjoint equation. It is easy to show that

$$\langle 0|T\{\bar{\psi}_\rho(x_\mu)\psi_{\rho'}(x'_\mu)\}|0\rangle(\gamma^\mu_{\rho\rho''}\overleftarrow{\partial}_{x_\mu}-\kappa) = -i\delta_{\rho'\rho''}, \tag{64}$$

where $\overleftarrow{\partial}_{x_\mu}$ acts to the left on any function of x_μ.† Therefore this function is the causal Green's function for the adjoint inhomogeneous Dirac equation. With these vacuum expectation values of the chronologically ordered operator pairs we can describe completely the propagation properties of the quantized free (spin-$\tfrac{1}{2}$) fermion field.

5. Charge conjugation; positronium decay

In Chapter III, § 11, it was shown that, in spite of first appearances, the charge of the fermion entered the classical Dirac theory in a symmetric way; it was unimportant whether we started from positive or negative particles. This symmetry was put in evidence by using the charge conjugation 4×4 matrix C. The properties of C which are important for the present section are (3.83), (3.84), and (3.85). To each (unquantized) four-component *wave function* $\psi(x_\mu)$ which satisfies Dirac's equation for a particle of charge e in the presence of an electromagnetic field, there corresponds a solution $\psi_c(x_\mu)$ of Dirac's equation for a particle of charge $(-e)$ in the same electromagnetic field. They are related by‡

$$\psi_c(x_\mu) = C\bar{\psi}_T(x_\mu) = C\gamma^4_T\psi^*(x_\mu). \tag{65}$$

We may call $\psi(x_\mu)$ and $\psi_c(x_\mu)$ the fermion and anti-fermion solutions. When there is no electromagnetic field present, $\psi(x_\mu)$ and $\psi_c(x_\mu)$ both

† Eqns. (12), (17), and (15) are used in proving (64).

‡ T denotes the transpose, * denotes the complex conjugate. ψ, ψ_c, ψ^*, $\bar{\psi}_T$ are column vectors.

obey the same Dirac equation (3.1). Because ψ_c is proportional to ψ^*, it follows that if $\psi(x_\mu)$ is written in the form

$$\psi(x_\mu) = w(k_\mu)e^{ik_\mu x_\mu},$$

then $\psi_c(x_\mu)$ is of the form

$$\psi_c(x_\mu) = w'(-k_\mu)e^{-ik_\mu x_\mu}.$$

Here $w(k_\mu)$, $w'(-k_\mu)$ are constant spinors obeying

$$(i\gamma^\mu k_\mu+\kappa)w(k_\mu) = 0, \qquad (-i\gamma^\mu k_\mu+\kappa)w'(-k_\mu) = 0.$$

Comparing with eqns. (18) and (19) above, we have the example

$$\psi(x_\mu) = u^{(s)}(\mathbf{k})e^{ik_\mu x_\mu}, \qquad \psi_c(x_\mu) = v^{(s)}(\mathbf{k})e^{-ik_\mu x_\mu}. \tag{66}$$

From (65) it follows that

$$u^{(s)}(\mathbf{k}) = C\bar{v}_T^{(s)}(\mathbf{k}), \qquad \bar{v}^{(s)}(\mathbf{k}) = \{C^{-1}u^{(s)}(\mathbf{k})\}_T. \tag{67}$$

Using (3.84), we see that $u^{(s)}(\mathbf{k})$, $v^{(s)}(\mathbf{k})$ have the correct spin dependence for (67)† (cf. eqn. (42)). Thus the spinors $u^{(s)}(\mathbf{k})$, $v^{(s)}(\mathbf{k})$ defined by (19) and (42) are charge conjugate to each other.

The charge conjugation operation

For any assembly of particles the *operation*‡ of charge conjugation C consists in changing the sign of the charge and the magnetic moment of each particle, while their mechanical properties are left unaltered. Individual particles which are related to each other in this way are called particle anti-particle pairs. Apart from the weak decay processes, such as β-decay mentioned in Chapter III, §§ 14, 15, the laws of elementary particle physics appear to be the same for any assembly of particles as they are for the corresponding anti-particle system. As is discussed in Chapter VII, § 5, any violation of this symmetry between 'particle laws' and 'anti-particle laws' is apt to be associated with right–left asymmetry. Such asymmetry has not been observed except for the weak decay processes; if for the present we ignore such processes, we shall require the Hamiltonian for interacting electromagnetic, electron, pion, nucleon, and other fields to be invariant under the charge conjugation operation C. The same must be true for the momentum operator $\mathbf{P}$, the angular momentum $\mathbf{M}$, the spin component $\mathbf{M}^{\mathrm{sp}}_{\mathrm{long}}$, etc.§ The total charge Q must, of course, anti-commute with C.

† This is because $[\gamma^\mu, \gamma^\nu]u^{(s)}(\mathbf{k}) = [\gamma^\mu, \gamma^\nu]C\bar{v}_T^{(s)} = -C[\gamma^\mu, \gamma^\nu]_T\bar{v}_T^{(s)}$. From (3.10), if $\frac{1}{2}\sigma^{12}u^{(s)}(\mathbf{k}) = s\hbar u^{(s)}(\mathbf{k})$, then $\frac{1}{2}\bar{v}^{(s)}(\mathbf{k})\sigma^{12} = -s\hbar\bar{v}^{(s)}(\mathbf{k})$.

‡ The operation of charge conjugation C should not be confused with the 4×4 matrix C (eqn. 65) of the unquantized theory.

§ The neutrino is an exception and is not to be included in the discussions of this section. The two-component theory of Chapter III, § 16, shows that the neutrino spin reverses on going over to the anti-particle.

With these assumptions, C is a constant of motion; it can be used to classify eigenstates and give absolute selection rules. Applying the charge conjugation operation twice gives the identity operation, so $\mathsf{C}^2 = 1$; therefore the only eigenvalues of C are $\mathsf{C}' = \pm 1$. Obviously any eigenstate of C must involve equal numbers of particles and anti-particles.

Now we consider the case of a quantized fermion field. First we discuss briefly the fermion field when an electromagnetic field is present. The field operator $\psi(x_\mu)$ and its adjoint $\bar{\psi}(x_\mu)$ obey the eqns. (3.6), (3.24)†,

$$\left.\begin{aligned} \gamma^\mu\left(\partial_\mu - \frac{ie}{\hbar c}A_\mu(x_\nu)\right)\psi(x_\nu) + \kappa\psi(x_\nu) &= 0 \\ \left(\partial_\mu + \frac{ie}{\hbar c}A_\mu(x_\nu)\right)\bar{\psi}(x_\nu)\gamma^\mu - \kappa\bar{\psi}(x_\nu) &= 0 \end{aligned}\right\}. \tag{68}$$

Here $A_\mu(x_\nu)$ is the electromagnetic field operator and e is the charge of the fermion. (A modified equation should be used for the neutron.‡) For convenience we denote by U that part of the charge conjugation operator C which acts on the fermion and the electromagnetic fields.§

Let us denote any state vector for this system by $|\,\rangle$. Then $U|\,\rangle$ gives the state in which the sign of charge of all particles is reversed. In this way we get a unitary|| transformation of all state vectors; there is a corresponding unitary transformation of the field operators. The *transformed operators* are written

$$\psi_c(x_\mu) = U\psi(x_\mu)U^{-1}, \quad \bar{\psi}_c(x_\mu) = U\bar{\psi}(x_\mu)U^{-1}, \quad A^c_\mu(x_\nu) = UA_\mu(x_\nu)U^{-1}. \tag{69}$$

By (69), the matrix element $\langle b|\psi(x_\mu)|a\rangle$ of $\psi(x_\mu)$ between any pair of states $|a\rangle$, $|b\rangle$ equals the matrix element $\langle b|\tilde{U}.\psi_c(x_\mu).U|a\rangle$ of $\psi_c(x_\mu)$ between the charge conjugate states $U|a\rangle$, $U|b\rangle$. Therefore ψ_c is obtained from ψ by reversing the charge properties; in particular $\psi_c(x_\mu)$ must obey the equation

$$\gamma^\mu\left(\partial_\mu + \frac{ie}{\hbar c}A_\mu(x_\nu)\right)\psi_c(x_\nu) + \kappa\psi_c(x_\nu) = 0. \tag{70}$$

It follows from the argument in Chapter III, § 11, that (70) is satisfied if

$$\psi_c(x_\mu) = C\bar{\psi}_T(x_\mu), \tag{71}$$

† From here on we assume the fermion has charge e and potential energy $e\phi$.

‡ A modified equation must be used for any fermion having an anomalous magnetic moment.

§ This avoids the danger of confusing the operator C and the 4×4 matrix C.

|| U must be unitary, because charge conjugation will not destroy the normal-orthogonal property of the state vectors.

where C is the constant 4×4 matrix (cf. eqn. (3.83)) and the notation $\bar{\psi}_T$ indicates that the four operators in $\bar{\psi}$ are written as a column vector. A similar argument shows that

$$\bar{\psi}_c(x_\mu) = \{C^{-1}\psi(x_\mu)\}_T, \tag{72}$$

where the notation ψ_T indicates that the four operators in ψ are to be written as a row vector.

Eqn. (70) should result from the first equation of (68) by applying the unitary transformation (69). This requires that

$$UA_\mu(x_\nu)U^{-1} = -A_\mu(x_\nu). \tag{73}$$

Now we return to the case of non-interacting fields. Because $\psi^{(+)}(x_\mu)$, $\bar{\psi}^{(-)}(x_\mu)$ destroy and create fermions, $\psi_c^{(+)}(x_\mu)$, $\bar{\psi}_c^{(-)}(x_\mu)$ should destroy and create anti-fermions; using (71) and (72) and taking positive and negative frequency parts, this is seen to be true. Similarly, $\bar{\psi}_c^{(+)}(x_\mu)$, $\psi_c^{(-)}(x_\mu)$ destroy and create fermions. Comparing (69) with (71) and (72) and using (67), requires that†

$$\left.\begin{aligned} Uc^{(s)}(\mathbf{k})U^{-1} &= d^{(s)}(\mathbf{k}), \qquad & Ud^{(s)}(\mathbf{k})U^{-1} &= c^{(s)}(\mathbf{k}) \\ U\tilde{c}^{(s)}(\mathbf{k})U^{-1} &= \tilde{d}^{(s)}(\mathbf{k}), \qquad & U\tilde{d}^{(s)}(\mathbf{k})U^{-1} &= \tilde{c}^{(s)}(\mathbf{k}) \end{aligned}\right\}. \tag{74}$$

The physical interpretation of (74) is obvious.‡

Because there is no charge distribution in the vacuum state of the non-interacting fields, this state $|0\rangle$ should be unaltered by charge conjugation. Thus we have§

$$U|0\rangle = |0\rangle. \tag{75}$$

If a fermion and an anti-fermion have the same momentum $\hbar\mathbf{k}$ and the same spin $s\hbar$, their state vector $\tilde{c}^{(s)}(\mathbf{k})\tilde{d}^{(s)}(\mathbf{k})|0\rangle$ is an eigenstate of the charge conjugation operator U with the eigenvalue (-1); the charge-conjugation operator exchanges the charge, and the anti-symmetric character of the state vector requires this change of sign. Eqn. (73) shows that any state vector describing N photons is an eigenstate of the charge conjugation operator with the eigenvalue $(-1)^N$. Because the Hamiltonians describing the interactions between fields commute with the charge conjugation operator, the statements made in this

† For the free field, the relations (69) can be split uniquely into positive and negative frequency parts.

‡ Eqns. (74) have been given by L. Wolfenstein and D. G. Ravenhall, *Phys. Rev.* **88** (1952) 279. These equations make it possible to write down explicitly that part of U which acts on fermions:

$$U = \pm\prod_{s,\mathbf{k}}\{1-\tilde{c}^{(s)}(\mathbf{k})c^{(s)}(\mathbf{k})-\tilde{d}^{(s)}(\mathbf{k})d^{(s)}(\mathbf{k})+\tilde{c}^{(s)}(\mathbf{k})d^{(s)}(\mathbf{k})+\tilde{d}^{(s)}(\mathbf{k})c^{(s)}(\mathbf{k})\} = U^{-1}.$$

§ Only the *change* in the charge conjugation eigenvalue C' enters the conservation law. We could have used $U|0\rangle = -|0\rangle$, but (75) is more convenient.

paragraph are still valid if interactions between the particles are included.†

Positronium decay

The electron field and the electromagnetic field are, of course, invariant under charge conjugation, and positronium decay provides a good example of a charge conjugation selection rule. Positronium, which consists of an electron and a positron bound together,‡ is an eigenstate of U because it is unaltered on reversing the charges (and magnetic moments). The ${}^3S_1$ state of positronium is symmetric in spin and orbital motion, therefore it is anti-symmetric in charge and it has the eigenvalue $C' = -1$; similarly the ${}^1S_0$ state has $C' = +1$. Hence on annihilation the ${}^3S_1$ state gives an odd number of photons and ${}^1S_0$ an even number. The ${}^1S_0$ state decays by two-photon emission with a mean life of $1{\cdot}2\times 10^{-10}$ sec; the ${}^3S_1$ state has a longer mean life ($1{\cdot}4\times 10^{-7}$ sec)§ because it annihilates into three photons.

It is of interest to notice that the S-states of positronium have odd parity, because of the opposite intrinsic parity of the electron and the positron (Chapter III, § 6). It is shown in Chapter VII, § 1, that if a particle of zero spin and odd parity annihilates to give two γ-rays, these must have perpendicular polarization. This perpendicular polarization of the γ-rays from ${}^1S_0$ positronium has been observed.‖

Charge symmetric formulation

This section is concluded by showing how the Hamiltonian (10), the momentum operator $\mathbf{P}$ (eqn. (29)), and the total charge Q (eqn. (31)) for the non-interacting fermion field can be written in an obviously charge conjugate form.†† Instead of developing the theory of fermion field quantization by using the operators $\psi(x_\mu)$, $\bar{\psi}(x_\mu)$, it would have been possible to use the operators $\psi_c(x_\mu)$, $\bar{\psi}_c(x_\mu)$. From (69), (16), and (17), these operators have the anti-commutation relations‡‡

$$\left.\begin{aligned}[\psi_{c\rho}(x_\nu),\psi_{c\rho'}(x'_\nu)]_+ &= [\bar{\psi}_{c\rho}(x_\nu),\bar{\psi}_{c\rho'}(x'_\nu)]_+ = 0\\ [\psi_{c\rho'}(x'_\nu),\bar{\psi}_{c\rho}(x_\nu)]_+ &= -iS_{\rho'\rho}(x'_\nu-x_\nu)\end{aligned}\right\}. \tag{76}$$

† i.e. we can replace the bare particle states by real particle states. Switching on the interaction gradually cannot alter the eigenvalue C'.

‡ For a survey of positronium see S. De Benedetti and H. C. Corben, *Ann. Rev. Nuclear Sci.* **4** (Annual Reviews Inc., Stanford, Cal., 1954); S. De Benedetti, *Suppl. Nuovo Cim.* **3** (1956) 1209.

§ The small coupling constant $(e^2/4\pi\hbar c)$ and the smaller volume of phase space give the much longer lifetime of ${}^3S_1$.

‖ R. C. Hanna, *Nature,* **162** (1948) 332; C. S. Wu and I. Shaknov, *Phys. Rev.* **77** (1950) 136.

†† J. Schwinger, *Phys. Rev.* **74** (1948) 1439.

‡‡ A. Pais and R. Jost, *Phys. Rev.* **87** (1952) 871.

The analysis in terms of creation and annihilation operators could be developed directly from (76). This would give the same results as §§ 3 and 4, apart from exchanging the role of fermions and anti-fermions.

Because the matrix C obeys $C_T = -C$,† eqns. (71), (72) give

$$\left.\begin{aligned} \bar{\psi}_c(x_\mu)\psi_c(x'_\mu) &= -\psi_T(x_\mu)\bar{\psi}_T(x'_\mu) \\ \bar{\psi}_c(x_\mu)\gamma^\nu\psi_c(x'_\mu) &= \psi_T(x_\mu)\gamma^\nu_T\bar{\psi}_T(x'_\mu) \\ \bar{\psi}_c(x_\mu)\gamma^\nu\gamma^\lambda\psi_c(x'_\mu) &= -\psi_T(x_\mu)\gamma^\nu_T\gamma^\lambda_T\bar{\psi}_T(x'_\mu) \\ \bar{\psi}_c(x_\mu)\gamma^5\psi_c(x'_\mu) &= -\psi_T(x_\mu)\gamma^5_T\bar{\psi}_T(x'_\mu) \end{aligned}\right\}, \tag{77}$$

also $$-\psi_T(x_\mu)\bar{\psi}_T(x'_\mu) = \bar{\psi}(x'_\mu)\psi(x_\mu) + i\sum_\rho S_{\rho\rho}(x_\mu - x'_\mu).$$

Therefore, on ignoring an (infinite) constant number, eqns. (10), (29), and (31) can be written‡

$$\mathbf{H} = \tfrac{1}{2}\hbar c\int d^3\mathbf{x}\,\{\bar{\psi}(\mathbf{x},t)(\boldsymbol{\gamma}.\mathrm{grad})\psi(\mathbf{x},t) + \kappa\bar{\psi}(\mathbf{x},t)\psi(\mathbf{x},t) + \\ + \bar{\psi}_c(\mathbf{x},t)(\boldsymbol{\gamma}.\mathrm{grad})\psi_c(\mathbf{x},t) + \kappa\bar{\psi}_c(\mathbf{x},t)\psi_c(\mathbf{x},t)\}, \tag{78}$$

$$\mathbf{P} = \frac{\hbar}{4i}\int d^3\mathbf{x}\,[\bar{\psi}(\mathbf{x},t)\gamma^4\,\mathrm{grad}\,\psi(\mathbf{x},t) - \{\mathrm{grad}\,\bar{\psi}(\mathbf{x},t)\}\gamma^4\,\psi(\mathbf{x},t) + \\ + \bar{\psi}_c(\mathbf{x},t)\gamma^4\,\mathrm{grad}\,\psi_c(\mathbf{x},t) - \{\mathrm{grad}\,\bar{\psi}_c(\mathbf{x},t)\}\gamma^4\psi_c(\mathbf{x},t)\}, \tag{79}$$

$$Q = \tfrac{1}{2}e\int d^3\mathbf{x}\,\{\bar{\psi}(\mathbf{x},t)\gamma^4\psi(\mathbf{x},t) - \bar{\psi}_c(\mathbf{x},t)\gamma^4\psi_c(\mathbf{x},t)\}. \tag{80}$$

These expressions are obviously in charge conjugate form.§ The charge conjugation operation clearly leaves $\mathbf{H}$ and $\mathbf{P}$ unchanged and reverses the sign of Q. Eqns. (78) to (80) give zero eigenvalues of energy, momentum, and charge for the vacuum.

6. Interacting fields: general remarks

The relativistic quantum theory of interacting fields is developed from a Lorentz invariant Lagrangian density $\mathscr{L}$ by the general formalism which is given in Chapter IX; this is a straightforward extension of the formalism which was used in Chapter II for quantizing boson fields, and at the beginning of the present chapter to quantize the Dirac field.

We assume that the independent field variables at time t are $\phi_B^{(\alpha)}(\mathbf{x},t)$

† See Chapter III, § 11.

‡ In deriving (78) and (79) it is necessary to integrate by parts. The infinite constant which is neglected in (78), (79), and (80) could have no effect on the quantum behaviour of the field.

§ The charge-current 4-vector is

$$j_\mu(x_\nu) = \tfrac{1}{2}iec\{\bar{\psi}(x_\nu)\gamma^\mu\psi(x_\nu) - \bar{\psi}_c(x_\nu)\gamma^\mu\psi_c(x_\nu)\}.$$

for the boson fields, and $\phi_F^{(\beta)}(\mathbf{x},t)$ for the fermion fields. The canonical momentum densities $\pi_B^{(\alpha)}(\mathbf{x},t)$, $\pi_F^{(\beta)}(\mathbf{x},t)$ are defined by the usual formulae:

$$\pi_B^{(\alpha)} = \partial\mathscr{L}/\partial\dot{\phi}_B^{(\alpha)}, \qquad \pi_F^{(\beta)} = \partial\mathscr{L}/\partial\dot{\phi}_F^{(\beta)}. \tag{81}$$

The canonical commutation rules for the field operators follow directly from the general formalism of Chapter IX. They are (cf. eqns. (6), (7) above, and (9.54), (9.57)):

$$\left.\begin{aligned}[\pi_B^{(\alpha)}(\mathbf{x},t),\phi_B^{(\alpha')}(\mathbf{x}',t)] &= (\hbar/i)\delta_{\alpha\alpha'}\,\delta^3(\mathbf{x}-\mathbf{x}')\\ [\pi_B^{(\alpha)}(\mathbf{x},t),\pi_B^{(\alpha')}(\mathbf{x}',t)] &= [\phi_B^{(\alpha)}(\mathbf{x},t),\phi_B^{(\alpha')}(\mathbf{x}',t)] = 0\end{aligned}\right\}; \tag{82}$$

$$\left.\begin{aligned}[\pi_F^{(\beta)}(\mathbf{x},t),\phi_F^{(\beta')}(\mathbf{x}',t)]_+ &= -(\hbar/i)\delta_{\beta\beta'}\,\delta^3(\mathbf{x}-\mathbf{x}')\\ [\pi_F^{(\beta)}(\mathbf{x},t),\pi_F^{(\beta')}(\mathbf{x}',t)]_+ &= [\phi_F^{(\beta)}(\mathbf{x},t),\phi_F^{(\beta')}(\mathbf{x}',t)]_+ = 0\end{aligned}\right\}. \tag{83}$$

Also, all fermion variables commute with all boson variables at the same time t.

The Hamiltonian operator H can be derived from the Lagrangian density in the standard way, and the Heisenberg equations of motion for the field variables are set up. The equations of motion, or the propagation equations, for interacting fields are in general much more complicated than the propagation equations for the free fields. Hence it is not possible to use the simple Green's function technique to write down the general field commutators (analogous to (2.27) and (16), (17) above). These general field commutators (e.g. $[\phi_B^{(\alpha)}(x_\mu),\phi_B^{(\alpha')}(x'_\mu)]$, $[\phi_F^{(\beta)}(x_\mu),\phi_F^{(\beta')}(x'_\mu)]_+$, etc.) will usually be complicated operator expressions, in contrast with the commutators or anti-commutators of the non-interacting fields, which are numbers. The physical reason for this is that the commutators (or anti-commutators) give a measure of the effect of disturbances of the fields at (x_μ) on the field amplitudes at (x'_μ);† a disturbance in one field at (x_μ) may produce new particles in the other fields at (x'_μ). Such effects are properly described by operators.

Neutral pions and nucleons

As an example of the quantization method we discuss the interaction of uncharged pseudo-scalar pions with protons (or neutrons). The Lagrangian density $\mathscr{L}$ is given by

$$\mathscr{L} = \mathscr{L}_P+\mathscr{L}_\pi+\mathscr{L}_{\text{int}}, \tag{84}$$

† This can be seen either, (i) from the well-known relation between the commutator $[A,B]$ and the uncertainty measure $\Delta A\,.\,\Delta B$ (for details of the field case see W. Heitler, *Quantum Theory of Radiation* (Clarendon Press, 3rd edn., 1954)), or (ii) from Peierls's general interpretation of Poisson brackets (R. E. Peierls, *Proc. Roy. Soc.* A, 214 (1952) 143).

where $\mathscr{L}_P$ and $\mathscr{L}_\pi$ are the Lagrangian densities for protons and neutral pions given by (3.25) and (2.18). The interaction term $\mathscr{L}_{\text{int}}$ has to be a Lorentz invariant Hermitian function of the variables of both fields. The commonly used form giving pseudo-scalar coupling is†

$$\mathscr{L}_{\text{int}} = -ig\bar{\psi}(x_\mu)\gamma^5\psi(x_\mu)\phi(x_\mu). \tag{85}$$

Here g is the (real) coupling constant. A pseudo-vector coupling between the fields is given by‡

$$\mathscr{L}_{\text{int}} = i(f/\mu)\bar{\psi}(x_\lambda)\gamma^\nu\gamma^5\psi(x_\lambda)\,\partial_\nu\,\phi(x_\lambda). \tag{86}$$

The presence of the 4×4 matrix γ^5 in (85) and (86) ensures that the interaction is invariant under a transition from a right-handed to a left-handed axes system; this gives a parity-conserving interaction. It should be noted that if the Lagrangian includes (85), the canonical momenta $\pi(x_\mu)$ have the same form as for the free fields. With (86) this is no longer so, because $\dot{\phi}(x_\mu)$ occurs in $\mathscr{L}_{\text{int}}$; the field commutators (82), (83) are then only valid if the new form of the pion canonical momentum $\pi(\mathbf{x}, t)$ is used.

It appears that neutral pions and protons have a pseudo-scalar interaction as given by (85); and the discussion is now restricted to this case. The Hamiltonian becomes

$$H = H_P + H_\pi + H_{\text{int}}, \tag{87}$$

where H_P and H_π have the same form as in eqn. (10) above and eqn. (2.20); also

$$H_{\text{int}} = ig\int d^3\mathbf{x}\,\phi(\mathbf{x}, t)\bar{\psi}(\mathbf{x}, t)\gamma^5\psi(\mathbf{x}, t). \tag{88}$$

On quantizing, the field variables *at one time t* obey the same commutation relations as the non-interacting fields:§

$$\left.\begin{aligned} [\phi(\mathbf{x}, t), \phi(\mathbf{x}', t)] = 0, \qquad [\pi(\mathbf{x}, t), \pi(\mathbf{x}', t)] = 0 \\ [\pi(\mathbf{x}, t), \phi(\mathbf{x}', t)] = (\hbar/i)\delta^3(\mathbf{x}-\mathbf{x}') \\ [\psi(\mathbf{x}, t), \psi(\mathbf{x}', t)]_+ = 0, \qquad [\bar{\psi}(\mathbf{x}, t), \bar{\psi}(\mathbf{x}', t)]_+ = 0 \\ [\bar{\psi}_\rho(\mathbf{x}, t), \psi_{\rho'}(\mathbf{x}', t)]_+ = \delta_{\rho\rho'}\delta^3(\mathbf{x}-\mathbf{x}') \end{aligned}\right\}, \tag{89}$$

where $\pi(\mathbf{x}, t) = \dot{\phi}(\mathbf{x}, t)$. Also, any pion variable commutes with any proton variable at the same time.

Using the Heisenberg representation, in which the state vectors are

† The factor $(-i)$ is required to make $\mathscr{L}_{\text{int}}$ Hermitian. The presence of both $\bar{\psi}$ and ψ ensures that in operator form $\mathscr{L}$ only has terms which leave unaltered N = (no. of protons)−(no. of anti-protons). (Cf. § 11 below.)

‡ The inverse pion Compton wavelength $\mu = m_\pi c/\hbar$ is introduced to give f the same dimensions as g.

§ This follows from (82), (83), and (85).

constant (in space and time), the Heisenberg equation of motion (11) gives the propagation equations for the field operators;†

$$\left.\begin{aligned} (\partial_\nu^2-\mu^2)\phi(x_\lambda) &= i(g/c^2)\bar{\psi}(x_\lambda)\gamma^5\psi(x_\lambda) \\ (\gamma^\nu\partial_\nu+\kappa)\psi(x_\lambda) &= (-ig/\hbar c)\gamma^5\psi(x_\lambda)\phi(x_\lambda) \\ \partial_\nu\bar{\psi}(x_\lambda)\gamma^\nu-\kappa\bar{\psi}(x_\lambda) &= (ig/\hbar c)\bar{\psi}(x_\lambda)\gamma^5\phi(x_\lambda) \end{aligned}\right\}. \tag{90}$$

The commutators and anti-commutators (89) are derived from the quantum theory form of the action principle (see Chapter IX); therefore these relations hold for any value of the common time t, and consequently the equations of motion (90) hold for all x_μ.‡

The action principle method is covariant, therefore several of the relations (89) can immediately be extended to any two space-time points x_μ, x'_μ having a space-like separation $[(x_\mu-x'_\mu)^2 > 0]$.§ In particular,

$$\left.\begin{aligned} [\phi(x_\mu),\phi(x'_\mu)] &= 0, \qquad [\bar{\psi}(x_\mu),\psi(x'_\mu)]_+ = 0 \\ [\psi(x_\mu),\psi(x'_\mu)]_+ &= 0, \qquad [\bar{\psi}(x_\mu),\bar{\psi}(x'_\mu)]_+ = 0 \end{aligned}\right\}. \tag{91}$$

Also, any pion variable at x_μ commutes with any proton variable at x'_μ. These commutation rules (91) are necessary in order that physical quantities‖ at points having a space-like separation should commute. If this were not so, we should find that measurements at points having a space-like separation would interfere with each other.

The solution of the quantum field equations (90), in contrast with the free field case, meets with considerable difficulties. For non-interacting fields, the field operators were expanded (by (2.30) and (20) above) in terms of the simple plane-wave solutions $f(x_\lambda)$, $w(x_\lambda)$ of the equations

$$(\partial_\nu^2-\mu^2)f(x_\lambda) = 0, \qquad (\gamma^\nu\partial_\nu+\kappa)w(x_\lambda) = 0.$$

This expansion is no longer possible, and the simple techniques which were used to derive the particle aspect for boson and fermion fields are no longer applicable for interacting fields. These remarks apply equally to any quantized interacting fields, and we shall return now to the discussion of the general case.

Comparatively few problems of interacting fields can be solved by

† The Compton wavelengths of the pion and the nucleon are μ^{-1} and κ^{-1} respectively.

‡ The older method for obtaining this result was: (*a*) assume (89) for one value of t; (*b*) assume any variable $A(t)$ obeys

$$A(t') = \exp[i(t'-t)H/\hbar]A(t)\exp[i(t-t')H/\hbar].$$

Hence (89) holds for all t'.

§ The relations involving π generalize to relations containing the derivative of ϕ in the direction normal to the space-like surface.

‖ Physical quantities containing fermion variables must be bilinear in $\bar{\psi}$, ψ (cf. § 2).

exact methods,† and in general approximation methods must be used. Two very important approximation methods will be described in the following sections. The first is an application of time-dependent perturbation theory; in the second, approximate eigenstates of the *total* Hamiltonian are used. A survey of the difficulties which occur in the application of these methods is given in § 9.

7. Perturbation theory for interacting fields: the interaction representation

Consider two interacting quantized fields '1' and '2' which have the total Hamiltonian

$$H = H_1+H_2+H_{\text{int}}, \tag{92}$$

where H_1, H_2 are the free-field Hamiltonians and H_{int} is the interaction term. Time-dependent perturbation theory may be used to investigate collisions between real particles, provided the Hamiltonian (92) is replaced by

$$H'(t) = H_1+H_2+H_{\text{int}}.\exp(-|t|/\tau), \tag{93}$$

where τ is a very large positive constant. In $H'(t)$ the interaction is gradually *switched on* and subsequently it is gradually *switched off*. The initial states ($t \to -\infty$) and the final states ($t \to +\infty$) are eigenstates of the free particle Hamiltonian H_1+H_2; therefore the initial and final states describe bare particles. It is assumed that τ is so large that the switching-on and switching-off are *adiabatic*; by this we mean that no particles are either created or destroyed by the switching processes themselves.‡

Suppose an initial state is chosen such that the individual incoming particles are described by wave packets of finite extent, and there is no overlap between these wave packets before the interaction has been fully switched on. In this case the switching-on process converts the bare incoming particles into real incoming particles before they collide; e.g. a bare incoming nucleon is converted into a real incoming nucleon (having the same mean momentum and spin) which is surrounded by

† Examples of exact solutions are: (i) vacuum polarization of the electron positron field (Chapter V, § 14); (ii) the emission of photons by a given (unquantized) current (see W. Thirring, *Quantenelektrodynamik* (F. Deuticke, Vienna, 1955), § 7); see also Chapter II, § 13 above, for the emission of low-frequency photons; (iii) neutral scalar mesons with scalar coupling to fixed sources (see L. van Hove, *Physica*, **18** (1952) 145, R. J. Glauber, *Phys. Rev.* **84** (1951) 395); (iv) neutral scalar mesons interacting in pairs with fixed sources (see G. Wentzel, *Helv. phys. Acta*, **25** (1952) 569, G. Morpurgo and B. F. Touschek, *Nuovo Cim.* **10** (1953) 1681; (v) Lee's theory (see T. D. Lee, *Phys. Rev.* **95** (1954) 1329).

‡ To ensure that the electromagnetic field behaved in an adiabatic way, it would be necessary to attribute a small non-zero rest mass (m) to all photons. The limit $m \to 0$ must be made at the end of the calculation.

its virtual pion field. Similarly, after the collision† the outgoing particles are real particles; if they have distinct velocities, the switching-off process ultimately yields the corresponding bare outgoing particles.‡ For the moment we assume that the collison does not lead to bound states. In this way, by using wave packets and the Hamiltonian $H'(t)$ (eqn. (93)), a precise physical picture of collision phenomena is obtained. The scattering cross-sections can be determined by applying time-dependent perturbation theory to find the transitions between the corresponding bare particle states.

A difficulty about using $H'(t)$ to calculate scattering cross-sections is that the results are not invariant under Lorentz transformations; also, the presence of the factor $\exp(-|t|/\tau)$ leads to complicated calculations.§ In order to carry out the renormalization programme it is desirable to have relativistically invariant results;‖ to achieve this, we take the limit $\tau \to \infty$ in (93) and think of the switching-on, and switching-off, occurring in the infinite past and the infinite future. The wave packets can now be limited to a very narrow spread of momenta, and they may without error be replaced by plane waves. A precise method for retaining the switching-on and switching-off process in the case $\tau \to \infty$ will be shown below.††

The interaction representation

Systematic and Lorentz invariant calculations for scattering problems are carried out with the aid of the *interaction representation* which will now be described. In the Heisenberg representation for two interacting fields, the Hamiltonian H (eqn. (92)) is a constant operator. However, H_1, H_2, and the interaction H_{int} in general vary with time. Any Heisenberg operator $A(t)$ (which is not explicitly time dependent) obeys

$$\partial A(t)/\partial t = (i/\hbar)[H_1(t)+H_2(t)+H_{\text{int}}(t), A(t)].$$

The interaction representation operator $\hat{A}(t)$ which corresponds to $A(t)$ is given by the unitary transformation

$$\hat{A}(t) = U(t)A(t)\tilde{U}(t). \tag{94}$$

The time dependence of the transformation operator $U(t)$ is chosen so

† It is assumed that the initial wave packets are so chosen that the collison occurs within the time interval $-\tau \leqslant t \leqslant \tau$.

‡ The use of wave packets in collision problems has been discussed by H. S. Snyder, *Phys. Rev.* **83** (1951) 1154.

§ F. J. Dyson, *Phys. Rev.* **83** (1951) 1207, has carried out calculations using a Hamiltonian of the form (93).

‖ See Chapter V, §§ 11–13.

†† Cf. Chapter V, § 1.

that the interaction representation operators vary with time in the same way as free field operators. This requires that $U(t)$ obeys

$$\frac{\partial U(t)}{\partial t} = -(i/\hbar)U(t)H_{\text{int}}(t), \tag{95}$$

so, by (94),

$$\frac{\partial \hat{A}(t)}{\partial t} = (i/\hbar)[\hat{H}_1+\hat{H}_2, \hat{A}(t)]. \tag{96}$$

The interaction representation operator $(\hat{H}_1+\hat{H}_2)$ is a constant.† A formal solution of (96) is

$$\hat{A}(t) = \exp\{i(t-t_0)(\hat{H}_1+\hat{H}_2)/\hbar\}\hat{A}(t_0)\exp\{-i(t-t_0)(\hat{H}_1+\hat{H}_2)/\hbar\}$$

for some fixed t_0.

The solution of the ordinary differential equation (95) is determined apart from an additive constant operator. It is possible to choose this constant so that the solution of (95) equals the identity operator at an arbitrary fixed time t_0. This solution will now be used; it is written $U(t,t_0)$, so

$$U(t,t_0) = I \quad \text{for } t = t_0. \tag{97}$$

The interaction representation operators are now identical with the Heisenberg operators at the time t_0.‡

The operator $U(t,t_0)$ is unitary on account of (95) and (97). For any time t,

$$\frac{\partial}{\partial t}\{U(t,t_0)\tilde{U}(t,t_0)\} = 0;$$

hence

$$U(t,t_0)\tilde{U}(t,t_0) = I. \tag{98}$$

Also

$$\frac{\partial}{\partial t}\{\tilde{U}(t,t_0)U(t,t_0)\} = -(i/\hbar)[\tilde{U}(t,t_0)U(t,t_0), H_{\text{int}}(t)],$$

so, by (97),

$$\frac{\partial}{\partial t}\{\tilde{U}(t,t_0)U(t,t_0)\}, \qquad \frac{\partial^2}{\partial t^2}\{\tilde{U}(t,t_0)U(t,t_0)\}, \quad \text{etc.},$$

vanish for $t = t_0$. Hence§

$$\tilde{U}(t,t_0)U(t,t_0) = I. \tag{99}$$

Eqns. (98) and (99) establish the unitary property of $U(t,t_0)$ when t and t_0 are *finite*;‖ if one or both of these times becomes infinite, it is again necessary to use the adiabatic switching process to *define* $U(t,t_0)$,

† Eqns. (95) and (96) are used whether $H_{\text{int}}(t)$ is explicitly or implicitly dependent on time. (H_{int} is explicitly dependent on t, if t occurs other than in the field amplitudes.)

‡ In considering time derivatives of operators, it may be necessary to distinguish between $\partial\hat{A}/\partial t$ and the transform of $(\partial A/\partial t)$.

§ Assuming the Taylor series expansion is valid for all t.

‖ A formal solution of (95), (97), if $H_{\text{int}}(t)$ is not explicitly dependent on time, is

$$U(t,t_0) = \exp[i(t-t_0)\{H_1(t_0)+H_2(t_0)\}/\hbar]\exp\{-i(t-t_0)H/\hbar\}.$$

and the proof of unitarity which has just been given is no longer valid. If bound states of the interacting system can occur, $U(t, \pm\infty)$ are not unitary, because a bound state cannot be expressed as a linear combination of free particle states. A careful discussion of this case is given in Chapter V, § 2; it is shown there that $U(\infty, -\infty)$ is always unitary.

From (94) and (95) we get

$$\frac{\partial U(t,t_0)}{\partial t} = -(i/\hbar)\hat{H}_{\text{int}}(t)U(t,t_0). \tag{100}$$

This equation for $U(t,t_0)$ is very convenient for actual calculations, because the dynamical variables which appear in $\hat{H}_{\text{int}}(t)$ propagate like free-field variables; eqn. (100) is the basic equation for the perturbation calculation of collision phenomena. From (94) it follows that any state vector in the interaction representation $|\Psi(t)\rangle$ is related to the corresponding Heisenberg state vector $|\,\rangle$ by

$$|\Psi(t)\rangle = U(t,t_0)|\,\rangle. \tag{101}$$

The two state vectors are identical at the time t_0. The perturbation theory approximation for $|\Psi(t)\rangle$ is deduced from the iterated solution of (100):

$$U(t,t_0) = I - \frac{i}{\hbar}\int_{t_0}^{t} dt_1\,\hat{H}_{\text{int}}(t_1) + \left(\frac{-i}{\hbar}\right)^2 \int_{t_0}^{t} dt_1 \int_{t_0}^{t_1} dt_2\,\hat{H}_{\text{int}}(t_1)\hat{H}_{\text{int}}(t_2) + \dots. \tag{102}$$

Collision phenomena

The interaction representation can be used as follows to describe collisions. A system for which the interaction representation state vector $|\Psi(t)\rangle$ is constant, has its time dependence described entirely by the interaction representation operators; this system therefore has the propagation properties of free fields, and no collision phenomena are observed. Further, in any system, the change which occurs in $|\Psi(t)\rangle$ describes the deviation from the free-particle behaviour. Suppose that $|\Psi(t)\rangle$ is specified by its representatives in free particle states, which we write $\langle \text{F.P.}|\Psi(t)\rangle$. Because $|\Psi(t_0)\rangle$ coincides with the Heisenberg state vector, it describes real particles. However, if each term $\hat{H}_{\text{int}}(t')$ occurring in (102) is multiplied by a factor $\exp(-\gamma|t'|)$, where γ is small and positive, the state vector $|\Psi(t_0)\rangle$ will tend to a free particle state vector as $t_0 \to -\infty$. For example, in the collision of two neutrons all representatives $\langle \text{F.P.}|\Psi(-\infty)\rangle$ vanish, except those with respect to the state vectors $|\mathbf{p}_1, s_1; \mathbf{p}_2, s_2\rangle$ for two free neutrons with momenta and spins $(\mathbf{p}_1, s_1)$, $(\mathbf{p}_2, s_2)$. These representatives are

$$\langle \mathbf{p}_1, s_1; \mathbf{p}_2, s_2|\Psi(-\infty)\rangle = \delta_{s_1 s_1'}\,\delta_{s_2 s_2'}\,\delta^3(\mathbf{p}_1-\mathbf{p}_1')\delta^3(\mathbf{p}_2-\mathbf{p}_2'), \tag{103}$$

where $(\mathbf{p}_1', s_1')$, $(\mathbf{p}_2', s_2')$ are the initial momenta and spins of the colliding neutrons. In evaluating $U(t, t_0)$ we take the limit $t_0 \to -\infty$ in (102) before letting γ tend to zero. This has the simple effect of removing from the multiple integrals all terms which for finite t_0 would depend on t_0 in a periodic way. After this limiting procedure is carried out the result is relativistically invariant (as will be seen in Chapter V).

The state vector $|\Psi(+\infty)\rangle$—which is given a precise meaning by an identical procedure—describes the system after the collision has been completed. Suppose we wish to find the probability that a pion $(\mathbf{p}'')$, a proton $(\mathbf{p}_1'', s_1'')$, and a neutron $(\mathbf{p}_2'', s_2'')$ are present after the two neutrons collide. It is

$$|\langle \mathbf{p}_1'', s_1''; \mathbf{p}_2'', s_2''; \mathbf{p}''|\Psi(+\infty)\rangle|^2, \tag{104}$$

where $|\mathbf{p}_1'', s_1''; \mathbf{p}_2'', s_2''; \mathbf{p}''\rangle$ is the corresponding free particle state vector. In evaluating (104) we shall find that it is possible to divide by the length of time and the volume over which the interaction occurs;† in this way the transition probabilities/unit time/unit volume, and hence the cross-sections, can be found.

By eqn. (101),

$$|\Psi(+\infty)\rangle = U(+\infty, -\infty)|\Psi(-\infty)\rangle. \tag{105}$$

Using (103), the probability (104) is

$$|\langle \mathbf{p}_1'', s_1''; p_2'', s_2''; \mathbf{p}''|U(\infty, -\infty)|\mathbf{p}_1', s_1', \mathbf{p}_2', s_2'\rangle|^2. \tag{106}$$

The operator $U(\infty, -\infty)$ is called the S-matrix;‡ the definition and structure of the S-matrix is further discussed in Chapter V, §§ 1, 2.

Bound states

The form of perturbation theory which has just been discussed is not valid if bound states can occur. Two colliding nucleons may emit a pion and move away from the collision region as a deuteron; a proton and an electron may (rarely) emit photons to form a hydrogen atom. The switching-on and switching-off which is implicit in the calculation of $U(\infty, -\infty)$ cannot take account of such situations. This is because the method is based upon relating the real outgoing particles to the

† Both the duration and the volume are infinite; however they can be divided out without any ambiguity (cf. Chapter V, pp. 218–19).

‡ The interaction representation was introduced by E. C. G. Stuckelberg, *Helv. phys. Acta*, **17** (1944) 43. For the S-matrix see W. Heisenberg, *Z. Phys.* **120** (1943) 513, 673; also C. Møller, *K. danske vidensk. Selsk. Skr.* **23** (1945), No. 1, and **26** (1946), No. 19.

corresponding bare outgoing particles; if the interaction is switched off, the outgoing deuteron state becomes a bare particle state for two nucleons. It follows that the method confuses the asymptotic form of the states for bound and unbound particles. Calculations based on eqn. (102) are only expected to be accurate if there is at most a small probability of a bound state being formed (for many high-energy collisions this is so). An adaptation of the perturbation theory method which is suitable for discussing radiative capture and similar phenomena is given in Chapter V, § 14.

8. The Tamm–Dancoff method

The coupling constant ($e^2/4\pi\hbar c \simeq \frac{1}{137}$) between the electron and the Maxwell field is small, and the interaction representation form of perturbation theory (eqn. (102)) gives an accurate description of the collision phenomena between electrons, positrons, photons, etc.† However, the coupling constant between the pion and nucleon fields is larger than unity, and perturbation theory is not satisfactory for describing the interactions between these fields. Instead a method due to Tamm and Dancoff‡ may be used. It consists in finding approximate eigenstates of the *total* Hamiltonian H for the interacting fields (eqn. (92)). Thus from the start the Tamm–Dancoff method attempts to use real particle states. In practice these eigenstates of the total Hamiltonian are expanded in terms of bare particle states (i.e. eigenstates of H_1+H_2), and the approximation (at the nth stage) is the omission of terms containing more than n bare particles.

As a simple illustration, the scattering of pions by nucleons at low energies is discussed. The pseudo-vector interaction (86) can be used, so that nucleon anti-nucleon pair effects may be ignored.§ It is assumed that only terms containing up to two bare pions need be included. The state vectors $|\rangle$ of the real pion-nucleon system satisfy

$$(H_N+H_\pi+H_{\text{int}}-E)|\rangle = 0. \tag{107}$$

Here H_N, H_π are the free-field Hamiltonians, and E is the energy of the state $|\rangle$. Eqn. (107) is projected on to the bare particle states

† It is, of course, necessary to use renormalized perturbation theory—see § 9.

‡ I. Tamm, *J. Phys.* (*U.S.S.R.*), **9** (1945) 449; S. M. Dancoff, *Phys. Rev.* **78** (1950) 382.

§ This gives

$$\begin{aligned} H_{\text{int}} &= -if/\mu \int d^3\mathbf{x}\, \bar{\psi}(\mathbf{x},t)\gamma\gamma^5\psi(\mathbf{x},t)\,.\,\text{grad}\,\phi(\mathbf{x},t) \\ &= f/\mu \int d^3\mathbf{x}\, \bar{\psi}(\mathbf{x},t)\{\boldsymbol{\sigma}'\,.\,\text{grad}\,\phi(\mathbf{x},t)\}\psi(\mathbf{x},t). \end{aligned}$$

See § 14 for a discussion.

$|N\rangle$, $|N',k'\rangle$, $|N'',k_1'',k_2''\rangle$ for a nucleon, a nucleon and a pion, and a nucleon and two pions respectively. This gives

$$\left.\begin{aligned}(E_N-E)\langle N|\,\rangle+\langle N|H_{\text{int}}|\,\rangle &= 0\\ (E_{N'k'}-E)\langle N'k'|\,\rangle+\langle N'k'|H_{\text{int}}|\,\rangle &= 0\\ (E_{N''k_1''k_2''}-E)\langle N''k_1''k_2''|\,\rangle+\langle N''k_1''k_2''|H_{\text{int}}|\,\rangle &= 0\end{aligned}\right\}. \tag{108}$$

Here E_N, $E_{N'k'}$, $E_{N''k_1''k_2''}$ are the energies of the free particle states.†

Because the bare particle state vectors $|B\rangle$ form a complete set, the Hilbert space identity operator can be written

$$I = \sum_B |B\rangle\langle B|,$$

where B runs over all bare particle states. Thus we can write

$$\langle N'k'|H_{\text{int}}|\,\rangle = \sum_B \langle N'k'|H_{\text{int}}|B\rangle\langle B|\,\rangle. \tag{109}$$

In the spirit of the approximation, the states $|B\rangle$ occurring on the right of (109) should be restricted to have at most two bare pions; the other matrix elements in (108) are expanded in a similar way. Only terms $\langle B|H_{\text{int}}|B'\rangle$ in which the number of pions changes by one can occur.‡ The Tamm–Dancoff equations therefore become

$$\left.\begin{aligned}(E_N-E)\langle N|\,\rangle+\sum_{N'k'}\langle N|H_{\text{int}}|N'k'\rangle\langle N'k'|\,\rangle &= 0\\ (E_{N'k'}-E)\langle N'k'|\,\rangle+\sum_{N}\langle N'k'|H_{\text{int}}|N\rangle\langle N|\,\rangle+ &\\ +\sum_{N''k_1''k_2''}\langle N'k'|H_{\text{int}}|N''k_1''k_2''\rangle\langle N''k_1''k_2''|\,\rangle &= 0\\ (E_{N''k_1''k_2''}-E)\langle N''k_1''k_2''|\,\rangle+\sum_{N'k'}\langle N''k_1''k_2''|H_{\text{int}}|N'k'\rangle\langle N'k'|\,\rangle &= 0\end{aligned}\right\}. \tag{110}$$

The homogeneous (integral) equations (110) have various sets of eigen-solutions (E is the eigenvalue). The real nucleon is described by the set which has the property that all $\langle N'k'|\,\rangle$, $\langle N''k_1''k_1''|\,\rangle$ vanish if $H_{\text{int}} \to 0$. Pion-nucleon scattering is derived from the sets in which all $\langle N|\,\rangle$, $\langle N''k_1''k_2''|\,\rangle$ vanish if $H_{\text{int}} \to 0$.

The Tamm–Dancoff method encounters the usual infinities which occur in the relativistic theory of interacting fields; for example it is not very difficult to see that the eigenvalue E for the real nucleon solution of (110) is infinite, unless the pion-nucleon interaction is cut off at high frequencies. These infinities can be avoided by a method which is analogous to renormalized perturbation theory. For details

† Thus $\langle N'k'|(H_N+H_\pi) = E_{N'k'}\langle N'k'|$, etc.

‡ This can be seen from the commutator of H_{int} with the operator which gives the total number of pions at time t (for a fixed time t the free field and interacting field commutators are identical).

of the renormalization of these equations the reader is referred to the literature.† The meson pair theory,‡ in which exact solutions for meson scattering on a fixed source are known, has been used to test the accuracy of the lowest order Tamm–Dancoff approximation; it is found that the approximation is superior to perturbation theory (for a large coupling constant) but the results of the Tamm–Dancoff method become noticeably unreliable if bound states can occur.§ It is not known whether the Tamm–Dancoff method converges as states containing greater numbers of bare particles are introduced; if we were sure that the theory of interacting quantized fields was well founded, it would be reasonable to expect the method to converge.

The Tamm–Dancoff method has been extensively used for pion-nucleon scattering at low energies, and it has been thoroughly discussed in the literature;|| the method will not be considered further in this volume. In Chapter VI pion–nucleon scattering is investigated following a method of Low and Chew,†† which is much easier to apply and which readily shows up the symmetry properties; its results are in good agreement with experiment.

9. Mathematical difficulties in the theory of interacting fields

In Chapter II and in the first five sections of the present chapter we set up a quantum theory of non-interacting (or free) fields; this made it possible to describe the mechanical properties (energy, momentum, spin, etc.) and the electrical properties of the elementary particles in a manner which combined the particle and the field aspects. Physically this description of free particles is straightforward and the mathematical techniques which were used are well established. The field operators can be set up in a separable Hilbert space in which the state vectors can be normalized without any difficulty.‡‡

Unfortunately it is not at all clear that the mathematical basis of the relativistic quantum theory of *interacting* fields is well established;

† F. J. Dyson, *Phys. Rev.* **91** (1953) 1543; A. Klein, ibid. **95** (1954) 1676. A detailed account is given by H. A. Bethe and F. de Hoffmann, *Mesons and Fields*, vol. ii (Row, Peterson & Co., Evanston, Ill., 1955).

‡ G. Wentzel, *Helv. phys. Acta,* **25** (1952) 569. In this theory there are *direct* matrix elements for the fixed nucleon source creating or destroying a *pair* of neutral mesons, and for the scattering of a neutral meson.

§ G. Morpurgo and B. F. Touscheck, *Nuovo Cim.* **10** (1953) 1681; see also G. Morpurgo, ibid. **11** (1954) 103.

|| See H. A. Bethe and F. de Hoffmann, loc. cit.

†† F. E. Low and G. F. Chew, *Phys. Rev.* **101** (1956) 1570.

‡‡ By *separable* is meant a Hilbert space of $\aleph_0$ dimensions; a non-separable space has $> \aleph_0$ dimensions.

any careful discussion of the mathematical foundations appears to encounter formidable difficulties.† As an example we mention van Hove's‡ discussion of a scalar boson field interacting (in a scalar manner) with fixed sources—the system is a crude model of the interaction between pions and nucleons. In this theory, it is easy to prove that any state vector of the non-interacting system which represents a finite number of bosons is *orthogonal* to all state vectors of the interacting system which represent a finite number of bosons.§ The vanishing of the inner product of such pairs of state vectors is caused by the high-frequency components of the interaction between the bosons and the sources.||

The general inference to be drawn from van Hove's work is that the customary free and uncritical use of operators, state vectors, and unitary transformations in Hilbert space may well be both unjustified and misleading for the case of interacting fields. This is borne out by the difficulties which have appeared in several other attempts to give a rigorous mathematical formulation†† of interacting fields.

A particular deduction from van Hove's work is that we cannot expect perturbation theory to be a reliable method for investigating the interactions between fields. This is because the validity of perturbation theory depends on the interaction between two systems producing only a small change in the state vectors of the systems;‡‡ in van Hove's example, even for any very small coupling constant between the bosons and the sources, the state vectors of the interacting and the free systems are orthogonal.§§

In order to avoid the difficulties arising from projecting real particle states on to bare particle states, it is necessary, so far as is possible,

† The physicist should note that since the theory is in obvious difficulties when it comes to answering practical questions, it may be useful to examine whether the basic equations are mathematically sensible or consistent.

‡ L. van Hove, *Physica*, **18** (1952) 145.

§ In other words, state vectors for a finite number of bare particles are orthogonal to all state vectors for a finite number of real particles.

|| If the interaction between two fields is not required to be relativistically invariant, it is possible to modify (or *cut off*) the high-frequency part of the interaction. In this way the difficulty can be avoided. Such non-relativistic theories have been of great value—for example that of G. F. Chew (*Phys. Rev.* **95** (1954) 285 for references) for pion-nucleon interactions (see Chapter VI). However, such theories are not satisfactory fundamental theories, and they do not hold for high-energy processes.

†† See, for example, R. Haag, *K. danske vidensk. Selsk.* (*Mat.-fys. Medd.*) **29** (1955), No. 12; A. S. Wightman and S. S. Schweber, *Phys. Rev.* **98** (1955) 812; A. S. Wightman, ibid. **101** (1956) 860, and later work by the same author.

‡‡ Apart from the degenerate resonance case, which does not affect the argument.

§§ In each case we refer to states of finite energy.

to work with real particle variables. Renormalized perturbation theory† is an attempt to modify perturbation theory in this direction. The most successful form‡ of Tamm–Dancoff theory uses the real vacuum as a basic state, instead of the bare particle vacuum. Finally, the current form of dispersion theory (cf. Chapter VI) works entirely with the real field (or Heisenberg) variables.

10. Renormalized perturbation theory

The results of perturbation theory, as derived in § 7, are in reasonable agreement with experiment so long as the coupling constant is small, as in electrodynamics (where $e^2/4\pi\hbar c \simeq \frac{1}{137}$), and so long as it is sufficient to calculate to the lowest-order (non-vanishing) approximation.§ For most interacting-field problems in which it is necessary to calculate the second-order approximation, perturbation theory gives infinite results, even for a small coupling constant. These divergences arise because we are dealing with systems having an infinite number of degrees of freedom; the divergences are not surprising in the light of van Hove's example (§ 9).

There is a class of field theories—the renormalizable theories||—in which the perturbation theory divergences can be avoided. In these theories, quantities which can be measured experimentally can be calculated by a modified perturbation theory.†† The calculated values are finite to all orders in the coupling constant. For example, the electron in a hydrogen atom interacts with the Coulomb field, and in addition it interacts with the quantized electromagnetic field by emitting and absorbing virtual photons. As a result the electron does not have exactly the same energy as is given by Dirac's theory of the hydrogen atom (Dirac's theory does not allow for the quantized radiation field). A straightforward perturbation theory calculation of the change ΔE in the electron's energy due to this virtual emission and absorption of photons gives an infinite result. The modified form of perturbation theory calculates the difference between the value of ΔE when the electron is moving freely outside the atom, and the value of ΔE when it is bound in the atom; an ingenious technique makes it

† See § 10 and Chapter V.

‡ F. J. Dyson, *Phys. Rev.* **91** (1953) 1543.

§ A comprehensive discussion of such solutions is given in the first edition of W. Heitler's book *Quantum Theory of Radiation* (Clarendon Press, 1936).

|| Amongst these are the physically useful theories of quantum electrodynamics, and the charged pseudo-scalar pion-nucleon (pseudo-scalar coupling) theory.

†† The renormalization theory is still not able to predict the masses of elementary particles, nor—what should be much easier—can it predict *mass differences* such as (proton—neutron), $(\pi^{\pm}-\pi^0)$.

possible, by using relativistic invariance, to give a precise (finite) value to the difference of the two divergent integrals which are involved. The result agrees perfectly with experiments.

In asserting that it is the difference between the values of ΔE for an electron outside and inside the atom which matters, we are attempting to work with a *real* rather than a *bare* electron. The real electron interacts with the quantized electromagnetic field always—not merely when it is inside the atom. Working consistently in this way, a *renormalized*† theory is constructed such that it gives finite results in perturbation calculations.‡ Renormalized quantum electrodynamics is in complete agreement with the experimental results, and as a method of calculation it is satisfactory. (Because of the large coupling constant the renormalized perturbation theory for pion-nucleon interactions is not reliable.)

In spite of this success the renormalized quantum electrodynamics can hardly be regarded as a completely satisfactory theory.§ It does not solve the problem of setting up a self-consistent scheme of operators and normalized state vectors to describe the interacting quantized electron and Maxwell fields. Presumably mathematicians would wish to be reasonably certain that such operators and state vectors existed, and physicists would wish to make simple calculations without having to subtract infinity from infinity.

11. Isotopic spin of nucleons and anti-nucleons

The isotopic spin of pions was discussed in Chapter II, § 8; here we treat the isotopic spin of nucleons, and in the next section the relation of isotopic spin to the pion-nucleon interaction is discussed.

The exclusion principle requires that the state vector for a number of protons and neutrons should change sign when any pair of protons is exchanged and when any pair of neutrons is exchanged. It is also necessary that the state vector should change sign when any proton

† The term 'renormalized' indicates that in the theory the actual masses, charges, etc., are used rather than the bare particle values of ordinary perturbation theory.

‡ The renormalization of the Tamm–Dancoff equations is more difficult—see p. 191, n. †.

§ Various difficulties within renormalized field theory have been suggested: (*a*) the series convergence difficulty after subtracting the infinite parts (C. A. Hurst, *Proc. Roy. Soc.* A, **214** (1952) 44, *Proc. Camb. Phil. Soc.* **48** (1952) 625, *Phys. Rev.* **85** (1952) 920; W. Thirring, *Helv. phys. Acta*, **26** (1953) 33; A. Petermann, ibid. 291, 731, *Arch. Genève*, **6** (1953) 3); (*b*) the *ghost* states (G. Källén and W. Pauli, *K. danske vidensk. Selsk.* (*Mat.-fys. Medd.*) **30** (1955), No. 7; W. Pauli, *Pisa Conference Proc., Suppl. Nuovo Cim.* **2** (1956) 703; see also the article by L. Landau in *Niels Bohr and the Development of Physics* (Pergamon, London, 1955).

is exchanged with any neutron; the reason for this can be seen as follows. Let $|P,\mathbf{p}',s';\, N,\mathbf{p}'',s'';\, P,\mathbf{p}''',s'''\rangle$ be the state vector for which the first particle is a proton of momentum and spin $(\mathbf{p}',s')$, the second is a neutron $(\mathbf{p}'',s'')$, etc. By β-decay the neutron can change to a proton, after which the nucleon component of the state vector is $|P,\mathbf{p}',s';\, P,\bar{\mathbf{p}},\bar{s};\, P,\mathbf{p}''',s'''\rangle$. If the initial state vector were $|P,\mathbf{p}',s';\, P,\mathbf{p}''',s''';\, N,\mathbf{p}'',s''\rangle$, the final state nucleon component would be $|P,\mathbf{p}',s';\, P,\mathbf{p}''',s''';\, P,\bar{\mathbf{p}},\bar{s}\rangle$ (assuming that both the emitted electron and neutrino in the two cases have the same momentum and spin values). Because the Hamiltonian for the β-decay cannot depend on the *order* in which the neutron appears in the initial state vector, it follows that the remaining factor in the final state vector is the same in the two cases. Therefore, since $|P,\mathbf{p}',s';\, P,\bar{\mathbf{p}},\bar{s};\, P,\mathbf{p}''',s'''\rangle$ changes sign on exchanging any pair of particles, this also holds for $|P,\mathbf{p}',s';\, N,\mathbf{p}'',s'';\, P,\mathbf{p}''',s'''\rangle$. Similar reasoning can be used in the general case.

This general form of the exclusion principle requires that the proton field operators and the neutron field operators anti-commute.† If $\psi_\rho^{(1)}(\mathbf{x},t)$, $\psi_\rho^{(2)}(\mathbf{x},t)$ $(\rho = 1,2,3,4)$ are the proton and neutron four-component field operators, then the nucleon field variables must satisfy (cf. eqn. (9))

$$\left.\begin{aligned} [\psi_\rho^{(l)}(\mathbf{x},t),\, \psi_{\rho'}^{(l')}(\mathbf{x}',t)]_+ = 0, \qquad [\tilde{\psi}_\rho^{(l)}(\mathbf{x},t),\, \tilde{\psi}_{\rho'}^{(l')}(\mathbf{x}',t)]_+ = 0 \\ [\tilde{\psi}_\rho^{(l)}(\mathbf{x},t),\, \psi_{\rho'}^{(l')}(\mathbf{x}',t)]_+ = \delta_{\rho\rho'}\delta_{ll'}\delta^3(\mathbf{x}-\mathbf{x}') \quad (l,l' = 1,2) \end{aligned}\right\}. \tag{111}$$

This general formalism for the nucleon field is now used to develop the idea of isotopic spin. The total charge in the nucleon field Q can be written in the charge conjugate form (80); with the help of (77) this gives

$$Q = \tfrac{1}{2}e\int d^3\mathbf{x}\,\{\tilde{\psi}^{(1)}(\mathbf{x},t)\psi^{(1)}(\mathbf{x},t)-\psi_T^{(1)}(\mathbf{x},t)\tilde{\psi}_T^{(1)}(\mathbf{x},t)\}. \tag{112}$$

The superscript $^{(1)}$ indicates that only protons contribute and the subscript $_T$ means that $\psi_T^{(1)}$, $\tilde{\psi}_T^{(1)}$ are written as four-component row and column vectors respectively. Because (112) is in charge conjugate form, it has the eigenvalue zero when acting on the vacuum state vector $|0\rangle$.

Isotopic notation

The charge Q can be written in isotopic notation by introducing the 2×2 matrix

$$\tau_3 = \begin{pmatrix} 1 & 0 \\ 0 & -1 \end{pmatrix},$$

where the rows and columns are labelled by l, $l' = 1, 2$. If I is the

† The argument is identical with that in § 1 above.

identity 2×2 matrix, the matrix $\frac{1}{2}(I+\tau_3)$ can be used to remove the neutron component from any nucleon field operator. This follows from

$$\left.\begin{aligned}\sum_{l'=1}^{2} \tfrac{1}{2}(I+\tau_3)_{ll'}\psi^{(l')} &= \psi^{(1)}\delta_{l1}\\ \sum_{l'=1}^{2} \bar{\psi}^{(l')}\tfrac{1}{2}(I+\tau_3)_{l'l} &= \bar{\psi}^{(1)}\delta_{l1}\end{aligned}\right\}.$$

Thus Q is written†

$$Q = \tfrac{1}{4}e\sum_{l,l'}\int d^3\mathbf{x}\,\{\bar{\psi}^{(l)}(\mathbf{x},t)(I+\tau_3)_{ll'}\psi^{(l')}(\mathbf{x},t)-\psi_T^{(l')}(\mathbf{x},t)(I+\tau_3)_{ll'}\bar{\psi}_T^{(l)}(\mathbf{x},t)\}. \tag{113}$$

The use of the 2×2 matrices for the proton-neutron characteristics of nucleons is analogous to the use of the 2×2 Pauli matrices for the spin characteristics of fermions (cf. eqn. (3.34)).

The operator Q can now be divided into two important constituents, viz.

$$Q/e = \tfrac{1}{2}N+T^{(3)}, \tag{114}$$

where
$$N = \tfrac{1}{2}\int d^3\mathbf{x}\sum_{l=1}^{2}\{\bar{\psi}^{(l)}(\mathbf{x},t)\psi^{(l)}(\mathbf{x},t)-\psi_T^{(l)}(\mathbf{x},t)\bar{\psi}_T^{(l)}(\mathbf{x},t)\}, \tag{115}$$

and‡
$$T^{(3)} = \tfrac{1}{2}\int d^3\mathbf{x}\sum_{l,l'}\bar{\psi}^{(l)}(\mathbf{x},t)(\tau_3)_{ll'}\psi^{(l')}(\mathbf{x},t). \tag{116}$$

The operator N is readily seen (on comparing with (112)) to be:

$$N = (\text{no. of nucleons})-(\text{no. of anti-nucleons}).$$

The conservation of N is strictly obeyed for all interactions so long as there is not sufficient energy available to create hyperons. When hyperons are created, the baryon conservation law appears to hold; one nucleon is destroyed for each hyperon which is created (cf. Chapter VII, § 6). For the present, hyperon creation is ignored, so the operator N must commute with the Hamiltonians for the interactions between nucleons, pions, mesons, and the lighter particles.§

Isotopic space

The operator $T^{(3)}$ is one component of the isotopic spin operator for the nucleon field. The other components are formed on replacing τ_3 in (116) by the two other independent 2×2 Hermitian matrices (cf. (3.34)),

$$\tau_1 = \begin{pmatrix}0 & 1\\ 1 & 0\end{pmatrix}, \qquad \tau_2 = \begin{pmatrix}0 & -i\\ i & 0\end{pmatrix}.$$

† The second term on the right of (113) is identical with the first apart from the change in the order of the field operators.

‡ In writing (116) we have used the last anti-commutation relation of (111) and the property trace$(\tau_3) = 0$.

§ Clearly N commutes with the Hamiltonian for free nucleons.

Thus the Hermitian operators $T^{(k)}$ are†

$$T^{(k)} = \tfrac{1}{2}\int d^3\mathbf{x} \sum_{l,l'} \bar{\psi}^{(l)}(\mathbf{x},t)(\tau_k)_{ll'}\psi^{(l')}(\mathbf{x},t) \quad (k = 1,2,3). \tag{117}$$

The matrices τ_1, τ_2 are associated with exchanging a proton and a neutron, and the τ_k $(k = 1,2,3)$ are analogous to the 2×2 Pauli matrices σ_k for the spin of a non-relativistic electron. Thus the proton-neutron degree of freedom of nucleons is associated with a spin in a three-dimensional space; this is called the *isotopic space*.‡ It is natural to expect that the proton and neutron represent the two possible directions of an isotopic spin of value $\frac{1}{2}$—eqn. (125) below shows this is true. For the nucleon field, as for the pion field in Chapter II, § 8, the isotopic spin has been deduced from the total charge operator. In both cases the third component of the isotopic spin is closely related to the total charge; the other components are the only two linearly independent operators of the same nature which can be formed. *It is therefore reasonable to expect that the isotopic space for pions and nucleons is identical*, and that it makes sense to add the isotopic spins of pions and nucleons; in § 12 it is shown that this is true.

The matrices τ_k can only describe the isotopic spin of a single nucleon; the operator $T^{(k)}$ gives the total isotopic spin of the nucleons in the field. This operator $T^{(k)}$ is related to τ_k in the same way that the total spin $\mathbf{M}^{\mathrm{sp}}$ of a fermion field (eqn. (41)) is related to the spin matrices $\boldsymbol{\sigma}$. A particular advantage of using $T^{(k)}$ is the easy and natural way in which the isotopic spin of anti-nucleons appears.

Using the anti-commutators (111) and the relations $[\tau_1, \tau_2] = 2i\tau_3$, etc., we have§

$$[T^{(1)}, T^{(2)}] = iT^{(3)} \quad \text{(and cyclic permutations).} \tag{118}$$

Also

$$[T^{(k)}, N] = 0 \quad (k = 1,2,3). \tag{119}$$

Eqns. (118) show that the operators $T^{(k)}$ have the properties of an angular momentum in the three-dimensional isotopic spin space. It is easy to show that each $T^{(k)}$ commutes with the total momentum $\mathbf{P}$ of the nucleon field, and, provided the small difference in the masses of the proton and neutron is ignored, each $T^{(k)}$ commutes with the Hamiltonian for the nucleon field (cf. (78)). Thus eigenstates of the nucleon field can be classified by the eigenvalues $T^{(3)\prime}$ and $\mathbf{T}^2 = T'(T'+1)$, where $\mathbf{T}^2 = \sum_{k=1}^{3} (T^{(k)})^2$. We also use the baryon number N'.

† Cf. J. Hamilton, *Proc. Pisa Conference, Suppl. Nuovo Cim.* **2** (1956) 803.

‡ The idea of isotopic variables is due to W. Heisenberg, *Z. Phys.* **77** (1932) 1.

§ The identity $[AB, CD] = A[B,C]_+D - AC[B,D]_+ + [A,C]_+DB - C[A,D]_+B$ is useful.

Isotopic spin eigenstates of the nucleon field

For a given value of T', one eigenstate can be obtained from another by applying the operators $T^{(1)}+iT^{(2)}$, $T^{(1)}-iT^{(2)}$, which, respectively, increase and decrease the eigenvalue of $T^{(3)}$ by unity. Also

$$\left.\begin{aligned} T^{(1)}+iT^{(2)} &= \int d^3\mathbf{x}\,\tilde{\psi}^{(1)}(\mathbf{x},t)\psi^{(2)}(\mathbf{x},t) \\ T^{(1)}-iT^{(2)} &= \int d^3\mathbf{x}\,\tilde{\psi}^{(2)}(\mathbf{x},t)\psi^{(1)}(\mathbf{x},t) \end{aligned}\right\}. \tag{120}$$

Because $T^{(k)}$ are constants of motion, when the integrand of the first eqn. (120) is split into positive and negative frequency parts we get†

$$T^{(1)}+iT^{(2)} = \int d^3\mathbf{x}\,[\{\tilde{\psi}^{(1)}(\mathbf{x},t)\}^{(+)}\{\psi^{(2)}(\mathbf{x},t)\}^{(-)}+\{\tilde{\psi}^{(1)}(\mathbf{x},t)\}^{(-)}\{\psi^{(2)}(\mathbf{x},t)\}^{(+)}]. \tag{121}$$

Substituting creation and annihilation operators as given in (26), and remembering that proton and neutron operators anti-commute, gives

$$T^{(1)}+iT^{(2)} = \sum_{(\alpha)} \{\tilde{c}_{P\alpha}c_{N\alpha}-\tilde{c}_{\bar{N}\alpha}c_{\bar{P}\alpha}\}. \tag{122}$$

Here α denotes the mechanical properties (momentum and spin), P, N denote proton and neutron, and $\bar{P}$, $\bar{N}$ their anti-particles, respectively; c is the (normalized) destruction operator and c the creation operator.

The summation is over all α. The Hermitian conjugate equation is

$$T^{(1)}-iT^{(2)} = \sum_{\alpha} \{\tilde{c}_{N\alpha}c_{P\alpha}-\tilde{c}_{\bar{P}\alpha}c_{\bar{N}\alpha}\}. \tag{123}$$

Finally, from (116) we have

$$T^{(3)} = \tfrac{1}{2}\{n_P-n_{\bar{P}}+n_{\bar{N}}-n_N\}, \tag{124}$$

where n_P is the total number operator for protons, etc.

The vacuum $|0\rangle$ is the eigenstate $T'=0$, $N'=0$.‡ By (122) to (124) the single particle eigenstates are

$$\left.\begin{aligned} N' &= 1, & T' &= \tfrac{1}{2};\; T^{(3)\prime} = \tfrac{1}{2}, -\tfrac{1}{2}: && |P\alpha\rangle,\ |N\alpha\rangle \\ N' &= -1, & T' &= \tfrac{1}{2};\; T^{(3)\prime} = \tfrac{1}{2}, -\tfrac{1}{2}: && |\bar{N}\alpha\rangle,\ -|\bar{P}\alpha\rangle \end{aligned}\right\}. \tag{125}$$

Here $|P\alpha\rangle$ is the state vector for a proton with mechanical properties α. The $T^{(3)}$ eigenvalues for anti-nucleons are the opposite of the corresponding nucleon eigenvalues.§

† Constants of motion cannot contain terms $\psi^{(+)}\psi^{(+)}$ or $\psi^{(-)}\psi^{(-)}$. In deriving the eigenstates we assume the free nucleon equations hold. Switching on an isotopic spin invariant interaction will not alter the form of the eigenstates.

‡ $N = n_P+n_N-(n_{\bar{P}}+n_{\bar{N}})$.

§ The sign in $-|\bar{P}\alpha\rangle$ arises from the minus sign in (123); it is only important if the relative phase of the eigenstates is required. The pair $(|\bar{P}\alpha\rangle, |\bar{N}\alpha\rangle)$ and the pair $(|P\alpha\rangle, |N\alpha\rangle)$ are *contravariant* under isotopic space rotations; hence $(|\bar{N}\alpha\rangle, -|\bar{P}\alpha\rangle)$ and $(|P\alpha\rangle, |N\alpha\rangle)$ are *covariant* pairs. For the theory of such binary vectors see B. L. van der Waerden, *Gruppentheoretische Methode in der Quantenmechanik* (Edwards, Ann Arbor, Mich., 1944), ch. 3.

The two-nucleon eigenstates of $\mathbf{T}^2$, $T^{(3)}$ are readily built up from (125). As was shown in Chapter I, § 11, these are ($N' = 2$)

$$\left.\begin{aligned} &T' = 1;\ T^{(3)\prime} = 1,\ 0,\ -1: \\ &\qquad |P\alpha_1 P\alpha_2\rangle,\ \frac{1}{\sqrt{2}}\{|P\alpha_1 N\alpha_2\rangle + |N\alpha_1 P\alpha_2\rangle\},\ |N\alpha_1 N\alpha_2\rangle \\ &T' = 0:\quad \frac{1}{\sqrt{2}}\{|P\alpha_1 N\alpha_2\rangle - |N\alpha_1 P\alpha_2\rangle\} \end{aligned}\right\}, \tag{126}$$

where $|P\alpha_1 N\alpha_2\rangle$ is the state vector in which the first particle is a proton of type α_1, and the second is a neutron of type α_2. There are similar sets for $T' = 1, 0$, formed from anti-nucleons ($N' = -2$).

Eigenstates of $\mathbf{T}^2$, $T^{(3)}$ for a nucleon and an anti-nucleon ($N' = 0$) are formed from (126) on replacing one nucleon state by one anti-nucleon state in the way indicated by (125). This gives:

$$\left.\begin{aligned} &T' = 1;\ T^{(3)\prime} = 1,\ 0,\ -1: \\ &\qquad |P\alpha_1 \bar{N}\alpha_2\rangle,\ \frac{1}{\sqrt{2}}\{|N\alpha_1 \bar{N}\alpha_2\rangle - |P\alpha_1 \bar{P}\alpha_2\rangle\},\ -|N\alpha_1 \bar{P}\alpha_2\rangle \\ &T' = 0:\quad \frac{1}{\sqrt{2}}\{|P\alpha_1 \bar{P}\alpha_2\rangle + |N\alpha_1 \bar{N}\alpha_2\rangle\} \end{aligned}\right\}. \tag{127}$$

In (126) the eigenstates of the set $T' = 1$ are symmetric, and the state $T' = 0$ is anti-symmetric in the isotopic variables. Thus the deuteron wave function, which is of the type $T' = 0$, must be symmetric in the spin and spatial variables. The set (127) have yet to be symmetrized in the charge variables. For the eigenstate $T' = 0$ there is a symmetrical form $T' = 0^s$ and an anti-symmetrical form $T' = 0^a$. They are†

$$\left.\begin{aligned} T' = 0^s:&\quad \tfrac{1}{2}\{|P\alpha_1 \bar{P}\alpha_2\rangle + |\bar{P}\alpha_1 P\alpha_2\rangle + |N\alpha_1 \bar{N}\alpha_2\rangle + |\bar{N}\alpha_1 N\alpha_2\rangle\} \\ T' = 0^a:&\quad \tfrac{1}{2}\{|P\alpha_1 \bar{P}\alpha_2\rangle - |\bar{P}\alpha_1 P\alpha_2\rangle + |N\alpha_1 \bar{N}\alpha_2\rangle - |\bar{N}\alpha_1 N\alpha_2\rangle\} \end{aligned}\right\}. \tag{128}$$

A nucleon and anti-nucleon in the $T' = 0^a$ state must be symmetrical in the spin and spatial variables, and so on. Similarly, for each of the eigenvalues $T^{(3)\prime} = 1, 0, -1$ there is a symmetrical state $T' = 1^s$ and an anti-symmetrical state $T' = 1^a$. An example is $T' = 1^a$, $T^{(3)\prime} = 1$:

$$\frac{1}{\sqrt{2}}\{|P\alpha_1 \bar{N}\alpha_2\rangle - |\bar{N}\alpha_1 P\alpha_2\rangle\}.$$

If there are two particles, the first and second having mechanical properties α_1, α_2 respectively, then each particle can be in one of four charge states (i.e. P, N, $\bar{P}$, $\bar{N}$). There are in all $4 \times 4 = 16$ independent charge combinations; this equals the total number of states given by

† See H. A. Bethe and J. Hamilton, *Nuovo Cim.* **4** (1956) 1.

(126), the corresponding expressions for anti-nucleons, and the sets $T' = 0^s$, 0^a; 1^s, 1^a coming from (127).

The relation between isotopic spin and the charge conjugation operation U of § 5 is discussed in Chapter VII, § 2. Here it is sufficient to notice that (because U exchanges particles and anti-particles), of the states just discussed, only those having $N' = 0$, $T^{(3)\prime} = 0$ can be eigenstates† of U. It is clear that $T' = 0^s$ and $T' = 1^s$, $T^{(3)\prime} = 0$ have the eigenvalue $U' = +1$, while $T' = 0^a$ and $T' = 1^a$, $T^{(3)\prime} = 0$ have the eigenvalue $U' = -1$.

It is important to remember that the charge conjugation operation gives a strict classification, and strict selection rules; isotopic spin does not give strict selection rules (cf. § 13).

12. Isotopic spin and the very strong interactions

We now examine what practical use is to be made of the isotopic spin formalism which was developed in the previous section and in Chapter II, § 8. It has been known for some time that the interactions between nucleons have important symmetry properties;‡ these are usually called *charge symmetry* and *charge independence*. In its simplest form, charge symmetry states that the force between two neutrons is the same as the force between two protons, apart from the Coulomb interaction, provided the two pairs are in the same state of spin and orbital motion. The evidence for this law comes from comparing the observed values of the energies of the ground states and the lower excited states of mirror nuclei.

The mirror B of a nucleus A is obtained by replacing all the protons in A by neutrons, and replacing all the neutrons by protons. After allowing for the difference in the Coulomb energies, the energy levels of A and B coincide (within reasonable errors).§ Some examples of the pairs of nuclei which are used for this purpose are H^3, He^3; B^{11}, C^{11}; C^{13}, N^{13}; also C^{14}, O^{14}; etc. The charge symmetry *operation* consists in replacing all protons by neutrons and vice versa, while preserving the spin and orbital states of the particles. The mirror nuclei properties show that the interactions between nucleons are invariant under the charge symmetry operation on ignoring Coulomb effects.|| ††

† For an eigenstate of U, $N' = 0$ is obviously necessary, as is $Q = 0$; from (114), $T^{(3)\prime} = 0$ follows.

‡ E. U. Condon, G. Breit, and R. D. Present, *Phys. Rev.* **50** (1936) 825.

§ The evidence is discussed by J. M. Blatt and V. F. Weisskopf, *Theoretical Nuclear Physics* (J. Wiley, New York, 1952).

|| It is unnecessary here to specify whether the forces are two-body or many-body.

†† Strictly, it is necessary to ignore *all* electromagnetic effects.

Charge independence

The charge independence rule states that on ignoring the Coulomb force, the proton-proton, proton-neutron, and neutron-neutron forces are identical if these pairs of nucleons are in the same spin and orbital states. Putting this into the language of isotopic spin, we say that the interaction between two nucleons depends only on their spin and orbital motion states and on the magnitude T' of their total isotopic spin; it is independent of the component $T^{(3)\prime}$ of the total isotopic spin.† We believe that the same rule holds when several nucleons interact, so that on allowing for the different Coulomb energies, many energy levels of certain sets of related nuclei will coincide. If any energy level has isotopic spin T', it may‡ occur in the $(2T'+1)$ isobaric nuclei for which $-T' \leqslant T^{(3)\prime} \leqslant T'$. Such states form an *isotopic spin multiplet*, and each member has the same parity and angular momentum. In some of the $(2T'+1)$ isobars this state may be the ground state, while in others it may be an excited state. (In general, it is not easy to find all members of such multiplets for $T' > 1$.)

An example is provided by the nuclei B^{12}, C^{12}, N^{12}. Because C^{12} has an even number of protons and of neutrons, its ground state has considerable symmetry and is a strongly bound $T' = 0$ state§ with angular momentum $J = 0$ and positive parity (i.e. 0^+). The nuclei B^{12} and N^{12} have $T^{(3)\prime} = -1, +1$ respectively, and their ground states are $T' = 1$ states at energies 13·37 MeV and 17·7 MeV respectively above the ground state of C^{12}; amongst the excited states of C^{12} the lowest energy $T' = 1$ state (and therefore the corresponding state) is at 15·09 MeV.|| Another example is taken from the nuclei C^{14}, N^{14}, O^{14}. The ground state of N^{14} is $T' = 0$, $J = 1^+$ and its first excited state at 2·31 MeV higher is $T' = 1$, $J = 0^+$. The ground state of C^{14} is a $T' = 1$, $J = 0^+$ state which is 0·155 MeV above the N^{14} ground state; the ground state of O^{14} is a $T' = 1$ state (presumably being 0^+) at 5·17 MeV|| above the ground state of N^{14}. The energy differences between these members of an isotopic state $T' = 1$ are accurately accounted for by the Coulomb energy.††

† The interaction also depends on the operator N; the nucleon–anti-nucleon forces are not identical with the nucleon–nucleon forces.

‡ The Coulomb force may prevent the existence of some members of the multiplet, for the more positive values of $T^{(3)\prime}$.

§ The nuclei of mass $4n$ such as He^4, Be^8, C^{12}, O^{16} have $T' = 0$ ground states; the nuclei H^2, Li^6, B^{10}, N^{14} which have less symmetry have less tightly bound $T' = 0$ ground states.

|| Cf. F. Ajzenberg and T. Lauritsen, *Rev. Mod. Phys.* **27** (1955) 77; ibid. **24** (1952) 321.

†† See D. H. Wilkinson, *Phil. Mag.* **1** (1956) 1031, for a survey of these Coulomb energy differences for light nuclei.

Further evidence for the charge independence of nuclear forces comes from the elastic nucleon-nucleon scattering experiments; the details are given in Chapter VIII, § 7, and will not be discussed here.† It has not yet been possible to examine whether nucleon-nucleon interactions are charge independent at energies so high that K-meson effects will contribute appreciably to the forces.

Assuming that the isotopic spins of the nucleon and the pion fields behave like angular momenta in the same isotopic space, these spins can be added by the usual vector additon method (Chapter I, § 10). For example, a state of one pion and one nucleon can have total isotopic spin $T = \frac{3}{2}$ (a quadruplet) and $T = \frac{1}{2}$ (a doublet). Experiments on elastic pion-nucleon scattering (Chapter VI) show that the total isotopic spin T (as well as the component $T^{(3)}$) is indeed conserved in the scattering. Therefore we assume that the fundamental pion-nucleon interaction conserves the total isotopic spin. In this way both the pion-scattering phenomena and the charge independence of nuclear forces are explained. Isotopic spin is not conserved in electromagnetic and β-decay interactions; the relation of isotopic spin to hyperon and K-meson interactions is discussed in Chapter VII. (*Note*: the charge symmetry of nuclear forces follows from charge independence; the converse is not true.)

The pion-nucleon interaction

The form of the charge-independent interaction between the pion field and the nucleon field has been given by Kemmer.‡ We consider pseudo-scalar charged and neutral pions interacting with nucleons via a pseudo-scalar coupling. A similar interaction for neutral pions and protons (or neutrons) is given in (88). Using the notation of Chapter II, § 7, the operator $\phi(x_\mu)$ destroys one unit of charge and $\tilde{\phi}(x_\mu)$ creates one unit of charge (cf. eqn. (2.112)). Also the operators $T^{(1)}+iT^{(2)}$, $T^{(1)}-iT^{(2)}$ of § 11 above create and destroy unit charge respectively.§ Therefore, remembering (117), the correct interaction Hamiltonian for charged pions, which is *symmetric* as between the neutron and the proton, is

$$H^{c}_{\text{int}} = \frac{iG}{\sqrt{2}} \int d^3\mathbf{x} \sum_{l,l'=1}^{2} \bar{\psi}^{(l)}(\mathbf{x},t)\gamma^5\{(\tau_1+i\tau_2)_{ll'}\phi(\mathbf{x},t)+(\tau_1-i\tau_2)_{ll'}\tilde{\phi}(\mathbf{x},t)\}\psi^{(l')}(\mathbf{x},t). \tag{129}$$

† For a review of the evidence supporting charge independence from nuclear forces and from pion interactions see the article by W. E. Burcham in *Progr. Nuclear Phys.* **4** (Pergamon, London, 1955). See also L. A. Radicati, *Proc. Phys. Soc.* A **66** (1953) 139.

‡ N. Kemmer, *Proc. Camb. Phil. Soc.* **34** (1938) 354.

§ The proton's charge is taken as $+e$.

In order to see the behaviour in isotopic space we write

$$\phi(x_\mu) = \frac{1}{\sqrt{2}}\{\phi_1(x_\mu)-i\phi_2(x_\mu)\}, \qquad \tilde{\phi}(x_\mu) = \frac{1}{\sqrt{2}}\{\phi_1(x_\mu)+i\phi_2(x_\mu)\},$$

where $\phi_1(x_\mu)$, $\phi_2(x_\mu)$ are the Hermitian field operators. Then

$$H^c_{\text{int}} = iG \int d^3\mathbf{x} \sum_{l,l'=1}^{2} \bar{\psi}^{(l)}(\mathbf{x},t)\gamma^5\{\tau_1\phi_1(\mathbf{x},t)+\tau_2\phi_2(\mathbf{x},t)\}_{ll'}\psi^{(l')}(\mathbf{x},t). \tag{130}$$

The neutral pion field operator $\phi_3(x_\mu)$ forms the third component of a vector in isotopic space: (ϕ_1, ϕ_2, ϕ_3) (cf. Chapter II, § 8). The way in which the π^0 interaction has to be added to (130) so as to give conservation of isotopic spin is now obvious. The interaction

$$H_{\text{int}} = iG \int d^3\mathbf{x} \sum_{l,l'=1}^{2} \bar{\psi}^{(l)}(\mathbf{x},t)\gamma^5\{\boldsymbol{\tau}.\phi(\mathbf{x},t)\}_{ll'}\psi^{(l')}(\mathbf{x},t) \tag{131}$$

has the required property, because

$$(\boldsymbol{\tau}.\boldsymbol{\varphi}) = \tau_1\phi_1+\tau_2\phi_2+\tau_3\phi_3$$

is invariant under rotations in isotopic space.† G is a real coupling constant. Comparing (2.105) and (2.151), the dimensions of ϕ are $(1/c)$ times the dimensions of the electromagnetic potential A_μ; comparing (2.188) and (131), it follows that in our units $G^2/\hbar c^3$ is a number. It will be noticed that the couplings of the neutral pion to the neutron and the proton have opposite signs; also each of these has a magnitude which is less than the charged pion coupling by a factor $2^{\frac{1}{2}}$. For pseudo-vector coupling the isotopic spin matrices τ_k must occur in the same way if charge independence is to hold. Thus, in this case (cf. (86))

$$H_{\text{int}} = -i(f/\mu) \int d^3\mathbf{x} \sum_{l,l'=1}^{2} \bar{\psi}^{(l)}(\mathbf{x},t)\gamma^\nu\gamma^5\{\boldsymbol{\tau}.\partial_\nu\boldsymbol{\varphi}(\mathbf{x},t)\}_{ll'}\psi^{(l')}(\mathbf{x},t). \tag{132}$$

13. Isotopic spin and electromagnetic interactions

Because the effect of the Coulomb force on the wave functions of light nuclei is small, it is possible to use isotopic spin to obtain new selection rules for the emission of γ-rays by light nuclei. The interaction which gives the emission of radiation by a nucleus arises from the charges of the protons and the magnetic moments μ_P and μ_N of the protons and neutrons (cf. Chapter I, § 19).‡ It is sufficient in the

† To be precise, $\bar{\psi}\gamma^5(\boldsymbol{\tau}.\boldsymbol{\varphi})\psi$ is invariant. The proof of this is the same as the proof that $\tilde{u}(\boldsymbol{\sigma}.\mathbf{x})u$ is invariant under spatial rotations, where u is a two-component Pauli spin wave function, $\boldsymbol{\sigma}$ is the 2×2 Pauli matrix, and $\mathbf{x}$ is a coordinate space vector.

‡ $\mu_P = 2{\cdot}97(e\hbar/2Mc)$, $\mu_N = -1{\cdot}91(e\hbar/2Mc)$ (M = proton mass).

simplest approximation to neglect relativistic effects in the motion of the nucleons, so the interaction with radiation becomes†

$$H^e = \frac{e}{Mc}\sum_P \{\mathbf{p}_P.\mathbf{A}(P)\} + \sum_P \mu_P\{\boldsymbol{\sigma}_P.\mathbf{H}(P)\} + \sum_N \mu_N\{\boldsymbol{\sigma}_N.\mathbf{H}(N)\}, \quad (133)$$

where $\sum_P$, $\sum_N$ denote summations over the protons and the neutrons, and $\boldsymbol{\sigma}_P$, $\boldsymbol{\sigma}_N$ are their Pauli spin matrices (M is the nucleon's mass).

This interaction Hamiltonian can be written in isotopic notation as

$$H^e = \frac{e}{2Mc}\sum_i \{\mathbf{p}_i.\mathbf{A}(\mathbf{x}_i)\}(1+\tau_3^{(i)}) + \sum_i \{\boldsymbol{\sigma}^{(i)}.\mathbf{H}(\mathbf{x}_i)\}\tfrac{1}{2}\{\mu_P(1+\tau_3^{(i)})+\mu_N(1-\tau_3^{(i)})\} \quad (134)$$

where $\sum_i$ is the sum over all nucleons, and $\tau_3^{(i)}$, $\boldsymbol{\sigma}^{(i)}$ are isotopic matrices and Pauli matrices for the ith nucleon. It is now possible to separate H^e into an isotopic scalar $H^e(0)$, and the third component of an isotopic vector $H^e(1_3)$. These are given by

$$\left.\begin{aligned} H^e &= H^e(0)+H^e(1_3) \\ H^e(0) &= \frac{e}{2Mc}\sum_i \{\mathbf{p}_i.\mathbf{A}(x_i)\} + \tfrac{1}{2}(\mu_P+\mu_N)\sum \{\boldsymbol{\sigma}^{(i)}.\mathbf{H}(\mathbf{x}_i)\} \\ H^e(1_3) &= \frac{e}{2Mc}\sum_i \tau_3^{(i)}\{\mathbf{p}_i.\mathbf{A}(\mathbf{x}_i)\} + \tfrac{1}{2}\sum_i \{\boldsymbol{\sigma}^{(i)}.\mathbf{H}(\mathbf{x}_i)\}\tau_3^{(i)}(\mu_P-\mu_N) \end{aligned}\right\}. \quad (135)$$

Because $H^e(0)$ is a scalar in isotopic space, it cannot cause a change in the isotopic spin T, so its selection rule is $\Delta T = 0$.‡ The matrix elements of $H^e(1_3)$ have the selection rules§

$$\left.\begin{aligned} \Delta T &= 0, \pm 1, \quad \text{for } T_3 \neq 0 \\ \Delta T &= \pm 1, \qquad \text{for } T_3 = 0 \end{aligned}\right\}.$$

Further information is obtained by expanding $\mathbf{A}(\mathbf{x})$ in plane wave form,

$$\mathbf{A}(\mathbf{x}) = (\text{const.})\,\mathbf{e}\exp(i\mathbf{k}.\mathbf{x}),$$

where $\mathbf{e}$, $\mathbf{k}$ are the polarization and propagation vectors. For radiation

† The first term in (133) is obtained from the non-relativistic form of (2.224) on replacing e by $-e$ and $\boldsymbol{\alpha}$ by $\mathbf{p}/Mc$. μ_P and μ_N are the actual values of the magnetic moments.

‡ These selection rules have been given by L. A. Radicati, *Phys. Rev.* **87** (1952) 521, and by M. Gell-Mann and V. L. Telegdi, ibid. **91** (1953) 169.

§ The first rule (for $T_3 \neq 0$) is similar to that for angular momenta changes in electric dipole radiation; the rule for $T_3 = 0$ is seen from the fact that $\cos\theta P_n(\cos\theta)$ contains only $P_{n+1}(\cos\theta)$ and $P_{n-1}(\cos\theta)$. We revert to the notation T, T_3 for the eigenvalues.

which has a wavelength that is long compared with nuclear dimensions, we can expand in powers of $|\mathbf{k}|$. The first term in $H^e(0)$ is of lower order in $|\mathbf{k}|$ than the second; it can be written

$$\frac{e}{2c}\mathbf{A}(\mathbf{x}=0).\frac{d}{dt}\Bigl(\sum_i \mathbf{x}_i\Bigr).$$

On neglecting the small recoil of the nucleus, this term vanishes;† hence $H^e(0)$ only gives a small $E1$ effect (arising from the remaining terms). Therefore strong $E1$ radiation will not occur between states having the same value of T in nuclei with equal numbers of protons and neutrons, whereas in neighbouring isobars ($T_3 = \pm 1$) strong $E1$ emission can occur between the same levels. For example, there is evidence that strong $E1$ emission occurs between the first excited and the ground states of C^{14}, both of which are $T = 1$ levels; the *corresponding* transition in N^{14} appears to be forbidden. A detailed discussion of the experimental evidence for these isotopic spin selection rules is given by Gell-Mann and Telegdi.‡ §

Photo-processes involving pions

We now show that similar isotopic spin selection rules hold for nucleon-pion-photon interactions.

The interaction between pions and the electromagnetic field is found by making the replacement (3.5) (or (4.68))

$$\partial_\mu \to \partial_\mu - \frac{ie}{\hbar c}A_\mu$$

in the Lagrangian (2.99) for charged pions.|| This gives

$$\mathscr{L} = -c^2\Bigl(\partial_\mu\tilde{\phi}+\frac{ie}{\hbar c}A_\mu\tilde{\phi}\Bigr)\Bigl(\partial_\mu\phi-\frac{ie}{\hbar c}A_\mu\phi\Bigr)-c^2\mu^2\tilde{\phi}\phi. \tag{136}$$

The canonical momenta become (cf. (2.107))

$$\pi = \dot{\tilde{\phi}}-\frac{ie}{\hbar}A_0\tilde{\phi}, \qquad \tilde{\pi} = \dot{\phi}+\frac{ie}{\hbar}A_0\phi.$$

† For a discussion of corrections arising from pions see G. Morpurgo, *Nuovo Cim.* **12** (1954) 60.

‡ loc. cit.; also D. H. Wilkinson, *Phil. Mag.* **1** (1956) 379. An examination of the isotopic state impurity due to Coulomb effects is given by L. A. Radicati, loc. cit.; also D. H. Wilkinson, *Phil. Mag.* **1** (1956) 1031.

§ G. Morpurgo (*Phys. Rev.* **110** (1958) 721) has pointed out that there is a similar reduction in the strength of $M1$ transitions with $\Delta T = 0$, $T_3 = 0$.

|| The reversed sign of $(ie/\hbar c)A_\mu$ compared with (3.5) is due to our charge convention for pions; notice that when acting on $\tilde{\phi}$, ∂_μ is replaced by $(\partial_\mu+(ie/\hbar c)A_\mu)$.

$A_0 = A_4/i$ is the scalar potential. The total Hamiltonian is

$$H = \int d^3\mathbf{x}\left\{\tilde{\pi}\pi + c^2\left(\operatorname{grad}\tilde{\phi} + \frac{ie}{\hbar c}\tilde{\phi}\mathbf{A}\right).\left(\operatorname{grad}\phi - \frac{ie}{\hbar c}\phi\mathbf{A}\right) + \right.$$

$$\left. + c^2\mu^2\tilde{\phi}\phi + \frac{ie}{\hbar}(\tilde{\pi}\tilde{\phi} - \pi\phi)A_0\right\} + H_{\text{E.M.}}, \quad (137)$$

where $H_{\text{E.M.}}$ is the Hamiltonian of the free electromagnetic field. The charge current 4-vector given by the general formula (9.43) is

$$j_\mu = -iec^2/\hbar\left\{\tilde{\phi}\left(\partial_\mu\phi - \frac{ie}{\hbar c}A_\mu\phi\right) - \left(\partial_\mu\tilde{\phi} + \frac{ie}{\hbar c}A_\mu\tilde{\phi}\right)\phi\right\} \quad (138)$$

instead of (2.110).†

Writing $H = H_\pi + H_{\text{E.M.}} + H^{(e)}_{\text{int}}$, where H_π has the same form as the free pion Hamiltonian (2.108), the pion-photon interaction $H^{(e)}_{\text{int}}$ is

$$H^{(e)}_{\text{int}} = \int d^3\mathbf{x}\left\{A_0\rho - \frac{1}{c}\mathbf{A}.\mathbf{j} - (e^2/\hbar^2)\tilde{\phi}\phi\,\mathbf{A}^2\right\} \quad (139)$$

with $j_\mu = (\mathbf{j}, ic\rho)$ given by (138). The first two terms on the right of (139) agree with the universal form of the interaction between charges and the Maxwell field. The third term gives rise to scattering and other processes involving two pions and two photons. On account of the extra factor e this term will be neglected. It is easy to see that $H^{(e)}_{\text{int}}$ is then the third component of a *vector* in isotopic space, because, as in Chapter II, § 8, the charge and current ρ, $\mathbf{j}$ are the O_3 components of an isotopic vector.

Photo-processes involving pions and nucleons are given by $H^{(e)}_{\text{int}}$ (eqn. (139)) together with the pion-nucleon interaction (131) which describes the induced pion field around a nucleon. The four-current j_μ does not contain the neutral pion component ϕ_3; however, neutral pions are created in photo-processes by charge exchange scattering of a (virtual) charged pion by a nucleon. Other contributions to photo-processes come from the direct interaction between nucleons and the electromagnetic field. This has been given by (133) or (135), and it is readily written in the quantized nucleon field variables without changing its isotopic spin dependence. In many cases the use of the magnetic moment terms as they stand in (133) can give rise to confusion,‡ because the anomalies in the magnetic moments of the proton and neutron must to a large extent be due to currents in the pion cloud

† $\mathscr{L}$ and j_μ obey gauge invariance of the type

$$A_\mu \to A_\mu + \partial_\mu\chi, \quad \phi \to \phi\exp(ie\chi/\hbar c), \quad \tilde{\phi} \to \tilde{\phi}\exp(-ie\chi/\hbar c).$$

‡ For a critical discussion of the ambiguity see G. F. Chew and F. E. Low, *Phys. Rev.* **101** (1956) 1579.

around the nucleon.† This overlapping cannot affect the isotopic selection rules, because the pion current j_μ (eqn. (138)) is an isotopic vector component.

To the *lowest* order in $(e^2/\hbar c)$ (and to any order in the pion-nucleon coupling $G^2/\hbar c^3$) the isotopic selection rules for photo-processes involving pions are

$$\left.\begin{array}{ll}\Delta T = 0, \pm 1, & \text{for } T_3 \neq 0 \\ \Delta T = \pm 1, & \text{for } T_3 = 0\end{array}\right\} \tag{140}$$

for all interactions except those involving $H^e(0)$ (eqn. (135)). For the latter the rule is $\Delta T = 0$.‡

We might have assumed that pions are coupled to nucleons by the pseudo-vector coupling (132) instead of the pseudo-scalar coupling (131) (cf. § 14 below). In that case there is an additional photon-pion-nucleon interaction which arises from making the substitution

$$\partial_\mu \rightarrow \partial_\mu \pm (ie/\hbar c)A_\mu$$

in the charged part of interaction (132). A simple calculation gives

$$H' = (ief/\mu c^2) \int d^3\mathbf{x}\, \bar{\psi}\gamma^\mu\gamma^5 A_\mu(\boldsymbol{\tau}\times\boldsymbol{\varphi})_3\psi, \tag{141}$$

where $(\boldsymbol{\tau}\times\boldsymbol{\varphi})_3 = \tau_1\phi_2-\tau_2\phi_1$. In writing (141) the isotopic indices l, l' have been omitted from the matrix $\boldsymbol{\tau}$ and from the nucleon field operators ψ, $\bar{\psi}$. Remembering that only transverse photons occur, H' can be written (using eqn. (3.10))

$$H' = -(ef/\mu c^2) \int d^3\mathbf{x}\, \bar{\psi}(\boldsymbol{\sigma}'.\mathbf{A})(\boldsymbol{\tau}\times\boldsymbol{\varphi})_3\psi, \tag{142}$$

where $\boldsymbol{\sigma}' = (\sigma^{23}, \sigma^{31}, \sigma^{12})$ is the nucleon spin operator and $(\boldsymbol{\sigma}'.\mathbf{A})$ is an inner product in coordinate space.§ Clearly H' is the third component of a vector in isotopic space. To the lowest order in $(e^2/\hbar c)$, the selection rules for processes involving (132), (139), and (142) are given by (140).

We summarize by referring to the photo-production of pions on a nucleon. (The angular distribution for photo-production of pions has been examined in Chapter I, § 21; a theorem relating to the threshold photo-production is given in Chapter V, § 16. Here we only discuss the isotopic spin rules.) The initial state is $T = \frac{1}{2}$, and, because of the strong interaction between pions and nucleons which occurs in the

† Subtracting the Dirac moment of the proton leaves the *anomalies* $\mu'_P = 1{\cdot}97$, $\mu_N = -1{\cdot}91$. The pion current (138) cannot give $\mu'_P+\mu_N \neq 0$; there must be a further (small) effect (the units are $e\hbar/2Mc$).

‡ These selection rules were given by K. M. Watson, *Phys. Rev.* **85** (1952) 852.

§ On expanding in powers of the propagation vector of the electromagnetic wave, the lowest-order term in (142) gives an $M1$ interaction whereas the lowest-order term in (139) gives $E1$.

$T = \frac{3}{2}$ state (cf. Chapter VI), there is a preference for a $T = \frac{3}{2}$ final state. The selection rules (140) show that this transition is indeed possible. The isotopic spin formalism can also be used to compare the photo-production on protons with that on neutrons. Any interaction $H(1_3)$, which is the O_3 component of an isotopic vector, acting on the initial isotopic state vector $|\frac{1}{2}, T_3\rangle$ gives

$$H(1_3)|\tfrac{1}{2}, T_3\rangle = \sum_{T=\frac{1}{2}}^{\frac{3}{2}} |T, T_3\rangle(1\,\tfrac{1}{2}\,0\,T_3|T T_3)h(T), \tag{143}$$

where $|T, T_3\rangle$ is the isotopic state vector, $(1\,\frac{1}{2}\,0\,T_3|T T^{(3)})$ is the Clebsch–Gordan coefficient, and $h(T)$ is independent of T_3. Using Table 2 on p. 131, it is easy to see that the scattering matrix element

$$\langle T_f, T_3|M(1_3)|\tfrac{1}{2}, T_3\rangle$$

which arises from $H(1_3)$ has the properties

$$\left.\begin{aligned} \langle\tfrac{1}{2}, T_3|M(1_3)|\tfrac{1}{2}, T_3\rangle &= \pm\mathscr{M}(\tfrac{1}{2}) \quad \text{for } T_3 = \pm\tfrac{1}{2} \\ \langle\tfrac{3}{2}, T_3|M(1_3)|\tfrac{1}{2}, T_3\rangle &= \mathscr{M}(\tfrac{3}{2}) \qquad \text{for } T_3 = \pm\tfrac{1}{2} \end{aligned}\right\},$$

where $\mathscr{M}(T)$ is independent of T_3. These relations make it possible to separate the isotopic scalar contribution from the isotopic vector contributions, if the scattering matrix is known.

A detailed discussion and analysis of the photo-pion effect is to be found in the literature.†

14. The pseudo-vector interaction and the equivalence theorem

Both the pseudo-scalar interaction (131) between pions and nucleons, and the pseudo-vector interaction (132) have been used in the preceding section. Field theorists believe that the correct interaction to use is the pseudo-scalar, because it is possible to carry out renormalization in this case (cf. Chapter V); no successful renormalization of the pseudo-vector interaction has been made. On the other hand, the physical process involved in pseudo-vector coupling is the simpler. Also, so long as the nucleon's motion is not relativistic, the pseudo-vector coupling (using a high-frequency cut-off) gives good agreement with the actual pion-nucleon phenomena (cf. Chapter VI). In the present section, after setting up the pseudo-vector theory, and giving an account of the basic physical processes, it is shown that, to the lowest order in the coupling constant, the two types of coupling are equivalent for low energy processes.

† Surveys are given by: M. Gell-Mann and K. M. Watson, *Ann. Rev. Nuclear Sci.* **4** (Annual Reviews Inc., Stanford, 1954); E. Fermi, *Suppl. Nuovo Cim.* **2** (1955) 1; G. Bernardini, ibid., p. 104.

The pion and nucleon fields interacting through a pseudo-vector coupling are given by the Lagrangian density (cf. (86) and (132))

$$\mathscr{L} = \mathscr{L}_0 + (if/\mu)\bar{\psi}\gamma^\nu\gamma^5(\boldsymbol{\tau}.\partial_\nu\boldsymbol{\varphi})\psi, \tag{144}$$

where $\mathscr{L}_0$ is the Lagrangian for the free pion and nucleon fields; $\boldsymbol{\varphi} = (\phi_1, \phi_2, \phi_3)$ is the pion amplitude written as an isotopic vector. The pion canonical momentum density $\boldsymbol{\pi} = (\pi_1, \pi_2, \pi_3)$ now involves the coupling; it is

$$\boldsymbol{\pi} = \dot{\boldsymbol{\varphi}} + (f/c\mu)\bar{\psi}\gamma^4\gamma^5\boldsymbol{\tau}\psi. \tag{145}$$

By the usual methods the Hamiltonian becomes

$$H = H_\pi + H_N - (f/\mu)\int d^3\mathbf{x}\left\{i\bar{\psi}\gamma^k\gamma^5(\boldsymbol{\tau}.\partial_k\boldsymbol{\varphi})\psi + \frac{1}{c}\bar{\psi}\gamma^4\gamma^5(\boldsymbol{\tau}.\boldsymbol{\pi})\psi\right\} + \\ + \tfrac{1}{2}(f/c\mu)^2\int d^3\mathbf{x}\,\bar{\psi}\gamma^4\gamma^5\boldsymbol{\tau}\psi.\bar{\psi}\gamma^4\gamma^5\boldsymbol{\tau}\psi, \tag{146}$$

where H_N is the nucleon Hamiltonian (cf. eqn. (10)) and H_π is the pion Hamiltonian (eqn. (2.136)); in both, $\boldsymbol{\pi}$ is given by (145). The fourth term in (146) is a point interaction between two nucleons; it appears because using (145) for $\boldsymbol{\pi}$ implies that H_π does not describe bare pions—H_π by itself gives a somewhat better approximation than (2.136).

The Hamiltonian

$$H = H_\pi + H_N + H_{(\text{p.v.})}, \tag{147}$$

with $H_{(\text{p.v.})}$ given by (132),

$$H_{(\text{p.v.})} = -i(f/\mu)\int d^3\mathbf{x}\,\bar{\psi}\gamma^\mu\gamma^5(\boldsymbol{\tau}.\partial_\mu\boldsymbol{\varphi})\psi, \tag{148}$$

is identical with the operator (146) apart from the f^2 term; the same commutation relations at a given time are used in the two cases. The distinction between these two Hamiltonians (146) and (147) is seen by (150) to vanish for zero velocity nucleons.

We now show that, so long as the nucleons have non-relativistic velocities and the pion energies are less than the nucleon rest energy, the interaction term containing $\dot{\boldsymbol{\varphi}}$ (or $\boldsymbol{\pi}$) can be neglected. The form (147) will be used. Using the spin matrices (cf. (3.10)) we have†

$$H_{(\text{p.v.})} = (f/\mu)\int d^3\mathbf{x}\,\bar{\psi}(\boldsymbol{\sigma}'.\text{grad})(\boldsymbol{\tau}.\boldsymbol{\varphi})\psi - \frac{f}{c\mu}\int d^3\mathbf{x}\,\bar{\psi}\gamma^5(\boldsymbol{\tau}.\dot{\boldsymbol{\varphi}})\psi. \tag{149}$$

In the representation (3.35) for the nucleon spinors,

$$\gamma^5 = \begin{pmatrix} 0 & -I \\ -I & 0 \end{pmatrix}, \qquad \sigma^{23} = \begin{pmatrix} \sigma_1 & 0 \\ 0 & \sigma_1 \end{pmatrix}, \tag{150}$$

where σ_1 is the 2×2 Pauli spin matrix, etc. Hence for a transition in which no anti-nucleons are created, $\bar{\psi}\gamma^5\psi$ is of order (v/c) relative to $\bar{\psi}\boldsymbol{\sigma}\psi$, where v is a measure of the nucleon's velocities. The term $\bar{\psi}\gamma^5\psi$

† grad does not act on $\boldsymbol{\tau}$.

may create a virtual pair consisting of a nucleon and an anti-nucleon, but the energy difference for this virtual state is of order $2Mc^2$;† it follows that for this process the second term in (149) is of order $(\hbar\omega_\pi/Mc^2)$ relative to the main contribution from the first term in (149) ($\hbar\omega_\pi =$ pion energy). Hence for pion energies $\hbar\omega_\pi$ up to around 350 MeV we can use (147) with

$$H_{(\mathrm{p.v.})} = (f/\mu)\int d^3\mathbf{x}\,\tilde{\psi}(\boldsymbol{\sigma}'.\mathrm{grad})(\boldsymbol{\tau}.\boldsymbol{\varphi})\psi; \tag{151}$$

this interaction has indeed been successfully used by Chew and others.‡

The virtual processes

Suppose a nucleon at rest emits a pion in a virtual process in which angular momentum (but not energy) is conserved. For the low pion energies considered above, the recoil of the nucleon is small, and it will most probably remain in an S-state. On account of its odd intrinsic parity, the pion must have odd angular momentum, and to conserve the total angular momentum the pion must be in a P-state; the nucleon spin must flip over. A similar process occurs when a low-energy pion is absorbed. In (151) $(\boldsymbol{\sigma}'.\mathrm{grad}\,\boldsymbol{\varphi})$ favours P-wave pions, and allows for the nucleon spin-flip; thus $H_{(\mathrm{p.v.})}$ provides a simple picture of the virtual processes which can be used to describe pion phenomena.

The interaction (131)

$$H_{(\mathrm{p.s.})} = iG\int d^3\mathbf{x}\,\tilde{\psi}\gamma^5(\boldsymbol{\tau}.\boldsymbol{\varphi})\psi \tag{152}$$

gives a different basic process at low energy. On account of the γ^5 operator, and the presence of $\boldsymbol{\varphi}$ itself, an S-wave pion disappears and a nucleon and an anti-nucleon—both in S-states—are created. Conversely, the nucleon-anti-nucleon pair disappear and an S-wave pion is created. Parity is conserved because the anti-nucleon has the opposite parity to the nucleon. Because of the large energy difference for the virtual state, the coupling constant G has to be particularly large. Experiment shows that at moderate energies P-wave pions interact strongly with nucleons; there is no simple *direct* way§ of seeing how this arises from $H_{(\mathrm{p.s.})}$.

We now discuss briefly how the pseudo-scalar interaction can be transformed into a form which contains the pseudo-vector interaction. Let $H^{(1)}$ be the Hamiltonian

$$H^{(1)} = H_\pi + H_N + H_{(\mathrm{p.s.})} + H^{(e)}, \tag{153}$$

† M is the nucleon mass.
‡ See G. F. Chew, *Phys. Rev.* **95** (1954) 285; also Chapter VI below.
§ See, however, footnote †, p. 191 above.

where H_π, H_N are the free pion and nucleon terms, $H_{(\text{p.s.})}$ is given by (152), and $H^{(e)}$ is the interaction of the Maxwell field with pions and nucleons.† Let $|\,\rangle_{\text{p.s.}}$ be any eigenstate of (153). The Hamiltonian $H^{(1)}$ is replaced by $H^{(2)} = \exp(iK)H^{(1)}\exp(-iK)$, where K is the Hermitian operator‡

$$K = \frac{G}{2Mc^2}\int \tilde{\psi}\gamma^5(\boldsymbol{\tau}.\boldsymbol{\varphi})\psi\, d^3\mathbf{x}.$$

Under this unitary transformation, the eigenstates of $H^{(2)}$ are

$$|\,\rangle_{(2)} = \exp(iK)|\,\rangle_{\text{p.s.}}.$$

Also, on expanding in powers of K,

$$H^{(2)} = H^{(1)}+i[K,H^{(1)}]+\frac{i^2}{2!}[K,[K,H^{(1)}]]+\dots. \tag{154}$$

Drell and Henley‡ have shown how the series (154) can be summed. It is easy to verify that§

$$H^{(2)} = H_\pi+H_N+H^{(e)}+\left(\frac{Gm_\pi}{2fM}\right)(H_{(\text{p.v.})}+H')+H(G^2), \tag{155}$$

where $H_{(\text{p.v.})}$ is the pseudo-vector interaction (149), H' is the interaction (142) between photons, pions, and nucleons, and $H(G^2)$ contains only G^2 and higher powers of the coupling constant. In the case of low-energy pions for which the nucleon motion is neglected, the dominant term in $H(G^2)$ is

$$\frac{G^2}{2Mc^2}\int \tilde{\psi}\psi\boldsymbol{\varphi}.\boldsymbol{\varphi}\, d^3\mathbf{x}. \tag{156}$$

Thus the pseudo-scalar coupling theory is at low energies equivalent to a theory having pseudo-vector coupling, where

$$f/m_\pi = G/2M, \tag{157}$$

together with the interaction (156). The latter term directly gives elastic scattering of pions by nucleons, and Drell and Henley‡ show that it corresponds to a short-range repulsive force. Clearly S-wave pions can be scattered according to (156); further, these authors show that, taking account of the short range of this interaction, a careful calculation could perhaps reconcile the observed small S-wave pion scattering with the observed strong P-wave interaction.

Pion-nucleon scattering is discussed in Chapter VI, §§ 4–8.

† $H^{(e)} = H^{(e)}_{\text{int}}+H^{(e)}_P$, where $H^{(e)}_{\text{int}}$ is given by (139), and $H^{(e)}_P = \frac{1}{2}iec\int\tilde{\psi}\gamma^\mu A_\mu(1+\tau_3)\psi\, d^3\mathbf{x}$.

‡ This transformation was used by S. D. Drell and E. M. Henley, *Phys. Rev.* **88** (1952) 1053.

§ m_π, M are the pion and nucleon masses.

V

THE S-MATRIX AND RENORMALIZATION

1. Scattering theory

IT is necessary to examine in more detail the properties of the S-matrix which was introduced in Chapter IV, § 7. In the present section an exact and simple form of scattering theory is developed, without using perturbation theory. The method is sufficiently general to apply, for example, (*a*) to the mutual scattering of two particles due to a given interaction potential, (*b*) to the various scattering, absorption, and creation processes which occur when the interaction between two quantized fields is switched on.†

Suppose the system has a Hamiltonian $H = H_0+H_{\text{int}}$, where H_0 describes the individual parts of the system and H_{int} is the interaction (i.e. in (*a*), H_0 describes the two particles at large separation, and in (*b*), the non-interacting fields). In the notation of Chapter IV, § 7, $H_0 = H_1+H_2$, where H_1, H_2 describe the two separate parts of the system. It is convenient to introduce the interaction representation via the Schrödinger representation. Any state vector in the latter representation $|\Psi^{(s)}(t)\rangle$ obeys

$$i\hbar\frac{d}{dt}|\Psi^{(s)}(t)\rangle = (H_0+H_{\text{int}})|\Psi^{(s)}(t)\rangle. \tag{1}$$

In the Schrödinger representation all the operators are independent of time. For quantized fields the operators obey the *single time* commutation relations, such as (4.82) and (4.83). For the treatment to be sufficiently general to include interacting fields, we must now multiply the interaction operator H_{int} by the factor $\exp(-\epsilon|t|/\hbar)$ (where ϵ is small and positive), so that H_{int} is switched on and off in an adiabatic manner‡ (cf. Chapter IV, § 7). In all time integrations this factor is to be included. Here the limit processes will be set out explicitly.

The corresponding interaction representation state vector $|\Psi(t)\rangle$ is defined by

$$|\Psi(t)\rangle = \exp(iH_0 t/\hbar)|\Psi^{(s)}(t)\rangle, \tag{2}$$

† The techniques which are used have been set out by B. A. Lippmann and J. Schwinger, *Phys. Rev.* **79** (1950) 469, and by M. Gell-Mann and M. L. Goldberger, ibid. **91** (1953) 398.

‡ Because the switching on and off is an *external* effect, it does not matter that the operator $H_{\text{int}}\exp(-\epsilon|t|/\hbar)$ varies with time.

and with this substitution, (1) becomes

$$i\hbar\frac{d}{dt}|\Psi(t)\rangle = \hat{H}_{\text{int}}(t)|\Psi(t)\rangle, \tag{3}$$

where

$$\hat{H}_{\text{int}}(t) = \exp(iH_0 t/\hbar)H_{\text{int}}\exp(-\epsilon|t|/\hbar)\exp(-iH_0 t/\hbar) \tag{4}$$

is the interaction representation operator (cf. eqn. (4.100)). Using (4.96) and (4), it is easy to verify that as $\epsilon \to 0$ the present definition of the interaction representation becomes identical with that in Chapter IV, § 7. By (2), $|\Psi(0)\rangle = |\Psi^{(s)}(0)\rangle$.

The S-matrix

The development of the interaction state vector with time is given by

$$|\Psi(t)\rangle = U(t,-\infty)|\Psi(-\infty)\rangle,$$

where $U(t,-\infty)$ obeys (4.100). Because of the adiabatic switching-on, $U(t,-\infty)$ and therefore $|\Psi(-\infty)\rangle$ are well defined.† $|\Psi(-\infty)\rangle$ is an eigenstate of H_0; it describes the initial state of the colliding particles before they begin to interact. It is convenient to write $|\Psi(-\infty)\rangle \equiv |\Phi_\alpha\rangle$ where this constant state vector obeys

$$H_0|\Phi_\alpha\rangle = E_\alpha|\Phi_\alpha\rangle. \tag{5}$$

As was explained in Chapter IV, § 7, $|\Phi_\alpha\rangle$ represents the infinite (or very long) wave trains which make up the initial state. We find the probability that after the collision the system is in the state $|\Phi_\beta\rangle$, where

$$H_0|\Phi_\beta\rangle = E_\beta|\Phi_\beta\rangle. \tag{6}$$

This probability is $|\langle\Phi_\beta|S|\Phi_\alpha\rangle|^2$, where $S = U(\infty,-\infty)$; it gives the fraction of the initial wave trains which is scattered into the state $|\Phi_\beta\rangle$. As we shall see in § 2, the matrix S is unitary, hence the total scattering probability adds up to unity; it is assumed that the eigenstates of H_0 are normalized so that‡

$$\sum_{(\text{all }\beta)}|\Phi_\beta\rangle\langle\Phi_\beta| = I. \tag{7}$$

In practice we require the rate at which particles are scattered out of the state $|\Phi_\alpha\rangle$ into $|\Phi_\beta\rangle$. This will be found by dividing $|\langle\Phi_\beta|S|\Phi_\alpha\rangle|^2$ by the time for which the interaction was switched on (cf. p. 218).

Writing $S = I-T$, we have to find $T_{\beta\alpha} = -\langle\Phi_\beta|U(\infty,-\infty)|\Phi_\alpha\rangle$ for $\beta \neq \alpha$. First, eqn. (4.100) is replaced by the integral equation

$$U(t,-\infty) = I-\frac{i}{\hbar}\int_{-\infty}^{t} dt'\hat{H}_{\text{int}}(t')U(t',-\infty). \tag{8}$$

† Cf. eqn. (8) below.

‡ I is the identity operator.

Clearly the correct initial condition, $U(t,-\infty) \to 1$ as $t \to -\infty$, is satisfied by (8). From (8)

$$T_{\beta\alpha} = \frac{i}{\hbar}\int\limits_{-\infty}^{\infty} dt\, \langle\Phi_\beta|\hat{H}_{\text{int}}(t)U(t,-\infty)|\Phi_\alpha\rangle. \tag{9}$$

Using (4) and (6) gives

$$T_{\beta\alpha} = \frac{i}{\hbar}\langle\Phi_\beta|H_{\text{int}}|\Psi_\alpha^{(+)}(E_\beta)\rangle \tag{10}$$

with

$$|\Psi_\alpha^{(+)}(E)\rangle = \int\limits_{-\infty}^{\infty} dt\, \exp\{i(E-H_0)t/\hbar\}\exp(-\epsilon|t|/\hbar)U(t,-\infty)|\Phi_\alpha\rangle. \tag{11}$$

The adiabatic switching factor has now been explicitly written; in (10) H_{int} is a *constant* operator.

An integral equation for $|\Psi_\alpha^{(+)}(E)\rangle$ is found by inserting (8) on the right of (11). This gives†

$$|\Psi_\alpha^{(+)}(E)\rangle = \int\limits_{-\infty}^{\infty} dt\, \exp\{i(E-E_\alpha)t/\hbar\}\exp(-\epsilon|t|/\hbar)|\Phi_\alpha\rangle -$$

$$-\frac{i}{\hbar}\int\limits_{0}^{\infty} dt\, \exp\{i(E-H_0)t/\hbar\}\exp(-\epsilon|t|/\hbar)H_{\text{int}}|\Psi_\alpha^{(+)}(E)\rangle. \tag{12}$$

Comparing with the Appendix (especially eqns. (A.35), (A.37)), we have for $\epsilon \to +0$,

$$\frac{i}{\hbar}\int\limits_{0}^{\infty} dt\, \exp\{i(E-H_0)t/\hbar\}\exp(-\epsilon|t|/\hbar) = 2\pi i\delta^{(+)}(H_0-E)$$

$$= i\pi\delta(E-H_0) - P\frac{1}{E-H_0}. \tag{13}$$

Eqn. (13) has a precise meaning when it is evaluated between eigenstates of H_0. The symbol P indicates that (on integration) the Cauchy principal value is to be taken. A convenient short notation for the right-hand side of (13) is

$$2\pi i\delta^{(+)}(H_0-E) = \frac{1}{H_0-E-i\epsilon}.$$

The integral equation for $|\Psi_\alpha^{(+)}(E)\rangle$ becomes

$$|\Psi_\alpha^{(+)}(E)\rangle = 2\pi\hbar\delta(E-E_\alpha)|\Phi_\alpha\rangle + \frac{1}{E-H_0+i\epsilon}H_{\text{int}}|\Psi_\alpha^{(+)}(E)\rangle \tag{14}$$

(where $\epsilon \to +0$).

† In the manipulation it is necessary to make an unimportant change in one of the adiabatic switching factors.

The scattering state

Multiplying eqn. (13) by the operator $(E-H_0+i\epsilon)$ and letting ϵ vanish gives†
$$(E-H_0-H_{\text{int}})|\Psi_\alpha^{(+)}(E)\rangle = 0.$$
Thus $|\Psi_\alpha^{(+)}(E)\rangle$ is an eigenstate of the *total* Hamiltonian H. Amongst these eigenstates there may be bound states (they are solutions of (14) for which $E \neq E_\alpha$). The eigenstates which describe scattering have the same energy E_α as the initial state $|\Phi_\alpha\rangle$. The scattering solutions are found by substituting in (14), $|\Psi_\alpha^{(+)}(E)\rangle = 2\pi\hbar\delta(E-E_\alpha)|\psi_\alpha^{(+)}\rangle$. The integral equation for $|\psi_\alpha^{(+)}\rangle$ is then‡
$$|\psi_\alpha^{(+)}\rangle = |\Phi_\alpha\rangle + \frac{1}{E_\alpha-H_0+i\epsilon} H_{\text{int}}|\psi_\alpha^{(+)}\rangle.\S \tag{15}$$
The factor $\delta(E-E_\alpha)$ which has been removed from $|\Psi_\alpha^{(+)}(E)\rangle$ is the *line-width* factor for the scattering state. This can be seen by retaining a small non-zero value of ϵ; $\delta(E-E_\alpha)$ is then replaced by
$$\frac{1}{\pi}\frac{\epsilon}{(E-E_\alpha)^2+\epsilon^2}.$$
The energy spread about E_α, which is of the order of ϵ, corresponds to the uncertainty in energy arising from the finite duration of the collision process as given by $H_{\text{int}}\exp(-\epsilon|t|/\hbar)$.

We now examine some properties of the scattering state $|\psi_\alpha^{(+)}\rangle$. The perturbation theory solution of (15) is an expansion in powers of H_{int}:
$$|\psi_\alpha^{(+)}\rangle = |\Phi_\alpha\rangle + \frac{1}{E_\alpha-H_0+i\epsilon} H_{\text{int}}|\Phi_\alpha\rangle + \\ + \frac{1}{E_\alpha-H_0+i\epsilon} H_{\text{int}} \frac{1}{E_\alpha-H_0+i\epsilon} H_{\text{int}}|\Phi_\alpha\rangle + \dots. \tag{16}$$
The operator products can be evaluated by using (7); for example
$$\frac{1}{E_\alpha-H_0+i\epsilon} H_{\text{int}}|\Phi_\alpha\rangle = \sum_\beta |\Phi_\beta\rangle \frac{1}{E_\alpha-E_\beta+i\epsilon} \langle\Phi_\beta|H_{\text{int}}|\Phi_\alpha\rangle. \tag{17}$$
Thus in general when $|\psi_\alpha^{(+)}\rangle$ is expanded in terms of the eigenstates $|\Phi_\beta\rangle$ of H_0, terms for which $E_\beta \neq E_\alpha$ will occur.

The presence of the small positive quantity ϵ shows how the integration over E_β in (17) is to be evaluated at $E_\beta = E_\alpha$. The Green's function
$$G(E_\alpha) = \frac{1}{E_\alpha-H_0+i\epsilon}$$

† The term in $|\Phi_\alpha\rangle$ disappears because $(E-E_\alpha)\delta(E-E_\alpha) = 0$.

‡ To see that the step from (14) to (15) is rigorous, we may retain ϵ as a small positive quantity; division by $\delta(E-E_\alpha)$ is then allowed.

§ The operator H_{int} in (14) and (15) contains no adiabatic switching factor.

is similar to the causal functions D_F (eqn. (A.64)) and S_F (eqn. (A.88)) which are associated with the chronological operator products (Chapter II, § 5, and Chapter IV, § 4).

Scattering by a central potential

As an example of the effect of $G(E_\alpha)$ we consider the *exact* solution of (15) for the scattering of a scalar particle of momentum $\mathbf{p}_\alpha$ by a central potential $V(r) \equiv H_{\text{int}}$. The eigenstates $|lmk\rangle$ describing a free particle having angular momentum (l, m) about the origin, and radial momentum k, are used to represent $|\psi_\alpha^{(+)}\rangle$:

$$|\psi_\alpha^{(+)}\rangle = \sum_{l,m,k} |lmk\rangle\langle lmk|\psi_\alpha^{(+)}\rangle.$$

The state $|lmk\rangle$ obeys

$$H_0|lmk\rangle = E_k|lmk\rangle;$$

for large r its spatial dependence is (cf. (2.92))

$$\langle \mathbf{x}|lmk\rangle \sim \frac{1}{kr}\sin(kr-\tfrac{1}{2}l\pi)Y_l^{(m)}(\theta,\phi).$$

In the present case

$$\langle \mathbf{x}|\Phi_\alpha\rangle = \exp\{i(\mathbf{p}.\mathbf{x})/\hbar\};$$

this is normalized so that there is one scalar particle per unit volume. Eqn. (15) has the spatial representative

$$\langle \mathbf{x}|\psi_\alpha^{(+)}\rangle = \langle \mathbf{x}|\Phi_\alpha\rangle + \sum_{l,m,k}\langle \mathbf{x}|lmk\rangle \frac{1}{E_\alpha - E_k + i\epsilon}\langle lmk|V(r)|\psi_\alpha^{(+)}\rangle. \quad (18)$$

If the potential $V(r)$ is of finite range, it is frequently the case† that $\langle lmk|V(r)|\psi_\alpha^{(+)}\rangle$ is not strongly dependent on k for $E_k \simeq E_\alpha$. Hence, by the analysis of Chapter II, § 6 (especially eqns. (2.97), (2.98)), the second term on the right of (18) has the asymptotic form $\exp(ik_\alpha r)/k_\alpha r$ of an outgoing wave (here $E_k = E_\alpha$). Therefore $\langle \mathbf{x}|\psi_\alpha^{(+)}\rangle$ consists of a plane incident wave $\langle \mathbf{x}|\Phi_\alpha\rangle$ and an outgoing scattered wave; this is just the boundary condition which is used to give the usual exact solution of the scattering by a central potential in terms of the phase shifts (cf. Chapter III, § 8, where the corresponding solution for the scattering of fermions is given).

The state $|\psi_\alpha^{(-)}\rangle$

A little manipulation with operators shows that the solution of (15) can be formally written

$$|\psi_\alpha^{(+)}\rangle = |\Phi_\alpha\rangle + \frac{1}{E_\alpha - H + i\epsilon} H_{\text{int}}|\Phi_\alpha\rangle. \quad (19)$$

† This is so if E_α is not close to a resonance.

This equation is of value in multiple scattering theory (§ 2 below). We sometimes have to use the solution $|\psi_\alpha^{(-)}\rangle$ of the equation obtained by reversing the sign of ϵ in (15):

$$|\psi_\alpha^{(-)}\rangle = |\Phi_\alpha\rangle + \frac{1}{E_\alpha - H_0 - i\epsilon} H_{\text{int}} |\psi_\alpha^{(-)}\rangle. \tag{20}$$

Obviously $|\psi_\alpha^{(-)}\rangle$ is also an eigenstate of the total Hamiltonian, satisfying

$$(E_\alpha - H)|\psi_\alpha^{(-)}\rangle = 0.$$

In the example of scattering by a central potential $V(r)$, the state $|\psi_\alpha^{(-)}\rangle$ corresponds to a plane wave $|\Phi_\alpha\rangle$ and an incoming spherical wave of asymptotic form $\exp(-ik_\alpha r)/(k_\alpha r)$. The corresponding row state vector, formed by taking the Hermitian conjugate, obeys

$$\langle\psi_\alpha^{(-)}| = \langle\Phi_\alpha| + \langle\psi_\alpha^{(-)}|H_{\text{int}} \frac{1}{E_\alpha - H_0 + i\epsilon}. \tag{21}$$

The scattering state $|\psi_\alpha^{(-)}\rangle$ is given by

$$|\Psi_\alpha^{(-)}(E)\rangle = 2\pi\hbar\delta(E - E_\alpha)|\psi_\alpha^{(-)}\rangle,$$

where $|\Psi_\alpha^{(-)}(E)\rangle$ obeys a modified form of equation (12):

$$|\Psi_\alpha^{(-)}(E)\rangle = \int_{-\infty}^{\infty} dt \exp\{i(E - H_0)t/\hbar\}\exp(-\epsilon|t|/\hbar)|\Phi_\alpha\rangle +$$

$$+\frac{i}{\hbar}\int_{-\infty}^{0} dt \exp\{i(E - H_0)t/\hbar\}\exp(-\epsilon|t|/\hbar)H_{\text{int}}|\Psi_\alpha^{(-)}(E)\rangle. \tag{22}$$

Between eqns. (12) and (22) the role of infinite past and infinite future has been exchanged. We trace this connexion a step farther by noticing that (22) can be written

$$|\Psi_\alpha^{(-)}(E)\rangle = \int_{-\infty}^{\infty} dt \exp\{i(E - H_0)t/\hbar\}\exp(-\epsilon|t|/\hbar)U(t,\infty)|\Phi_\alpha\rangle, \tag{23}$$

where

$$U(t,\infty) = I + \frac{i}{\hbar}\int_{t}^{\infty} dt' \hat{H}_{\text{int}}(t')U(t',\infty). \tag{24}$$

The operator $U(t,\infty)$ given by (24) equals $\lim_{t_0\to\infty} U(t,t_0)$, where $U(t,t_0)$ is given by eqns. (4.95), (4.97).† The switching-off factor ensures that $U(t,\infty)$ is well defined. Also, $U(t,\infty) \to I$ as $t \to \infty$.

Clearly $|\psi_\alpha^{(-)}\rangle$ describes the collision process for which the *final* state

† It is convenient to use

$$U(t,t_0) = I - (i/\hbar)\int_{t_0} dt' \hat{H}_{\text{int}}(t')U(t',t_0).$$

is $|\Phi_\alpha\rangle$. A boundary condition of this form is of no practical value; we only introduce $|\psi_\alpha^{(-)}\rangle$ because it has mathematical use below (§ 2). Using (21) and a form similar to (19), gives the symmetry property

$$\langle\Phi_\beta|H_{\text{int}}|\psi_\alpha^{(+)}\rangle = \langle\psi_\beta^{(-)}|H_{\text{int}}|\Phi_\alpha\rangle \qquad (E_\beta = E_\alpha). \tag{25}$$

The scattering matrix

The matrix element (10) can be written

$$T_{\beta\alpha} = 2\pi i\delta(E_\beta - E_\alpha)\mathbf{T}_{\beta\alpha}, \tag{26}$$

where†

$$\mathbf{T}_{\beta\alpha} = \langle\Phi_\beta|H_{\text{int}}|\psi_\alpha^{(+)}\rangle.$$

$\mathbf{T}$ is called the *scattering matrix.*

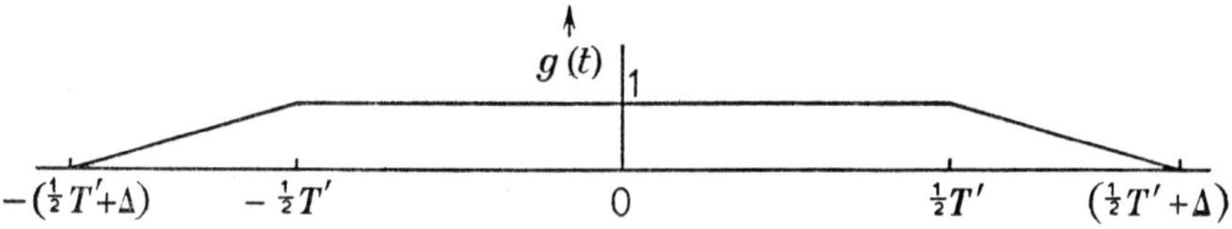

FIG. 6. The switching factor $g(t)$.

The probability that the system, initially in state $|\Phi_\alpha\rangle$, is finally in state $|\Phi_\beta\rangle$ is

$$|T_{\beta\alpha}|^2 = (4\pi)^2\{\delta(E_\beta - E_\alpha)\}^2|\mathbf{T}_{\beta\alpha}|^2.$$

Here one δ-function factor gives $(T'/2\pi\hbar)$ where T' is the time for which the interaction has been switched on.‡ This is seen by suitably modifying the first integral in (12), which was written

$$2\pi\hbar\delta(E_\beta - E_\alpha) = \int\limits_{-\infty}^{\infty} dt\, \exp\{i(E_\beta - E_\alpha)t/\hbar\}\exp(-\epsilon|t|/\hbar). \tag{27}$$

A δ-function also results in the limit $T' \to \infty$ if we replace the adiabatic switching factor $\exp(-\epsilon|t|/\hbar)$ by a function $g(t)$ such as is shown in Fig. 6. This function equals unity between $t = -\frac{1}{2}T'$ and $t = \frac{1}{2}T'$; outside this range it decreases smoothly to zero in a large but fixed interval Δ. For $E_\beta = E_\alpha$ eqn. (27) then gives (as $T' \to \infty$) $2\pi\hbar\delta(0)/T' \to 1$. Hence the transition probability per unit time from the state $|\Phi_\alpha\rangle$ to the state $|\Phi_\beta\rangle$ is

$$W_{\beta\alpha} = \frac{2\pi}{\hbar}\delta(E_\beta - E_\alpha)|\mathbf{T}_{\beta\alpha}|^2. \tag{28}$$

† The notation is almost identical with that of B. A. Lippman and J. Schwinger, *Phys. Rev.* **79** (1950) 469.

‡ $|T_{\alpha\beta}|^2$ cannot be increased indefinitely by increasing T'. A large time T' requires long wave trains; the latter require a large periodic box and corresponding small density in the waves. Normalization is discussed in detail by M. Gell-Mann and M. L. Goldberger, *Phys. Rev.* **91** (1953) 398.

The remaining factor $\delta(E_\beta - E_\alpha)$ expresses the line width of the final state.

As an example of the application of (28), consider the collision of two monoenergetic beams of nucleons. Let $\rho(E_\beta)\,d\Omega_\beta\,dE_\beta$ be the number of states in the (total) energy interval dE_β for which the final momentum $\mathbf{p}$ of one nucleon lies in the small solid angle $d\Omega_\beta$. Considering unit volume, we have

$$\rho(E_\beta) = \frac{p^2\,dp}{(2\pi\hbar)^3\,dE_\beta}.$$

Integrating over the energy E_β of the final state, the total transition probability/unit time for scattering into the solid angle $d\Omega_\beta$ is

$$\Gamma\,d\Omega_\beta = \frac{2\pi}{\hbar}\rho(E_\beta)\,d\Omega_\beta\,|\mathbf{T}_{\beta\alpha}|^2. \tag{29}$$

Because there is one particle of each kind per unit volume, the differential cross-section for scattering into $d\Omega_\beta$ is

$$\sigma.d\Omega_\beta = \frac{2\pi\rho(E_\beta)\,d\Omega_\beta}{\hbar v}|\mathbf{T}_{\beta\alpha}|^2, \tag{30}$$

where v is the relative velocity of the colliding nucleons. In a similar way (28) can be applied to more general cases.

From the unitary condition† $\tilde{S}.S = I$, we have

$$\tilde{T}.T = T+\tilde{T}.$$

Substituting (26) and removing one δ-function factor gives

$$\pi\sum_\beta |\mathbf{T}_{\beta\alpha}|^2\,\delta(E_\beta - E_\alpha) = -\mathrm{im}(\mathbf{T}_{\alpha\alpha}), \tag{31}$$

where the summation is over *all* values of β. From eqn. (28),

$$\mathrm{im}(\mathbf{T}_{\alpha\alpha}) = -\tfrac{1}{2}\hbar\sum_{\beta\neq\alpha} W_{\beta\alpha}, \tag{32}$$

it is assumed that the term $\beta = \alpha$ can be omitted from the summation in (31) without error. Eqn. (32) is the generalization of (1.35) which relates the forward scattering amplitude for no spin-flip to the total cross-section (the optical theorem).

The energy shift

The theory given above assumes that the interaction H_{int} makes a negligible change in the energy of the collision states relative to the free particle values. For quantized fields this is not true; however, the

† See also § 2 below.

difficulty can readily be avoided as follows.† Suppose the eigenstates of H_0+H_{int} for *real* particles at a large separation are $|\Psi'_\alpha\rangle$, so that

$$(H_0+H_{\text{int}})|\Psi'_\alpha\rangle = (E_\alpha+\Delta_\alpha)|\Psi'_\alpha\rangle.$$

E_α is the energy of the corresponding bare particle state $|\Phi_\alpha\rangle$, and Δ_α is the energy displacement due to H_{int} (Δ_α may be infinite). Clearly Δ_α is the *sum* of the energy displacements for the individual real particles in $|\Psi'_\alpha\rangle$. The total Hamiltonian may be written:

$$H_0+H_{\text{int}} = (H_0+\Delta)+(H_{\text{int}}-\Delta),$$

where

$$\Delta = \sum_\alpha |\Phi_\alpha\rangle\,\Delta_\alpha\,\langle\Phi_\alpha|.$$

If $(H_{\text{int}}-\Delta)$ is now taken as the interaction, there will be no displacement of the energy values.

2. The unitary condition

Because the interaction is switched on and switched off by the adiabatic switching factor, the matrix $S = U(\infty,-\infty)$, which describes transitions from eigenstates $|\Phi_\alpha\rangle$ of H_0 to eigenstates $|\Phi_\beta\rangle$ of H_0, will be unitary. The usual methods of calculating the operator $U(t,-\infty)$ (for finite t) will not give a unitary result if bound states can occur. We now examine the unitary properties in more detail.

Eqn. (11) can be written

$$2\pi\hbar\delta(E-E_\alpha)|\psi_\alpha^{(+)}\rangle$$
$$= \int\limits_{-\infty}^{\infty} dt\,\exp\{i(E-H_0)t/\hbar\}\exp(-\epsilon|t|/\hbar)U(t,-\infty)|\Phi_\alpha\rangle. \quad (33)$$

Multiplying by $\exp(-iEt'/\hbar)$ and integrating over E from $-\infty$ to ∞, gives (for finite t)

$$\exp(-iE_\alpha t/\hbar)|\psi_\alpha^{(+)}\rangle = \exp(-iH_0 t/\hbar)\,\exp(-\epsilon|t|/\hbar)\,U(t,-\infty)|\Phi_\alpha\rangle.$$

Hence

$$|\psi_\alpha^{(+)}\rangle = U(0,-\infty)|\Phi_\alpha\rangle. \quad (34)$$

By (7) this gives

$$U(0,-\infty) = \sum_\alpha |\psi_\alpha^{(+)}\rangle\langle\Phi_\alpha|. \quad (35)$$

The operator $U(0,-\infty)$ is the *wave matrix* of Møller.‡ It follows from (35) that

$$\tilde{U}(0,-\infty)U(0,-\infty) = \sum_\alpha |\Phi_\alpha\rangle\langle\Phi_\alpha| = I, \quad (36)$$

because the scattering states form a normal orthogonal set, i.e.

$$\langle\psi_\alpha^{(+)}|\psi_\beta^{(+)}\rangle = \delta_{\alpha\beta}.$$

† J. Pirenne, *Helv. phys. Acta*, **21** (1948) 226; *Phys. Rev.* **86** (1952) 395. See also M. Gell-Mann and M. L. Goldberger, p. 218, n. ‡.

‡ C. Møller, *K. danske vidensk. Selsk.* **23** (1945), No. 1; **22** (1946), No. 19.

However, $$U(0,-\infty)\tilde{U}(0,-\infty) = \sum_{\alpha} |\psi_{\alpha}^{(+)}\rangle\langle\psi_{\alpha}^{(+)}|.$$

This is not equal to the identity if bound states of the total Hamiltonian H exist. Because the set of scattering *plus* bound states $|\psi_b\rangle$ is complete, we have†
$$U(0,-\infty)\tilde{U}(0,-\infty) = I - \sum_{b} |\psi_b\rangle\langle\psi_b|. \tag{37}$$

The effect of bound states

The reason for obtaining a non-unitary value of $U(0,-\infty)$ is seen by referring to the definitions (8) and (24) for $U(t,-\infty)$ and $U(t,\infty)$ respectively. In these equations the adiabatic switching factor is included in $\hat{H}_{\text{int}}(t)$. Consider a bound state: for example, the deuteron. The bound state is specified by the energy E_b and by other eigenvalues B (angular momentum, charge, etc.). The adiabatic switching-off leaves the eigenvalues B unaltered, but it raises E_b slowly. The bound state necessarily has an energy lower than that of all unbound states with eigenvalues B. It follows that when the switching-off is complete, the bound state will have become a state having zero kinetic energy‡ and eigenvalues B. The deuteron will become a $^3S_1$ state of energy $(M_P+M_N)c^2$, where M_P, M_N are the proton and neutron masses. Clearly such states are spread over an infinite volume of space.

Let $|\Phi_b\rangle$ denote this free particle state of zero kinetic energy which results from adiabatically switching off the interaction in the bound state $|\psi_b\rangle$. Similarly, adiabatically switching on the interaction converts $|\Phi_b\rangle$ into the bound state $|\psi_b\rangle$. We may write symbolically
$$|\psi_b\rangle = U(0,-\infty)|\Phi_b\rangle = U(0,\infty)|\Phi_b\rangle. \tag{38}$$
If we assert that the incoming parts $|\Phi_\alpha\rangle$ of the scattering states *plus* the states $|\Phi_b\rangle$ form a complete set (cf. eqn. (7)), then using (38) we get the unitary expression
$$U(0,-\infty) = \sum_{\alpha} |\psi_{\alpha}^{(+)}\rangle\langle\Phi_\alpha| + \sum_{b} |\psi_b\rangle\langle\Phi_b|.$$
In this way we can understand why the expression (35) is non-unitary;§ however, it is obvious that in any practical scattering calculation‖ we must use the form (35) for $U(0,-\infty)$.

Practical unitary relations

The investigation of the unitary properties is continued. For this purpose we use the practical equations like (33)—that is, we ignore the

† S. T. Ma, *Phys. Rev.* **87** (1952) 652.

‡ The motion of the centre of mass is ignored in this discussion.

§ The derivation of (35) includes only scattering states because the bound states are obtained from (14) by taking $\delta(E-E_\alpha) = 0$.

‖ For an adaptation of the method of § 1 to fast protons picking up electrons from hydrogen (and similar phenomena) see T. Pradhan, *Phys. Rev.* **105** (1957) 1250.

states $|\Phi_b\rangle$ which appear in (38). The scattering state $|\Psi'^{(-)}_\alpha(E)\rangle$ is obtained from $|\Psi'^{(+)}_\alpha(E)\rangle$ by exchanging past and future. Hence in addition to (35), we expect

$$U(0,\infty) = \sum_\alpha |\psi_\alpha^{(-)}\rangle\langle\Phi_\alpha|. \tag{39}$$

From (23) it is easy to verify this relation. From eqn. (4.100) (which is identical with (8) and (24)), we can readily prove

$$U(t,t')U(t',t_0) = U(t,t_0)$$

for finite t, t', t_0. Defining $U(\infty,t)$ by

$$U(\infty,t) = I-(i/\hbar)\int\limits_t^\infty dt'\hat{H}_{\text{int}}(t')U(t',t), \tag{40}$$

it follows directly on multiplying by $U(t,t_0)$, that

$$U(\infty,t)U(t,t_0) = U(\infty,t_0). \tag{41}$$

Moreover, this holds in the two limiting cases,† so

$$\left.\begin{aligned} U(\infty,-\infty) &= U(\infty,0)U(0,-\infty) \\ \text{and} \qquad U(\infty,0)U(0,\infty) &= I \end{aligned}\right\}. \tag{42}$$

From (39),

$$\tilde{U}(0,\infty)U(0,\infty) = I \tag{43}$$

and

$$U(0,\infty)\tilde{U}(0,\infty) = I-\sum_b |\psi_b\rangle\langle\psi_b|, \tag{44}$$

where $|\psi_b\rangle$ is a bound state. Comparing the second equation in (42) with (43) gives‡

$$U(\infty,0) = \tilde{U}(0,\infty). \tag{45}$$

By (39) and (45) we have

$$U(\infty,0) = \sum_\alpha |\Phi_\alpha\rangle\langle\psi_\alpha^{(-)}|. \tag{46}$$

The physical meaning of (35) and (46) is clear; $U(0,-\infty)$ converts the bare particle (or non-interacting) state $|\Phi_\alpha\rangle$ into the state $|\psi_\alpha^{(+)}\rangle$ which is the corresponding eigenstate after the interaction has been adiabatically switched on. $U(\infty,0)$ gives the analogous relation for the switching-off process.

The proof that S is unitary now follows readily. From the eqns. (42), (37), and (44),

$$\begin{aligned} U(\infty,-\infty)\tilde{U}(\infty,-\infty) &= \sum_\alpha |\Phi_\alpha\rangle\langle\psi_\alpha^{(-)}|\Big(I-\sum_b |\psi_b\rangle\langle\psi_b|\Big)\sum_\beta |\psi_\beta^{(-)}\rangle\langle\Phi_\beta| \\ &= \sum_\alpha |\Phi_\alpha\rangle\langle\Phi_\alpha| = I; \end{aligned}$$

also,

$$\tilde{U}(\infty,-\infty)U(\infty,-\infty) = I,$$

† Cf. M. Gell-Mann and M. L. Goldberger, p. 218, n. ‡.

‡ This can also be deduced as the limiting form of the relation $U(t,t') = \tilde{U}(t',t)$ (cf. Chapter IV, § 7).

because any bound state $|\psi_b\rangle$ is orthogonal to any scattering state $|\psi_\alpha^{(-)}\rangle$. Finally we notice that the matrix elements of S can be written (using (42), (35), (46))

$$S_{\beta\alpha} \equiv \langle\Phi_\beta|S|\Phi_\alpha\rangle = \langle\psi_\beta^{(-)}|\psi_\alpha^{(+)}\rangle. \tag{47}$$

The energy continuum

Because δ-functions containing the total energy have appeared in our analysis, it is now convenient to consider the continuum of values of the total energy. We assume that amongst the commuting dynamical variables used to specify the states $|\Phi_\alpha\rangle$ is the total energy E_α. The remaining variables required to specify $|\Phi_\alpha\rangle$ will be written† as α, but we avoid confusion by writing any summation over these remaining variables as $\sum_{(\alpha)}$. All terms in this summation refer to the *same* total energy. Any initial state vector $|\,\rangle$ can be expressed as

$$|\,\rangle = \sum_{(\alpha)} \int |\Phi_\alpha\rangle \, dE_\alpha \langle\Phi_\alpha|\,\rangle. \tag{48}$$

With this set of basic vectors, the identity operator (which appears in the relation $S = I-T$, and on the right of (43), etc.) is given by

$$\langle\Phi_\beta|I|\Phi_\alpha\rangle = \delta_{\alpha\beta}\,\delta(E_\alpha-E_\beta).$$

Here, with an obvious notation, the factor $\delta_{\alpha\beta}$ refers to the variables other than the total energy. Using (26),

$$\left.\begin{aligned} S_{\beta\alpha} &= \delta(E_\beta-E_\alpha)\mathbf{S}_{\beta\alpha} \\ \text{where} \qquad \mathbf{S}_{\beta\alpha} &= 1-2\pi i\mathbf{T}_{\beta\alpha} \end{aligned}\right\}. \tag{49}$$

The operators $\mathbf{S}$ and $\mathbf{T}$ only relate states all of which have the same energy; they are sometimes called *energy shell* operators. Since we can work with monoenergetic incident beams, all information about the scattering is contained in the matrix $\mathbf{S}$. It is easy to verify that $\mathbf{S}$ has the unitary properties‡

$$\sum_{(\alpha)} \mathbf{S}^*_{\beta\alpha}\mathbf{S}_{\gamma\alpha} = \delta_{\beta\gamma}; \qquad \sum_{(\alpha)} \mathbf{S}^*_{\alpha\beta}\mathbf{S}_{\alpha\gamma} = \delta_{\beta\gamma}, \tag{50}$$

where $\sum_{(\alpha)}$ is the summation over the energy shell.

The eigenstates of $\mathbf{S}$

Because $\mathbf{S}$ is a unitary matrix, if it is transformed into diagonal form, its eigenvalues§ λ all satisfy $|\lambda|^2 = 1$. It is to be expected that the

† Strictly, we should write $|\Phi_\alpha(E_\alpha)\rangle$.

‡ It is convenient but not necessary to assume that the variables on the energy shell are discrete.

§ $\mathbf{S}$ is in general not Hermitian, so its eigenvalues λ need not be real.

eigenstates of **S** are of considerable physical importance; they will be illustrated by the example of the scattering of a scalar particle by a central potential $V(r)$. **S** converts the initial interaction representation state vector $|\Psi(-\infty)\rangle$ into the final state vector $|\Psi(\infty)\rangle$. For an eigenstate† of **S** these two state vectors can only differ by a constant phase factor λ; therefore before and after the 'collision' *all* measurable quantities must be the same.

The only states satisfying this condition are the standing wave eigenstates of $H_0+V(r)$; these states have no net flux into, or out of, the scattering centre. The asymptotic form of such an eigenstate $|lmk\rangle$, having angular momentum (l,m) and radial momentum k, is

$$\begin{aligned}\langle \mathbf{x}|lmk\rangle &\sim \frac{1}{kr}\sin\{kr-\tfrac{1}{2}l\pi+\delta_l(k)\}Y_l^{(m)}(\theta,\phi)\\ &= \frac{1}{2ikr}[\exp\{i(kr-\tfrac{1}{2}l\pi+\delta_l)\}-\exp\{-i(kr-\tfrac{1}{2}l\pi+\delta_l)\}]Y_l^{(m)}(\theta,\phi),\end{aligned} \tag{51}$$

where $\delta_l(k)$ is the usual phase shift.‡ The first exponential in (51) gives the outgoing component, the second gives an ingoing component of equal intensity. These states $|lmk\rangle$ are the stationary states belonging to the continuous spectrum of $H_0+V(r)$; they are eigenstates of **S**.

The interaction representation state vector $|\Psi(t)\rangle$ gives the change in the Schrödinger state vector for the system $H_0+V(r)$ relative to that for the free particles (H_0). The free particle stationary state (cf. § 1 above) is of the form

$$\langle \mathbf{x}|lmk\rangle \sim \frac{1}{2ikr}[\exp\{i(kr-\tfrac{1}{2}l\pi)\}-\exp\{-i(kr-\tfrac{1}{2}l\pi)\}]Y_l^{(m)}(\theta,\phi). \tag{52}$$

Remembering that $|\Psi(-\infty)\rangle$, $|\Psi(\infty)\rangle$ are associated with the terms $\exp(-ikr)$, $\exp(+ikr)$ respectively, and comparing (51) and (52), we see that the eigenvalue of **S** for the state (51) is $\exp\{2i\delta_l(k)\}$.

In other situations the interpretation of the eigenstates of **S** is not so simple. For example, at high energies a pion striking a nucleon may either be scattered elastically, or it may produce other pions; suppose it can only produce one other pion. The eigenstates of **S** will consist of a mixture of single-pion and two-pion states; the mixture is 'scattered' into itself, apart from a phase factor $\exp(2i\delta)$. If the probability

† Clearly **S** leaves unaltered the energy E_α, momentum, and angular momentum of the initial states $|\Phi_\alpha\rangle$; thus **S** commutes with the corresponding operators H_0, **P**, **M**, etc.

‡ N. F. Mott and H. S. W. Massey, *Theory of Atomic Collisions* (Clarendon Press, 2nd edn., 1949), ch. 2.

of inelastic processes were small, the mixture could be divided into two sets (*a*) and (*b*); in (*a*) the single-pion component would predominate, while in (*b*) the two-pion component would be greatest.

A method for finding bound states by using eigenstates of **S** having phases $\delta = n\pi$, where n is a positive integer, can be used in some cases.†

3. The reaction matrix

In addition to the causal solutions $|\psi_\alpha^{(\pm)}\rangle$ which were used in § 1, there is a family of eigenstates of the total Hamiltonian H which are symmetric between past and future. These states $|\psi_\alpha^{(1)}\rangle$ obey an integral equation whose kernel is the average of the kernels of eqns. (15) and (20) for $|\psi_\alpha^{(+)}\rangle$ and $|\psi_\alpha^{(-)}\rangle$, viz.

$$|\psi_\alpha^{(1)}\rangle = |\Phi_\alpha\rangle + P\frac{1}{E_\alpha - H_0} H_{\text{int}}|\psi_\alpha^{(1)}\rangle, \tag{53}$$

where P denotes the principal value. We now show how the solutions of (53) can be related to the scattering matrix to give some important results.

First we set up the related time-dependent solution of eqn. (3). By eqns. (A.36), (A.37) of the Appendix the Fourier transform of the principal value is given by

$$P\frac{1}{a} = \frac{1}{2i}\int\limits_{-\infty}^{\infty} e^{ias}\epsilon(s,0)\,ds, \tag{54}$$

where
$$\epsilon(s,s') = \begin{cases} +1 & (s > s') \\ -1 & (s < s'). \end{cases}$$

Instead of $U(t, -\infty)$ given by (8) and $U(t, \infty)$ given by (24), the solution of (4.100) which will show past–future symmetry is $V(t)$ which obeys‡

$$V(t) = 1 - \frac{i}{2\hbar}\int\limits_{-\infty}^{\infty} dt'\,\epsilon(t,t')\hat{H}_{\text{int}}(t')V(t'). \tag{55}$$

The factor $\epsilon(t,t')$ corresponds to taking the principal value of the energy denominators arising from (53). It is now necessary to relate the boundary conditions of (55) to those of the equations for $U(t, -\infty)$ or

† This depends on using (38) to give $|\Phi_b\rangle = U(\infty, -\infty)|\Phi_b\rangle$; the Bethe–Salpeter equation can be deduced. See J. Hamilton, *Proc. Camb. Phil. Soc.* **49** (1953) 97. (In this paper it is necessary to put the eigenvalue $\lambda = 1$ in eqn. (1), and to ignore eqns. (5) to (9)).

‡ Cf. J. Schwinger, *Phys. Rev.* **74** (1948) 1492.

$U(t,\infty)$. Assuming V^{-1} exists, the interaction representation state vector $|\Psi'(t)\rangle$ is related to some constant basic vector $|\Psi'\rangle$ by

$$|\Psi'(t)\rangle = V(t)|\Psi'\rangle.$$

Using this relation for $|\Psi'(\infty)\rangle$ and $|\Psi'(-\infty)\rangle$ it follows, since $|\Psi'\rangle$ is arbitrary, that

$$S.V(-\infty) = V(\infty). \tag{56}$$

By (55), this gives

$$S.(I+\tfrac{1}{2}iK) = (I-\tfrac{1}{2}iK), \tag{57}$$

where

$$K = \frac{1}{\hbar}\int\limits_{-\infty}^{\infty} dt'\hat{H}_{\text{int}}(t')V(t'). \tag{58}$$

Multiplying (55) to the left by $\tilde{V}(t)\hat{H}_{\text{int}}(t)$ and integrating over the range $-\infty \leqslant t \leqslant \infty$, and operating in a similar way on the Hermitian conjugate equation for $V(t)$, it follows that K is Hermitian.†

Analogous to (10) and (11) we can write

$$K_{\beta\alpha} = \langle\Phi_\beta|K|\Phi_\alpha\rangle = \frac{1}{\hbar}\langle\Phi_\beta|H_{\text{int}}|\Psi'^{(1)}_\alpha(E_\beta)\rangle,$$

where (it is easy to show)

$$|\Psi'^{(1)}_\alpha(E)\rangle = 2\pi\hbar\delta(E-E_\alpha)|\psi^{(1)}_\alpha\rangle$$

and $|\psi^{(1)}_\alpha\rangle$ is given by (53). Hence

$$K_{\beta\alpha} = 2\pi\delta(E_\beta-E_\alpha)\mathbf{K}_{\beta\alpha};$$

the Hermitian matrix $\mathbf{K}$ is defined only on the energy shell. Its value is

$$\mathbf{K}_{\beta\alpha} = \langle\Phi_\beta|H_{\text{int}}|\psi^{(1)}_\alpha\rangle \quad (\text{for } E_\beta = E_\alpha). \tag{59}$$

$\mathbf{K}$ is the *reaction matrix.*

Virtual processes

An important property of $\mathbf{K}$ follows from using the perturbation theory expansion of (53) (cf. eqns. (16) and (17)):

$$\begin{aligned}\mathbf{K}_{\beta\alpha} = {} & \langle\Phi_\beta|H_{\text{int}}|\Phi_\alpha\rangle + \\ & + P\sum_\gamma \frac{1}{E_\alpha-E_\gamma}\langle\Phi_\beta|H_{\text{int}}|\Phi_\gamma\rangle\langle\Phi_\gamma|H_{\text{int}}|\Phi_\alpha\rangle + \\ & + P\sum_\gamma \frac{1}{E_\alpha-E_\gamma}P\sum_\delta \frac{1}{E_\alpha-E_\delta}\times \\ & \times\langle\Phi_\beta|H_{\text{int}}|\Phi_\gamma\rangle\langle\Phi_\gamma|H_{\text{int}}|\Phi_\delta\rangle\langle\Phi_\delta|H_{\text{int}}|\Phi_\alpha\rangle + \ldots. \end{aligned} \tag{60}$$

Because the principal value is taken in each energy integration $\left(\sum_\gamma, \sum_\delta,\right.$ etc.$\left.\right)$, no intermediate states for which any of the *intermediate energies* E_γ, E_δ,... are equal to E_α can occur in the expansion (60). We can say

† Cf. Schwinger, loc. cit.

that each term in (60) necessarily corresponds to a *virtual* process in which only the final state $|\Phi_\beta\rangle$ has the same energy as the initial state $|\Phi_\alpha\rangle$. It follows that the matrix elements $\mathbf{K}_{\beta\alpha}$ describe single scattering processes, but they do not include what we may call *compound scattering*. In the latter, the energy at some intermediate state (or states) equals the initial energy E_α; interference may occur between this state and the initial or final states. Compound scattering can be regarded as made up of successive single scattering processes (i.e. virtual processes). This compound scattering is important for strong interactions, for which, as we shall see, it gives rise to damping effects. It is not to be confused with the multiple scattering which occurs when a fast particle on traversing a nucleus is scattered by several nucleons (cf. § 4).

The damping equation

The properties of the reaction matrix are further illustrated with the help of (57) which shows that $\mathbf{S}$ is a function of the matrix $\mathbf{K}$.†

Substituting (26) we see that the scattering matrix $\mathbf{T}$ obeys the integral equation‡

$$\mathbf{T}_{\beta\alpha}+i\pi\sum_{E_\gamma}\sum_{(\gamma)}\mathbf{K}_{\beta\gamma}\,\delta(E_\gamma-E_\alpha)\mathbf{T}_{\gamma\alpha} = \mathbf{K}_{\beta\alpha}, \tag{61}$$

where $E_\beta = E_\alpha$, and γ now denotes the variables on the energy shell E_γ. If $\rho_\gamma(E)\,dE$ is the number of states in the energy interval E, $E+dE$ which have the value γ for the variables other than the energy,§ eqn. (61) can be written

$$\mathbf{T}_{\beta\alpha} = \mathbf{K}_{\beta\alpha}-i\pi\sum_{(\gamma)}\mathbf{K}_{\beta\gamma}\,\rho_\gamma(E_\alpha)\mathbf{T}_{\gamma\alpha}. \tag{62}$$

All quantities in (62) refer to the energy shell. The structure of eqn. (62) shows how the total scattering which is given by $\mathbf{T}$ is built up out of the single scattering processes given by $\mathbf{K}$.

Eqn. (62) is the general form of the *radiation damping* equation which was developed by Heitler and others.‖ Older calculations based on the approximation of taking $\mathbf{T}_{\beta\alpha}$ equal to $\mathbf{K}_{\beta\alpha}$ were only valid for weakly

† It follows that $\mathbf{S}$ and $\mathbf{K}$ commute; hence $\mathbf{T}$ and $\mathbf{K}$ commute.

‡ Eqns. (61) and (62) are called integral equations because in general $\sum_{(\gamma)}$ is to be replaced by an integral over angles or relative momenta.

§ The definition of $\rho_\gamma(E)$ differs from that of the (less general) density $\rho(E)$ on p. 219. The relation between them is $\rho_\gamma(E) = \rho(E)\,d\Omega_\gamma$; in (62) $\sum_{(\gamma)}$ is now replaced by the $\int$ sign.

‖ W. Heitler, *Proc. Camb. Phil. Soc.* **37** (1941) 291; A. H. Wilson, ibid. 301; W. Heitler and H. W. Peng, ibid. **38** (1942) 296; see also J. Hamilton, *Proc. Phys. Soc.* **49** (1947) 917. The fact that, given $\mathbf{K}$, the radiation damping equation (62) gave the correct transition probabilities was, for some time, somewhat obscured by the noticeably incorrect values of $\mathbf{K}$ which were used in the early applications.

interacting systems, such as quantum electrodynamics. For strongly interacting systems it is necessary to use (62) which always leads to a unitary S-matrix. In such systems the rate of attenuation of the incident beams, due to the strong interaction, is an important factor in calculating the scattering; the unitary calculation using (62) (or using **T** directly) makes proper allowance for this damping effect.

The eigenvalues of **K**

The relation between the reaction matrix and the scattering matrix is further illustrated by their eigenvalues. Formally, by (49) and (57),

$$\mathbf{S}(1+i\pi\mathbf{K}) = (1-i\pi\mathbf{K}). \tag{63}$$

Also, **K** and **S** clearly have common eigenstates. Corresponding to the eigenvalue $\mathbf{S}' = \exp(2i\delta)$, eqns. (63) and (49) give the following eigenvalues for **K** and **T**:†

$$\left.\begin{aligned} \mathbf{K}' &= -\frac{1}{\pi}\tan\delta \\ \mathbf{T}' &= -\frac{1}{\pi}\sin\delta\exp(i\delta) \end{aligned}\right\}. \tag{64}$$

However large $|\mathbf{K}'|$ becomes, $|\mathbf{T}'|$ cannot exceed $1/\pi$. The general character of the damping effect which occurs when $|\mathbf{K}'|$ is large is shown by the formula

$$|\mathbf{T}'| = \frac{|\mathbf{K}'|}{\{1+\pi^2|\mathbf{K}'|^2\}^{\frac{1}{2}}}. \tag{65}$$

In practice we can estimate whether the approximation $\mathbf{T} \simeq \mathbf{K}$ is accurate by examining the size of the factor $\rho_\gamma \mathbf{K}$ in (62). For pion-nucleon interactions it is generally large.

The reaction matrix **K** is closely related to the derivative matrix $\mathscr{R}$ for the theory of nuclear scattering and resonance formulae.‡

Off-shell values

We conclude with a remark on notation. Using eqns. (7), (53), and (59), the reaction matrix element is written

$$\begin{aligned} \mathbf{K}_{\beta\alpha} &= \langle\Phi_\beta|\mathbf{K}|\Phi_\alpha\rangle \\ &= \langle\Phi_\beta|H_{\text{int}}|\Phi_\alpha\rangle + P\sum_\gamma \langle\Phi_\beta|H_{\text{int}}|\Phi_\gamma\rangle\frac{1}{E_\alpha-E_\gamma}\langle\Phi_\gamma|H_{\text{int}}|\psi_\alpha^{(1)}\rangle, \end{aligned} \tag{66}$$

where $\sum_\gamma$ includes summation over the energy E_γ. This equation

† Cf. B. A. Lippmann and J. Schwinger, *Phys. Rev.* **79** (1950) 469.

‡ Cf. J. M. Blatt and V. F. Weisskopf, *Theoretical Nuclear Physics* (J. Wiley, New York, 1952), ch. 10. A mathematical discussion is given by E. P. Wigner and J. von Neumann, *Ann. Math.* **3** (1954) 418.

suggests that we extend the definition of **K** to include energy values off the energy shell. We write

$$\mathbf{K}_{\gamma\alpha}(E_\alpha) = \langle\Phi_\gamma|H_{\text{int}}|\psi_\alpha^{(1)}\rangle \quad (\text{for any } E_\gamma,\ E_\alpha).$$

Now (66) can be extended to the general matrix form†

$$\mathbf{K}(E_\alpha) = H_{\text{int}} + PH_{\text{int}}\frac{1}{E_\alpha - H_0}\mathbf{K}(E_\alpha). \tag{67}$$

It is sometimes convenient to find the reaction matrix by solving eqn. (67). If this is done, the matrix element $\mathbf{K}_{\beta\alpha}$ is given by the energy-shell value:

$$\mathbf{K}_{\beta\alpha} = \langle\Phi_\beta|\mathbf{K}(E_\alpha)|\Phi_\alpha\rangle \quad (E_\beta = E_\alpha).$$

In a similar way the definition (26) of the scattering matrix $\mathbf{T}_{\beta\alpha}$ can be extended to energies off the energy shell by writing

$$\mathbf{T}_{\gamma\alpha}(E_\alpha) = \langle\Phi_\gamma|\mathbf{T}(E_\alpha)|\Phi_\alpha\rangle = \langle\Phi_\gamma|H_{\text{int}}|\psi_\alpha^{(+)}\rangle \quad (\text{any } E_\gamma,\ E_\alpha). \tag{68}$$

By eqn. (15) this matrix obeys

$$\mathbf{T}(E_\alpha) = H_{\text{int}} + H_{\text{int}}\frac{1}{E_\alpha - H_0 + i\epsilon}\mathbf{T}(E_\alpha). \tag{69}$$

On solving (69) we need only retain the components of $\mathbf{T}(E_\alpha)$ on the energy shell to give the scattering matrix $\mathbf{T}_{\beta\alpha}$.

Although eqns. (66) and (69) are used frequently in manipulations (cf. § 4 below) it should be emphasized that the extension of **T** and **K** to values off the energy shell is a mathematical device which has no physical significance.

4. Example: Multiple scattering theory

In Chapter I, §§ 6 and 8, the optical model was used to describe the passage of fast pions or fast nucleons through a nucleus. As an example of scattering theory we now consider an attempt to justify this optical model in terms of the individual pion-nucleon or nucleon-nucleon collisions. It should be emphasized that the simple treatment which will be given is *only* valid for the passage of fast particles through the nucleus. The results of the calculation may be regarded as a generalization of formula (1.39 b) which relates the refractive index of an infinite medium to the forward scattering amplitude. The method is due to K. M. Watson.‡

As a preliminary we show the relation between the scattering amplitude $f(\theta)$ of Chapter I, § 7, and the scattering matrix **T**. If two particles

† As usual P indicates that the principal value is to be used.

‡ See K. M. Watson, *Phys. Rev.* **89** (1953) 575; N. C. Francis and K. M. Watson, ibid. **92** (1953) 291; G. Takeda and K. M. Watson, ibid. **94** (1954) 1087; ibid. **97** (1955) 1336.

collide in the centre of mass system with relative momentum $\mathbf{p} = \hbar\mathbf{k}$, the wave function describing the scattering can be written

$$\langle \mathbf{x}|\psi^{(+)}\rangle \simeq \exp(i\mathbf{k}.\mathbf{x})+\frac{f(\theta)}{r}e^{ikr} \quad (\text{for } r \to \infty), \tag{70}$$

where (θ, ϕ) are polar angles relative to $\mathbf{p}$, and r is the separation of the particles. Although it is convenient to use the simple form (70), the scattering amplitude f can be a function of the azimuthal angle ϕ as well as of θ, and f can also be a matrix in spin and isotopic spin space.

Using (15) and (26) gives

$$\langle \mathbf{x}|\psi^{(+)}\rangle = \langle \mathbf{x}|\mathbf{p}\rangle + \int d^3\mathbf{p}' \, \langle \mathbf{x}|\mathbf{p}'\rangle \frac{1}{E-E_{p'}+i\epsilon} \langle \mathbf{p}'|\mathbf{T}|\mathbf{p}\rangle, \tag{71}$$

where we have used the relation†

$$\int d^3\mathbf{p}' \, |\mathbf{p}'\rangle\langle \mathbf{p}'| = I.$$

Substituting $\langle \mathbf{x}|\mathbf{p}'\rangle = \exp(i\mathbf{k}'.\mathbf{x})$ and integrating (cf. p. 15),

$$\langle \mathbf{x}|\psi^{(+)}\rangle \simeq \exp(i\mathbf{k}.\mathbf{x}) - (2\pi)^2\frac{dp}{dE}\hbar p\langle \bar{\mathbf{p}}|\mathbf{T}|\mathbf{p}\rangle \exp(ikr)/r; \tag{72}$$

the integration over the function $\delta^{(+)}(E-E_{p'})$ gives the outgoing wave only (cf. pp. 78, 216). Thus

$$f(\theta) = -(2\pi)^2\frac{dp}{dE}\hbar p \, \langle \bar{\mathbf{p}}|\mathbf{T}|\mathbf{p}\rangle \quad (\text{c.m. system}); \tag{73}$$

here E is the *total* c.m. energy of the particles and $\bar{\mathbf{p}} = \mathbf{x}p/r$ lies at an angle θ to the incident momentum $\mathbf{p}$. The generalization for a scattering amplitude $f(\theta, \phi)$ which depends on spins, etc., is obvious. The derivation of (73) can be extended; for example, (73) will be true for *forward* scattering in the laboratory system. (E is now the total laboratory ene

Passage of a fast particle through a nucleus

We now discuss the passage of a fast particle through a medium or large nucleus in which multiple scattering can occur. Mostly we refer to the passage of a fast pion through the nucleus, but the arguments apply with a few modifications to the passage of a nucleon.

In the first instance we ignore the possibility of the pion being absorbed. We consider the matrix $\mathbf{T}(j)$ which describes the scattering of the pion by the jth nucleon *in the nucleus*. By (19) and (26) we can write

$$\mathbf{T}(j) = V(j)+V(j)\frac{1}{E-H_0-V(j)+i\epsilon}V(j) \qquad (\epsilon \to +0). \tag{74}$$

† This agrees with the normalization $\langle \mathbf{p}|\mathbf{p}'\rangle = \delta^3(\mathbf{p}-\mathbf{p}') = V\delta_{\mathbf{p},\mathbf{p}'}(2\pi\hbar)^{-3}$.

Here $V(j)$ is the interaction between the pion and nucleon j, and H_0 is the sum of the Hamiltonians H_N and h_π for the nucleus and the free pion respectively. E is the energy shell to which $\mathbf{T}(j)$ relates. It would be possible to improve (74) on replacing the denominator by $(E-H_0-V(j)+V_c+i\epsilon)$, where V_c gives the depth of the potential well in which the pion moves inside the nucleus; this would allow for the propagation vector of the pion having a different value inside the nucleus. However, as a first approximation we use (74); the estimates of the potential well depth given in Chapter I, § 6, show that for pions (or nucleons) of 100 MeV or more, this should be a reasonable approximation. Corrections can be made at a later stage.

We wish to relate $\mathbf{T}(j)$ to the scattering matrix $\mathbf{T}^{(0)}(j)$ for pion scattering by a *free* nucleon (the index (j) is now only written for ease of comparison of the symbols). This latter scattering matrix obeys

$$\mathbf{T}^{(0)}(j) = V(j)+V(j)\frac{1}{e-h_\pi-h(j)-V(j)+i\epsilon}V(j), \tag{75}$$

where $h(j)$ is the Hamiltonian for the free nucleon and e is the total energy of pion and nucleon. The energy e can later be adjusted so that the pion described by $\mathbf{T}^{(0)}(j)$ has the same wavelength as the pion in the nucleus. The difference between the operators $(e-h_\pi-h(j))$ in (75) and $(E-H^0)$ in (74) will be small, provided that the change in the binding energy of the *struck nucleon* during the collision is small. This change may be of the order of 20 MeV, and is unimportant if the incident particle has energy higher than (about) 100 MeV. Treating the *struck* nucleon in this way as if it were independent of the nucleus gives the *impulse approximation*.† Finally, on comparing $\mathbf{T}(j)$ and $\mathbf{T}^{(0)}(j)$ we must remember that the exclusion principle can reduce the scattering cross-section within the nucleus.‡ This effect, which is small for high-energy incident particles, can be allowed for in the subsequent calculations.§

If the multiple scattering which occurs inside the nucleus is to be accurately related to successive scatterings described by $\mathbf{T}^{(0)}(j)$, it is necessary that the mean free path (λ) between collisions should be sufficiently long for the energy of the scattered particle to be well defined between each collision. The energy spread ΔE has the size

$$\Delta E \simeq \hbar v/\lambda,$$

† G. F. Chew and C. G. Wick, *Phys. Rev.* **85** (1952) 636; G. F. Chew and M. L. Goldberger, ibid. **87** (1952) 778.

‡ Cf. footnote ||, p. 12, in Chapter I, § 6.

§ M. L. Goldberger, *Phys. Rev.* **74** (1948) 1269; M. H. Johnson, ibid. **83** (1951) 510.

where v is the velocity of the particle. For nucleons of energy E greater than 100 MeV, the relative spread $(\Delta E/E)$ is small. For pions of about 200 MeV, $(\Delta E/E)$ becomes appreciable;† this will lead to errors because the scattering cross-section changes quickly in the same energy range.

The matrix $\mathbf{T}$ for the scattering of the pion *by the nucleus* obeys (cf. eqn. (69))

$$\mathbf{T} = V + V\frac{1}{E - H_0 + i\epsilon}\mathbf{T}, \tag{76}$$

where $V = \sum_j V(j)$, the summation going over all nucleons; $\mathbf{T}$ is the *multiple scattering matrix*. The fundamental mathematical theorem‡ is that $\mathbf{T}$ can be written as a sum of the $\mathbf{T}(j)$ thus:

$$\mathbf{T} = \sum_j \mathbf{T}(j) + \sum_{(j_1,j_2)} \mathbf{T}(j_1)\frac{1}{E-H_0+i\epsilon}\mathbf{T}(j_2) + \\ + \sum_{(j_1,j_2,j_3)} \mathbf{T}(j_1)\frac{1}{E-H_0+i\epsilon}\mathbf{T}(j_2)\frac{1}{E-H_0+i\epsilon}\mathbf{T}(j_3) + \ldots, \tag{77}$$

where $(j_1, j_2, \ldots, j_k)$ indicates that in the sum over $j_1, \ldots, j_k$ no two *adjacent* indices are to be equal. The physical interpretation of the terms in (77) is clear; the particle is scattered at different nucleons and propagates freely in between. Eqn. (77) is verified by substituting it on the right of (76) and using eqn. (74) in the form (cf. (69))

$$\mathbf{T}(j) = V(j) + V(j)\frac{1}{E-H_0+i\epsilon}\mathbf{T}(j). \tag{78}$$

Elastic scattering

The scattering matrix $\mathbf{T}$ is to be evaluated between pairs of states of the nucleus as well as between the initial and final states of the scattered particle. For *elastic* scattering the expectation value of $\mathbf{T}$ for the ground state of the nucleus is used. The calculation is simplified because we can assume that after each collision the penetrating particle, on account of its high energy ($\geqslant$ 100 MeV), will outrun the disturbance which it has caused; subsequent collisions will therefore start with the struck nucleon in the ground state.§ If $\langle\,\rangle$ denotes the ground-state expectation value, we can write

$$\langle\mathbf{T}\rangle = \sum_j \langle\mathbf{T}(j)\rangle + \sum_j \langle\mathbf{T}(j)\rangle\frac{1}{E-H_0+i\epsilon}\langle\mathbf{U}(j)\rangle, \tag{79}$$

† R. M. Frank, J. L. Gammel, and K. M. Watson, *Phys. Rev.* **101** (1956) 891.

‡ K. M. Watson, p. 229, n. ‡. See also, *Phys. Rev.* **105** (1957) 1388.

§ For nucleon-nucleus collisions there is some difficulty because of the exchange effect. G. Takeda and K. M. Watson (*Phys. Rev.* **97** (1955) 1336) distinguish the *scattered* nucleon as that which has the greatest kinetic energy.

where

$$\mathbf{U}(j) = \sum_{(j_1 \neq j)} \mathbf{T}(j_1) + \sum_{\substack{(j_1, j_2) \\ (j_1 \neq j)}} \mathbf{T}(j_1) \frac{1}{E - H_0 + i\epsilon} \mathbf{T}(j_2) + \dots .$$

In the last term in (79) the expectation value $\langle \mathbf{T}(j)\mathbf{U}(j) \rangle$ has been replaced by $\langle \mathbf{T}(j) \rangle \langle \mathbf{U}(j) \rangle$; this is the mathematical form of the statement that at each new collision the struck nucleon is found in the ground state. If the velocity of the penetrating particle is low, this approximation cannot be made and the following simple analysis is not possible.

For a large nucleus we further approximate by replacing $\mathbf{U}(j)$ by $\mathbf{T}$ (for smaller nuclei this replacement necessitates a small correction). In the denominator of (79) $(E - H_0 + i\epsilon)$ can be replaced by the operator $(E_p - h_\pi + i\epsilon)$, where E_p is the energy of the penetrating pion and h_π is its free Hamiltonian; this change is made because in (79) the nucleus is everywhere in the ground state. Therefore

$$\langle \mathbf{T} \rangle = \sum_j \langle \mathbf{T}(j) \rangle + \sum_j \langle \mathbf{T}(j) \rangle \frac{1}{E_p - h_\pi + i\epsilon} \langle \mathbf{T} \rangle, \tag{80}$$

where $\langle \mathbf{T} \rangle$ is the elastic scattering matrix for the pion. It follows that inside the nucleus the pion obeys the Schrödinger equation

$$\Big(E_p - h_\pi - \sum_j \langle \mathbf{T}(j) \rangle\Big) | \Psi \rangle = 0; \tag{81}$$

as always $\langle\ \rangle$ is the expectation value with respect to the nuclear ground state, and $\sum_j$ is the sum over all nucleons in the nucleus.

The effective potential for elastic scattering

In order to use this simple result we must evaluate $\mathbf{T}_c \equiv \sum_j \langle \mathbf{T}(j) \rangle$. We find the matrix element $\langle \mathbf{p}' | \mathbf{T}_c | \mathbf{p} \rangle$, where $\mathbf{p}, \mathbf{p}'$ are the momenta of the pion before and after a collision with a nucleon in the nucleus. Suppose the struck nucleon's initial and final momenta are $\mathbf{P}_1$, $\mathbf{P}_1'$ (to be definite we call this the first of the A nucleons). Then

$$\langle \mathbf{p}' | \mathbf{T}_c | \mathbf{p} \rangle = A \int d^3\mathbf{P}_1 \int d^3\mathbf{P}_1' \prod_{k=2}^{A} d^3\mathbf{P}_k \, \psi^*(\mathbf{P}_1') \delta^3(\mathbf{p} + \mathbf{P}_1 - \mathbf{p}' - \mathbf{P}_1') \times$$
$$\times \langle \mathbf{p}', \mathbf{P}_1' | \mathbf{T}(1) | \mathbf{p}, \mathbf{P}_1 \rangle \psi(\mathbf{P}_1), \tag{82}$$

where A is the atomic weight and $\psi(\mathbf{P}_1, \mathbf{P}_2, \dots, \mathbf{P}_A)$ is the ground state wave function (in momentum representation). For convenience in (82) we have written $\psi(\mathbf{P}_1) \equiv \psi(\mathbf{P}_1, \mathbf{P}_2, \dots, \mathbf{P}_A)$, $\psi(\mathbf{P}_1') \equiv \psi(\mathbf{P}_1', \mathbf{P}_2, \dots, \mathbf{P}_A)$.

A quantity $v_{\alpha'\alpha}(\mathbf{x}_1',\mathbf{x}_1)$ is defined by

$$v_{\alpha'\alpha}(\mathbf{x}_1',\mathbf{x}_1) \equiv \int \prod_{k=2}^{A} d^3\mathbf{x}_k\, \psi^*_{\alpha'}(\mathbf{x}_1',\mathbf{x}_2,\ldots,\mathbf{x}_A)\psi_\alpha(\mathbf{x}_1\mathbf{x}_2\ldots\mathbf{x}_A), \tag{83}$$

where $\psi(\mathbf{x}_1,\ldots,\mathbf{x}_A)$ is the configuration space form of the nuclear ground-state wave function. (α, α') denotes the spin and isotopic spin of the first nucleon; it is assumed that in (83) we sum over the spins and charges of the other nucleons. Clearly $v_{\alpha\alpha}(\mathbf{x}_1,\mathbf{x}_1)\, d^3\mathbf{x}_1$ is the probability of the first nucleon being in the volume $d^3\mathbf{x}_1$ about $\mathbf{x}_1$ and having spin and charge α. In terms of this coefficient eqn. (82) becomes

$$\langle\mathbf{p}'|\mathbf{T}_c|\mathbf{p}\rangle = \frac{A}{(2\pi\hbar)^3}\int d^3\mathbf{P}_1 \int d^3\mathbf{x}_1 \int d^3\mathbf{x}_1' \exp\{-i(\mathbf{p}-\mathbf{p}').\mathbf{x}_1'/\hbar\}\times$$
$$\times\exp\{-i\mathbf{P}_1.(\mathbf{x}_1'-\mathbf{x}_1)/\hbar\}\sum_{\alpha,\alpha'} v_{\alpha'\alpha}(\mathbf{x}_1',\mathbf{x}_1)\times$$
$$\times\langle\mathbf{p}',\mathbf{P}_1+\mathbf{p}-\mathbf{p}',\alpha'|\mathbf{T}(1)|\mathbf{p},\mathbf{P}_1,\alpha\rangle, \tag{84}$$

where the coefficients α, α' have been written explicitly in the scattering matrix $\mathbf{T}(1)$.

We now assume for simplicity that, for given pion momenta $\mathbf{p}$, $\mathbf{p}'$, the dependence of $\mathbf{T}(1)$ on the nucleon momentum $\mathbf{P}_1$ can be ignored.† This is a rough approximation which leads to a plausible result.‡ All pion scattering matrix elements will now refer to the laboratory system. Integrating over $\mathbf{P}_1$ in (84) gives

$$\langle\mathbf{p}'|\mathbf{T}_c|\mathbf{p}\rangle = A\overline{\langle\mathbf{p}'|\mathbf{T}(1)|\mathbf{p}\rangle}\int d^3\mathbf{x}\exp\{i(\mathbf{p}-\mathbf{p}').\mathbf{x}/\hbar\}v(\mathbf{x},\mathbf{x}). \tag{85}$$

$\overline{\langle\mathbf{p}'|\mathbf{T}(1)|\mathbf{p}\rangle}$ denotes§ an average of the scattering matrix $\mathbf{T}(j)$ over the spins and charges of the nucleons in the ground state of the nucleus, (it should be a weighted average over the momenta $\mathbf{P}_j$ of the nucleons). $v(\mathbf{x},\mathbf{x})$ is the nucleon density; *correlations* of nucleon spin or isotopic spin are neglected in (85), i.e. the indices α, α' are dropped.

Neglecting nuclear structure we have $v(\mathbf{x},\mathbf{x}) = \rho(\mathbf{x})/\mathrm{v}_A$, where v_A is the nuclear volume, and $\rho(\mathbf{x})$ is the density of nucleons, normalized to unity inside the nucleus. Eqn. (85) shows that the matrix elements of $\mathbf{T}_c$ will be small for $|\mathbf{p}-\mathbf{p}'| > (\hbar/R)$, where R is the nuclear radius. It follows from the Schrödinger equation (81) that the elastic scattering of fast particles by a nucleus will be small outside an angle of the order $(\hbar/R|\mathbf{p}|)$.

† A large change (by nuclear standards) in $\mathbf{P}_1$ gives a small change in the c.m. values (cf. R. M. Frank, J. L. Gammel, and K. M. Watson, p. 232, n. †).

‡ For a discussion see K. M. Watson, p. 229, n. ‡. For large $|\mathbf{x}_1-\mathbf{x}_1'|$, a small range of $\mathbf{P}_1$ is sufficient to give a good approximation; for small $|\mathbf{x}_1-\mathbf{x}_1'|$, $\psi(\mathbf{x}_1'\,\mathbf{x}_2\ldots\mathbf{x}_A)$ and $\psi(\mathbf{x}_1\,\mathbf{x}_2\ldots\mathbf{x}_A)$ do not differ appreciably.

§ This average is discussed on p. 235.

The potential well depth

For a very large nucleus an approximation to (85) is

$$\langle \mathbf{p}'|\mathbf{T}_c|\mathbf{p}\rangle \simeq \frac{A}{\mathrm{V}_A}(2\pi\hbar)^3\,\delta^3(\mathbf{p}'-\mathbf{p})\overline{\langle \mathbf{p}|\mathbf{T}(1)|\mathbf{p}\rangle}. \tag{86}$$

For pions of momentum $|\mathbf{p}|$ we find the effective potential energy by going over to the configuration space form of $\mathbf{T}_c$. As $|\mathbf{p}-\mathbf{p}'|/p$ is always small, eqn. (85) gives, approximately,

$$\langle \mathbf{x}'|\mathbf{T}_c|\mathbf{x}\rangle \simeq \frac{A}{\mathrm{V}_A}(2\pi\hbar)^3\,\delta^3(\mathbf{x}-\mathbf{x}')\overline{\langle \mathbf{p}|\mathbf{T}(1)|\mathbf{p}\rangle}\rho(\mathbf{x}). \tag{87}$$

In (85), (86), (87), $\mathbf{T}(1)$ can be replaced by the appropriate element of the matrix $\mathbf{T}^{(0)}$ for the scattering of a pion by an unbound nucleon (cf. eqn. (75)). Substituting (87) into the Schrödinger equation (81) gives

$$\{E_p-h_\pi+V_c\rho(\mathbf{x})\}|\Psi\rangle = 0; \tag{88}$$

thus the pion moves in a potential well whose *depth* V_c is given by

$$V_c = -\frac{A}{\mathrm{V}_A}(2\pi\hbar)^3\overline{\langle \mathbf{p}|\mathbf{T}^{(0)}|\mathbf{p}\rangle}. \tag{89}$$

For elastic pion-nucleus scattering we have the following situation. By eqn. (73) the matrix element $\langle \mathbf{p}|\mathbf{T}^{(0)}|\mathbf{p}\rangle$ can be written in terms of the forward scattering amplitude $f(0)$ for pion-nucleon scattering. The average $\overline{f(0)}$ over the protons and neutrons has to be made.† (If the nucleus is randomly orientated, terms in $\mathbf{T}^{(0)}$ (in (85)) which are linear in the nucleon spin will average to zero; thus for any $\mathbf{p}'$ only the component of $\mathbf{T}^{(0)}$ relating to no spin-flip occurs.‡) Eqn. (89) gives

$$V_c = 2\pi\hbar^2\frac{A}{\mathrm{V}_A}\frac{dE}{dp}\frac{1}{p}\overline{f(0)}; \tag{90}$$

this is the generalization of formula (1.39 b) which relates the refractive index of matter to the forward scattering amplitude for individual scatterers.

As a check on (90) we can use eqn. (1.35) relating $\mathrm{Im}\{f(0)\}$ to the total cross-section σ_T for scattering of a pion by a nucleon. This gives

$$\mathrm{Im}\,V_c = \hbar v/2\lambda_s, \tag{91}$$

where v is the pion velocity and $\lambda_s = \mathrm{V}_A/(\bar{\sigma}_T A)$ is its mean free path (for

† For $\pi^\pm$ and nuclei with $Z \simeq \frac{1}{2}A$ this gives $\overline{f(0)} = \frac{2}{3}f_{\frac{3}{2}}(0)+\frac{1}{3}f_{\frac{1}{2}}(0)$, where $f_{\frac{3}{2}}(0), f_{\frac{1}{2}}(0)$ are the forward scattering amplitudes for total isotopic spin $T = \frac{3}{2}, \frac{1}{2}$ respectively.

‡ For pion-nucleon scattering $\mathbf{T}^{(0)} = g(\theta)+h(\theta)\boldsymbol{\sigma}.\mathbf{n}$, where $\boldsymbol{\sigma}$ is the nucleon spin, $\mathbf{n}$ the normal to the plane of scattering, and g, h are scalar functions of the scattering angle θ. (Cf. Chapter VI, § 4.)

scattering) in nuclear matter.† The arguments of Chapter I, § 6, show that (91) is the correct value for $\operatorname{Im} V_c$.

Absorption of pions

The absorption of pions in the nucleus can be described by adding an imaginary term to the Hamiltonian; for example in (76) and (78) we replace the denominator by $(E-H_0+i\Delta+i\epsilon)$, where the positive number Δ is proportional to the rate of absorption of pions in nuclear matter. It is obvious that this replaces the Schrödinger equation (88) by

$$\{E_p-h_\pi+(i\Delta+V_c)\rho(\mathbf{x})\}|\Psi\rangle = 0. \tag{92}$$

Comparing with eqn. (91), we see that the correct value for Δ is $\hbar v/2\lambda_a$, where λ_a is the mean free path for pion *absorption* in nuclear matter.‡

Using eqn. (88) it is possible to discuss the propagation of pions through nuclei in terms of the known forward scattering amplitudes§ for pions on unbound nucleons.‖ It is also possible to improve the accuracy of the calculations by a self-consistent type of calculation in which the well depth V_c given by (89) is inserted in the basic equation (74).‖

Elastic scattering of nucleons

The elastic scattering of nucleons by nuclei, and in particular the polarization occurring in these collisions (cf. Chapter VIII, § 4), can be understood in terms of nucleon-nucleon scattering in a similar way. In (85) we replace $\mathbf{T}(1)$ by the scattering matrix for nucleon-nucleon collisions (eqn. (83), Chapter VIII). On averaging over the nucleons in the nucleus, terms which are linear in the spin of these nucleons will vanish, and we have

$$\overline{\langle\mathbf{p}'|\mathbf{T}(1)|\mathbf{p}\rangle} = \bar{A}+i\bar{C}(\boldsymbol{\sigma}.\mathbf{p}'\times\mathbf{p}), \tag{93}$$

where $\mathbf{p}$, $\mathbf{p}'$ are the initial and final momenta of the scattered nucleon; $\bar{A}$, $\bar{C}$ are some scalar functions of the scattering angle θ, and $\boldsymbol{\sigma}$ is the spin of the scattered nucleon. To the first order $\bar{A}$ and $\bar{C}$ should be

† The total cross-section $\bar{\sigma}_T$ is the average over the protons and neutrons in the nucleus (cf. p. 235, n. †).

‡ For a more fundamental discussion of the absorption term (which involves pairs of nucleons because of the large energy transferred) see K. M. Watson, p. 229, n. ‡, and K. Breuckner, R. Serber, and K. M. Watson, *Phys. Rev.* **84** (1951) 258.

§ If we wish to transform to the centre of mass frame, it is useful to remember that

$$(E_1 . E_2 \ldots)^{\frac{1}{2}}\langle\mathbf{p}_1, \mathbf{p}_2,\ldots|\mathbf{T}|\mathbf{p}_\alpha, \mathbf{p}_\beta,\ldots\rangle(E_\alpha . E_\beta \ldots)^{\frac{1}{2}}$$

is an invariant under Lorentz transformations. (E_1 is the total energy associated with $\mathbf{p}_1$, etc.) Cf. C. Møller, *K. danske vidensk. Selsk.* **23** (1945), No. 1.

‖ See R. M. Frank, J. L. Gammel, and K. M. Watson, *Phys. Rev.* **101** (1956) 891, for details.

constant for small angles θ (cf. Chapter VIII, § 8). Going over from (85) to the configuration space form (analogous to (87)) we have, for a large nucleus,

$$\langle \mathbf{x}'|\mathbf{T}_c|\mathbf{x}\rangle = \frac{A}{V_A}(2\pi\hbar)^3\{\bar{A}+i\bar{C}\hbar^2(\boldsymbol{\sigma}.\nabla_{\mathbf{x}'}\times\nabla_{\mathbf{x}})\}\rho(\mathbf{x})\delta^3(\mathbf{x}-\mathbf{x}').$$

Assuming that $\rho(\mathbf{x})$ only depends on the distance r from the centre of the nucleus, we can now write

$$\langle \mathbf{x}'|\mathbf{T}_c|\mathbf{x}\rangle = \frac{A}{V_A}(2\pi\hbar)^3\left\{\bar{A}\rho(r)+\hbar\bar{C}(\boldsymbol{\sigma}.\mathbf{L})\frac{1}{r}\frac{d\rho}{dr}\right\}\delta^3(\mathbf{x}-\mathbf{x}'), \qquad (94)$$

where $\boldsymbol{\sigma}$ and $\mathbf{L}$ are the spin and orbital angular momentum of the

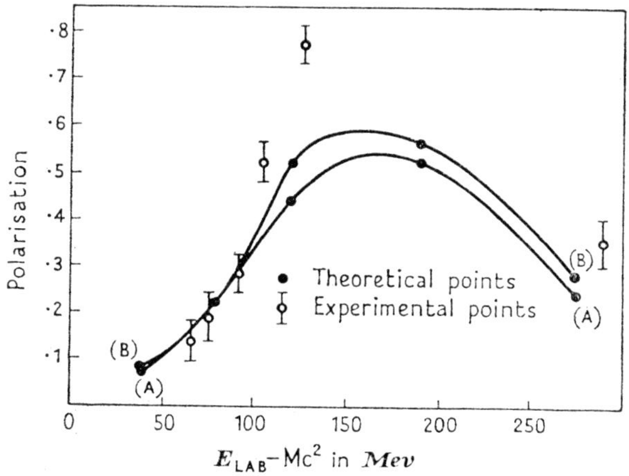

FIG. 7. The polarization of nucleons scattered from carbon at $\theta_{\text{lab}} = 20°$ as calculated† from eqn. (94). Curves (A) and (B) are derived from the sets A and B of nucleon-nucleon phase shifts given by H. Feshbach and E. Lomon (*Phys. Rev.* **102** (1956) 891). References for the experimental values are given in Chapter VIII, § 4.

scattered nucleon.† Both $\bar{A}$ and C contain imaginary (attenuation) terms which allow for the loss to the beam by elastically scattered nucleons, or inelastic collisions which leave the nucleus in an excited state, or even break it up. When (94) is inserted in the Schrödinger equation (88) it gives an ordinary potential well, together with a spin-orbital interaction occurring near the surface of the nucleus (cf. eqn. (43), Chapter VIII).

Using nucleon-nucleon phase shifts the nucleon-nucleus polarization resulting from (94) can be calculated and compared with experiment† (cf. Fig. 7).

† W. B. Reisenfeld and K. M. Watson, *Phys. Rev.* **102** (1956) 1157.

5. The perturbation theory of the S-matrix

For the remainder of this chapter we discuss the Lorentz invariant perturbation theory of the S-matrix describing the interaction between two quantized fields. It was pointed out in Chapter IV, § 7, that this method is only valid for weakly interacting fields; for this reason quantum electrodynamics will mostly be used to provide illustrations of the techniques. The analysis depends on using the interaction representation which was introduced in Chapter IV, § 7. Except where it is specifically mentioned to the contrary, all dynamical variables occurring in the remainder of this chapter will be interaction representation variables. For convenience they will be written $A(t)$ (*not* $\hat{A}(t)$ as in Chapter IV, § 7). The advantage of using the interaction representation operators is that they obey the equations of motion for free (i.e. non-interacting) fields.

The perturbation theory expansion for $S \equiv U(\infty, -\infty)$ follows from the formula (4.102) for $U(t,t_0)$ on letting $t \to \infty$, $t_0 \to -\infty$ and, if necessary, using the adiabatic switching to give well-defined limits. The series in (4.102) can be written in a simple form by using the chronological ordering operator T.† This operator rearranges any product of the operators $H_{\text{int}}(t)$ in chronological order with the factor H_{int} containing the latest time to the left. For example,

$$T\{H_{\text{int}}(t_1)H_{\text{int}}(t_2)H_{\text{int}}(t_3)\} = H_{\text{int}}(t_2)H_{\text{int}}(t_1)H_{\text{int}}(t_3), \quad \text{if } t_2 > t_1 > t_3.$$

Therefore we can write

$$S = I + \left(\frac{-i}{\hbar}\right) \int_{-\infty}^{\infty} dt_1\, H_{\text{int}}(t_1) + \left(\frac{-i}{\hbar}\right)^2 \frac{1}{2!} \int_{-\infty}^{\infty} dt_1 \int_{-\infty}^{\infty} dt_2\, T\{H_{\text{int}}(t_1)H_{\text{int}}(t_2)\} +$$
$$+ \left(\frac{-i}{\hbar}\right)^3 \frac{1}{3!} \int_{-\infty}^{\infty} dt_1 \int_{-\infty}^{\infty} dt_2 \int_{-\infty}^{\infty} dt_3\, T\{H_{\text{int}}(t_1)H_{\text{int}}(t_2)H_{\text{int}}(t_3)\} + \dots. \tag{95}$$

The factors $1/2!$, $1/3!$, etc., are necessary to allow for the $n!$ different chronological orderings of $t_1,\dots, t_n$ which occur when each variable is integrated over the range $(-\infty, \infty)$.

The interaction Hamiltonian $H_{\text{int}}(t)$ is an integral over all configuration space

$$H_{\text{int}}(t) = \int d^3\mathbf{x}\, \mathscr{H}_1(\mathbf{x}, t), \tag{96}$$

where, for electrodynamics (cf. eqn. (2.188)),

$$\mathscr{H}_1(x_\mu) = -\frac{1}{c} j_\mu(x_\nu) A_\mu(x_\nu). \tag{97}$$

† F. J. Dyson, *Phys. Rev.* **75** (1949) 486, is responsible for this fruitful idea.

Here $A_\mu(x_\nu)$ is the 4-vector potential operator for the free Maxwell field (cf. Chapter II, § 9) and j_μ is the 4-vector current generated by the electrons: in its full charge-conjugate form (Chapter IV, § 5)

$$j_\mu(x_\nu) = \tfrac{1}{2}iec\{\bar{\psi}(x_\nu)\gamma^\mu\psi(x_\nu) - \bar{\psi}_c(x_\nu)\gamma^\mu\psi_c(x_\nu)\}. \tag{98}$$

The free electron field operators $\psi(x_\nu)$, $\psi_c(x_\nu)$ are described in Chapter IV, §§ 1–5.

For the pseudo-scalar pion field coupled to the nucleon field by a charge-independent pseudo-scalar coupling, we have, in the notation of Chapter IV, § 12 (especially eqn. (4.131)),

$$\mathscr{H}_1(x_\nu) = iG\bar{\psi}(x_\nu)\gamma^5(\boldsymbol{\tau}.\boldsymbol{\varphi})\psi(x_\nu). \tag{99}$$

It should be noticed that in both these examples $\mathscr{H}_1(x_\nu)$ is invariant under Lorentz transformations; this property makes it possible to develop a Lorentz invariant expansion of the S-matrix.

Lorentz invariance

We have applied the chronological ordering operator T to products† of the form $\mathscr{H}_1(x_1)\mathscr{H}_1(x_2)\ldots\mathscr{H}_1(x_n)$; in a given Lorentz frame this leads to a unique ordering. In addition, the resulting expression $T\{\mathscr{H}_1(x_1),\ldots,\mathscr{H}_1(x_n)\}$ is invariant under Lorentz transformations; therefore the ordering operator T is independent of the Lorentz frame which was used. This important result follows from the commutation relation

$$[\mathscr{H}_1(x_i), \mathscr{H}_1(x_j)] = 0 \quad \text{for } (x_i - x_j)^2 > 0. \tag{100}$$

Eqn. (100) shows that the order of any pair of operators $\mathscr{H}_1(x_i)$, $\mathscr{H}_1(x_j)$ can be reversed, provided (x_i), (x_j) have a space-like separation. A Lorentz transformation can only alter the time sequence of points whose separation is space-like; it follows that $T\{\mathscr{H}_1(x_1),\ldots,\mathscr{H}_1(x_n)\}$ is Lorentz invariant. Eqn. (100) holds because (*a*) boson field operators at any points having a space-like separation will commute (e.g. eqn. (2.27)); (*b*) the Hamiltonian must contain an even number of fermion field amplitudes.‡ The commutators of pairs of fermion amplitudes at points whose separation is space-like will vanish, because the anti-commutators of single fermion amplitudes at such points all vanish (cf. eqns. (4.16) and (4.17)).

† Greek suffixes, e.g. x_ν, are used to show the 4-vector character; the notation x_1, x_2,..., x_r,... is used to distinguish space-time points.

‡ See Chapter IV, § 11.

The integrals in (95) can now be expressed in four-dimensional form:

$$S = I+\left(\frac{-i}{\hbar c}\right)\int\limits_{-\infty}^{\infty} d^4x_1\,\mathscr{H}_1(x_1)+\frac{1}{2!}\left(\frac{-i}{\hbar c}\right)^2\int\limits_{-\infty}^{\infty} d^4x_1\int\limits_{-\infty}^{\infty} d^4x_2\,T\{\mathscr{H}_1(x_1)\mathscr{H}_1(x_2)\}+$$
$$+\frac{1}{3!}\left(\frac{-i}{\hbar c}\right)^3\int\limits_{-\infty}^{\infty} d^4x_1\int\limits_{-\infty}^{\infty} d^4x_2\int\limits_{-\infty}^{\infty} d^4x_3\,T\{\mathscr{H}_1(x_1)\mathscr{H}_1(x_2)\mathscr{H}_1(x_3)\}+\dots \quad (101)$$

Each integration in (101) is over the whole of space-time.

Physical interpretation

The physical interpretation of (101) is seen from the relation

$$|\Psi(\infty)\rangle = S|\Psi(-\infty)\rangle$$

between the initial and final interaction representation states. Because of the adiabatic switching, these state vectors describe non-interacting particles. The field variables A_μ, ϕ, $\bar{\psi}$, ψ, etc., appearing in $\mathscr{H}_1(x)$ obey the equations for non-interacting fields; therefore they can be analysed into operators which destroy or create particles, as in Chapters II and IV. The destruction operators remove particles which are present in the initial state $|\Psi(-\infty)\rangle$, and the creation operators give particles in the final state $|\Psi(\infty)\rangle$ which are not present in the initial state. Obviously it is necessary to move all the destruction operators to the right of all creation operators, so that the destruction operators can act on the initial state.

For example, using the electrodynamics interaction (97), we examine the first two integrals in (101). By Chapter IV, § 3, and Chapter II, § 9, the operators $\psi^{(+)}$, $\bar{\psi}^{(+)}$, $A_\mu^{(+)}$ destroy electrons, positrons, and photons respectively, while $\bar{\psi}^{(-)}$, $\psi^{(-)}$, $A_\mu^{(-)}$ create electrons, positrons, and photons respectively.† The first integrand has the operator form

$$\{\bar{\psi}^{(+)}(x_1)+\bar{\psi}^{(-)}(x_1)\}\{\psi^{(+)}(x_1)+\psi^{(-)}(x_1)\}\{A_\mu^{(+)}(x_1)+A_\mu^{(-)}(x_1)\}. \quad (102)$$

This corresponds to processes in which, for example, an electron and a positron are destroyed and a photon is created (i.e. the term $A_\mu^{(-)}\bar{\psi}^{(+)}\psi^{(+)}$). (This and the other terms in (102) must give zero contribution because the conservation of energy and momentum cannot be satisfied in such processes.)

We examine one typical term from the second integrand in (101), viz.

$$\bar{\psi}^{(-)}(x_1)\psi^{(+)}(x_1)\bar{\psi}^{(-)}(x_2)\psi^{(+)}(x_2)A_\mu^{(+)}(x_1)A_{\mu'}^{(-)}(x_2). \quad (103)$$

It is useful to remember the commutation relations (4.34), (4.35), (4.36),

† There is no need to worry about the treatment of longitudinal photons; the methods of Chapter II, § 11, are used below.

and (2.155); all positive and negative frequency parts of ψ, $\bar{\psi}$ anti-commute with each other, except

$$\left.\begin{aligned}[\psi_{\rho'}^{(+)}(x_1), \bar{\psi}_{\rho}^{(-)}(x_2)]_+ &= -iS_{\rho'\rho}^{(+)}(x_1-x_2)\\ [\psi_{\rho'}^{(-)}(x_1), \bar{\psi}_{\rho}^{(+)}(x_2)]_+ &= -iS_{\rho'\rho}^{(-)}(x_1-x_2)\end{aligned}\right\} \tag{104}$$

(where ρ, ρ' are the usual spinor indices). All positive and negative frequency parts of A commute with each other, except for (see (2.151) and (2.43))†

$$[A_\mu^{(+)}(x_1), A_{\mu'}^{(-)}(x_2)] = i\hbar c\,\delta_{\mu\mu'} D^{(+)}(x_1-x_2). \tag{105}$$

All boson variables commute with all fermion variables. Moving destruction operators to the right, (103) becomes

$$\bar{\psi}^{(-)}(x_1)\{-\bar{\psi}^{(-)}(x_2)\psi^{(+)}(x_1)+[\bar{\psi}^{(-)}(x_2), \psi^{(+)}(x_1)]_+\}\times$$
$$\times\psi^{(+)}(x_2)\{A_{\mu'}^{(-)}(x_2)A_\mu^{(+)}(x_1)+[A_\mu^{(+)}(x_1), A_{\mu'}^{(-)}(x_2)]\}.$$

The physical interpretation is now simple; for example, the term

$$\bar{\psi}^{(-)}(x_1)[\bar{\psi}^{(-)}(x_2), \psi^{(+)}(x_1)]_+\psi^{(+)}(x_2)A_{\mu'}^{(-)}(x_2)A_\mu^{(+)}(x_1) \tag{106}$$

describes the Compton scattering of an electron, because (by (104)) the anti-commutator is not an operator.

A term, like (106), which has been ordered so that all the destruction operators are to the right is called a *normal product*. The physical interpretation of normal products in the S-matrix is always obvious, and we shall show how the general term in the series (101) can be resolved into a sum of normal products.

6. Normal products and graphs

A normal ordering operator N is now defined. Acting on any product of field operators, N rearranges them so that all destruction operators are to the right; all the functions $S^{(+)}$, $S^{(-)}$, $D^{(+)}$ arising from this rearrangement (by (104) and (105)) are to be omitted. Thus, for example,

$$N\{A_\mu(x_1)A_{\mu'}(x_2)\} = A_\mu^{(-)}(x_1)A_{\mu'}^{(-)}(x_2)+A_\mu^{(+)}(x_1)A_{\mu'}^{(+)}(x_2)+$$
$$+A_\mu^{(-)}(x_1)A_{\mu'}^{(+)}(x_2)+A_{\mu'}^{(-)}(x_2)A_\mu^{(+)}(x_1) \tag{107}$$

and

$$N\{\psi_\rho(x_1)\bar{\psi}_{\rho'}(x_2)\} = \psi_\rho^{(-)}(x_1)\bar{\psi}_{\rho'}^{(-)}(x_2)+\psi_\rho^{(+)}(x_1)\bar{\psi}_{\rho'}^{(+)}(x_2)+$$
$$+\psi_\rho^{(-)}(x_1)\bar{\psi}_{\rho'}^{(+)}(x_2)-\bar{\psi}_{\rho'}^{(-)}(x_2)\psi_\rho^{(+)}(x_1). \tag{108}$$

The negative sign before the last term in (108) is due to the change in order of the fermion operators. It should be noted that, for the same reason,

$$N\{\psi_\rho(x_1)\bar{\psi}_{\rho'}(x_2)\} = -N\{\bar{\psi}_{\rho'}(x_2)\psi_\rho(x_1)\}. \tag{109}$$

† These rules are summed up by saying that an operator describing the creation of one kind of particle commutes (or anti-commutes) with all operators, except that which destroys the same kind of particle.

The vacuum expectation value of any normal product must be zero. Also, the commutator of any pair of field amplitudes (or the anti-commutator of any pair of fermion amplitudes) is a number. Therefore we can write†

$$A_\mu(x_1)A_{\mu'}(x_2) = N\{A_\mu(x_1)A_{\mu'}(x_2)\}+\langle 0|A_\mu(x_1)A_{\mu'}(x_2)|0\rangle, \quad (110)$$

$$\psi_\rho(x_1)\bar{\psi}_{\rho'}(x_2) = N\{\psi_\rho(x_1)\bar{\psi}_{\rho'}(x_2)\}+\langle 0|\psi_\rho(x_1)\bar{\psi}_{\rho'}(x_2)|0\rangle. \quad (111)$$

Similar relations hold for other pairs of field amplitudes.

Expansion in normal products

Eqns. (110) and (111) are examples of the general formula for expressing any product of field amplitudes $ABC\ldots Z$ as a sum of normal products. The rule (which we prove below) is

$$\begin{aligned} ABC\ldots Z = {} & N(ABC\ldots Z)+\delta_P\langle AB\rangle_0 N(C\ldots Z)+ \\ & +\delta_P\langle AC\rangle_0 N(B\ldots Z)+\ldots+\delta_P\langle AB\rangle_0\langle CD\rangle_0 N(E\ldots Z)+ \\ & +\delta_P\langle AC\rangle_0\langle BE\rangle_0 N(D\ldots Z)+\ldots+ \\ & +\delta_P\langle AB\rangle_0\langle CD\rangle_0\langle EF\rangle_0\ldots N(L\ldots Z)+\ldots. \end{aligned} \quad (112)$$

Apart from the ordered product $N(AB\ldots Z)$, the right-hand side of (112) is formed by selecting *all distinct sets of one, two, three,... pairs* of the operators A, B, C,..., Z. We take the vacuum expectation value of each pair, which, for conciseness, is written $\langle AB\rangle_0$ instead of $\langle 0|AB|0\rangle$. The two operators in each pair are to be written in the same relative order as they had in the original product $AB\ldots Z$. The normal ordering operator N is written in front of the operators which remain after all the pairs have been formed. The factor δ_P is $+1$ or -1 according as the order of the *fermion* field operators in the term concerned differs by an even or an odd permutation from their order in $ABC\ldots Z$.

As an example (112) is written for four variables:

$$\begin{aligned} ABCD = {} & N(ABCD)+\delta_P\langle AB\rangle_0 N(CD)+\delta_P\langle AC\rangle_0 N(BD)+ \\ & +\delta_P\langle AD\rangle_0 N(BC)+\delta_P\langle BC\rangle_0 N(AD)+ \\ & +\delta_P\langle BD\rangle_0 N(AC)+\delta_P\langle CD\rangle_0 N(AB)+\delta_P\langle AB\rangle_0\langle CD\rangle_0+ \\ & +\delta_P\langle AC\rangle_0\langle BD\rangle_0+\delta_P\langle AD\rangle_0\langle BC\rangle_0. \end{aligned} \quad (113)$$

If A, B, C, D are all fermion amplitudes, the coefficients δ_P appearing on the right of (113) have the values $+1$, -1, $+1$, $+1$, -1, $+1$, $+1$, -1, $+1$ respectively. Because (112) arises from a product of operators

† In other words, the difference between $A_{(1)}A_{(2)}$ and $N(A_{(1)}A_{(2)})$ is a number; this number is conveniently evaluated by taking the vacuum expectation value.

$\mathscr{H}_1(x_\nu)$, there is necessarily an even number of fermion operators in $AB...Z$; there may be an even or an odd number of boson operators. For a single (boson) operator A, we have $N(A) = A$.

In general, a number of the terms which have been written in (112) will vanish. By the commutation rules and the interpretation of positive and negative frequency parts, both $\langle\psi(x_\nu)\psi(x'_\nu)\rangle_0$ and $\langle\bar{\psi}(x_\nu)\bar{\psi}(x'_\nu)\rangle_0$ vanish. By (104), (105) the non-vanishing pairs are

$$\left.\begin{aligned} \langle\psi_\rho(x_\nu)\bar{\psi}_{\rho'}(x'_\nu)\rangle_0 &= \langle\psi_\rho^{(+)}(x_\nu)\bar{\psi}_{\rho'}^{(-)}(x'_\nu)\rangle_0 = -iS_{\rho\rho'}^{(+)}(x_\nu-x'_\nu) \\ \langle\bar{\psi}_{\rho'}(x'_\nu)\psi_\rho(x_\nu)\rangle_0 &= -iS_{\rho\rho'}^{(-)}(x_\nu-x'_\nu) \\ \langle A_\mu(x_\nu)A_{\mu'}(x'_\nu)\rangle_0 &= i\hbar c\,\delta_{\mu\mu'}D^{(+)}(x_\nu-x'_\nu) \end{aligned}\right\}. \tag{114}$$

Proof of the rearrangement theorem

Now we prove the fundamental relation† (112). The order of any adjacent factors P, Q in the product $ABC...PQ...Z$ can be altered by writing

$$PQ = \pm QP + (PQ \mp QP), \tag{115}$$

where the upper sign is to be used except when *both* P and Q are fermion operators; the expression $(PQ \mp QP)$ is not an operator. By repeated application of (115) we get‡

$$AB...Z = N(AB...Z) + W. \tag{116}$$

Here W is a sum of terms each of the form§

$$(PQ \mp QP)O,$$

where O is a product of field amplitude operators. In $N(AB...Z)$ all destruction operators are to the right, so $\langle RS\rangle_0$ would vanish for *any* pair of operators appearing in this order in $N(AB...Z)$. Thus, using (116), we see that the expansion (112) is true for $AB...Z$, provided it holds for W.

Relation (112) is obviously true for single operators or for pairs of operators (e.g. eqns. (110), (111)). We now assume that (112) holds for any operator O_n which contains n field amplitudes. Then it follows that (112) holds for any operator of the form‖

$$O' = (PQ \mp QP)O_n. \tag{117}$$

† Eqn. (112) is frequently called Wick's theorem (C. G. Wick, *Phys. Rev.* **80** (1950) 268). Earlier statements of the relation are A. Houriet and A. Kind, *Helv. phys. Acta*, **22** (1949) 319; F. J. Dyson, *Phys. Rev.* **75** (1949) 486. The proof given here follows an (unpublished) form given by Dyson; it is probably the neatest proof.

‡ It is assumed that splitting into positive and negative frequency parts is used wherever necessary.

§ W may contain several factors of the type $(PQ \mp QP)$: only one need be mentioned explicitly in the sequel.

‖ The sign convention is always that the lower sign is only to be used if both P and Q are fermion amplitudes.

This is because when PQO_n and $\pm QPO_n$ are substituted on the *right* of (112), they give identical terms except for those in which P and Q are paired. Hence substituting O' on the right of (112) gives

$$\{\langle PQ\rangle_0 \mp \langle QP\rangle_0\}O_n. \tag{118}$$

Because $PQ \mp QP$ is not an operator, the expression (118) is identical with (117); hence (112) is true for O'.

Finally we consider any operator O_{n+2}. Using (116) we see that W is now of the form O'; hence (112) is true for O_{n+2}. This completes the proof by induction. It will be noted that it is essential for the validity of the proof that the operators are in the interaction representation. In (112) the operation of bringing A and B together to form $\langle AB\rangle_0$ is called *contraction*.

The S-matrix for electrodynamics

The theorem (112) will be applied to the S-matrix series (101) for electrodynamics; for $\mathscr{H}_1(x_\nu)$ eqn. (97) is used. Contracting fermion variables $\bar{\psi}(x_\nu)$, $\psi(x_\nu)$ which belong to the same point x_ν gives the vacuum expectation value $\langle j_\mu(x_\nu)\rangle_0$. This vanishes when the correct charge conjugate form (98)† is used for j_μ (cf. Chapter IV, § 5). It follows that we need only contract variables belonging to distinct points $x_\nu \neq x'_\nu$. For such contractions it is sufficient to use the form

$$j_\mu(x_\nu) = iec\,\bar{\psi}(x_\nu)\gamma^\mu\psi(x_\nu). \tag{119}$$

The difference between this form and (98) cannot appear in contractions with variables at other points x'_ν.

The order of the operators in the integrand is determined by the chronological operator T. On the left of (112) we replace $AB\ldots Z$ by $\mathsf{T}(AB\ldots Z)$, and on the right all contractions such as $\langle AB\rangle_0$ are therefore to be replaced‡ by $\langle \mathsf{T}(AB)\rangle_0$. Thus to evaluate the contractions arising in the S-matrix we only require (cf. (4.62) and (2.184))

$$\langle \mathsf{T}\{\psi_\rho(x_\nu)\bar{\psi}_{\rho'}(x'_\nu)\}\rangle_0 \equiv -\langle \mathsf{T}\{\bar{\psi}_{\rho'}(x'_\nu)\psi_\rho(x_\nu)\}\rangle_0$$
$$= -\tfrac{1}{2}\{S_F(x_\nu - x'_\nu)\}_{\rho\rho'} \tag{120}$$

and
$$\langle \mathsf{T}\{A_\mu(x_\nu)A_{\mu'}(x'_\nu)\}\rangle_0 = \tfrac{1}{2}\hbar c\delta_{\mu\mu'}D_F(x_\nu - x'_\nu). \tag{121}$$

In (120) the form of the chronological operator for a pair of fermion variables is identical with (4.57); the change of sign which occurs in (120) on changing the order of the fermion variables gives agreement with the definition of δ_P in (112). In Chapter II, § 11, it was shown

† This is because j_n changes sign under charge conjugation.

‡ Because $\bar{\psi}$, ψ always occur together, $N(\mathsf{T}(AB\ldots Z)) = N(AB\ldots Z)$ on the left.

that there is no difficulty about the role of longitudinal photons in connexion with (121).

The use of the ordering theorem (112) is illustrated by sorting out the various physical phenomena which are contained in the double integral in the S-matrix series (101). Using (97) and (119) this term is written

$$S_2 = \frac{1}{2!}\left(\frac{e}{\hbar c}\right)^2 \int d^4x_1 \int d^4x_2\, T\{\bar{\psi}(x_1)\gamma^{\mu}\psi(x_1)\bar{\psi}(x_2)\gamma^{\mu'}\psi(x_2)\}T\{A_{\mu}(x_1)A_{\mu'}(x_2)\}. \tag{122}$$

The photon component gives two terms:

$$T\{A_{\mu}(x_1)A_{\mu'}(x_2)\} = N\{A_{\mu}(x_1)A_{\mu'}(x_2)\}+\langle T\{A_{\mu}(x_1)A_{\mu'}(x_2)\}\rangle_0. \tag{123 a}$$

The electron-positron component gives four terms; ignoring the γ^{μ} matrices for the moment, we have†

$$N\{\bar{\psi}(x_1)\psi(x_1)\bar{\psi}(x_2)\psi(x_2)\}+\langle T\{\bar{\psi}(x_1)\psi(x_2)\}\rangle_0 N\{\psi(x_1)\bar{\psi}(x_2)\}+$$
$$+\langle T\{\psi(x_1)\bar{\psi}(x_2)\}\rangle_0 N\{\bar{\psi}(x_1)\psi(x_2)\}+$$
$$+\langle T\{\bar{\psi}(x_1)\psi(x_2)\}\rangle_0\langle T\{\psi(x_1)\bar{\psi}(x_2)\}\rangle. \tag{123 b}$$

Multiplying (123 a) by (123 b) there are eight processes in all.

Graphs

These processes are illustrated by graphs as follows.‡ For each fermion contraction $\langle T\{\bar{\psi}(x_i)\psi(x_j)\}\rangle_0$ (or $\langle T\{\psi(x_j)\bar{\psi}(x_i)\}\rangle_0$) we draw a solid line from point x_i to point x_j; for each photon contraction

$$\langle T\{A_{\mu}(x_k)A_{\mu'}(x_l)\}\rangle_0$$

we draw a broken line joining x_k and x_l. Each operator $\bar{\psi}(x_j)$ appearing in a normal product is represented by a solid line directed away from x_j (to the edge of the diagram) and each operator $\psi(x_i)$ is represented by a line directed towards x_i. Each operator $A_{\mu}(x_m)$ appearing in a normal product is represented by a broken line from x_m to the edge of the diagram. It will be seen that the fermion lines are continuous; this expresses the conservation of the difference between the number of fermions and the number of anti-fermions.

The eight processes given by (123 a) and (123 b) lead to the six *topologically distinct* graphs which are shown in Fig. 8. The remaining two terms are obtained by exchanging x_1 and x_2 in Fig. 8 (3) and (4). Fig. 8 (1) is the term $N\{\bar{\psi}(x_1)\psi(x_1)\bar{\psi}(x_2)\psi(x_2)\}N\{A_{\mu}(x_1)A_{\mu'}(x_2)\}$; it represents scattering processes which give zero contribution when the integrations over x_1, x_2 are performed, because such processes cannot

† For each term in (123 b) $\delta_P = +1$.

‡ F. J. Dyson, *Phys. Rev.* **75** (1949) 486.

conserve energy and momentum.† Fig. 8 (6) represents the product of three contractions, and it describes spontaneous fluctuations which are not related to any particular initial or final state; we shall see below that these are the vacuum state fluctuations. The remaining graphs describe real processes; Fig. 8 (2), (3), (4), and (5) are, respectively, Møller scattering, Compton effect (and pair annihilation or creation),

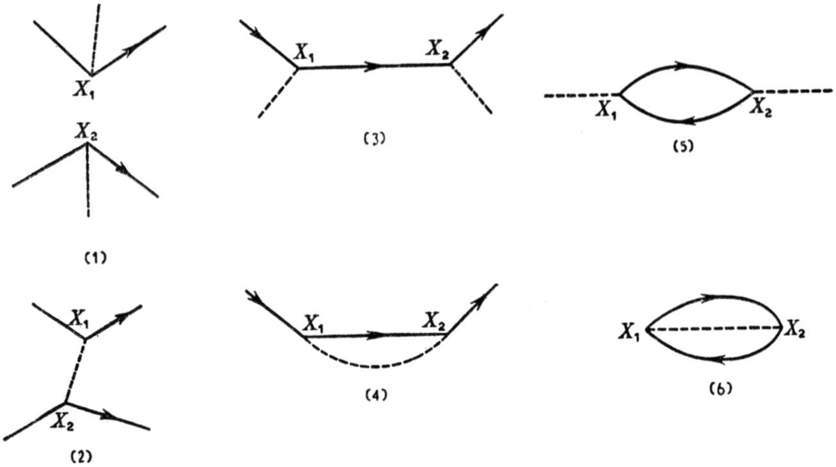

FIG. 8. The six distinct processes which arise from the integral S_2 (eqn. (122)).

fermion self-energy, photon self-energy. S_2 gives the lowest-order matrix elements for these four phenomena.

Feynman graphs

An elaboration of the graphical notation makes it possible to distinguish much more detail in the physical processes. We now assume in addition that fermion lines which are directed up the page describe electrons and those directed down the page describe positrons. This idea is made more substantial if we remember that the time dependence of the unquantized Dirac solutions has positive frequency for electron solutions and negative frequency for positron solutions (cf. Chapter III, § 6). The new convention therefore corresponds to assuming that time increases up the page, and ascribing the direction of motion which would be given by these simple Dirac solutions. This gives the useful fiction that positrons can be regarded as electrons which move backwards in time;‡ it leads to no ambiguity in interpreting graphs, and enables us to distinguish electron and positron processes. Graphs in

† See § 7 for the details of energy-momentum conservation.
‡ R. P. Feynman, *Phys. Rev.* **76** (1949) 749.

which this new convention is used will be distinguished from the more general variety above by calling them *Feynman graphs*.

Fig. 8 (2) gives rise to four Feynman graphs; these are shown in Fig. 9. Fig. 9 (1) and (2) are electron-electron and positron-positron scattering

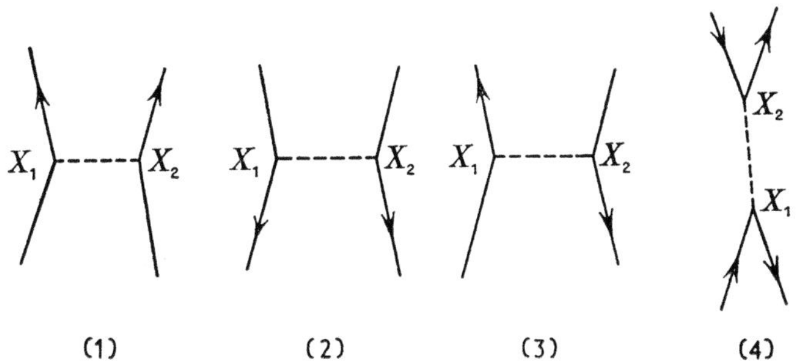

FIG. 9. The four Feynman graphs arising from Fig. 8 (2).

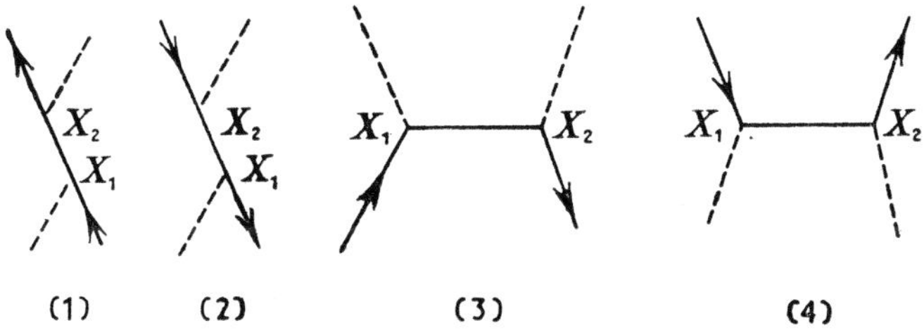

FIG. 10. Four Feynman graphs arising from Fig. 8 (3).

respectively. Fig. 9 (3) and (4) give electron-positron scattering; the last is distinguished by the nature of its intermediate state.

Another example comes from Fig. 8 (3) which gives the four Feynman graphs in Fig. 10. Fig. 10 (1) and (2) give Compton scattering on electrons and positrons respectively. Fig. 10 (3) and (4) respectively give the two-photon annihilation of an electron-positron pair, and the inverse pair production process.

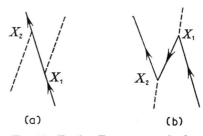

FIG. 11. Further Feynman graphs for Compton scattering on electrons.

Still further details can be described by Feynman graphs. For example, Compton scattering on electrons, in addition to Fig. 10 (1), can have the forms in Fig. 11. The diagram (*a*) indicates that the final photon is emitted at x_1. Diagram (*b*) shows that the initial photon creates an electron-positron pair at x_2; the positron annihilates the incident electron at x_1 and produces the final photon. The distinction between Fig. 11 (*a*) and (*b*) only arises if we give a physical interpretation to the intermediate state or process; both terms come from the same doubly infinite integral over x_1 and x_2 in the S-matrix. In the subsequent discussion they will not be distinguished.

The choice between the various processes shown in Fig. 10 (1) to (4) and Fig 11 depends entirely on whether we take the positive or the negative frequency parts of the various operators within the normal products. (The normal products for these processes are shown in eqns. (123 a, b).)

Finally we notice that all lines joining two points in the graphs—we call them *internal lines*—are described by contractions of chronological products. These lines denote virtual processes,† and by Chapter II, §§ 5 and 11, and Chapter IV, § 4, it follows that the associated contractions are *causal* Green's functions for the propagation of disturbances of the fields.

7. The evaluation of matrix elements: Compton scattering

As an illustration of the evaluation of a simple matrix element consider the Compton scattering of an electron described by the S-matrix element S_2 (eqn. (122)). The related graph is Fig. 8 (3),‡ which describes the matrix element

$$M_2 \equiv \left(\frac{e}{\hbar c}\right)^2 \int d^4x_1 \int d^4x_2 \langle \mathrm{T}\{\bar{\psi}_\rho(x_1)\psi_{\sigma'}(x_2)\}\rangle_0 \times$$
$$\times N\{\psi_{\rho'}(x_1)\bar{\psi}_\sigma(x_2)\} N\{A_\mu(x_1)A_{\mu'}(x_2)\}\gamma^\mu_{\rho\rho'}\gamma^{\mu'}_{\sigma\sigma'}. \quad (124)$$

Because $T\{\mathscr{H}_1(x_1)\mathscr{H}_1(x_2)\}$ is symmetric in x_1, x_2, the two terms in the expansion (112) which give the topological form Fig. 8 (3) are equal. This is allowed for by dropping the factor (1/2!) appearing in (122).

The electron in the initial state is to be destroyed and another electron created; hence it is sufficient to write

$$N\{\psi_{\rho'}(x_1)\bar{\psi}_\sigma(x_2)\} = -\bar{\psi}^{(-)}_\sigma(x_2)\psi^{(+)}_{\rho'}(x_1). \quad (125\,\mathrm{a})$$

The photon operators give two terms according as the incident photon is destroyed§ at x_1 or x_2; we write

$$N\{A_\mu(x_1)A_{\mu'}(x_2)\} = A^{(-)}_\mu(x_1)A^{(+)}_{\mu'}(x_2) + A^{(-)}_{\mu'}(x_2)A^{(+)}_\mu(x_1). \quad (125\,\mathrm{b})$$

In the initial state the electron has propagation vector $\mathbf{k}$ and spin s; the photon has propagation vector $\mathbf{q}$ and polarization $\mathbf{e}$. In the final

† See, however, § 8 below.

‡ This is not a Feynman graph.

§ Cf. Fig. 10 (1), (2), and Fig. 11.

state the corresponding values are $\mathbf{k}'$, s'; $\mathbf{q}'$, $\mathbf{e}'$. The matrix element between these states is written $\langle \mathbf{k}, s'; \mathbf{q}', \mathbf{e}' | M_2 | \mathbf{k}, s; \mathbf{q}, \mathbf{e} \rangle$. We require the transverse electromagnetic component $A_{\mathbf{e}}^{(+)}(x_\mu)$ in the direction $\mathbf{e}$, and the component $A_{\mathbf{e}'}^{(-)}(x_\mu)$ in the direction $\mathbf{e}'$. By (2.154) and (2.156) these operators can be written in terms of the normalized photon destruction and creation operators $a_{\mathbf{e}}(\mathbf{q})$, $\tilde{a}_{\mathbf{e}'}(\mathbf{q}')$. Using the state density $\rho_{\mathbf{q}} = V/8\pi^3$ for a periodic box of volume V we have

$$A_{\mathbf{e}}^{(+)}(x_\mu) = V^{-\frac{1}{2}} \sum_{\mathbf{q}} \left(\frac{\hbar c}{2|\mathbf{q}|}\right)^{\frac{1}{2}} a_{\mathbf{e}}(\mathbf{q}) e^{i(\mathbf{q}.\mathbf{x}-|\mathbf{q}|x_0)}; \tag{126}$$

the summation is over all values of $\mathbf{q}$. $A_{\mathbf{e}}^{(-)}$ is given by the Hermitian conjugate expression. (We use a simplified notation $A_{\mathbf{e}}$.)

By (4.26) and (4.46) we can write

$$\left.\begin{aligned} \psi_\rho^{(+)}(x_\mu) &= V^{-\frac{1}{2}} \sum_{s=-\frac{1}{2}}^{\frac{1}{2}} \sum_{\mathbf{k}} c^{(s)}(\mathbf{k}) u_\rho^{(s)}(\mathbf{k}) e^{i(\mathbf{k}.\mathbf{x}-\omega_k t)} \\ \bar{\psi}_\rho^{(-)}(x_\mu) &= V^{-\frac{1}{2}} \sum_{s=-\frac{1}{2}}^{\frac{1}{2}} \sum_{\mathbf{k}} \tilde{c}^{(s)}(\mathbf{k}) \bar{u}_\rho^{(s)}(\mathbf{k}) e^{-i(\mathbf{k}.\mathbf{x}-\omega_k t)} \end{aligned}\right\}, \tag{127}$$

where $c^{(s)}(\mathbf{k})$, $\tilde{c}^{(s)}(\mathbf{k})$ are the *normalized* destruction and creation operators for electron $(\mathbf{k}, s)$. The spinors are normalized according to scheme (i) of Chapter IV, § 3, so that (by 4.25)†

$$\bar{u}^{(s)}(\mathbf{k}).u^{(s')}(\mathbf{k}) = \frac{c\kappa}{\omega_k}\delta_{ss'} \quad (s, s' = \tfrac{1}{2} \text{ or } -\tfrac{1}{2}).$$

The corresponding expressions for the destruction and creation of positrons would be respectively

$$\left.\begin{aligned} \psi_\rho^{(+)}(x_\mu) &= V^{-\frac{1}{2}} \sum_{s=-\frac{1}{2}}^{\frac{1}{2}} \sum_{\mathbf{k}} d^{(s)}(\mathbf{k}) \bar{v}_\rho^{(s)}(\mathbf{k}) e^{i(\mathbf{k}.\mathbf{x}-\omega_k t)} \\ \bar{\psi}_\rho^{(-)}(x_\mu) &= V^{-\frac{1}{2}} \sum_{s=-\frac{1}{2}}^{\frac{1}{2}} \sum_{\mathbf{k}} \tilde{d}^{(s)}(\mathbf{k}) v_\rho^{(s)}(\mathbf{k}) e^{-i(\mathbf{k}.\mathbf{x}-\omega_k t)} \end{aligned}\right\}, \tag{128}$$

where the spinor normalization is

$$\bar{v}^{(s)}(\mathbf{k}).v^{(s')}(\mathbf{k}) = -\frac{c\kappa}{\omega_k}\delta_{ss'}.$$

Using (120) and (125) to (127) the matrix element

$$\langle \mathbf{k}', s'; \mathbf{q}', \mathbf{e}' | M_2 | \mathbf{k}, s; \mathbf{q}, \mathbf{e} \rangle$$

is

$$-\left(\frac{e^2}{4\pi\hbar c}\right)\frac{\pi}{(|\mathbf{q}||\mathbf{q}'|)^{\frac{1}{2}}} V^{-2} \int_{-\infty}^{\infty} d^4x_1 \int_{-\infty}^{\infty} d^4x_2 \times$$

$$\times\{\bar{u}^{(s')}(\mathbf{k}')(\boldsymbol{\gamma}.\mathbf{e}) S_F(x_2-x_1)(\boldsymbol{\gamma}.\mathbf{e}') u^{(s)}(\mathbf{k}) e^{i(qx_2-q'x_1)} +$$
$$+\bar{u}^{(s')}(\mathbf{k}')(\boldsymbol{\gamma}.\mathbf{e}') S_F(x_2-x_1)(\boldsymbol{\gamma}.\mathbf{e}) u^{(s)}(\mathbf{k}) e^{i(qx_1-q'x_2)}\} e^{i(kx_1-k'x_2)}; \tag{129}$$

† Always $\omega_k = +c(\mathbf{k}^2+\kappa^2)^{\frac{1}{2}}$; $\kappa = mc/\hbar$ (m = electron mass).

here $\boldsymbol{\gamma} \equiv (\gamma^1, \gamma^2, \gamma^3)$ and $q \equiv (\mathbf{q}, i|\mathbf{q}|)$, $k \equiv (\mathbf{k}, i\omega_k/c)$, etc. The expression qx_2 is the scalar product of the 4-vectors q and x_2, etc. The two terms in the integrand correspond to the two terms in (125 b).

Replacing the contraction term by the integral expression (cf. eqn. (A.101) and eqn. (120))

$$-\tfrac{1}{2}S_F(x) = \lim_{\epsilon \to +0} \frac{i}{(2\pi)^4} \int_{-\infty}^{\infty} d^4k'' \frac{e^{ik''x}(i\gamma k'' - \kappa)}{(k''^2 + \kappa^2 - i\epsilon)}, \tag{130}$$

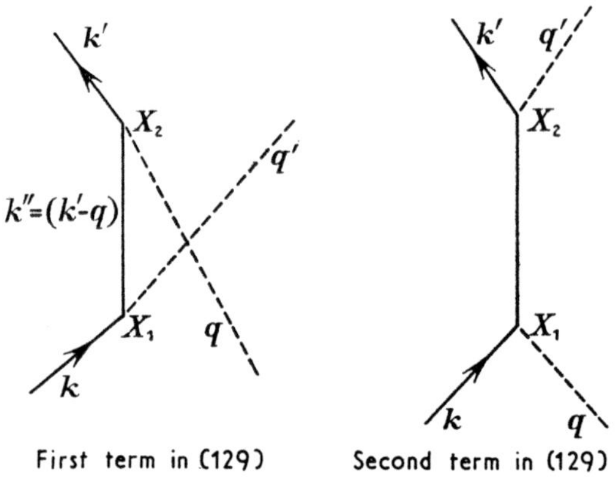

FIG. 12. Energy-momenta integration variables for the integral (129).

the integrations over x_1, x_2 can be completed. That over x_2 gives for the first term in the integrand,

$$\int d^4x_2 \exp\{ik''x_2 + iqx_2 - ik'x_2\} = (2\pi)^4 \delta^3(\mathbf{k}'' + \mathbf{q} - \mathbf{k}')\delta(k_0'' + q_0 - k_0'). \tag{131}$$

This shows that if we ascribe the energy-momentum 4-vectors

$$k'' = (\mathbf{k}'', ik_0'')$$

to the internal line, with k'' pointing from x_1 to x_2, energy and momentum will be conserved at the *vertex* x_2; by a similar consideration it is conserved at x_1. These energy-momentum values are shown in Fig. 12. Finally we have

$$\langle \mathbf{k}', s'; \mathbf{q}', \mathbf{e}' | M_2 | \mathbf{k}, s; \mathbf{q}, \mathbf{e} \rangle$$
$$= V^{-2}(2\pi)^4 \delta^{(4)}(k + q - k' - q')\left(\frac{e^2}{4\pi\hbar c}\right)\frac{2\pi i}{(|\mathbf{q}||\mathbf{q}'|)^{\frac{1}{2}}} \bar{u}^{(s')}(\mathbf{k}') \mathsf{O} u^{(s)}(\mathbf{k}), \tag{132}$$

where

$$\mathsf{O} = \left\{(\boldsymbol{\gamma}.\mathbf{e})\frac{i\gamma(k'-q)-\kappa}{(k'-q)^2+\kappa^2}(\boldsymbol{\gamma}.\mathbf{e}') + (\boldsymbol{\gamma}.\mathbf{e}')\frac{i\gamma(k+q)-\kappa}{(k+q)^2+\kappa^2}(\boldsymbol{\gamma}.\mathbf{e})\right\}. \tag{133}$$

In (133), ϵ has been allowed to vanish because there cannot be any ambiguity about the denominators.† By $\delta^{(4)}(k)$ we mean $\delta^3(\mathbf{k})\delta(k_0)$. Clearly the energy-momentum conservation at each vertex yields the overall conservation of energy and momentum; it is not difficult to see that this must be true for any graph, however complicated.

The notation in (132) is not quite consistent because the finite normalization volume V implies discrete momentum values. Comparing with (131) we see that the factor $V^{-1}(2\pi)^3\delta^3(\mathbf{k}+\mathbf{q}-\mathbf{k}'-\mathbf{q}')$ should be replaced by unity,‡ and we should only consider momenta such that

$$\mathbf{k}+\mathbf{q} = \mathbf{k}'+\mathbf{q}'.$$

The scattering matrix $\mathbf{T}$ is given by (26) above. Using the relation $\delta(k_0) = \hbar c\delta(E)$, the contribution $\mathbf{T}_2$ arising from M_2 is (with $V = 1$)

$$\langle \mathbf{k}', s'; \mathbf{q}', \mathbf{e}'|\mathbf{T}_2|\mathbf{k}, s; \mathbf{q}, \mathbf{e}\rangle = -\alpha\frac{2\pi\hbar c}{(|\mathbf{q}||\mathbf{q}'|)^{\frac{1}{2}}}\bar{u}^{(s')}(\mathbf{k}')\mathbf{O}u^{(s)}(\mathbf{k}), \quad (134)$$

where $\alpha = e^2/4\pi\hbar c \simeq \frac{1}{137}$. The transition probability W per unit time is now given by formulae (28) or (29).

The cross-section

The relativistic Klein–Nishina formula for Compton scattering can be evaluated in a straightforward way; it is given in detail by a number of authors, and the derivation will not be repeated here.§ The completion of the calculation is illustrated for the case of low-energy photons striking an electron; the electron can be assumed to remain at rest. The density of the final states is

$$\rho(E) = \frac{q^2}{(2\pi)^3}d\Omega\frac{dq}{dE} \qquad \left(\text{with } \frac{dq}{dE} = \frac{1}{\hbar c}\right),$$

where the photon goes off in the solid angle $d\Omega$. Also, ignoring terms of relative order (q/κ) $(= \hbar q/mc)$, we have‖

$$\bar{u}^{(s')}\mathbf{O}u^{(s)} = \frac{1}{2\kappa}\bar{u}^{(s')}\{(\boldsymbol{\gamma}.\mathbf{e})\gamma^4(\boldsymbol{\gamma}.\mathbf{e}')+(\boldsymbol{\gamma}.\mathbf{e}')\gamma^4(\boldsymbol{\gamma}.\mathbf{e})\}u^{(s)} = -(\mathbf{e}.\mathbf{e}')\delta_{ss'}/\kappa.$$

† The denominators in (133) cannot vanish, because k'' cannot satisfy the real particle condition $k''^2+\kappa^2 = 0$. This is not the general case (cf. § 8).

‡ The matrix element now varies as V^{-1}, as it should.

§ See, for example, W. Heitler, *Quantum Theory of Radiation* (Clarendon Press, 3rd edn., 1954); J. M. Jauch and F. Rohrlich, *Theory of Photons and Electrons* (Addison-Wesley, Cambridge, Mass., 1955).

‖ Neglecting the electron's momentum, the first term in $\mathbf{O}$ is

$$-(\boldsymbol{\gamma}.\mathbf{e})\{\gamma^4(\kappa-q_0)+\kappa\}(\boldsymbol{\gamma}.\mathbf{e}')/\{\kappa^2-(\kappa-q_0)^2\}.$$

For the numerator $\bar{u}^{(s')}(\boldsymbol{\gamma}.\mathbf{e})(1+\gamma^4) = 0$; the denominator is approximately $2\kappa q_0$.

The differential cross-section for scattering into the solid angle $d\Omega$ is†

$$d\sigma = \frac{2\pi}{\hbar c}\rho(E)|\mathbf{T}_2|^2$$
$$= d\Omega(\mathbf{e}.\mathbf{e}')^2\left(\frac{e^2}{4\pi mc^2}\right)^2. \tag{135}$$

This gives J. J. Thomson's famous formula.‡ The derivation shows that covariant perturbation theory as developed above is also a straightforward practical method.

The reaction matrix

We return to the general formula (134) for the (second-order) scattering matrix $\mathbf{T}_2$ for the Compton effect. The Hermitian conjugate§ of $\bar{u}^{(s')}(\mathbf{k}')\mathsf{O}u^{(s)}(\mathbf{k})$ is $\bar{u}^{(s)}(\mathbf{k})\gamma^4\tilde{\mathsf{O}}\gamma^4u^{(s')}(\mathbf{k}')$. Also, from (133), $\gamma^4\tilde{\mathsf{O}}\gamma^4 = \mathsf{O}$. It follows that $\mathbf{T}_2$ is a Hermitian matrix. This property is connected with the relation of $\mathbf{T}_2$ to the reaction matrix $\mathbf{K}$ (cf. § 3), and it is also a consequence of the fact that the intermediate state (cf. Fig. 12) is necessarily a virtual state (i.e. $k''+\kappa^2 \neq 0$). From eqn. (62) it is obvious that, to order e^2, $\mathbf{T}$ and $\mathbf{K}$ are identical. Because $\mathbf{K}$ cannot have real intermediate states, the same must be true for $\mathbf{T}_2$. It also follows from (62) that it is essential, if a *unitary* scattering matrix $\mathbf{T}$ is to be given by the perturbation method, that there should be higher-order graphs which describe successive scatterings. An example of this type of graph is given in the next section.

8. Higher-order processes

As an illustration we again consider Compton scattering. The next relevant matrix elements in the series (101) are of order e^4; typical graphs are shown in Fig. 13. In Fig. 13 (1) and (2), external and internal electron lines respectively have been modified; we say that an *electron self-energy part* has been inserted in these lines. In general we define an *electron self-energy part* (E.S.E.) as a portion of a graph which is connected to the remainder of the graph by two electron lines only (cf. Fig. 13 (6)). A *photon self-energy part* (P.S.E.) is defined similarly (cf. Fig. 13 (6)); Fig. 13 (3) shows a photon self-energy part of the lowest order inserted in an external photon line. A *vertex part* is defined as a

† $d\sigma$ is found by dividing the transition probability by the relative velocity c after putting the normalizing volume V equal to unity. $(e^2/4\pi mc^2)$ is the classical electron radius.

‡ J. J. Thomson, *Conduction of Electricity through Gases* (Cambridge University Press, 3rd edn., 1933), vol. ii.

§ $\tilde{\mathsf{O}}$ is the Hermitian conjugate of O.

portion of a graph which is connected to the remainder by a photon line and two electron lines only (cf. Fig. 13 (6)). Fig. 13 (4) shows a vertex part of the lowest order inserted at x_2.

The E.S.E., P.S.E., and vertex parts give divergent integrals in the perturbation series (101); in § 10 we show how to extract the correct finite contributions from such terms. For the present we examine the correction to Compton scattering which comes from the finite term in

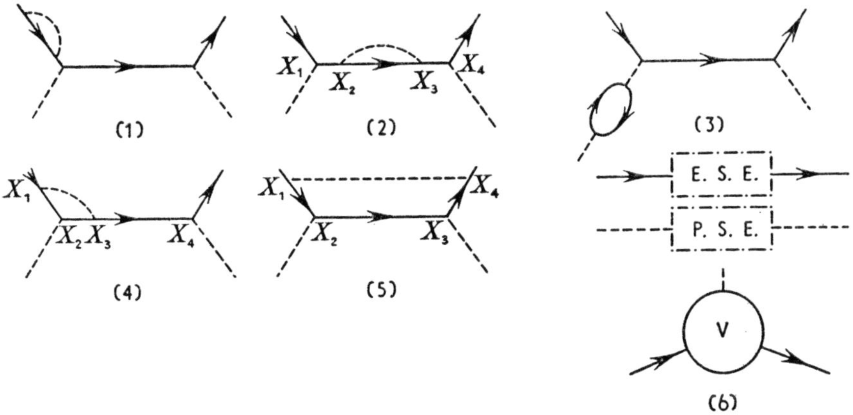

FIG. 13. Graphs of order e^4 for Compton scattering. No. (6) shows the general notation for insertions.

Fig. 13 (5). This graph is obtained by extracting from the fourth-order integral in (101) the term

$$(+1)N\{\psi(x_1)\bar{\psi}(x_4)\}N\{A(x_2)A(x_3)\}\langle T\{\bar{\psi}(x_1)\psi(x_2)\}\rangle_0\langle T\{\bar{\psi}(x_2)\psi(x_3)\}\rangle_0\times$$
$$\times\langle T\{\bar{\psi}(x_3)\psi(x_4)\}\rangle_0\langle T\{A(x_1)A(x_4)\}\rangle_0. \quad (136)$$

In the expansion (112) there are 4! terms of the same type as (136), arising from all permutations of $x_1,\ldots, x_4$; if we omit the factor 1/4! before the integral in (101) we need only consider the term (136).

Using (120), (121), (124), and (125), the S-matrix term is

$$M_4 = -\left(\frac{e}{\hbar c}\right)^4\frac{\hbar c}{2^4}\int d^4x_1 \ldots \int d^4x_4\,\bar{\psi}^{(-)}(x_4)\gamma^{\mu_4}S_F(x_4-x_3)\gamma^{\mu_3}\times$$
$$\times\{A^{(-)}_{\mu_3}(x_3)S_F(x_3-x_2)A^{(+)}_{\mu_2}(x_2)+A^{(-)}_{\mu_2}(x_2)S_F(x_3-x_2)A^{(+)}_{\mu_3}(x_3)\}\times$$
$$\times\gamma^{\mu_2}S_F(x_2-x_1)\gamma^{\mu_4}\psi^{(+)}(x_1)D_F(x_1-x_4). \quad (137)$$

Here the 4-vector indices μ_2, μ_3, μ_4 appearing twice are to be summed. Using (126) and (127), this matrix element can be evaluated in the same way as (129).†

† For details of the calculation see L. M. Brown and R. P. Feynman, *Phys. Rev.* **85** (1952) 231. See also J. M. Jauch and F. Rohrlich, op. cit.

The unitary property

We use (137) as an illustration of how the unitary character of the S-matrix expansion (101) arises. Using (130) and the corresponding expression for a photon line (cf. eqn. (A.64)),

$$-\tfrac{1}{2}D_F(x_\mu) = \lim_{\epsilon\to+0}\frac{i}{(2\pi)^4}\int\limits_{-\infty}^{\infty} d^4k''\,\frac{e^{ik''_\mu x_\mu}}{k''^2_\mu-i\epsilon}, \tag{138}$$

the term $M_4^{(1)}$ of (137) which contains $A_{\mu_3}^{(-)}(x_3)A_{\mu_2}^{(+)}(x_2)$ reduces to†

$$M_4^{(1)} = -\alpha^2\frac{8\pi^2}{(|\mathbf{q}||\mathbf{q}'|)^{\frac{1}{2}}}\delta^{(4)}(k+q-k'-q')\int\limits_{-\infty}^{\infty} d^4k''\,\bar{u}^{(s')}(\mathbf{k}')\gamma^\lambda\times$$
$$\times\frac{i\gamma(k''-q')-\kappa}{(k''-q')^2+\kappa^2-i\epsilon}(\boldsymbol{\gamma}.\mathbf{e}')\frac{i\gamma k''-\kappa}{k''^2+\kappa^2-i\epsilon'}(\boldsymbol{\gamma}.\mathbf{e})\times$$
$$\times\frac{i\gamma(k''-q)-\kappa}{(k''-q)^2+\kappa^2-i\epsilon''}\gamma^\lambda u^{(s)}(\mathbf{k})\frac{1}{(k''-k'-q')^2-i\epsilon'''}. \tag{139}$$

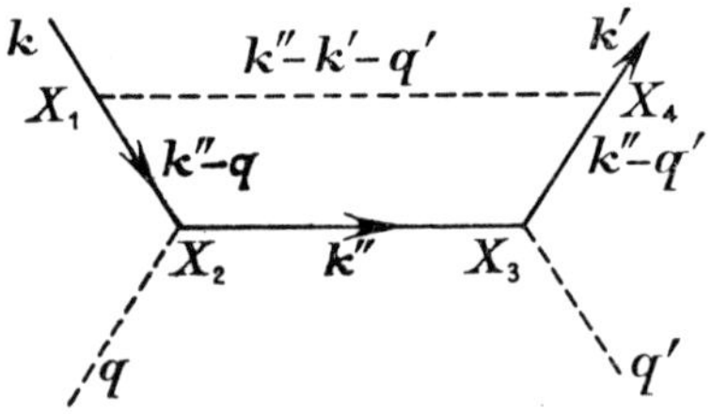

FIG. 14. Energy-momentum variables for integrating the process in Fig. 13 (5).

The 4-momenta ascribed to the lines is shown in Fig. 14.

The small positive numbers, ϵ, ϵ', ϵ'', ϵ''' show how the integration over k''_0 is to be carried out near the poles of the integrand. It is, however, possible to find a value of k'' for which *both* $k''^2+\kappa^2$ and $(k''-k'-q')^2$ vanish; this *coincident pole* corresponds to the situation in which the photon which is propagated between x_1 and x_4 and the electron which is propagated between x_2 and x_3 are *both* free particles. The contribution to $M_4^{(1)}$ from the coincident pole gives what we called compound scattering (cf. § 3); in this case $M_4^{(1)}$ is made up of two successive scattering processes of order e^2. Coincident poles can also occur in the graphs Fig. 13 (2) and (4). The coincident pole contribution can be separated off unambiguously. This can be seen from (139); here the important denominators are $(k''^2+\kappa^2-i\epsilon')$ and $\{(k''-k'-q')^2-i\epsilon'''\}$. Integrating over k''_0, a pole (i.e. δ-function) contribution from the first denominator gives $k''_0 = \pm\{\sqrt{(\mathbf{k}''^2+\kappa^2)}-i\eta\}$ (where $\eta > 0$). Now we substitute this value of k''_0 in the second denominator and take the pole (or δ-function) contribution of the integration over k''_1. This gives

† $\alpha = e^2/4\pi\hbar c$.

the coincident pole contribution; the remaining terms all contain at least one principal value integration.†

Let $\mathbf{T}_4$ be the *total* scattering matrix of order e^4 for Compton scattering. We can separate $\mathbf{T}_4$ into the contribution $\mathbf{T}_4^c$ from the coincident poles discussed above, and the remainder $\mathbf{T}_4^v$. By using eqn. (62) we can build up $\mathbf{T} = \mathbf{T}_2+\mathbf{T}_4$ in terms of the reaction matrix elements $\mathbf{K}_2$ and $\mathbf{K}_4$ of order e^2 and e^4 respectively. Clearly $\mathbf{T}_4^v$ must be identical with $\mathbf{K}_4$. Also, by (62),

$$\mathbf{T}_4^c = -i\pi \mathbf{K}_2 \rho(E)\mathbf{K}_2. \tag{140}$$

These matrices are only defined on the energy shell, and the multiplication of matrices in (140) involves summation over the states on the energy shell. $\mathbf{T}_4^v$ must be Hermitian, and clearly $\mathbf{T}_4^c$ is anti-Hermitian. For *no scattering* $\mathbf{T}_4^c$ gives‡ (using (140) and remembering $\mathbf{T}_2 = \mathbf{K}_2$):

$$\langle \mathbf{k}, s; \mathbf{q}, \mathbf{e}|\mathbf{T}_4^c|\mathbf{k}, s; \mathbf{q}, \mathbf{e}\rangle = -i\pi \sum_{\mathbf{k}',s',\mathbf{e}'} \rho(E)|\langle \mathbf{k}', s'; \mathbf{q}', \mathbf{e}'|\mathbf{T}_2|\mathbf{k}, s; \mathbf{q}, \mathbf{e}\rangle|^2. \tag{141}$$

Thus the *interference* with the original beam due to second-order scattering only appears in the fourth order. Non-forward elements of $\mathbf{T}_4^c$ are also expected to show some interference. In general, it follows from eqn. (62) and § 3 that the total scattering matrix contribution $\mathbf{T}_{2n}^v$ from strictly virtual processes of order e^{2n} equals the corresponding reaction matrix term $\mathbf{K}_{2n}$.

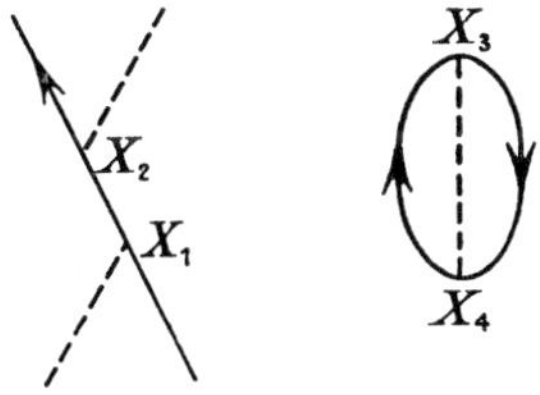

FIG. 15. A fourth-order graph which includes a vacuum part.

9. The analysis of graphs; Furry's theorem

Vacuum loops

Among the fourth-order matrix elements for Compton scattering are terms of the type shown in Fig. 15. This term comes from the pairing (in the fourth-order term in (101))

$$(+1)N\{\psi(x_1)\bar{\psi}(x_2)\}\langle T\{\bar{\psi}(x_1)\psi(x_2)\}\rangle_0 N\{A(x_1)A(x_2)\}\langle T\{\bar{\psi}(x_3)\psi(x_4)\}\rangle_0 \times$$
$$\times \langle T\{\psi(x_3)\bar{\psi}(x_4)\}\rangle_0 \langle T\{A(x_3)A(x_4)\}\rangle_0. \tag{142}$$

The factor (+1) indicates that no change of sign is required because of the change in order of the fermion operators. The first three factors in (142) are identical with the factors giving the second-order matrix

† For a detailed investigation see J. Hamilton, *Proc. Camb. Phil. Soc.* **48** (1952) 640.

‡ Eqn. (141) is of course a special case of (32), or the optical theorem (1.35). See also S. N. Gupta, *Proc. Camb. Phil. Soc.* **47** (1951) 454.

element (124). The remaining three factors are not connected to the first three, either by spinor indices or by space-time integration. The pairing (142) gives the matrix element

$$-\tfrac{1}{2}M_2\left(\frac{e}{\hbar c}\right)^2\cdot\frac{1}{2^3}\hbar c\int d^4x_1\int d^4x_2\times$$

$$\times\,\mathrm{spur}\{S_F(x_4-x_3)\gamma^\mu S_F(x_3-x_4)\gamma^\mu\}D_F(x_3-x_4). \quad (143)$$

Spur denotes the diagonal sum over the spinor indices;† M_2 is given by (124). The numerical factor $\frac{1}{2}$ in front of the matrix element results from multiplying the original factor 1/4! (in (101)) by the number of

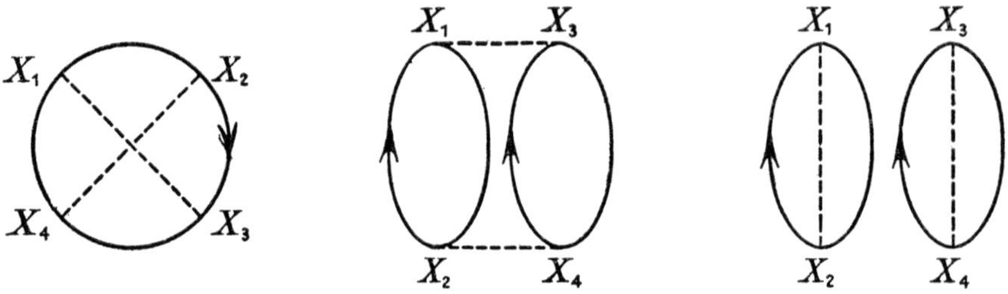

FIG. 16. Fourth-order vacuum parts.

ways of permuting $x_1 \dots x_4$ to give the same topological form.‡ Substituting (130) and (138) for S_F and D_F, the integrations in (143) give an infinite constant; if we use a cut-off at high frequencies the integral becomes a large pure imaginary number. This is because the closed loop in Fig. 15 is a strictly virtual process.§

Those parts of graphs which represent spontaneous vacuum processes such as we have just discussed are called vacuum loops. In Fig. 16 (*a*), (*b*), and (*c*) are shown fourth-order vacuum processes which can appear in the sixth-order matrix element (101) for Compton scattering. Both Fig. 16 (*a*) and (*b*) are virtual processes; they contribute purely imaginary (infinite) integrals similar to that in (143). Fig. 16 (*c*) is a succession of two virtual processes;‖ it contributes the square of the integral appearing in (143).

† $\mathrm{Spur}(A) = \sum_{\alpha=1}^{4} A_{\alpha\alpha}$, where A is any function of the γ^λ.

‡ The closed loop in (67) offers no means of distinguishing x_3 and x_4.

§ By this we mean that the graph cannot be divided into two other graphs which are joined by lines all of which simultaneously have free particle energy-momentum values. By (62) the corresponding part of S is anti-Hermitian.

‖ Fig. 16 (c) may be regarded as a *compound* vacuum to vacuum scattering (cf. § 8).

The summation of vacuum loops

Now we consider all the vacuum loops which can appear together with a graph which represents any observable processes.† Suppose that in a graph G there are *in all n* vertices and r of these lie on a vacuum loop or loops V (obviously r must be even). Let the matrix element for the process described by the graph be $M_n(G)$. The number of ways of choosing r out of $x_1,..., x_n$ to form the vertices of the vacuum part V is $\{n!/(n-r)!\,r!\}$. Remembering that there is a factor $(1/n!)$ outside the nth order term in the S-matrix series (101), it follows that‡

$$M_n(G) = M_{(n-r)}(G')M_{(r)}(V). \tag{144}$$

Here $M_{(r)}(V)$ and $M_{(n-r)}(G')$ are the matrix elements for the vacuum part V and the remainder of the graph G', as calculated directly from the rth order and $(n-r)$th order terms in (101) respectively.§ From (144) it follows that the total S-matrix contribution M for any observable process can be written

$$M = M'.M(\textstyle\sum V), \tag{145}$$

where M' is the sum of all the matrix elements which do not contain vacuum parts, and $M(\sum V)$ is the sum of all possible vacuum parts (plus the identity operator). For example, for Compton scattering M' is the sum of the terms given by Fig. 8 (3), Fig. 13 (1) to (5), etc.; the lowest order terms in $M(\sum V)$ (besides identity) are the loop in Fig. 15 and Fig. 16 (*a*), (*b*), and (*c*).

The elimination of vacuum parts

We now show that $M(\sum V)$, which is necessarily a number, is the exponential of an imaginary quantity. Suppose the vacuum part V is made up of two separate vacuum loops, V_1 and V_2, which have r_1 and r_2 vertices, respectively; we assume that the loops are not identical. The r vertices‖ in V can be divided between the two loops in $(r!/r_1!\,r_2!)$ ways. Therefore the matrix element $M_{(r)}(V)$ of V is given by

$$M_{(r)}(V) = M_{(r_1)}(V_1)M_{(r_2)}(V_2), \tag{146}$$

where $M_{(r_1)}(V_1)$ is the matrix element for V_1, etc. Consider another vacuum part V which consists of s identical vacuum loops V_1 each of which has r_1 vertices. The number of distinct ways of distributing the r $(= sr_1)$

† An observable process necessarily has external lines (i.e. lines going to the edge of the figure).

‡ It is easy to verify that the factor δ_P in (112) gives no difficulty.

§ Having selected $x_{i1},..., x_{ir}$ for V, a number of exchanges of these vertices will give the same topological form; the same is true for G'.

‖ $r = r_1+r_2$.

vertices over the loops is $\{r!/s!\,(r_1!)^s\}$. The extra factor $s!$ appears because the loops are identical. Thus

$$M_{(r)}(V) = \frac{1}{s!}\{M_{(r_1)}(V_1)\}^s. \tag{147}$$

It follows from (146), (147), and similar formulae that

$$M(\sum V) = \exp\Big\{\sum_i M(\overline{V}_i)\Big\}, \tag{148}$$

where $\sum_i$ denotes the sum over all connected or *proper* vacuum loops $\overline{V}_i$. The arguments of § 8 show that all the numbers $M(\overline{V}_i)$ are purely imaginary, because each refers to a single strictly virtual process. We can now write the vacuum to vacuum S-matrix element as

$$\langle 0|S|0\rangle = \exp\Big\{\sum_i M(\overline{V}_i)\Big\}. \tag{149}$$

Because of the adiabatic switching on and off it is to be expected that the vacuum to vacuum transition probability $|\langle 0|S|0\rangle|^2$ will be unity; eqn. (149) shows this is so. We can in future ignore all vacuum processes† and evaluate cross-sections, etc., by using the matrix elements M' of eqn. (145).‡

If, in addition to the quantized electromagnetic field $A_\mu(x)$ there is a given (external) field $A_\mu^{(e)}(x)$ (cf. § 13 below), the vacuum to vacuum transition probability need not be unity, because electron-positron pairs can be created or destroyed. The matrix elements corresponding to $M(\overline{V}_i)$ can then have non-zero *real* parts because they describe processes which are not entirely virtual.§

Furry's theorem

The number of graphs which we have to consider is further reduced by Furry's theorem; this states that all graphs vanish which contain one or more closed electron loops having an odd number of vertices. Such a loop is shown in Fig. 17 (*a*); the photon lines coming from the vertices x_1, x_3, x_4 may either be external lines, or they may join the

† In graphs M some vacuum fluctuations would be suppressed by the exclusion principle. These terms are cancelled by other terms in M (such as Fig. 8 (4) with $(x_2)_0 < (x_1)_0$) which themselves violate the exclusion principle. The latter terms also occur in M', and they just make it correct to ignore the dependence of the vacuum fluctuations on the presence of other particles.

‡ The original derivation of (148) was given by R. P. Feynman, *Phys. Rev.* **76** (1949) 749. The form of eqn. (145) is closely related to the use of the Fredholm method for solving the integral equation for the S-matrix (eqn. (8) above); $\langle 0|S|0\rangle$ is then related to the discriminant. For a mathematical discussion see J. Hamilton, *Phys. Rev.* **91** (1953) 1524, where other references are given.

§ See J. Schwinger, *Phys. Rev.* **93** (1954) 615, for a comprehensive discussion.

loop to the remainder of the graph. Corresponding to Fig. 17 (*a*) there must be a graph Fig. 17 (*b*) in which the arrow on the electron loop is reversed, but all other quantities are the same. The second graph is obtained from the first on replacing $\bar{\psi}(x_i)\gamma^\mu\psi(x_i)$ by† $\psi_T(x_i)\gamma_T^\mu\,\bar{\psi}_T(x_i)$ for $i = 1, 2,..., 5$. By eqn. (4.77) this means replacing $\bar{\psi}(x_i)\gamma^\mu\psi(x_i)$ by its charge conjugate $\bar{\psi}_c(x_i)\gamma^\mu\psi_c(x_i)$, so the second graph is the charge conjugate of the first.

From the expression (98) for the current $j_\mu(x_i)$, it follows that the

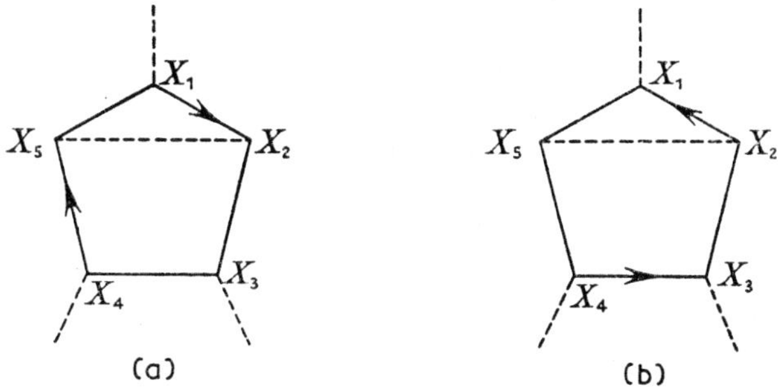

FIG. 17. Electron loops which cancel by Furry's theorem.

matrix elements M_1, M_2 arising from graphs like Fig. 17 (*a*), (*b*) are related by

$$M_1 = (-1)^p M_2,$$

where p is the number of vertices on the closed loop. When p is odd the total contribution therefore vanishes. Graphs in which a closed electron loop is connected to the rest of the graph by an odd number of photon lines vanish by Furry's theorem.

10. The divergent graphs

The infra-red divergences

We now discuss the divergences which occur when we attempt to evaluate the matrix elements for general electrodynamic processes.‡ The divergences in perturbation theory may arise from the low-frequency limit of the integrations over virtual states as well as from the high-frequency limit. It can be shown that the divergences in the radiative corrections to cross-sections which arise from low-frequency virtual photons can always be cancelled; it is only necessary to add on the perturbation theory corrections to the cross-section which allow for the *emission* of low-frequency photons.§ At each stage both types of

† ψ_T is a 4-component row vector, etc.

‡ We follow the fundamental discussion given by F. J. Dyson, *Phys. Rev.* **75** (1949) 1736.

§ A full discussion is given by J. M. Jauch and F. Rohrlich, *Theory of Photons and Electrons* (Addison-Wesley, Cambridge, Mass., 1955), ch. 16.

correction should be taken to the same order in $(e^2/4\pi\hbar c)$. The emission of such low-frequency photons cannot be distinguished from the main scattering process (cf. Chapter II, § 13). To avoid infinities in such calculations we replace the denominator in the photon propagator (138) by $(k''^2+\lambda^2-i\epsilon)$; the constant λ is equated to zero after the calculation. This is in effect a neutral vector meson propagator. In finding the contribution from low energy emission, longitudinal as well as transverse photons must be included. This is because when $\lambda \neq 0$ longitudinal quanta can occur—a Lorentz transformation of a transverse wave can give a longitudinal part. Neglect of longitudinal emission gives a (small) error even after putting $\lambda = 0$. For full details see Jauch and Rohrlich, loc. cit. § 15–2.

The high-frequency divergences

The high-frequency divergences present a more serious problem. In order to see where they occur it is necessary to examine the structure of matrix elements in some detail. Consider any graph which has n vertices, F internal lines, and E external lines.† The graph corresponds to some pairing of operators given by (112); let p_j $(j = 1, 2, \ldots, E)$ be the energy momenta of the free particles described by the external lines. Each internal electron and photon line give propagators S_F, D_F respectively; these propagators are expressed by integrals (130) and (138) over 4-vector momentum space. At each vertex the energy momentum is conserved; therefore, allowing for the overall conservation of energy and momentum for the graph, there are

$$f = F-n+1$$

independent (4-vector) variables of integration k_i $(i = 1, 2, \ldots, f)$.

The integrand of the (multiple) integral has in its denominator F factors of the type

$$\sum_{i,j} (c_i k_i + d_j p_j)^2 + \begin{pmatrix} \kappa^2 \\ 0 \end{pmatrix} - i\epsilon, \tag{150}$$

where κ^2 only appears for electron lines; c_i, d_j are constant coefficients whose values depend on the line concerned. The numerator of the integrand contains F_e factors which are linear in the k_i (F_e is the number of internal electron lines).

Each variable of integration k_i appears in at least two factors (150). We discuss the case of k_i appearing in two factors only; the other cases

† External lines only meet a vertex at one end.

can be treated similarly. Keeping all variables fixed except k_i, the relevant factors in the denominator can be written†

$$\{(k_i+q)^2+\kappa^2-i\epsilon\}\{(k_i+t)^2+\kappa^2-i\epsilon'\}, \tag{151}$$

where q, t are 4-vectors. The path of integration and the poles for $(k_i)_0$ are as shown in Fig. 18 (a) or (b).

The integration over $(k_i)_0$ converges absolutely at infinity, therefore the line of integration can be rotated through 90° about any point on the real axis; this gives Fig. 19 (a) and (b) respectively. In the second case we must add on the contribution from the isolated pole as shown.

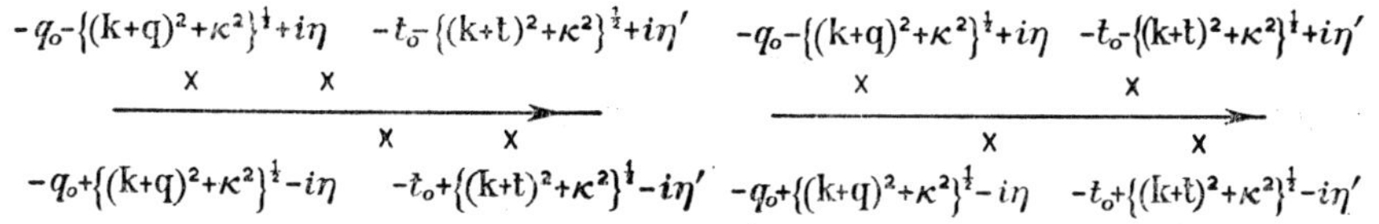

FIG. 18. The path of integration and the poles for $(k_i)_0$.

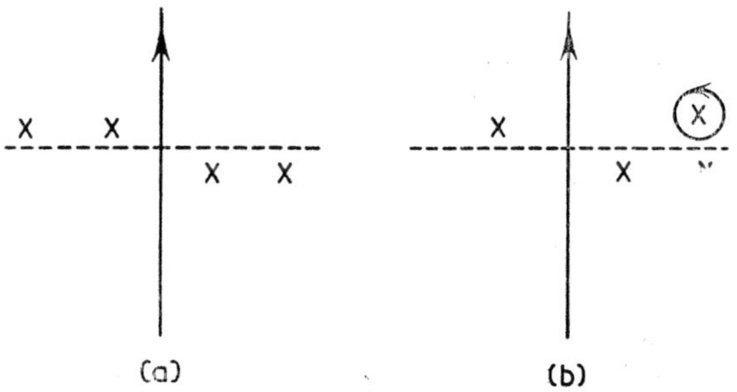

FIG. 19. The rotated path of integration; (b) shows an isolated pole.

It is easy to see that this contribution cannot alter the convergence property of the integral;‡ in future, such contributions will be ignored. Because of the rotation of the path of integration, the factors (151) give predominantly positive values for large $|k_0|$ and large $|\mathbf{k}|$.

Primitive divergents

A *primitive divergent* graph is defined as a graph which does not have an absolutely convergent integral, but which would converge absolutely if *any* one 4-vector of integration k_i were kept fixed. In other words, replacing any internal line in a primitive divergent graph by two

† κ^2 can be absent from either or both terms. λ^2 may occur in photon lines.

‡ The isolated pole contribution only arises when

$$\{(\mathbf{k}+\mathbf{q})^2+\kappa^2\}^{\frac{1}{2}}+\{(\mathbf{k}+\mathbf{t})^2+\kappa^2\}^{\frac{1}{2}} \leqslant q_0+t_0.$$

Therefore the region of integration over $\mathbf{k}$ is bounded, and the integrations over $d^3\mathbf{k}$ cannot diverge.

external lines gives a convergent graph.† For example, we shall see that Fig. 20 (*a*) and (*b*) are primitive divergent graphs; Fig. 20 (*c*) is divergent, but is not a primitive divergent. For an absolutely convergent graph, by counting the powers of the variables of integration k_i which appear in the numerator and the denominator, we clearly require

$$2F - F_e - 4f \geqslant 1.$$

Therefore, for a primitive divergent graph,

$$2F - F_e - 4f < 1. \tag{152 a}$$

This condition can be written‡

$$\tfrac{3}{2}E_e + E_p < 5, \tag{152 b}$$

where E_e, E_p are the number of external electron and photon lines.

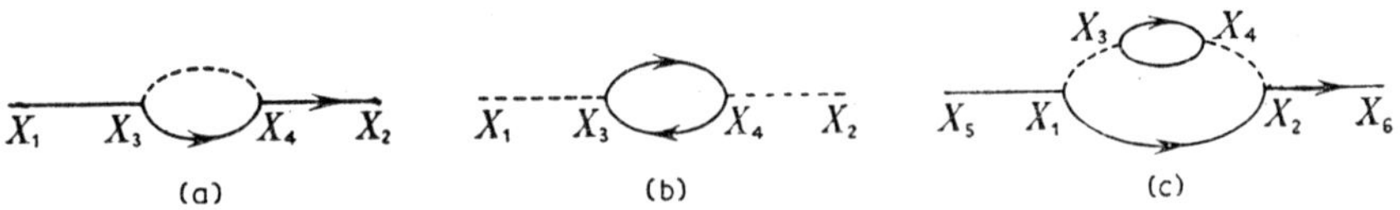

FIG. 20. Divergent parts. (*a*) and (*b*) are primitive divergents, (*c*) is divergent, but is not primitive.

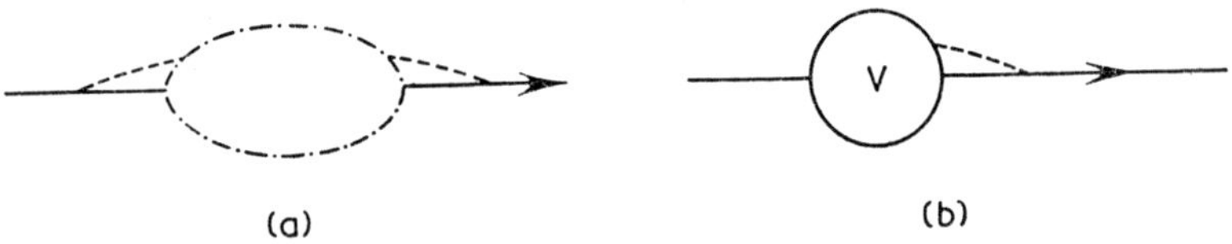

FIG. 21. (*a*) is the general E.S.E. part. In (*b*) it is drawn to show that it contains a vertex part.

Remembering Furry's theorem, it follows that the graphs satisfying (152 b) are: all electron and photon self-energy parts, all vertex parts,§ and all graphs describing the scattering of light by light (i.e. $E_p = 4$, $E_e = 0$). Clearly all these graphs are not primitive divergents, and we now have to pick out the latter.

In Fig. 21 (*a*) the general electron self-energy part is shown, and, drawing it as in (*b*), it is obvious that Fig. 20 (*a*) is the only primitive divergent electron self-energy part. Similarly Fig. 20 (*b*) is the only

† A primitive divergent graph need not diverge; it may converge for special reasons (cf. p. 263). The graphs Fig. 20 (*a*) and (*b*) do diverge, but Fig. 20 (*b*) does not diverge so fast as is indicated by counting powers of the variables.

‡ If F_e, F_p are the numbers of internal lines, then

$$2F_e + E_e = 2n, \qquad 2F_p + E_p = n;$$

eqn. (152 b) follows on using $f = F - n + 1$.

§ E.S.E., P.S.E., and vertex parts are defined in § 8; they are $E_e = 2$, $E_p = 0$; $E_e = 0$, $E_p = 2$; $E_e = 2$, $E_p = 1$, respectively.

primitive divergent photon self-energy part. There is an infinity of primitive divergent vertex parts; two are shown in Fig. 22.

Scattering of light by light

Fig. 22 (c) shows a primitive divergent for the scattering of light by light; it turns out that such graphs give convergent matrix elements. This can be seen in two ways: either we may make a careful gauge invariant calculation,† or we can argue simply from general principles; the second method is given. Let $M^{(4)}_{\lambda\mu\nu\rho}(p_1, p_2, p_3, p_4)$ be the total matrix

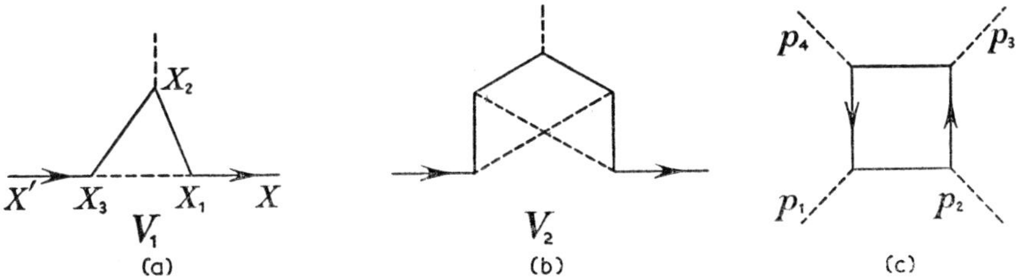

FIG. 22. (a) and (b) are primitive divergent vertex parts; (c) is a primitive divergent for the scattering of light by light.

element coming from primitive divergent graphs describing the scattering of photons 1 and 2 into photons 3 and 4; λ, μ, ν, ρ will indicate their polarizations. This matrix element is given by an integral of the form

$$M^{(4)}_{\lambda\mu\nu\rho}(p_1, p_2, p_3, p_4) = \int d^4k\, R_{\lambda\mu\nu\rho}(p_1, p_2, p_3, p_4;\, k); \tag{153}$$

on counting powers of k it is clear that this is at most a logarithmic divergent. Hence if we write

$$M^{(4)}_{\lambda\mu\nu\rho}\,(p_1, p_2, p_3, p_4) = \int d^4k\,\{R_{\lambda\mu\nu\rho}(p_1, p_2, p_3, p_4;\, k) - R_{\lambda\mu\nu\rho}(0,0,0,0;\, k)\} + M^{(4)}_{\lambda\mu\nu\rho}(0,0,0,0) \tag{154}$$

the first term on the right is a convergent integral.

The scattering of light by light arises because of the polarization of the electron-positron vacuum which is produced by the light waves, and it obviously must vanish at zero frequency because the polarization can only be caused by the electric and magnetic fields of the light

† Three graphs like Fig. 22 (c) contribute to the light-light scattering matrix element. The other two are obtained by replacing the energy momenta p_1, p_2, p_3, p_4 of the external lines by p_1, p_2, p_4, p_3, and p_1, p_3, p_2, p_4 respectively. Their sum is finite. Cf. R. Karplus and M. Neuman, *Phys. Rev.* **80** (1950) 380, for details of the calculation. This direct calculation is only practicable for the lowest order graph, i.e. Fig. 22 (c).

waves.† Hence $M^{(4)}_{\lambda\mu\nu\rho}(0,0,0,0)$, which gives scattering at zero frequency, must vanish.‡ Therefore $M^{(4)}_{\lambda\mu\nu\rho}(p_1,p_2,p_3,p_4)$ is finite.

The cross-section for photon-photon scattering is very small. In the centre of mass system, for small photon energies $\hbar\omega$, the total cross-section§ varies as ω^6; it rises to a maximum of about 3×10^{-30} cm² for $\hbar\omega \simeq 2m_e c^2$. Above this energy the graph Fig. 22 (c) can have real intermediate states on account of the production and subsequent annihilation of a real electron-positron pair; thus for $\hbar\omega > 2m_e c^2$ the corresponding $\mathbf{T}_4$ has an imaginary as well as a real term (cf. §§ 3, 8).

11. Separation of infinities in electrodynamics

The renormalization procedure is based on the fundamental role of the primitive divergents (except for light-light scattering which can now be ignored). Extracting the correct finite part from primitive divergents is easy, because it is only the last integration which diverges. Also *any* divergent graph, however complicated, can be given a finite value by successively replacing the contributions of primitive divergent parts by the correct finite values. For example, in the graph Fig. 13 (2) (§ 8) the self-energy part is replaced by a finite propagator $S^{(2)}_{F_c}(x_4-x_1)$ (of order e^2); this propagator allows for the fact that the electron while passing from x_1 to x_4 may interact with the electromagnetic field. In the graph Fig. 13 (4) the vertex part (x_1,x_2,x_3) is replaced by a finite contribution Γ.

On replacing primitive divergents by their finite contributions we must work outwards from the inner divergent parts. For example, if an electron line in a graph contains the part Fig. 20 (c) (§ 10), we first replace the photon line between x_1 and x_2 by a finite propagator (of order e^2) $D^{(2)}_{F_c}(x_1-x_2)$; this leaves an electron self-energy part which differs from that of Fig. 20 (a). The integral for this self-energy part is still divergent, and we must once more extract a finite part; the final result is a finite electron propagator of the fourth order $S^{(4)}_{F_c}(x_6-x_5)$.

Electron self-energy

First we show how to extract the finite part from the primitive divergent E.S.E. part,‖ Fig. 20 (a). It is convenient to use the nota-

† A gauge invariant calculation of the vacuum polarization by plane waves is given by J. Schwinger, *Phys. Rev.* **82** (1951) 664.

‡ Alternatively, we can say that the scattering can be described by a Lagrangian term containing a fourth power of the electromagnetic field variables; by gauge invariance this can be $(\mathbf{E}^2-\mathbf{H}^2)^2$ or $(\mathbf{E}.\mathbf{H})^2$ but it cannot be $\mathbf{A}^4$.

§ See p. 263, n. †.

‖ We use the contractions E.S.E. and P.S.E. for electron and photon self-energy, respectively.

tion†
$$S_F(k) = \frac{1}{2\pi i}\frac{i\gamma k-\kappa}{k^2+\kappa^2-i\epsilon}; \qquad D_F(k) = \frac{1}{2\pi i}\frac{1}{k^2+\lambda^2-i\epsilon}, \tag{155}$$
where k_μ is any 4-vector. By (130) and (138),
$$\left.\begin{aligned} S_{F(\kappa)}(x_\mu) &= \frac{1}{4\pi^3}\int d^4k\, e^{ik_\mu x_\mu} S_F(k) \\ D_F(x_\mu) &= \frac{1}{4\pi^3}\int d^4k\, e^{ik_\mu x_\mu} D_F(k) \end{aligned}\right\}. \tag{156}$$
The self-energy part in Fig. 20 (*a*) has the effect of replacing the electron propagator $\frac{1}{2}S_F(x_2-x_1)$ for the line joining x_1 and x_2 by‡
$$\frac{1}{2^4}\frac{e^2}{\hbar c}\int d^4x_3 \int d^4x_4\, S_F(x_2-x_4)\gamma^\mu S_F(x_4-x_3)\gamma^\mu S_F(x_3-x_1)D_F(x_3-x_4).$$
Writing $S_F(x_2-x_1)$ in terms of $S_F(p)$ by (156) it is easy to verify that the E.S.E. part replaces $S_F(p)$ by
$$\left.\begin{aligned} S_F^{(2)}(p) &= S_F(p)\Sigma(p)S_F(p) \\ \text{where§}\qquad \Sigma(p) &= 2\alpha \int d^4k\, \gamma^\mu S_F(p+k)\gamma^\mu D_F(k) \end{aligned}\right\}. \tag{157}$$
Obviously $\Sigma(p)$ is a Lorentz invariant, and on substituting (155) we see it diverges linearly. The linearly divergent part is independent of p; it can be removed by *renormalizing the mass* of the electron.‖ An addition δm to the mass m ($m = \hbar\kappa/c$) appearing in the free electron Hamiltonian (4.10) is counteracted on replacing the interaction (97) by
$$\mathscr{H}_1(x_\nu) = -\frac{1}{c}j_\mu(x_\nu)A_\mu(x_\nu) - \hbar c\,\delta\kappa\,\bar{\psi}(x_\nu)\psi(x_\nu). \tag{158}$$
$\delta\kappa$ is to be expressed as a power series in e^2 (commencing with e^2). The perturbation calculation using the interaction (158) makes it possible, at all orders of e^2, to cancel the self-mass terms arising from the interaction of the electron with the electromagnetic field. For the present we show how $\delta\kappa$ is determined to order e^2.

The lowest order correction to the propagator for an electron between x_1 and x_2 which arises from the self-mass term (158) is shown graphically in Fig. 23. The contribution from this term is
$$-i\,\delta\kappa\frac{1}{2^2}\int d^4x'\, S_F(x_2-x')S_F(x'-x_1). \tag{159}$$

† In $D_F(k)$ the term λ gives a small photon mass (cf. § 10).

‡ The repeated index μ in (157) is to be summed.

§ $\alpha = e^2/4\pi\hbar c \simeq 1/137$.

‖ Renormalization of the mass so as to include the electromagnetic mass in the total inertia was suggested by H. A. Kramers in 1948 (H. A. Kramers, *Collected Scientific Papers* (North-Holland Publishing Co., 1956), p. 845). An early application is given by H. W. Lewis, *Phys. Rev.* **73** (1948) 173.

The two factors S_F appear because the contractions are now made between x_2 and x', and between x' and x_1; the minus sign arises from a necessary change in the order of the fermion operators. The contribution (159) is equivalent to replacing the propagator $S_F(p)$ by

$$-2\pi i\,\delta\kappa\,S_F(p)S_F(p). \tag{160}$$

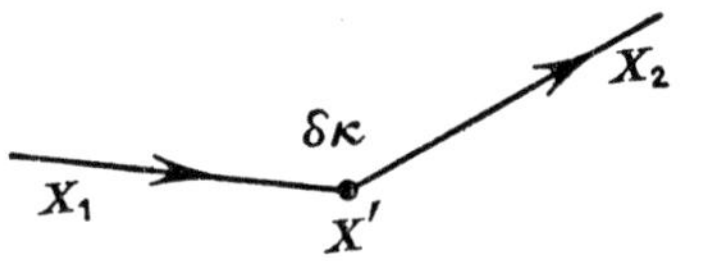

FIG. 23. The electron mass correction insertion.

Separation of the infinities

The infinite terms in $\Sigma(p)$ are separated off in a unique way as follows. The matrices γ^μ in (157) are moved together giving

$$\Sigma(p) = \frac{\alpha}{\pi^2}\int d^4k\,\frac{i\gamma(p+k)+2\kappa}{(p+k)^2+\kappa^2-i\epsilon}\,\frac{1}{k^2+\lambda^2-i\epsilon'}. \tag{161}$$

An integral Σ_0 is obtained from $\Sigma(p)$ on making the substitutions

$$i\gamma p+\kappa = 0, \qquad p^2+\kappa^2 = 0 \tag{162}$$

in the integrand (161). Σ_0 is an invariant which is independent of p_μ, hence it must be a (divergent) number A. From (162) it follows that Σ_0 and $\Sigma(p)$ give identical results when they operate on the Dirac wave function $u(p)$, for a free electron (p_μ). The substitutions (162) determine Σ_0, because $\Sigma(p)$, which is an invariant function of p_μ, can only be a function† of $\gamma^\mu p_\mu$ and p_μ^2. The number A must be pure imaginary; this is because the S-matrix element $\bar{u}(p)\Sigma_0\,u(p)$ describes transitions from a state satisfying (162) to the same state It follows that the intermediate states (which are given by the variable k_μ) are strictly virtual states; therefore by the arguments of §§ 3 and 8,

$$i\bar{u}(p)\Sigma_0\,u(p)$$

is Hermitian (i.e. real).

In practice the calculation of Σ_0 is lengthy because of the term $(p+k)^2$ in the denominator in (161). The following technique due to Feynman is commonly used.‡ The relation

$$\frac{1}{ab} = \int\limits_0^1 \frac{du}{[(a-b)u+b]^2} \tag{163}$$

† We use the notation $p^2 = p_\mu p_\mu$, $\gamma p = \gamma^\mu p_\mu$.
‡ R. P. Feynman, *Phys. Rev.* **76** (1949) 769.

permits us to write the integral (161) as

$$\int_0^1 du \int d^4k \frac{i\gamma(p+k)+2\kappa}{[(k+pu)^2+(\kappa^2-i\epsilon)u+p^2u(1-u)+(\lambda^2-i\epsilon)(1-u)]^2}. \tag{164}$$

The integration over the auxiliary variable u is performed last. The 4-variable of integration k_μ is changed to $k'_\mu = k_\mu+up_\mu$ and (164) becomes

$$\int_0^1 du \int d^4k' \frac{i\gamma p(1-u)+i\gamma k'+2\kappa}{[k'^2+(\kappa^2-i\epsilon)u+p^2u(1-u)+(\lambda^2-i\epsilon)(1-u)]^2}+$$
$$+p_\mu \int_0^1 du\, u \int d^4k' \frac{\partial}{\partial k'_\mu}\left(\frac{i\gamma k'}{[k'^2+(\kappa^2-i\epsilon)u+p^2u(1-u)+(\lambda^2-i\epsilon)(1-u)]^2}\right). \tag{165}$$

The last term is the surface integral which must be added to allow for the shift of the origin of integration in a linearly divergent integral;† this term vanishes for a logarithmically divergent integral.‡ The second integral in (165) is seen to be a multiple§ of $p_\mu \gamma^\mu$.

Replacing the integral in (161) by (165) we can make the substitutions (162) and obtain Σ_0. Also, using (165) we can write

$$\Sigma(p)-\Sigma_0 = (i\gamma p+\kappa)\int_0^1 du \int d^4k' I(p,k',u), \tag{166}$$

where $I(p,k',u)$ is an invariant function of p_μ, k'_μ, and u, and it contains the γ^μ matrices at most linearly. The integration over k' in (166) diverges logarithmically. A function $I_0(k',u)$ is obtained from $I(p,k',u)$ on making the substitutions (162). Now (166) can be written||

$$\Sigma(p) = A-(i\gamma p+\kappa)iB+(i\gamma p+\kappa)\int_0^1 du \int d^4k' \{I(p,k',u)-I_0(k',u)\}; \tag{167}$$

† Cf. R. Karplus and N. M. Kroll, *Phys. Rev.* **77** (1950) 536.

‡ The shift of origin is equivalent to writing

$$f(k+pu) = f(k)+up_\mu \frac{\partial}{\partial k_\mu} f(k)+\tfrac{1}{2}u^2 p_\mu p_\nu \frac{\partial^2}{\partial k_\mu \partial k_\nu} f(k)+\dots .$$

For convergent or log. divergent integrals only $f(k)$ gives a non-zero contribution; for linearly divergent integrals, the second term on the right appears, and so on.

§ This is because

$$p_\mu \frac{\partial}{\partial k'_\mu}(\gamma k') = p_\mu \gamma^\mu, \quad \text{and} \quad p_\mu \frac{\partial}{\partial k'_\mu}(k'^2) = 2p_\mu \gamma^\mu . k_\nu \gamma^\nu.$$

|| Σ_0 equals the (infinite) number A.

the number B is given by the invariant divergent integral

$$B = i\int\limits_0^1 du \int d^4k' I_0(k', u). \tag{168}$$

It can be shown with the aid of Ward's theorem (§ 12 below) that B must be a real number.† Also

$$S_c(p) \equiv i\int\limits_0^1 du \int d^4k' \{I(p,k',u) - I_0(k',u)\} \tag{169}$$

is a convergent integral. $S_c(p)$ is an invariant function of p_μ which vanishes when we make the substitutions (162). $(\gamma p - i\kappa)S_c(p)$ is the unique finite part of $\Sigma(p)$ which has been separated off by a form of expansion about the unbound electron energy-momentum values (162).

Renormalization of the electron propagator

Now we can evaluate the complete electron propagator‡ $S'_F(p)$ up to order e^2; this is found by adding to $S_F(p)$ the contributions from (157) and from the mass correction term (160). We have, using (167) and (155),

$$S'_F(p) = S_F(p) + S_F(p)(A - 2\pi i\delta\kappa)S_F(p) + \frac{1}{2\pi}BS_F(p) + \frac{1}{2\pi}S_c(p)S_F(p).$$

The correct electron mass renormalization to order e^2 is obtained by putting

$$\delta\kappa = A/2\pi i$$

in (158). Hence, to order e^2,

$$S'_F(p) = \left(1 + \frac{1}{2\pi}B\right)S_F(p) + \frac{1}{2\pi}S_c(p)S_F(p). \tag{170}$$

Following Dyson§ we define a *renormalization constant* Z_2 to order e^2 by

$$Z_2 = 1 + \frac{1}{2\pi}B. \tag{171}$$

Now (170) can be written *correctly to order* e^2 in the form‖

$$S'_F(p) = Z_2\left\{S_F(p) + \frac{1}{2\pi}S_c(p)S_F(p)\right\}. \tag{172}$$

Eqn. (172) shows (to order e^2) that the radiative corrections to any internal electron line are given by an infinite (log. divergent) multiplicative constant Z_2, together with a *finite* correction to the propagator;

† See footnote †† on p. 272.

‡ $S_F(p)$ is called a propagator because it obeys $(i\gamma p + \kappa)S_F(p) = i/2\pi$.

§ F. J. Dyson, *Phys. Rev.* **75** (1949) 1736.

‖ Eqn. (172) holds because $S_c(p)$ and B are both of order e^2; any error in (172) is of order e^4. It will be noticed that the renormalization scheme depends on strict adherence to the correct orders of e^2 at each stage.

this finite correction to the propagator vanishes for free electrons.† The constants Z_2 arising from *all* internal electron lines in a graph can be removed by redefining, or *renormalizing*, the electron's charge; this is illustrated in § 12 below.

Radiative correction to the photon propagator

The second-order correction to the photon propagator $D_F(x_1-x_2)$ arises from the primitive divergent P.S.E. part, Fig. 20(*b*); it gives a propagator $D_F^{(2)}(x_1-x_2)_{\mu_1\mu_2}$ such that‡

$$\tfrac{1}{2}\hbar c D_F^{(2)}(x_1-x_2)_{\mu_1\mu_2} = -\frac{e^2}{2^4}\int d^4x_3 \int d^4x_4\, D_F(x_1-x_3)\times$$
$$\times \mathrm{spur}\{\gamma^{\mu_1}S_F(x_3-x_4)\gamma^{\mu_2}S_F(x_4-x_3)\}D_F(x_4-x_2). \quad (173)$$

Using (156) it is easy to show that on inserting this P.S.E. part in an internal photon line, the original propagator $D_F(p)\delta_{\mu_1\mu_2}$ is replaced by (cf. eqn. (157))

$$\left.\begin{aligned} D_F^{(2)}(p)_{\mu_1\mu_2} &= D_F(p)\Pi_{\mu_1\mu_2}(p)D_F(p) \\ \text{where}\quad \Pi_{\mu_1\mu_2}(p) &= -2\alpha\int d^4k\, \mathrm{spur}\{\gamma^{\mu_1}S_F(p+k)\gamma^{\mu_2}S_F(k)\} \end{aligned}\right\}. \quad (174)$$

The integrand transforms as a second rank tensor; also, because the spur (or diagonal sum) is taken, the integral must be of the form

$$\Pi_{\mu_1\mu_2}(p) = \Pi(p)\delta_{\mu_1\mu_2}+F(p)p_{\mu_1}p_{\mu_2}, \quad (175)$$

where $\Pi(p)$ and $F(p)$ are invariant functions of the photon's energy momentum; hence they are functions of p^2.

The term $F(p)p_{\mu_1}p_{\mu_2}$ cannot give a non-zero contribution in any graph. If in Fig. 20(*b*) the line (x_1, x_2) is an internal photon line, the current operator $j(x_1)$ must act at x_1 (and $j(x_2)$ acts at x_2). On integration by parts over x_1, the factor p_{μ_1} appearing in $\Pi_{\mu_1\mu_2}(p)$ replaces $j_{\mu_1}(x_1)$ by $\partial_{\mu_1}j_{\mu_1}(x_1)$; this operator vanishes by the conservation of charge. If the photon line reaching x_3 is an external line, then $p_{\mu_1}A_{\mu_1}(p)$ vanishes, because $A_\mu(p)$ describes transverse vibrations.§ Hence we can ignore the term $F(p)p_{\mu_1}p_{\mu_2}$; the propagator correction term then becomes

$$D_F^{(2)}(p)_{\mu_1\mu_2} = \delta_{\mu_1\mu_2}D_F(p)\Pi(p)D_F(p). \quad (176)$$

† In (170) the order of $S_c(p)$ and $S_F(p)$ can be exchanged because both are functions of (γp).

‡ One, not two, pairings in (112) gives the closed electron loop, but it can be joined to the rest of the graph in two ways.

§ If $A(p)$ represents an *external field* (§ 13 below), then $p_\mu A_\mu(p)$ vanishes provided we use the Lorentz gauge for $A(p)$.

Renormalization of the photon propagator

Using the device (163), the integral (174) is written

$$\Pi_{\mu_1\mu_2}(p) = \frac{2\alpha}{\pi^2}\int\limits_0^1 du \int d^4k \times$$

$$\times \frac{\delta_{\mu_1\mu_2}\{(p.k)+k^2+\kappa^2\}-\{p_{\mu_1}k_{\mu_2}+p_{\mu_2}k_{\mu_1}+2k_{\mu_1}k_{\mu_2}\}}{[(k+pu)^2+p^2u(1-u)+\kappa^2-i\epsilon]^2}. \quad (177)$$

This integral is quadratically divergent, and on changing the variable of integration to $k' = k_\mu+up_\mu$, it is necessary to add two terms to allow for the effect of changing the origin.† It is now easy, if tedious, to pick out all the contributions to $\Pi(p)$ from (177); we shall assume this has been done.‡

Because $\Pi(p)$ is a function of p^2, it follows that $\{\Pi(p)-\Pi(0)\}$ is a logarithmically divergent integral whose divergent part is proportional to p^2. Proceeding in this way we have (analogous to (167) and (168))

$$\Pi(p) = A'+Cp^2+p^2D_c(p), \quad (178)$$

where $A' = \Pi(0)$, C is a constant,§ and the finite term $D_c(p)$ is an invariant function of p^2 which vanishes when $p^2 = 0$.

When (174) is evaluated by a gauge invariant calculation,|| the constant term A' is found to be zero. It can be seen as follows that A' should vanish. A non-zero A' gives a photon mass effect (this is obvious on comparison with the electron mass correction term A in (167)). The Lagrangian term required to remove this mass effect is of the form $\delta(\mu^2)A_\nu(x)A_\nu(x)$; this correction term is not gauge invariant.†† A non-zero A' would mean that the vacuum was polarized by a single electromagnetic wave; for such a wave the vacuum would therefore have a dielectric constant different from unity.

The total photon propagator to order e^2 is given by (155), (176), and (178) with $A' = 0$. (For simplicity we have here taken $\lambda^2 = 0$):

$$D'_F(p) = \left(1+\frac{1}{2\pi i}C\right)D_F(p)+\frac{1}{2\pi i}D_c(p)D_F(p). \quad (179)$$

† See p. 267, n. ‡.

‡ For details see J. Schwinger, *Phys. Rev.* **74** (1948) 1439, and G. Wentzel, ibid. 1070.

§ C is logarithmically divergent.

|| Such a calculation is given by J. Schwinger, *Phys. Rev.* **82** (1951) 664. Gauge invariance (eqn. (2.168)) requires that any expression of the type $A_{\mu_1}(p)\Pi_{\mu_1\mu_2}(p)A_{\mu_2}(p)$ is unaltered if we replace $A_\mu(p)$ by $A_\mu(p)+p_\mu\Lambda(p)$. This requires $p_{\mu_1}\Pi_{\mu_1\mu_2}(p) = 0$, $\Pi_{\mu_1\mu_2}(p)p_{\mu_2} = 0$; hence $\Pi_{\mu_1\mu_2}(p)$ must be of the form $(p_{\mu_1}p_{\mu_2}-\delta_{\mu_1\mu_2}p^2)F(p)$, where $F(p)$ is a function of p^2. Thus $A' = 0$.

†† An alternative discussion of the photon mass correction effect is given by S. N. Gupta, *Proc. Phys. Soc.* A **64** (1951) 426.

The renormalization constant Z_3 is defined, to order e^2, by

$$Z_3 = 1+\frac{1}{2\pi i}C. \tag{180}$$

So (to order e^2),

$$D'_F(p) = Z_3\left\{D_F(p)+\frac{1}{2\pi i}D_c(p)D_F(p)\right\}. \tag{181}$$

The radiative corrections are given by the finite term $D_c(p)D_F(p)$ which vanishes for $p^2 = 0$. We shall see that the factor Z_3 can be removed by redefining the electron's charge.

Vertex parts

From (152) it follows that all primitive divergent vertex parts are logarithmically divergent. We shall show how to separate off the divergent part of the lowest order vertex part, Fig. 22 (*a*); the same method can be used for the graph of Fig. 22 (*b*) or any higher order primitive divergent vertex part. A simple vertex at x_2 which is joined to x and x' by electron lines gives the term

$$S_F(x-x_2)\gamma^\mu S_F(x_2-x'). \tag{182}$$

In Fig. 22 (*a*) this is replaced by

$$\frac{1}{2^3}\frac{e^2}{\hbar c}\int d^4x_1 \int d^4x_3\, S_F(x-x_1)\gamma^\nu S_F(x_1-x_2)\times \times\gamma^\mu S_F(x_2-x_3)\gamma^\nu S_F(x_3-x')D_F(x_1-x_3). \tag{183}$$

If the momentum space form of (182) is taken to be

$$S_F(p_1)\gamma^\mu S_F(p_2), \tag{184}$$

the term (183) is equivalent to replacing γ^μ in (184) by

$$L_\mu(p_1,p_2) = 2\alpha\int d^4k\, \gamma^\nu S_F(p_1+k)\gamma^\mu S_F(k+p_2)\gamma^\nu D_F(k). \tag{185}$$

The 4×4 matrix $L_\mu(p_1,p_2)$ transforms like a 4-vector. The divergent part of the integral is independent of p_1, p_2, and must therefore be a multiple of γ^μ. A reasonable separation of the finite part is given by

$$L_\mu(p_1,p_2) = L\gamma^\mu+\Lambda_c^\mu(p_1,p_2), \tag{186}$$

where L is a logarithmically divergent number, and the finite part $\Lambda_c^\mu(p_1,p_2)$ vanishes when we substitute

$$p_1 = p_2,\quad i\gamma p_1+\kappa = 0,\quad p_1^2+\kappa^2 = 0. \tag{187}$$

Thus the finite part gives no contribution to a freely moving electron which suffers no deflexion. The separation (186) is made by moving the terms $i(\gamma p_1)$, $i(\gamma p_2)$ in (185) to the left and right respectively and then using (187); the resulting integral† is $L\gamma^{\mu}$. The infinite number L must be real.‡

A renormalization constant Z_1 is defined, to order e^2, by

$$Z_1 = 1-L. \tag{188}$$

Thus (to order e^2) the vertex contributions may be written

$$Z_1^{-1}\{\gamma^{\mu}+\Lambda_c^{\mu}(p_1,p_2)\}. \tag{189}$$

Z_1 will be removed by charge renormalization.

12. Ward's identity and charge renormalization

From the definition of $S_F(k)$ in (155) it follows that

$$\frac{\partial S_F(k)}{\partial k_{\mu}} = -2\pi S_F(k)\gamma^{\mu}S_F(k). \tag{190}$$

This formula enables us to relate electron self-energy parts and vertex parts; for example, by (157) and (185),

$$\frac{\partial \Sigma(p)}{\partial p_{\mu}} = -2\pi L_{\mu}(p,p). \tag{191}$$

Therefore, differentiating the primitive divergent E.S.E. part of Fig. 20 (*a*) is equivalent to inserting an external photon line of *zero energy-momentum* ($(p_3)_{\mu} = 0$) into the internal electron line, as in Fig. 24 (*a*). Comparing (167) and (186) we have§

$$\left.\begin{aligned} \frac{1}{2\pi}B &= -L \\ \frac{\partial}{\partial p_{\mu}}\Sigma_c(p) &= -2\pi\Lambda_c^{\mu}(p,p) \end{aligned}\right\},\| \tag{192}$$

where $$\Sigma_c(p) = -i(i\gamma p+\kappa)S_c(p)$$

is the finite part of $\Sigma(p)$. The first relation shows that†† (cf. (171) and (188))

$$Z_1 = Z_2. \tag{193}$$

A *proper* graph is a graph which cannot be divided into two parts connected only by a single line. For example, Fig. 24 (*b*) is not a proper

† The details of this separation are given by R. Karplus and N. M. Kroll, *Phys. Rev.* **77** (1950) 536.

‡ Under the conditions (187), $L_{\mu}(p_1,p_2)$ represents a virtual process, so $i\bar{u}(p_1)L\gamma^{\mu}A_{\mu}u(p_1)$ must be Hermitian; i.e. L is real.

§ To obtain (192) we separate the constants terms from those which vanish for $p^2+\kappa^2 = 0$.

‖ J. C. Ward, *Phys. Rev.* **78** (1950) 182.

†† Because L is real (n. ‡ above), it follows that B is real.

graph. Ward extended his identity (191) to the contribution $\Sigma^*(p)$ arising from *any* proper E.S.E. part W; this gives

$$\frac{\partial \Sigma^*(p)}{\partial p_\mu} = -2\pi \sum_{V_i} L_\mu(p,p;V_i), \tag{194}$$

where V_i is a vertex part obtained by inserting an external photon line into any internal electron line in W. $L_\mu(p_1,p_2;V_i)$ is the (divergent) contribution from the vertex part V_i, analogous to (185); in (194) the summation runs over *all* vertex parts V_i which can be formed from W in this way. For example, for the E.S.E. part in Fig. 24 (c) there are three vertex parts V_i as shown in Fig. 24 (d).

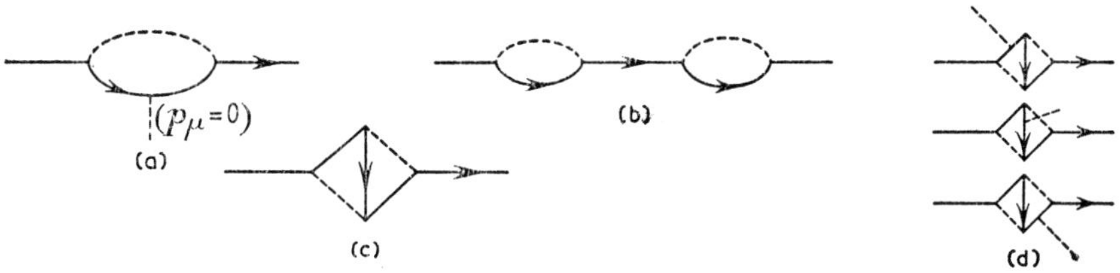

FIG. 24. (a) is the result of differentiating the E.S.E. part in Fig. 20 (a). (b) is an improper E.S.E. part. (d) shows the three vertex parts which result from differentiating the E.S.E. part (c).

In order to prove (194) we notice that in the integral expression for $\Sigma^*(p)$ (analogous to (157)), the 4-vectors of integration k_i can be assigned so that any internal electron line which is connected by electron lines to the two external electron lines is given by $S_F\left(p+\sum_i c_i k_i\right)$ (the c_i are constant coefficients). Factors S_F and D_F relating to all other lines are independent of p_μ. Applying (190) gives formula (194), where V_i are the vertex parts obtained by inserting an external photon line into all electron lines having propagators of the form $S_F(p+\sum c_i k_i)$. The remaining electron lines form closed electron loops; by Furry's theorem the sum of the matrix elements obtained by inserting an external photon line into the electron lines of a closed loop must vanish. This completes the proof.

It is clear that (194) holds when $\Sigma^*(p)$ is the sum of all proper electron self-energy parts of order e^{2n}, provided V_i runs over all proper vertex parts of order e^{2n}. In this form the relation (194) can be used to renormalize the perturbation expansion up to any order in e. Here we give the method for order e^4 only; that is sufficient to indicate how the general case is treated.

Renormalization of vertex parts to order e^4

First it is necessary to consider all proper vertex parts up to order e^4. The *irreducible*† vertex parts V_1 and V_2 of order e^2 and e^4 are shown in Fig. 22 (*a*) and (*b*). Slightly altering the notation of (186) we can write their contributions $L_\mu(p_1, p_2)$ in the form

$$L_1(e)\gamma^\mu + \Lambda_c^\mu(p_1, p_2; V_1), \qquad L_2(e)\gamma^\mu + \Lambda_c^\mu(p_1, p_2; V_2),$$

respectively. $L_1(e)$, $L_2(e)$ are logarithmically divergent real numbers of order e^2 and e^4, while $\Lambda_c^\mu(p_1, p_2; V_1)$, $\Lambda_c^\mu(p_1, p_2; V_2)$ are the finite parts. These finite parts vanish under the conditions (187).

In addition to V_2 there are six *reducible* vertex parts of order e^4, which are obtained by inserting the second E.S.E., P.S.E., and vertex parts

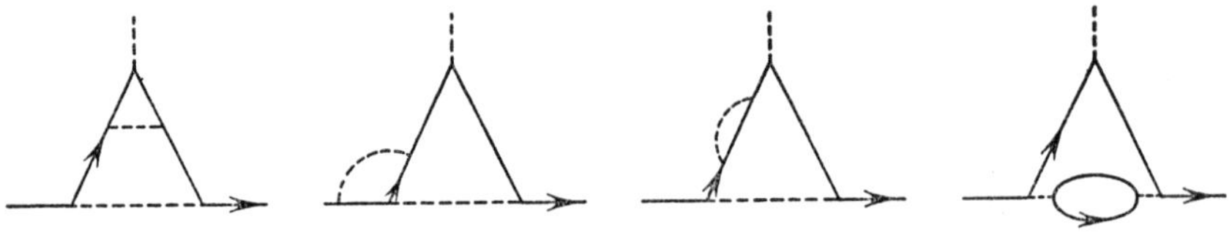

FIG. 25. Four of the fourth-order reducible vertex parts.

in V_1. Four of these are shown in Fig. 25. The total contribution of these six reducible graphs and of V_1 is obtained from (185) on replacing S_F, D_F, γ^μ (or γ^ν) in the integrand by S'_F (eqn. (170)), D'_F (eqn. (179)), and L_μ (eqn. 186), respectively. Including V_2, the sum of the vertex parts to order e^4 becomes‡

$$L_\mu^{(2)} = \gamma^\mu\left\{1+L_1(e)\left(1+\frac{1}{2\pi}B(e)\right)^2\left(1+\frac{1}{2\pi i}C(e)\right)\{1+L_1(e)\}^3+L_2(e)+L_2^{(2)}(e)\right\}+ \\ +\left(1+\frac{1}{2\pi}B(e)\right)^2\left(1+\frac{1}{2\pi i}C(e)\right)\{1+L_1(e)\}^3\Lambda_c^\mu(p_1 p_2; V_1)+ \\ +\Lambda_c^{\mu(2)}(p_1, p_2; V_1)+\Lambda_c^\mu(p_1, p_2; V_2). \quad (195)$$

Here $\Lambda_c^{\mu(2)}(p_1, p_2; V_1)$ is the finite term of order e^4 which arises from the insertion of the finite parts $S_c\, S_F$, $D_c\, D_F$, $\Lambda_c^\mu(p_1, p_2; V_1)$ in the lines and vertices of V_1. $L_2^{(2)}(e)\gamma^\mu$ is the corresponding infinite term.§

Defining the *renormalized charge* e_1 of the electron by

$$e_1^2 = e^2\{1+L_1(e)\}^2\left(1+\frac{1}{2\pi}B(e)\right)^2\left(1+\frac{1}{2\pi i}C(e)\right) \quad (196)$$

† An irreducible graph contains no E.S.E., P.S.E., or vertex parts (except itself, if it is divergent).

‡ We write B, C of eqns. (170), (179) as $B(e)$, $C(e)$; these real infinite constants are both of order e^2 in the present case.

§ Explicit calculations show S_c, $D_c \to 0$ as $p \to \infty$; the divergence in $L_2^{(2)}(e)$ is at most logarithmic, coming from $\Lambda_c^\mu(V_1)$ insertions.

and working to order e^4 (or e_1^4), we can rewrite (195) as†

$$L_\mu^{(2)}(p_1,p_2) = Z_1^{-1}\Gamma_c^\mu(p_1,p_2;\, e_1), \tag{197}$$

where

$$Z_1 = 1-L_1(e_1)-L_2(e_1)-L_2^{(2)}(e_1) \tag{198}$$

and‡

$$\Gamma_c^\mu(p_1,p_2;\, e_1) = \gamma^\mu+\Lambda_c^\mu(p_1,p_2;\, V_1,e_1)+ +\Lambda_c^{\mu(2)}(p_1,p_2;\, V_1,e_1)+\Lambda_c^\mu(p_1,p_2;\, V_2,e_1). \tag{199}$$

In (199) the value of the electron's charge which appears in the radiative correction terms is written explicitly. Eqn. (197) shows that, to the fourth order, the vertex part contributions can be expressed as an infinite multiple (Z_1^{-1}) of the *finite* contribution $\Gamma_c^\mu(p_1,p_2;\, e_1)$. In general, Γ_c^μ is expressed as a power series in $(e_1^2/4\pi\hbar c)$, where e_1 is the renormalized or physical charge, and the coefficients in the power series are all finite. Under the substitution (187), Γ_c^μ reduces to γ^μ.§

Renormalization of electron propagators to order e^4

It is now possible to renormalize all electron self-energy graphs up to order e^4. Let $\Sigma^*(p)$ be the contribution of the proper E.S.E. graphs up to order e^4; then, by (194) and (197),

$$\frac{\partial\Sigma^*(p)}{\partial p_\mu} = -2\pi\{L_\mu^{(2)}(p,p)-\gamma^\mu\}. \tag{200}$$

Defining the divergent number $B(e_1)$ by (cf. (192))

$$-(1/2\pi)B(e_1) = L_1(e_1)+L_2(e_1)+L_2^{(2)}(e_1), \tag{201}$$

we have, on integrating (200),

$$\Sigma^*(p)-\Sigma_0 = \left(1-\frac{1}{2\pi}B(e_1)\right)\{B(e_1)(\gamma p-i\kappa)+F_c(p,e_1)\}. \tag{202}$$

Σ_0 is the value of $\Sigma^*(p)$ when $(i\gamma p+\kappa)$ is put equal to zero. $F_c(p,e_1)$ arises from the finite terms Λ_c^μ on the right of (199); clearly it can be written (cf. (192))

$$F_c(p,e_1) = (\gamma p-i\kappa)S_c(p,e_1), \tag{203}$$

where $S_c(p,e_1)$ vanishes on making the substitution (162). Thus

$$S_F(p)\Sigma^*(p) = \left(1-\frac{1}{2\pi}B(e_1)\right)\left\{A(e_1)S_F+\frac{1}{2\pi}B(e_1)+\frac{1}{2\pi}S_c(p,e_1)\right\}, \tag{204}$$

† The coefficient of γ^μ becomes (to order e_1^4)

$$1+L_2(e_1)+L_2^{(2)}(e_1)+L_1(e_1)\{1+L_1(e_1)\} = \{1-L_1(e_1)-L_2(e_1)-L_2^{(2)}(e_1)\}^{-1}.$$

‡ Here we write

$$(e_1^2/e^2)\{1+L_1(e)\}\Lambda_c^\mu(p_1,p_2;\, V_1) = \{1+L_1(e)\}\Lambda_c^\mu(p_1,p_2;\, V_1,e_1) = \{1-L_1(e_1)\}^{-1}\Lambda_c^\mu(p_1,p_2;\, V_1,e_1).$$

§ In order to make $\Lambda_c^{\mu(2)}(p_1,p_2;\, V_1)$ vanish for conditions (187) it may be necessary in (195) to add a finite contribution to the infinite constant $L_2^{(2)}(e)$. This causes no difficulty.

where we define the constant $A(e_1)$ by

$$A(e_1)\left(1-\frac{1}{2\pi}B(e_1)\right) = \Sigma_0. \tag{205}$$

We take account of the mass renormalization term (160) and the improper E.S.E. graphs (Fig. 26 (*a*), (*b*), (*c*), etc.) by using the solution $S'_F(p)$ of the implicit equation

$$S'_F(p) = S_F(p)-2\pi i\,\delta\kappa\, S_F(p)S'_F(p)+$$
$$+\left(1-\frac{1}{2\pi}B(e_1)\right)\left\{A(e_1)S_F(p)+\frac{1}{2\pi}\{B(e_1)+S_c(p,e_1)\}\right\}S'_F(p). \tag{206}$$

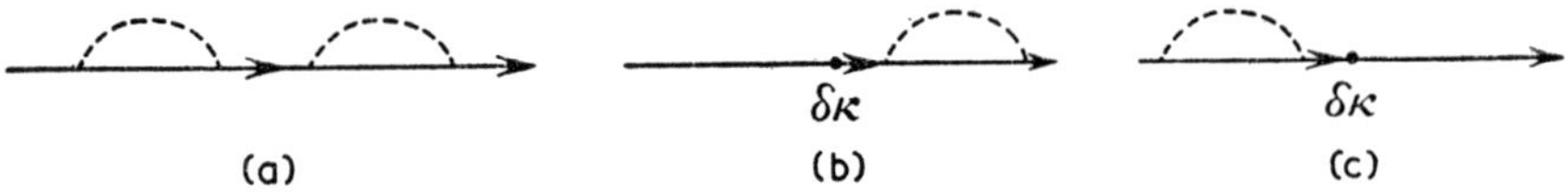

FIG. 26. Improper E.S.E. graphs in the lowest order (graph $(\delta\kappa)^2$ is not shown).

Defining†

$$Z_2 = 1+\frac{1}{2\pi}B(e_1)$$

(so by (198) and (201), $Z_1 = Z_2$), we use

$$\delta\kappa = \frac{1}{2\pi i}Z_2^{-1}A(e_1) \tag{207}$$

to give electron mass renormalization to order e^4. Also (to order e^4), by (206),

$$S'_F(p) = Z_2\left\{1+\frac{1}{2\pi}S_c(p,e_1)+\left(\frac{1}{2\pi}S_c(p,e_1)\right)^2\right\}S_F(p). \tag{208}$$

Apart from Z_2, all terms on the right of (208) are finite. Thus eqn. (172) has been extended to order e^4.

Renormalizing in this way by using Ward's relation (194), we avoid the difficult *overlapping divergences* which occur in graphs like Fig. 24 (*c*). This graph can be regarded as a vertex part insertion at either vertex of the primitive divergent E.S.E. graph (Fig. 20 (*a*)); thus the process of first removing the innermost divergence is not unambiguous.‡ In the treatment above, that difficulty does not arise.

† Although $Z_1 = Z_2$, it is useful to write Z_1 when we discuss vertex parts and Z_2 when we discuss E.S.E. parts.

‡ A detailed, but difficult, prescription for removing overlapping divergences has however been given by A. Salam, *Phys. Rev.* **82** (1951) 217.

The photon propagator

Renormalization of the photon propagator can be carried out by a similar method. Analogous to (194), Ward derived a relation†

$$\frac{\partial\Pi^*(p)}{\partial p_\mu} = -2\pi \sum_{V_i} M_\mu(p, p; V_i), \tag{209}$$

where $\Pi^*(p)$ is the total contribution from all proper P.S.E. parts of order e^{2n}. V_i are graphs with three external photon lines which are obtained by inserting an external photon line into internal lines of the P.S.E. parts.‡ By (152), such graphs ($E_p = 3$, $E_e = 0$) might be expected to diverge linearly, but in fact they are only logarithmically divergent. All matrix elements $M_\mu(p_1, p_2; V_i)$ do not vanish by Furry's theorem, because in V_i we should not insert the photon line into both directions of the electron lines. For the details of the method the reader is referred to the literature.§

External line renormalization

By such methods formulae (179), (197), and (208) can be extended to any order in e_1; also, the relation (193) between the renormalization constants holds to any order. Finally, it is necessary to consider the insertions which can be made in the external lines of any graph. For external electron lines a few of these insertions are shown in Fig. 27.

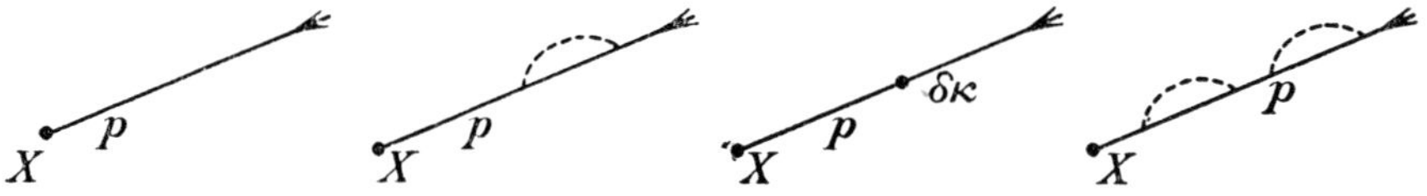

FIG. 27. (*a*) an external electron line; (*b*) and (*c*) are lowest order insertions in this line; (*d*), a higher order insertion.

These parts conserve energy and momentum, and thus they can only multiply the renormalized operator $\psi(x)$ by a constant R, giving an operator $\psi'(x) = R\psi(x)$. Similarly, there is an operator $\bar{\psi}'(x) = R^*\bar{\psi}(x)$. A difficulty in finding R is that certain expressions become indeterminate for free particle energy-momentum values. Writing

$$\bar{u}'(p) = Ru(p), \tag{210}$$

† J. C. Ward, *Phys. Rev.* **78** (1950) 182.

‡ The external photon line must sometimes be inserted in an internal photon line $D_F(p+k)$; it gives a *vertex* contribution $(p+k)_\mu$. The evaluation of such integrals is straightforward.

§ Cf. J. C. Ward, p. 272, n. ||. See also J. M. Jauch and F. Rohrlich, *Theory of Photons and Electrons* (Addison-Wesley, Cambridge, Mass., 1955), for a detailed discussion.

the 4×4 matrix R is given by

$$R = 1+S_F(p)\{\Sigma^*(p)-2\pi i\,\delta\kappa\}+\dots.$$

$\Sigma^*(p)-2\pi i\,\delta\kappa$ is the sum of the contributions from all proper E.S.E. parts (cf. (202)). By eqn. (204) (which holds to any order),

$$S_F(p)\{\Sigma^*(p)-2\pi i\,\delta\kappa\} = \frac{1}{2\pi}Z_2^{-1}\{B(e_1)+S_c(p)\}, \tag{211}$$

where the finite part $S_c(p)$ vanishes for free electrons. Hence in (210) we get a different value for $Ru(p)$ according as we first use (211) or first multiply† $\Sigma^*(p)-\Sigma_0^*$ into $u(p)$.

We avoid this difficulty by evaluating $\langle T(\bar\psi'(x)\psi'(x'))\rangle_0$ which gives the complete electron propagator S_F'. This can be done without ambiguity if we notice that (208) can be extended to any order e^{2n}.

Letting p tend to free electron values, gives

$$|R|^2 = Z_2.$$

Thus we take‡

$$\psi'(x) = Z_2^{\frac{1}{2}}\psi(x). \tag{212}$$

Similarly,§

$$A_\mu'(x) = Z_3^{\frac{1}{2}}A_\mu(x) \tag{213}$$

shows the effect of insertions in external photon lines.

Renormalized calculations

The effect of making all possible insertions in all the vertices and internal and external lines of the graph|| for any scattering process therefore leads to a *finite* matrix element which is multiplied by the factors (cf. (181), (197), (208), (212), (213))

$$e^n Z_2^{\frac{1}{2}E_e} Z_3^{\frac{1}{2}E_p} Z_2^{F_e} Z_3^{F_p} Z_1^{-n}. \tag{214}$$

Generalizing the definition (196) of the renormalized charge to

$$e_1 = eZ_1^{-1}Z_2\,Z_3^{\frac{1}{2}} = eZ_3^{\frac{1}{2}}, \tag{215}$$

the factor (214) becomes e_1^n. Hence the renormalizing constants have the effect of replacing the charge e by the renormalized, or the actual, charge e_1. In the same way the mass of the electron which appears in the results of calculations is the actual mass of the electron. The original mass m and charge e are not determined by any experiments.

For processes involving only free electrons and photons the radiative corrections are in general quite small. The calculation of such effects

† As above, $\Sigma_0^* = 2\pi i\,\delta\kappa$ always (cf. (207)).

‡ The phases in (212), (213) are chosen to give the correct overall charge renormalization in eqn. (214).

§ For a careful discussion see R. Karplus and N. M. Kroll, loc. cit.

|| This graph has n vertices, F_e, F_p internal lines, etc.

is obviously lengthy, and the reader is referred to the original papers for the details.† Thirring‡ has shown, by using relation (190) twice, that in the limit of zero frequency the radiative corrections to Compton scattering must vanish; this is because in this limit the corrections are proportional to the finite part $S_c(p)$ of the electron self-energy term.

13. External field problems

In a number of important problems it is necessary to find the radiative corrections to the motion of an electron or positron in the electromagnetic field of a nucleus. This latter field is determined by the known charge distribution and magnetic moment of the nucleus; thus it is a classical electromagnetic field. It will be called the *external electromagnetic field* $A_\mu^{(e)}(x)$. $A_\mu^{(e)}(x)$ may be regarded as the expectation value of the quantized field when no photons (and no other charges) are present;§ the quantum fluctuations in the field $A_\mu(x)$ are superimposed on the value $A_\mu^{(e)}(x)$.

The interaction Hamiltonian (158) is replaced by $\{\mathscr{H}_1(x_\nu)+\mathscr{H}^{(e)}(x_\nu)\}$, where

$$\left.\begin{aligned} \mathscr{H}_1(x_\nu) &= -\frac{1}{c}j_\mu(x_\nu)A_\mu(x_\nu)-\hbar c\,\delta\kappa\,\bar{\psi}(x_\nu)\psi(x_\nu) \\ \mathscr{H}^{(e)}(x_\nu) &= -\frac{1}{c}j_\mu(x_\nu)A_\mu^{(e)}(x_\nu) \end{aligned}\right\}. \tag{216}$$

For collision problems it is often sufficient to use the perturbation theory obtained on replacing $\mathscr{H}_1(x_\nu)$ in the S-matrix expansion (101) by $\{\mathscr{H}_1(x_\nu)+\mathscr{H}^{(e)}(x_\nu)\}$. If the resulting expression is written as a power series in $\mathscr{H}^{(e)}(x_\nu)$ we get the Born expansion, or the Born approximation,‖ for the scattering of an electron or positron by the electromagnetic field of a nucleus.

† For radiative corrections to Compton scattering see M. R. Schafroth, *Helv. phys. Acta*, **23** (1950) 542; L. M. Brown and R. P. Feynman, *Phys. Rev.* **85** (1952) 231. See also R. P. Feynman, ibid. **76** (1949) 769 (Appendix), and R. Karplus and N. M. Kroll, ibid. **77** (1950) 536, for the general methods of calculation.

‡ W. Thirring, *Phil. Mag.* **41** (1950) 1193. The proof is similar to that of the Kroll–Ruderman theorem in § 16 below.

§ The Coulomb field $\mathbf{E}_N$ of a nucleus is in general much larger than the radiation field $\mathbf{E}_R$ of a scattered electron. At distance r from the electron $|\mathbf{E}_R| \simeq |\ddot{\mathbf{Z}}|/4\pi c^2 r$ (eqn. (2.217)), and $\ddot{\mathbf{Z}} = e^2\mathbf{E}_N/m$. Hence

$$|\mathbf{E}_R| \simeq |\mathbf{E}_N|\left(\frac{e^2}{4\pi mc^2}\right)\frac{1}{r} \simeq |\mathbf{E}_N|10^{-13}\,\text{cm}/r.$$

This shows the importance of the external field phenomena.

‖ For a discussion on the validity of the Born approximation see W. Kohn, *Rev. Mod. Phys.* **26** (1954) 292.

The Born approximation

Now we consider the first Born approximation, for which the S-matrix is (cf. (101))†

$$S = I+\left(\frac{-i}{\hbar c}\right)\int\limits_{-\infty}^{\infty} d^4x_1\,\mathscr{H}^{(e)}(x_1)+\left(\frac{-i}{\hbar c}\right)^2\int\limits_{-\infty}^{\infty} d^4x_1\int\limits_{-\infty}^{\infty} d^4x_2\,\mathsf{T}\{\mathscr{H}^{(e)}(x_1)\mathscr{H}_1(x_2)\}+$$
$$+\frac{1}{2!}\left(\frac{-i}{\hbar c}\right)^3\int\limits_{-\infty}^{\infty} d^4x_1\int\limits_{-\infty}^{\infty} d^4x_2\int\limits_{-\infty}^{\infty} d^4x_3\,\mathsf{T}\{\mathscr{H}^{(e)}(x_1)\mathscr{H}_1(x_2)\mathscr{H}_1(x_3)\}+\ldots. \tag{217}$$

On the right of (217) the first integral gives the first Born approximation ignoring radiation effects, the second integral gives bremsstrahlung

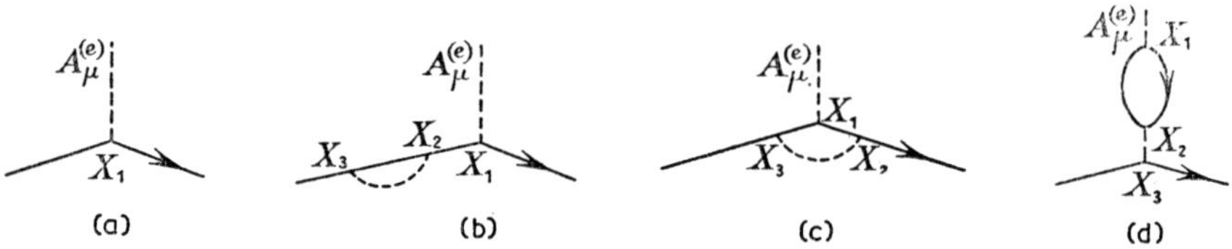

FIG. 28. The lowest order processes in the scattering of an electron, or a positron, by an external electromagnetic field $A_\mu^{(e)}$.

with the emission of one photon, the third integral gives the emission of two photons together with radiative corrections to scattering. The various terms in (217) can be represented by graphs in which $A_\mu^{(e)}(x_1)$ is shown as a broken line from x_1 to the edge of the diagram; the remaining terms are expressed in normal products by the theorem (112), using eqns. (120) and (121) for the contractions.

It follows from (217) that the effect of field quantization is to replace the simple scattering interaction $\mathscr{H}^{(e)}(x_1)$ of the first Born approximation by

$$\mathscr{H}^{(e)}(x_1)+\left(\frac{-i}{\hbar c}\right)\int\limits_{-\infty}^{\infty} d^4x_2\,\mathsf{T}\{\mathscr{H}^{(e)}(x_1)\mathscr{H}_1(x_2)\}+$$
$$+\frac{1}{2!}\left(\frac{-i}{\hbar c}\right)^2\int\limits_{-\infty}^{\infty} d^4x_2\int\limits_{-\infty}^{\infty} d^4x_3\,\mathsf{T}\{\mathscr{H}^{(e)}(x_1)\mathscr{H}_1(x_2)\mathscr{H}_1(x_3)\}+\ldots. \tag{218}$$

The lowest order terms in (217) for electron or positron scattering are shown in Fig. 28. Fig. 28 (*b*) shows an electron self-energy part in the external line; the effect of all such parts is to replace the renormalized operator $\psi(x_1)$ by $Z_2^{\frac{1}{2}}\psi(x_1)$. A similar term gives

$$\bar\psi'(x_1) = Z_2^{\frac{1}{2}}\bar\psi(x_1).$$

† Apart from identity, we include only terms linear in $A_\mu^{(e)}$.

The graph in Fig. 28 (c) shows a vertex part at x_1. This can be evaluated by the analysis of § 11, if we write

$$A_{\mu}^{(e)}(x_{\nu}) = \int d^4p\, e^{ip_{\nu}x_{\nu}} A_{\mu}^{(e)}(p). \tag{219}$$

Because $A_{\mu}^{(e)}(x_{\nu})$ arises from sources, p^2 (in (219)) does not in general vanish. If the energy-momenta of the incoming and outgoing fermion are p_2, p_1 respectively, eqn. (189) shows that the total effect of the graphs Fig. 28 (a) and (c) is to replace the factors $\gamma^{\mu}A_{\mu}^{(e)}(p)$ appearing in $\mathscr{H}^{(e)}(x)$ by

$$Z_1^{-1}\{\gamma^{\mu}+\Lambda_c^{\mu}(p_1,p_2)\}A_{\mu}^{(e)}(p), \tag{220}$$

where $p_2-p_1 = p$. The effect of inserting all proper vertex parts is given by formula (197) (extended to any order in e_1); $\gamma^{\mu}A_{\mu}^{(e)}(p)$ is replaced by

$$Z_1^{-1}\Gamma_c^{\mu}(p_1,p_2;\, e_1)A_{\mu}^{(e)}(p), \tag{221}$$

where $\Gamma_c^{\mu}(p_1,p_2;\, e_1)$ is finite. The factor Z_1 contributes to the charge renormalization;† for practical calculations we take $Z_1 = 1$ and replace γ^{μ} by $\Gamma_c^{\mu}(p_1,p_2;\, e_1)$.

Vacuum polarization

Graph Fig. 28 (d) is the lowest order *vacuum polarization* effect; the field $A_{\mu}^{(e)}(x)$ acting on the fermion vacuum tends to produce a separation of charge.‡

The effect of the fermion loop in this graph is to replace $A_{\mu}^{(e)}(p)$ by§

$$A_{\mu}^{(e)}(p)\Pi_{\mu\mu'}(p)D_F(p),$$

where $\Pi_{\mu\mu'}(p)$ is the second-order photon self-energy term given by (174). Choosing the Lorentz gauge (cf. eqn. (1.17)) the external field obeys

$$p_{\mu}A_{\mu}^{(e)}(p) = 0.$$

Therefore, as in (176), $A_{\mu}^{(e)}(p)$ is replaced by

$$A_{\mu}^{(e)}(p)\Pi(p)D_F(p). \tag{222}$$

The vacuum polarization modifies the external field, irrespective of the scattered particle. Higher-order vacuum polarization corrections can readily be included by using higher-order evaluations of $\Pi(p)$.

† Charge renormalization requires that in (218) we replace the external field $A_{\mu}^{(e)}(x)$ by $Z_3^{\frac{1}{2}}A_{\mu}^{(e)}(x)$. $A_{\mu}^{(e)}$ is the field which would be given by renormalized (external) charges.

‡ R. Serber, *Phys. Rev.* **48** (1935) 49; E. A. Uehling, ibid. 55. See also V. F. Weisskopf, *K. danske vidensk. Selsk.* **14** (1936), No. 6, for a discussion of early work on vacuum polarization.

§ This replacement is obviously equivalent to replacing $D_F(p)$ by $D_F^{(2)}(p)_{\mu\mu'}$ in eqn. (174).

Substituting (178) in (222), we see that the graphs† Fig. 28 (*a*) and (*d*) have the effect of replacing $A_\mu^{(e)}(p)$ (to relative order e^2) by

$$A_\mu^{(e)\prime}(p) = Z_3\left\{A_\mu^{(e)}(p)+\frac{1}{2\pi i}D_c(p)A_\mu^{(e)}(p)\right\}, \tag{223}$$

where Z_3 is the renormalization constant given by (180) and (181). Charge renormalization allows us to replace Z_3 by unity in (223). Using the methods given in § 11 the finite term $D_c(p)$ is readily evaluated. This gives‡ §

$$A_\mu^{(e)\prime}(p) = A_\mu^{(e)}(p)+\alpha\frac{p^2}{\pi}\int\limits_0^1 du\,\frac{u^2(1-\frac{1}{3}u^2)}{4\kappa^2+p^2(1-u^2)}A_\mu^{(e)}(p). \tag{224}$$

If the external field does not vary very rapidly (in space or time) we can neglect the dependence of the integrand on p^2. In that case the *additional* field $\delta A_\mu^{(e)}(p)$ arising from the vacuum polarization is

$$\delta A_\mu^{(e)}(p) = \frac{\alpha}{15\pi\kappa^2}p^2A_\mu^{(e)}(p) = \frac{\alpha}{15\pi\kappa^2}J_\mu(p), \tag{225}$$

where
$$J_\mu(x_\nu) = \int d^4p\, e^{ip_\nu x_\nu}J_\mu(p)$$

is the charge-current which gives rise to the external field $A_\mu^{(e)}(x)$. In other words, $J_\mu(p)$ induces a current $\delta j_\mu(p)$ in the vacuum, where‖

$$\delta j_\mu(p) = \frac{\alpha p^2}{15\pi\kappa^2}J_\mu(p). \tag{226}$$

It should be noted that there is a singularity in the intergrand in (224) if $p^2+4\kappa^2 \leqslant 0$. Under these conditions the external field varies (in time) so rapidly that real electron-positron pairs are produced in the vacuum; in this case a stable vacuum may not be possible.

The vacuum polarization leads to small deviations from Dirac's solution for the motion of an electron in the Coulomb field of an atom. It contributes -27 mc/sec to the difference ($\simeq +1{,}058$ mc/sec) between the $2p_{\frac{1}{2}}$ and $2s_{\frac{1}{2}}$ energy levels in hydrogen (see § 14). The good agreement between the theoretical and experimental values for this energy difference confirms the existence of vacuum polarization.

Vacuum polarization effects should have greater importance relative to the other radiative corrections for the energy levels of μ-mesic

† We have already used Fig. 28 (*a*) in deriving (220); we now replace $A_\mu^{(e)}(p)$ in (220) by $A_\mu^{(e)\prime}(p)$ of (223).

‡ R. Karplus and N. M. Kroll, *Phys. Rev.* **77** (1950) 536; for a clear account of the fourth-order calculations see G. Källén and A. Sabry, *K. danske vidensk. Selsk.* **29** (1955), No. 17.

§ $\alpha = e_1^2/4\pi\hbar c = 1/137{\cdot}039$; $\kappa = m_e c/\hbar$.

‖ E. A. Uehling, p. 281, n. ‡.

atoms;† the effect should be greatest in μ-mesic atoms of large atomic number.‡ It has been suggested that vacuum polarization can also be detected in the phase shifts for proton-proton scattering at a few MeV.§

Radiative corrections to scattering

Eqns. (217) or (218) may be used|| to find the radiative corrections to the scattering of an electron by a nucleus. It is obvious from the discussion in Chapter II, § 13, that the corrections will depend on the energy resolution ΔE of the experiment.†† Using the Born approximation for the electron-nucleus interaction, the first-order correction is‡‡ of the form

$$\sigma_{\text{rad}}(e^2) = -\delta . \sigma_{\text{el}},$$

where σ_{el} is the usual Born approximation elastic scattering differential cross-section. For electrons of very relativistic energy E which are scattered through an angle θ,§§

$$\delta \simeq \frac{4\alpha}{\pi}\log\left(\frac{2E}{m_e c^2}\sin\tfrac{1}{2}\theta\right)\log(E/\Delta E).$$

Except at very high energies, this radiative correction is small.||||

The anomalous magnetic moment

Eqn. (218)††† can also be used to find the radiative correction to the magnetic moment μ_0 of the electron. An anomalous magnetic moment

† L. L. Foldy and E. Eriksen, *Phys. Rev.* **95** (1954) 1048. The μ-mesons move closer to the nucleus in a stronger Coulomb field; their greater mass reduces the other corrections. Vacuum polarization is then comparable with the nuclear size effect.

‡ Vacuum polarization in a strong Coulomb field, and its application to μ-mesic atoms and the X-ray spectra of heavy atoms are discussed by E. H. Wichmann and N. M. Kroll, *Phys. Rev.* **101** (1956) 843; see also A. B. Mickelwait and H. C. Corben, ibid. **96** (1954) 1145. Vacuum polarization may be important for π-mesic atoms; for a discussion see M. Stearns and M. B. Stearns, ibid. **103** (1956) 1534. For a bibliography for μ-mesic and π-mesic atoms see M. Camac, A. D. McGuire, J. B. Platt, and H. J. Schulte, ibid. **99** (1955) 897; S. de Benedetti, *Suppl. Nuovo Cim.* **3** (1956) 1209.

§ E. Eriksen, L. L. Foldy, and W. Rarita, *Phys. Rev.* **103** (1956) 781.

|| For a critical discussion of the use of higher-order Born approximations for Coulomb scattering see R. H. Dalitz, *Proc. Roy. Soc.* A **206** (1951) 509.

†† The emission of l.f. photons of energy up to ΔE is included in the 'elastic' scattering.

‡‡ J. Schwinger, *Phys. Rev.* **76** (1949) 790; H. Suura, ibid. **99** (1955) 1020.

§§ The presence of the factor $\log(E/\Delta E)$ indicates how this h.f. photon formula joins on to the formula (2.249).

|||| For discussion and references see R. G. Newton, *Phys. Rev.* **97** (1955) 1162; **98** (1955) 1514. Also, D. R. Yennie and H. Suura, ibid. **105** (1957) 1378; R. Hofstadter, *Rev. Mod. Phys.* **28** (1956) 214.

††† The scattering of light by the Coulomb field of a nucleus (Delbrück scattering) is given by a graph like Fig. 22 (*c*), with the Coulomb field acting at two vertices. The cross-section is therefore much larger than light-light scattering (it can be as large as 10 millibarns at a few MeV for large Z). Cf. F. Rohrlich and R. L. Gluckstein, *Phys. Rev.* **86** (1952) 1. The calculation uses the related pair production in the Coulomb field.

$\delta\mu$ would give rise to an interaction

$$\mathscr{H}'(x) = -\delta\mu.\tfrac{1}{2}f_{\mu\nu}(x)\bar{\psi}(x)\sigma^{\mu\nu}\psi(x),$$

where $f_{\mu\nu}$ is the electromagnetic field strength and $\sigma^{\mu\nu}$ is the electron's spin operator (3.10). In momentum space this interaction is of the form

$$\bar{\psi}(p_1)\sigma^{\mu\nu}\psi(p_2)(p_1-p_2)_\mu A_\nu(p_1-p_2). \tag{227}$$

On picking out the terms linear in (p_1-p_2) from the matrix elements for Fig. 28 (*b*), (*c*), (*d*), the magnetic moment of the electron is found to be†

$$\mu_0+\delta\mu = \left(1+\frac{\alpha}{2\pi}\right)\frac{e_1\hbar}{2m_e c}.$$

C. M. Sommerfield‡ has evaluated the corrections to the fourth order, and gets

$$\mu_0+\delta\mu = \left(1+\frac{\alpha}{2\pi}-0{\cdot}328\frac{\alpha^2}{\pi^2}\right)\frac{e_1\hbar}{2m_e c} = 1{\cdot}001159\frac{e_1\hbar}{2m_e c}.$$

This result is in agreement with experiment.§

14. Bound state problems

Furry's representation

The Born approximation methods which were discussed in § 13 are not the best for finding the radiative corrections to the motion of an electron inside an atom; an elegant method has been invented by Furry for this purpose.‖ We assume, as in § 13, that the nucleus gives rise to a field $A_\mu^{(e)}(x_\nu)$, so that the interaction representation state vector $|\Psi(t)\rangle$ obeys (cf. eqns. (4.100) and (4.101))

$$i\hbar\frac{\partial}{\partial t}|\Psi(t)\rangle = \int d^3\mathbf{x}\,\{\mathscr{H}_1(\mathbf{x},t)+\mathscr{H}^{(e)}(\mathbf{x},t)\}|\Psi(t)\rangle, \tag{228}$$

where $\mathscr{H}_1(x)$, $\mathscr{H}^{(e)}(x)$ are expressed by (216) above in terms of the interaction representation variables $\bar{\psi}(x)$, $\psi(x)$, $A_\mu(x)$. Now we use a unitary transformation to give a new representation in which the state vector $|\Psi_F(t)\rangle$ obeys the equation

$$i\hbar\frac{\partial}{\partial t}|\Psi_F(t)\rangle = \int d^3\mathbf{x}\,\mathscr{H}_1(\mathbf{x},t)_F|\Psi_F(t)\rangle. \tag{229}$$

The notation $\mathscr{H}_1(\mathbf{x},t)_F$ indicates that $\mathscr{H}_1(x)$ is written in terms of the field variables $\bar{\psi}_F(x)$, $\psi_F(x)$, $A_\mu(x)_F$ of the new representation:

$$\mathscr{H}_1(x)_F = -\frac{1}{c}j_\mu(x)_F A_\mu(x)_F - \hbar c\,\delta\kappa\,\bar{\psi}(x)_F\psi(x)_F \tag{230}$$

† J. Schwinger, *Phys. Rev.* **73** (1948) 416.

‡ *Phys. Rev.* **107** (1957) 328; A. Petermann, *Helv. phys. Acta*, **30** (1957) 407.

§ S. Koenig, A. G. Pradell, and P. Kusch, *Phys. Rev.* **88** (1952) 191.

‖ W. H. Furry, *Phys. Rev.* **81** (1951) 115.

with (cf. (4.77) and (98))†

$$j_\mu(x)_F = \tfrac{1}{2}iec\{\bar{\psi}(x)_F\gamma^\mu\psi(x)_F - \psi(x)_F\gamma_T^\mu\bar{\psi}(x)_F\}. \tag{231}$$

This new representation is called the *bound state interaction representation*. The required unitary transformation is

$$\left.\begin{aligned} |\Psi(t)\rangle &= V(t)|\Psi_F(t)\rangle \\ O_F(t) &= \{V(t)\}^{-1}O(t)V(t) \end{aligned}\right\}, \tag{232}$$

where $O(t)$ and $O_F(t)$ are corresponding operators in the interaction representation and the new representation. The transformation operator $V(t)$ must satisfy‡

$$i\hbar\frac{\partial V(t)}{\partial t} = \int d^3\mathbf{x}\,\mathscr{H}^{(e)}(\mathbf{x},t).V(t). \tag{233}$$

Eqns. (232) and (233) lead directly to (229).

The electromagnetic field operator is unaltered by the transformation:

$$A_\mu(x)_F = A_\mu(x). \tag{234}$$

The change in the electron field operator can easily be seen from its propagation equation. By (232)

$$\frac{\partial}{\partial t}O_F(t) = \{V(t)\}^{-1}\frac{\partial O(t)}{\partial t}V(t) + \left[O_F(t), \{V(t)\}^{-1}\frac{\partial V(t)}{\partial t}\right],$$

also

$$i\hbar\{V(t)\}^{-1}\frac{\partial V(t)}{\partial t} = -\frac{1}{c}\int d^3\mathbf{x}\, j_\mu(\mathbf{x},t)_F A_\mu^{(e)}(\mathbf{x},t).$$

It follows§ that $\psi_F(x)$ obeys

$$\gamma^\mu\left(\partial_\mu - \frac{ie}{\hbar c}A_\mu^{(e)}(x)\right)\psi_F(x) + \kappa\psi_F(x) = 0. \tag{235}$$

Similarly,

$$\left(\partial_\mu + \frac{ie}{\hbar c}A_\mu^{(e)}(x)\right)\bar{\psi}_F(x)\gamma^\mu - \kappa\bar{\psi}_F(x) = 0. \tag{236}$$

Thus the operators $\psi_F(x)$, $\bar{\psi}_F(x)$ obey the Dirac equation for the presence of an external electromagnetic field $A_\mu^{(e)}(x)$ (cf. (4.68)).

The great advantage of this method is that eqns. (235) and (236) can be solved as exactly as we wish, while eqn. (229) which contains the radiation effects can be solved by the perturbation method. Thus

$$|\Psi_F(t'')\rangle = U(t'',t')|\Psi_F(t')\rangle,$$

† The full form of $j_\mu(x)_F$ is given, because the vacuum expectation value of $j_\mu(x)_F$ does not vanish.

‡ By (233) $\partial/\partial t\{\tilde{V}(t)V(t)\} = 0$, and we can ensure that $V(t)$ is unitary by choosing $V(t_0)$ at the initial time t_0 such that $\tilde{V}(t_0)V(t_0) = I$.

§ The anti-commutators of $\psi_F(\mathbf{x}, t)$, $\bar{\psi}_F(\mathbf{x}', t)$ for the same time t are unaltered by the transformation. Here the electron has charge e and potential energy eA_0.

where

$$U(t'',t') = 1+\left(\frac{-i}{\hbar c}\right)\int\limits_{t'}^{t''} d^4x_1\,\mathscr{H}_1(x_1)_F+$$

$$+\left(\frac{-i}{\hbar c}\right)^2\frac{1}{2!}\int\limits_{t'}^{t''} d^4x_1\int\limits_{t'}^{t''} d^4x_2\,T\{\mathscr{H}_1(x_1)_F\mathscr{H}_1(x_2)_F\}+$$

$$+\left(\frac{-i}{\hbar c}\right)^3\frac{1}{3!}\int\limits_{t'}^{t''} d^4x_1\int\limits_{t'}^{t''} d^4x_2\int\limits_{t'}^{t''} d^4x_3\,T\{\mathscr{H}_1(x_1)_F\mathscr{H}_1(x_2)_F\mathscr{H}_1(x_3)_F\}+\dots. \tag{237}$$

The chronological products in these integrands can be expanded into normal products by (112), and the various radiative effects can be represented by graphs similar to those for the S-matrix. It is important to notice that an electron line can form a closed loop having *one* vertex only (cf. Fig. 29); this is because the external potential polarizes the vacuum, so $j_\mu(x)_F$ has a non-zero vacuum expectation value. In order to find the energy shifts of atomic levels due to radiative corrections, it is only necessary to know $U(\infty,-\infty)$. Eqns. (235) to (237) show that $U(\infty,-\infty)$ is a Lorentz invariant;† this fact makes it easy to separate off the divergent terms in a unique way.

The electron field in the presence of a nucleus

Suppose that $A_\mu^{(e)}$ is the field of a nucleus; we now use the frame of reference in which the nucleus is at rest. The operators $\psi_F(x)$, $\bar{\psi}_F(x)$ can be expanded in terms of the c-number solutions $\phi_\alpha(x)$ of the Dirac equation (235). Thus

$$\left.\begin{aligned}\psi_F(x) &= \sum_{(\alpha)} B_\alpha\phi_\alpha(x)\\ \bar{\psi}_F(x) &= \sum_{(\alpha)} \tilde{B}_\alpha\bar{\phi}_\alpha(x)\end{aligned}\quad (\bar{\phi}_{(\alpha)} = \tilde{\phi}_\alpha\gamma^4)\right\}, \tag{238}$$

where B_α, $\tilde{B}_\alpha$ are constant operator coefficients. The summation runs over *all* states ϕ_α both of positive and negative energy eigenvalues E_α. The expansion (238) is a simple extension of the expansion (4.21) of the free field electron operators $\psi(x)$, $\bar{\psi}(x)$ in terms of the plane-wave solutions of Dirac's equation.

Let $\phi_{\alpha+}(x)$, $\phi_{\alpha-}(x)$ be solutions for energies $E_\alpha>0$, $E_\alpha<0$, respectively. As in Chapter IV, § 3, we can interpret $B_{\alpha+}$, $\tilde{B}_{\alpha+}$ as the operators destroying and creating an electron in the state $\phi_{\alpha+}$; also $\tilde{B}_{\alpha-}$, $B_{\alpha-}$ are

† The presence of $A_\mu^{(e)}$ cannot cause disturbances in $\psi_F(x)$, $\bar{\psi}_F(x)$ to propagate faster than light; therefore all operators $\psi_F(x)$, $\bar{\psi}_F(x)$ anti-commute at space-like separations. Hence the chronological operator T is Lorentz invariant.

the operators destroying and creating a positron in the state $\phi_{\alpha-}$. The vacuum state $|0\rangle$ in the presence of the external field $A_\mu^{(e)}$ is therefore defined by†

$$\psi_F^{(+)}(x)|0\rangle = 0, \qquad \bar{\psi}_F^{(+)}(x)|0\rangle = 0. \tag{239}$$

The electron propagator

The contractions of the electron-positron field variables which appear when (237) is expanded in normal products are the vacuum expectation values (cf. (120))

$$\begin{aligned}\langle T\{\bar{\psi}_{\rho' F}(x')\psi_{\rho F}(x)\}\rangle_0 &= -\langle T\{\psi_{\rho F}(x)\bar{\psi}_{\rho' F}(x')\}\rangle_0 \\ &= \tfrac{1}{2}S^{(e)}_{F\rho\rho'}(x,x').\end{aligned} \tag{240}$$

By (238),‡

$$\tfrac{1}{2}S^{(e)}_{F\rho\rho'}(x,x') = \begin{Bmatrix} -\sum\limits_{(\alpha+)} \phi_{\alpha+}(x)_\rho \bar{\phi}_{\alpha+}(x')_{\rho'} & (x_0 > x_0') \\ +\sum\limits_{(\alpha-)} \phi_{\alpha-}(x)_\rho \bar{\phi}_{\alpha-}(x')_{\rho'} & (x_0 < x_0') \end{Bmatrix}, \tag{241}$$

where $\sum\limits_{(\alpha+)}$, $\sum\limits_{(\alpha-)}$ denote summations over positive and negative energy states respectively. $S_F^{(e)}(x,x')$ can be evaluated by using (241); it should be noticed that it is not in general a function of $(x-x')$.

We define $S^{(e)}_{F\rho\rho'}(x,x)$ as the average of the two limiting values obtained by letting x' tend to x from the past and from the future. It follows from (231) and (240) that the vacuum expectation value of the current is§

$$\langle j_\mu(x)_F\rangle_0 = \tfrac{1}{2}iec\,\mathrm{spur}\{\gamma^\mu S_F^{(e)}(x,x)\}. \tag{242}$$

This gives the value of the closed single vertex loops such as that in Fig. 29 (*b*). From (235) and the methods of Chapter IV, § 4, it is easy to verify that $\tfrac{1}{2}S^{(e)}_{F\rho\rho'}(x,x')$ is the causal Green's function‖ obeying (cf. (4.60))

$$\left\{\gamma^\mu\left(\partial_{x_\mu} - \frac{ie}{\hbar c}A_\mu^{(e)}(x)\right) + \kappa\right\}\tfrac{1}{2}S_F^{(e)}(x,x') = i\delta^{(4)}(x-x'). \tag{243}$$

The energy corrections

Let $|\alpha\rangle$ be the bound interaction representation state vector for a single electron (or positron) in the state $\phi_\alpha(x)$. The radiative effects give a correction ΔE_α to the energy of this state, where††

$$-\frac{i}{\hbar}\Delta E_\alpha = \lim_{(t''-t')\to\infty} \frac{1}{(t''-t')}\langle\alpha|U(t'',t')-1|\alpha\rangle. \tag{244}$$

† For the radiation field $A_\mu(x)$ the usual vacuum definition holds.

‡ It can readily be seen that if $\phi_\alpha(x)$ are the normalized solutions ($\bar{\phi}_\alpha\cdot\phi_\alpha = 1$) then B_α, $\tilde{B}_\alpha$ are the normalized creation-annihilation operators.

§ J. Schwinger, *Phys. Rev.* **82** (1951) 664.

‖ Schwinger (loc. cit.) has given a gauge invariant evaluation of this Green's function for special values of the external field $A_\mu^{(e)}(x)$; the vacuum polarization can then be deduced by (242).

†† N. M. Kroll and F. Pollock, *Phys. Rev.* **86** (1952) 876.

This relation is seen to be true if we assume that the total effect of radiative corrections to the energy level is equivalent to replacing

$$\int d^3\mathbf{x}_1\,\mathscr{H}_1(\mathbf{x}_1,t_1)$$

in the first integral in (237) by ΔE_α. The real part of ΔE_α is the energy shift, the imaginary part gives the rate of decay of the state $|\alpha\rangle$ due to radiative transitions to lower energy levels.

The radiative energy corrections to order e^2 are given by the graphs†

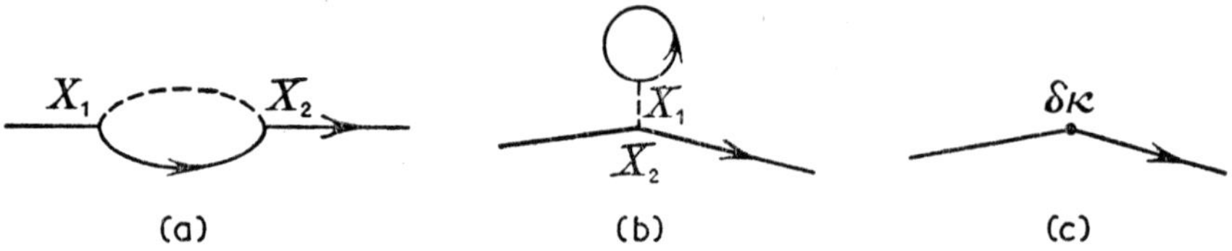

FIG. 29. The lowest order bound state corrections. (a) gives rise to the fluctuation energy; (b) gives rise to the polarization energy; (c) is used to renormalize the electron's mass.

Fig. 29 (a), (b), (c). By the usual methods (cf. §§ 8, 9) we get‡ (for $t'\to-\infty$, $t''\to+\infty$)

$$-\frac{i}{\hbar}(t''-t')\Delta E_\alpha$$
$$=-\frac{1}{4}\frac{e^2}{\hbar c}\int\limits_{t'}^{t''}d^4x_1\int\limits_{t'}^{t''}d^4x_2\,\bar{\phi}_\alpha(x_2)\gamma^\mu S_F^{(e)}(x_2,x_1)\gamma^\mu\phi_\alpha(x_1)D_F(x_2-x_1)+$$
$$+\frac{1}{4}\frac{e^2}{\hbar c}\int\limits_{t'}^{t''}d^4x_1\int\limits_{t'}^{t''}d^4x_2\,\bar{\phi}_\alpha(x_2)\gamma^\mu\phi_\alpha(x_2)D_F(x_2-x_1)\mathrm{spur}\{\gamma^\mu S_F^{(e)}(x_1,x_1)\}+$$
$$+i\delta\kappa\int\limits_{t'}^{t''}\bar{\phi}_\alpha(x_1)\phi_\alpha(x_1)\,d^4x_1. \quad (245)$$

The first integral in (245) which arises from Fig. 29 (a) gives the *fluctuation energy*; on emitting the virtual photon, the electron has a recoil so that its potential energy is slightly altered. The effect is comparatively large if the relative change in the potential energy due to the recoil is appreciable; this is the case for s-states only.§ Because $S_F^{(e)}(x_1,x_2)$ describes propagation in the Coulomb field, the graph of Fig. 29 (a) also includes the effect of the radiative correction to the electron's magnetic moment. For high-frequency virtual processes,

† N. M. Kroll and F. Pollock, loc. cit.
‡ Eqn. (245) is the correction for an *electron*.
§ In s-states there is an appreciable probability that the electron is near the nucleus.

this graph gives a contribution which is identical with the electron self-energy part of Fig. 20 (a) (§ 10). The third integral in (245) can be used to renormalize the mass and remove the most divergent term.

The polarization energy

The renormalization process will be illustrated by the case of the second integral in (245). This is the *polarization energy* which arises from the interaction of the electron with the vacuum polarization current (Fig. 29 (b)). It can be written†

$$\Delta E_P = -\frac{ie}{c}\lim \frac{1}{t''-t'}\int\limits_{t'}^{t''} \bar{\phi}_\alpha(x_1)\gamma^\mu A_\mu^P(x_1)\phi_\alpha(x_1)\, d^4x_1, \tag{246}$$

where
$$A_\mu^P(x_1) = \frac{i}{2c}\int\limits_{-\infty}^{\infty} D_F(x_1-x_2)\langle j_\mu(x_2)_F\rangle_0\, d^4x_2. \tag{247}$$

Here $A_\mu^P(x)$ is the field produced by the vacuum polarization. Using (2.182) and (2.184), it follows from (247) that

$$\partial_\mu^2 A_\nu^P(x) = -\frac{1}{c}\langle j_\nu(x)_F\rangle_0.$$

From (241) it is seen that we can write

$$S_F^{(e)}(x_2, x_1) = \frac{1}{4\pi^3}\iint d^4p_1\, d^4p_2\, S_F^{(e)}(p_2, p_1)\delta\{(p_2-p_1)_0\}e^{i(p_2x_2-p_1x_1)}, \tag{248}$$

where $(p_2-p_1)_0$ is the zero component of (p_2-p_1). In the frame of reference in which the nucleus is at rest we can also write

$$\left.\begin{aligned} A_\mu^{(e)}(x) &= \int A_\mu^{(e)}(\mathbf{p})\delta(p_0)e^{ipx}\, d^4p \\ A_\mu^P(x) &= \int A_\mu^P(\mathbf{p})\delta(p_0)e^{ipx}\, d^4p \end{aligned}\right\}. \tag{249}$$

Using (242) and (156) we deduce from (247)

$$A_\mu^P(\mathbf{k}) = -\frac{e}{4\pi^2}\int d^4p_1\, D_F(\mathbf{k}, 0)\mathrm{spur}[\gamma^\mu S_F^{(e)}\{\mathbf{p}_1+\mathbf{k}, (p_1)_0; \mathbf{p}_1, (p_1)_0\}]. \tag{250}$$

This is evaluated by using (243) to find the high-frequency dependence of $S_F^{(e)}(p_2, p_1)$. Substituting (248) in (243) gives

$$(i\gamma p_2+\kappa)S_F^{(e)}(p_2, p_1) = \frac{i}{2\pi}\delta^3(\mathbf{p}_2-\mathbf{p}_1)+\frac{ie}{\hbar c}\int d^3\mathbf{p}\,\gamma^\mu A_\mu^{(e)}(\mathbf{p}_2-\mathbf{p})S_F^{(e)}(p, p_1), \tag{251}$$

† See p. 287, n. ††.

where $(p_1)_0 = (p_2)_0 = p_0$. Also, we can use (236) to derive the generalized form of the associated Green's equation (4.64); this gives

$$S_F^{(e)}(p_2,p_1)(i\gamma p_1+\kappa) = \frac{i}{2\pi}\delta^3(\mathbf{p}_2-\mathbf{p}_1)+\frac{ie}{\hbar c}\int d^3\mathbf{p}\, S_F^{(e)}(p_2,p)\gamma^\mu A_\mu^{(e)}(\mathbf{p}-\mathbf{p}_1), \tag{252}$$

where $(p_1)_0 = (p_2)_0 = p_0$. Using (251) and then (252) we have

$$S_F^{(e)}(p_2,p_1) = S_F(p_2)\delta^3(\mathbf{p}_2-\mathbf{p}_1)+\frac{2\pi e}{\hbar c}S_F(p_2)\gamma^\mu A_\mu^{(e)}(\mathbf{p}_2-\mathbf{p}_1)S_F(p_1)+$$
$$+\left(\frac{2\pi e}{\hbar c}\right)^2 S_F(p_2)\iint d^3\mathbf{p}d^3\mathbf{p}'\,\gamma^\mu A_\mu^{(e)}(\mathbf{p}_2-\mathbf{p})\times$$
$$\times S_F^{(e)}(p,p')\gamma^\mu A_\mu^{(e)}(\mathbf{p}'-\mathbf{p}_1)S_F(p_1). \tag{253}$$

In this equation those terms which are predominant for large values of p_2^2 or p_1^2 have been separated from the remainder.† Substituting (253) in (250), the first term in (253) gives zero,‡ and we are left with

$$A_\mu^P(\mathbf{k}) = A_\mu^{(e)}(\mathbf{k})\Pi(\mathbf{k},0)D_F(\mathbf{k},0)+\delta A_\mu^P(\mathbf{k}). \tag{254}$$

$\Pi(\mathbf{k},0)$ is the photon self-energy contribution (eqn. (176)); it arises from the second term on the right of (253). The third term in (253) gives rise to $\delta A_\mu^P(\mathbf{k})$, which is a finite polarization contribution; it is only important for strong fields $A_\mu^{(e)}$.

The first term on the right of (254) is identical with the vacuum polarization effect which was found in § 13. Applying charge renormalization,§ the remaining (finite) part of this term is given by the value of $\{A_\mu^{(e)\prime}(\mathbf{k})-A_\mu^{(e)}(\mathbf{k})\}$ in eqn. (224).

The electron's wave function $\phi_\alpha(x)$ is transformed to the momentum representation by using||

$$\phi_\alpha(x) = \int d^4p\,\phi_\alpha(\mathbf{p})\delta(p_0-p_\alpha)e^{ipx}. \tag{255}$$

Substituting (254), (255), and (224) in (246) gives

$$\Delta E_P = -ie(2\pi)^2\alpha\int du\, 2u^2(1-\tfrac{1}{3}u^2)\times$$
$$\times\int d^3\mathbf{p}\int d^3\mathbf{p}'\,\bar{\phi}_\alpha(\mathbf{p})\frac{(\mathbf{p}-\mathbf{p}')^2\gamma^\mu A_\mu^{(e)}(\mathbf{p}-\mathbf{p}')}{4\kappa^2+(1-u^2)(\mathbf{p}-\mathbf{p}')^2}\phi_\alpha(\mathbf{p}')-$$
$$-ie(2\pi)^3\int d^3\mathbf{p}\int d^3\mathbf{p}'\,\bar{\phi}_\alpha(\mathbf{p})\gamma^\mu\delta A_\mu^P(\mathbf{p}-\mathbf{p}')\phi_\alpha(\mathbf{p}'). \tag{256}$$

This formula can be used to evaluate the second-order polarization energy. (It should be noted that the first term on the right of (256)

† Obviously, for $A_\mu^{(e)}\to 0$, $S_F^{(e)}(x_2,x_1)\to S_F(x_2-x_1)$ (by eqns. (248) and (156)).
‡ Because we require $\mathbf{k}\neq 0$.
§ We renormalize to the second order in the radiative effects.
|| $E_\alpha = \hbar c p_\alpha$ is the energy of the state ϕ_α.

could be obtained directly from (246) and the vacuum polarization calculations of § 13.) The fluctuation energy ΔE_F arising from Fig. 29 (a) is calculated by a very similar method.†

Applications of the theory

Several elegant calculations of the radiative corrections to atomic energy levels have been carried out using these or similar methods.†‡ For hydrogen the second-order radiative corrections give an energy difference between the $2s_{\frac{1}{2}}$ and $2p_{\frac{1}{2}}$ levels of about 1,052 Mc/sec;§ fourth-order corrections modify this to (1,058·0±0·1) Mc/sec. This is in good agreement with Lamb's experimental‖ value of (1,057·8±0·1) Mc/sec. For deuterium†† the fourth-order calculations‡‡ give a $2s_{\frac{1}{2}}-2p_{\frac{1}{2}}$ level separation of (1,059·2±0·1) Mc/sec which is to be compared with the experimental value (1,059·0±0·1) Mc/sec.‖ The same method has been used to calculate the radiative corrections to the hyperfine structure of atomic energy levels.† §§

A simple estimate of the energy levels of *positronium* may be found from the Schrödinger equation for an electron and a positron subject to a Coulomb attraction. The corrections are not so easily found as for atoms. Because both particles have a large magnetic moment there is a large 'hyperfine' structure. For the ^3S state there is a virtual process corresponding to one quantum annihilation; this raises the ^3S level relative to the ^1S level.‖‖ For the ^1S state there is a smaller correction due to (virtual or real) two-quantum annihilation. In addition there are recoil effects which are not important in the atomic case.††† The calculation of these corrections requires the theory of two-

† N. M. Kroll and F. Pollock, loc. cit. M. H. Mittleman, *Phys. Rev.* **107** (1957) 1170.

‡ M. Baranger, H. A. Bethe, and R. P. Feynman, *Phys. Rev.* **92** (1953) 482.

§ Of this total, $\Delta E_P = -27$ Mc/sec (1 Mc/sec $= 4{\cdot}13\times10^{-9}$ eV).

‖ W. E. Lamb and R. C. Retherford, *Phys. Rev.* **72** (1947) 241; S. Triebwasser, E. S. Dayhoff, and W. E. Lamb, ibid. **89** (1953) 106; the latter paper contains further references. For a careful comparison of the theoretical and experimental values see C. M. Sommerfield, *Phys. Rev.* **107** (1957) 328.

†† The Lamb shift of (14,043±13) Mc/sec for He^+ agrees closely with the theoretical value (see R. Novick, E. Lipworth, and P. F. Yergin, *Phys. Rev.* **100** (1955) 1153).

‡‡ For a careful comparison of the calculations for H and D see E. E. Salpeter, *Phys. Rev.* **89** (1953) 92. The finite size of the deuteron contributes 0·7 Mc/sec, but the electron-nucleon interaction gives only 0·02 Mc/sec in the $2s$ state of H, and gives a much smaller value for D.

§§ For the effect of the electromagnetic structure of the proton on the hyperfine splitting in H see A. C. Zemach, *Phys. Rev.* **104** (1956) 1771. Proton size increases the Lamb shift by 0·1 Mc/sec (W. Aron and A. J. Zuchelli, ibid. **105** (1957) 1681).

‖‖ This virtual process cannot occur for the ^1S state because of the charge conjugation selection rules given in Chapter IV, § 5.

††† For a detailed discussion of the effect of recoil on the hyperfine splitting in H see W. A. Newcomb and E. E. Salpeter, *Phys. Rev.* **97** (1955) 1146.

body propagators;† the reader is referred to the original papers for the details of this theory.‡ The theoretical value for the energy difference between the ^3S and ^1S states is (to order α^5)§

$$E_{^3S}-E_{^1S} = 2{\cdot}0337\times 10^5 \text{ Mc/sec.}$$

This is in very good agreement with the experimental value $(2{\cdot}0335\pm 0{\cdot}0005)\times 10^5$ Mc/sec.‖

15. Renormalization of meson theories

The possibility of using the renormalization method to give finite results for pion-nucleon interactions and for pion-nucleon-photon interactions was first considered by Matthews.†† He used the perturbation-theory method which has been applied to electrodynamics in previous sections. The S-matrix (95) is again analysed into normal products and a graphical notion is easily devised.

In pion-nucleon interactions the presence of a derivative coupling (such as (4.132)) would make it impossible to renormalize,‡‡ because the derivative gives rise to a four-momentum factor at each vertex and any graph with many vertices will therefore be highly divergent. The number of types of primitive divergents is not bounded, and the renormalization programme cannot be carried out.§§

The renormalizable theories of practical importance‖‖ are scalar, or pseudo-scalar, mesons having scalar, or pseudo-scalar, coupling with nucleons; the mesons may be charged or neutral. We consider *charged pseudo-scalar* mesons as an example. The interaction Hamiltonian is

$$H_{\text{int}} = H^{(c)}_{\text{int}}+H^{(e)}_{\text{int}}+H^{(P)}_{\text{int}}, \tag{257}$$

† See Chapter VI, § 2.

‡ E. E. Salpeter and H. A. Bethe, *Phys. Rev.* **81** (1951) 1232, *Encyclopedia of Physics*, Vol. 35 (Springer, Berlin, 1957); J. Schwinger, *Proc. Nat. Acad. Sci.* **37** (1951) 455.

§ Detailed calculations for positronium are given by G. V. B. Berestetski, *Zh. eksp. teor. Fiz.* **19** (1949) 1130; T. Fulton and P. C. Martin, *Phys. Rev.* **95** (1954) 811, where references to earlier work are given. See also a survey article on positronium by S. de Benedetti, *Suppl. Nuovo Cim.* **3** (1956) 1209.

‖ R. Weinstein, M. Deutsch, and S. Brown, *Phys. Rev.* **94** (1954) 758.

†† P. T. Matthews, *Phil. Mag.* **41** (1950) 185; **42** (1951) 221; *Phys. Rev.* **80** (1950) 292, 293; **81** (1951) 936. See also K. M. Watson and J. V. Lepore, ibid. **76** (1949) 1157 and F. Rohrlich, ibid. **80** (1950) 666.

‡‡ An exception is neutral vector mesons with vector coupling. See P. T. Matthews, *Phys. Rev.* **76** (1949) 1254.

§§ See, however, R. Arnowitt and S. Deser, *Phys. Rev.* **100** (1955) 349, for an attempt to renormalize derivative coupling theories.

‖‖ A β-decay type theory in which four fermion fields interact at a point is not renormalizable. The methods of § 10 show that the degree of divergence increases with the number of vertices (cf. Chapter III, § 14).

where $H_{\text{int}}^{(c)}$, $H_{\text{int}}^{(e)}$, $H_{\text{int}}^{(P)}$ are the pion-nucleon, pion-photon, and photon-proton interactions given by (4.131), (4.139), and (97) respectively.

Each charged pion internal line in a graph corresponds to a contraction factor† (cf. (2.63) and (2.105))

$$\langle T\{\tilde{\phi}(x_\mu)\phi(x'_\mu)\}\rangle_0 = \frac{1}{2}\frac{\hbar}{c}\Delta_F(x_\mu - x'_\mu), \tag{258}$$

where

$$\Delta_F(x_\mu) = \frac{1}{4\pi^3}\int d^4k\, e^{ik_\nu x_\nu}\Delta_F(k) = \frac{1}{8\pi^4 i}\int d^4k \frac{e^{ik_\nu x_\nu}}{k^2+\mu^2-i\epsilon}. \tag{259}$$

A simple modification of the graphical notation makes it possible to represent the conservation of charge as well as the conservation of

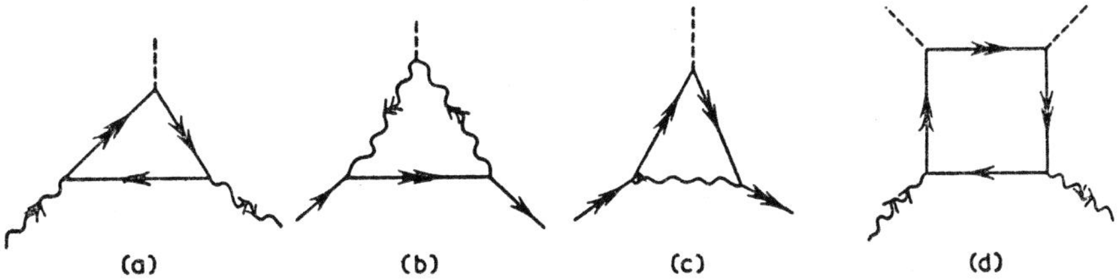

FIG. 30. Photon-pion-nucleon graphs. The double arrow indicates the motion of the charge; the single arrow completes the description of nucleon anti-nucleon conservation. (*a*) is a primitive divergent charged pion-photon vertex part. (*b*) is a contribution to the anomalous magnetic moment of the neutron. (*c*) is a proton-photon vertex part. (*d*) is a primitive divergent *C*-part.

nucleons. This is shown in Fig. 30; mesons are shown by wavy lines and the double arrow indicates how the charge moves. $H_{\text{int}}^{(c)}$ gives a three-vertex where one pion and two nucleon lines meet. This vertex contributes a factor $(G/\hbar c)\gamma^5\boldsymbol{\tau}(2\pi)^4\delta^{(4)}(p_1-p_2+p_3)$ to the matrix element; p_1, p_2, p_3 are the four-momenta of the nucleon and pion lines. $H_{\text{int}}^{(P)}$ gives a three-vertex where one photon and two proton lines meet; it contributes $-(e/\hbar c)\gamma^\mu(2\pi)^4\delta^{(4)}(p_1-p_2+p_3)$ (using an obvious notation). $H_{\text{int}}^{(e)}$ gives two types of vertices; the first is a pion-photon three-vertex coming from the term (cf. (4.137))

$$\frac{iec}{\hbar}A_\mu\{\tilde{\phi}\,\partial_\mu\phi - (\partial_\mu\tilde{\phi})\,\phi\}.$$

It contributes $$\frac{ie}{\hbar^2}(p_1+p_2)_\mu(2\pi)^4\delta^{(4)}(p_1-p_2+p_3),$$

where p_1, p_2 are the pion line four-momenta. The remaining term in

† It is convenient to denote the pion propagators by Δ_F and the photon propagators by D_F.

$H_{\text{int}}^{(e)}$ (i.e. $-(e^2/\hbar^2)A_\mu^2\tilde{\phi}\phi$) gives a four-vertex where two photon and two pion lines meet; it contributes†

$$(ie^2/\hbar^3c)\delta_{\mu\nu}(2\pi)^4\delta^{(4)}(p_1-p_2+p_3-p_4).$$

The primitive divergents

From these rules it is easy to apply the method of § 10 above for finding primitive divergent graphs. This shows that for primitive divergents we require

$$\tfrac{3}{2}E_n+E_m+E_p < 5, \tag{260}$$

where E_n, E_m, E_p are the number of external nucleon, meson, and photon lines respectively. This becomes the same as eqn. (152) if we fail to distinguish between external pions and photons. The boson and fermion self-energy graphs are similar to those of electrodynamics; however, the pion self-energy part is actually a quadratic divergent‡ and pion mass renormalization is necessary. There are various logarithmic divergent vertex parts ($E_n = 2$, $E_m = 1$; $E_n = 2$, $E_p = 1$; $E_m = 2$, $E_p = 1$), but the three-pion vertex part cannot occur (for charged pions) on account of charge conservation.§ The square parts ($E_p = 4$) giving light-light scattering do not diverge,|| but there are two logarithmic divergent square parts (($E_p = 2$, $E_n = 2$), and ($E_m = 4$)) which correspond to Compton scattering and Møller scattering respectively. These will be called C-parts and M-parts.

The quadratic divergences in the pion self-energy, the linear divergence in the nucleon self-energies, and the logarithmic divergence in the M-parts are removed by adding to the interaction Hamiltonian the terms (cf. eqn. (158) for electrodynamics)

$$H' = -\int d^3\mathbf{x}\,[\hbar c\,\delta\kappa_P\,\bar{\psi}_P(x)\psi_P(x)+\hbar c\,\delta\kappa_N\,\bar{\psi}_N(x)\psi_N(x)+ \\ +c^2\delta(\mu^2)\tilde{\phi}(x)\phi(x)+\tfrac{1}{2}c^2\delta\lambda\{\tilde{\phi}(x)\phi(x)\}^2]. \tag{261}$$

$\delta\kappa_P$, $\delta\kappa_N$ give the mass renormalizations for protons and neutrons and ψ_P, ψ_N are the proton and neutron field variables; the other terms are the

† The rules for calculating matrix elements are given in precise form by J. C. Ward, *Phys. Rev.* **84** (1951) 897.

‡ Gauge invariances arguments cannot be used to reduce the degree of divergence as for photons.

§ Furry's theorem cannot be used to exclude such vertex parts. In the case of neutral pseudo-scalar pions three-pion vertex parts are excluded by parity conservation. They can occur for neutral scalar pions, and their infinite parts are to be cancelled by adding a term $-\chi\phi^3(x)$ to the interaction Hamiltonian. χ is a log. divergent constant. Cf. P. T. Matthews, *Phys. Rev.* **81** (1951) 936, for a detailed discussion.

|| This is due to gauge invariance (cf. § 10).

pion mass and M-part subtractions.† The remaining divergences are to be removed by renormalizing the charge e and the coupling constant G.

Coupling constant renormalization

Matthews† states necessary conditions for this renormalization to be possible. They are:

(i) The infinite multiples arising from inserting vertex parts like Fig. 30 (a) in Fig. 31 (a) must be identical with the multiples obtained by renormalizing the C-parts like Fig. 30 (d). These processes relate

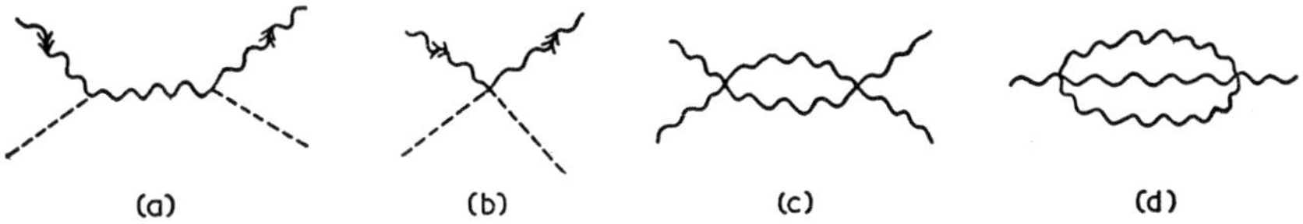

FIG. 31. (a) is a finite C-part formed from two pion-photon three-vertices. (b) is the pion-photon four-vertex. (c) and (d) are new divergences arising from the renormalization term $\delta\lambda(\tilde{\phi}\phi)^2$. ($c$) is an M-part and (d) is a pion self-energy.

to pion-photon charge renormalization; they enable us to express the renormalized pion charge e_1 as a function of e and G: $e_1 = e_1(e, G)$.

(ii) The renormalized proton charge, which is obtained by making all insertions (such as Fig. 30 (c)) in the proton-photon vertex, must be identical with e_1. In addition it is necessary that the renormalization method deals with the new divergent graphs, such as Fig. 31 (c) and (d), which are introduced by the last term in (261);‡ also, Matthews† points out that because the neutron carries no charge, all the *infinite parts* arising from vertex parts with two neutron lines and one photon line (such as Fig. 30 (b)) should cancel out.§

Matthews has verified that the renormalization scheme works up to the fourth order in the coupling constant;‖ general verifications up to any order have been given by Salam†† and by Ward.‡‡ We quote Ward's form of the results of renormalization. Let $S_F^{P\prime}$, $S_F^{N\prime}$, Δ_F', D_F'

† P. T. Matthews, *Phys. Rev.* **80** (1950) 293. $\delta\mu^2$ and $\delta\lambda$ are constants; the latter is to be determined by experiment.

‡ These *new* divergent parts have been examined in detail by A. Salam, *Phys. Rev.* **82** (1951) 217.

§ The infinite parts of neutron-photon vertex parts cancel out because Ward's relation (190) can be adapted to relate proton and pion self-energy parts to photon vertex parts (cf. eqn. (191)). By differentiation of the internal line variables (*not* the external line variables) the result follows (cf. A. Salam, *Phys. Rev.* **79** (1950) 911).

‖ P. T. Matthews, *Phil. Mag.* **42** (1951) 221.

†† A. Salam, *Phys. Rev.* **82** (1951) 217; **84** (1951) 426. The method involves a complicated subtraction procedure for the various types of overlapping divergence.

‡‡ J. C. Ward, *Phys. Rev.* **84** (1951) 897. This treatment avoids the overlapping divergence difficulty and is consequently easier to follow. It is analogous to the treatment in § 12 above.

be the propagators, including *all* corrections, for protons, neutrons, pions (charged),† and photons (compare, for example, with (170), (179), (206)). Also, let V_μ, Γ_μ, Γ_5 be the sums of all photon-pion,‡ photon-proton, pion-nucleon vertex parts (cf. eqn. (195)), let $C_{\mu\nu}$ be the sum of all C-part contributions and N the sum of all M-part contributions. Then we have (cf. (197), (208))

$$\left.\begin{aligned} \Delta'_F &= Z_1\,\Delta_c(e_1, G_1), & S^{P'}_F &= Z_6\,S_{Pc}(e_1, G_1) \\ D'_F &= Z_3\,D_c(e_1, G_1), & S^{N'}_F &= Z_7\,S_{Nc}(e_1, G_1) \\ V_\mu &= Z_1^{-1}V_{\mu c}(e_1, G_1), & \Gamma_\mu &= Z_6^{-1}\Gamma_{\mu c}(e_1, G_1) \\ C_{\mu\nu} &= Z_1^{-1}C_{\mu\nu c}(e_1, G_1), & \Gamma_5 &= Z_5^{-1}\Gamma_{5c}(e_1, G_1) \\ N &= Z_1^{-2}N_c(e_1, G_1), & & \end{aligned}\right\}, \tag{262}$$

where the functions having subscript c are the *finite* renormalized propagators, vertex parts, etc.; they are expressed in terms of the renormalized (or the observed) coupling constants e_1, G_1. Z_1, Z_3, Z_5, Z_6, Z_7 are logarithmic divergent constants, and e_1, G_1 are given by

$$e_1 = Z_3^{\frac{1}{2}}e, \qquad G_1 = (Z_1\,Z_6\,Z_7)^{\frac{1}{2}}Z_5^{-1}G. \tag{263}$$

Requirement (i) on p. 295 follows from the presence of the same constant Z_1 in four equations in the first column of (262). Requirement (ii) is satisfied because for each photon-proton vertex the factor Z_6^{-1} cancels with a factor Z_6 from the proton lines; for a photon-pion vertex the factor Z_1 similarly disappears.§ (See also eqn. (270).)

Definition of the renormalized coupling constants

In electrodynamics the renormalized coupling constant e_1 was defined by the requirement that radiative corrections give no contribution to a freely moving electron which suffers a small deflexion in an electromagnetic field. Another definition is obtained by requiring that e_1 gives the correct value for Thomson scattering in the limit of low frequency (cf. eqn. (135) with e replaced by e_1). Because the radiative corrections to Thomson scattering vanish in this limit (cf. the end of § 12), these two definitions of e_1 give the same result. These definitions give a unique result because they both involve slowly varying electromagnetic fields; for such fields radiative corrections are necessarily unimportant.‖

In pion theory there may be some ambiguity about the definition of

† Neutral pions can easily be included.

‡ Neutron-photon vertices are finite (cf. n. §, p. 295).

§ The relation of (262) to Matthews's notation is that his coefficients Z'_i obey $Z'_1 = Z'_2 = Z'_4$. Also, his Z'_1 = our Z_1 of (262). The infinite constants of (262) are not equal to the similar constants of § 12.

‖ For a discussion see S. Deser, W. E. Thirring, and M. L. Goldberger, *Phys. Rev.* **94** (1954) 711; G. Källén, *Nuovo Cim.* **12** (1954) 217.

the renormalized coupling constant G_1. If p_1 and p_2 both obey the free nucleon relations (162) then Lorentz invariance shows that Γ_{5c} must be of the form

$$\Gamma_{5c}(p_1, p_2) = \gamma^5 f((p_1-p_2)^2), \tag{264}$$

where $f((p_1-p_2)^2)$ is some function of the invariant $(p_1-p_2)^2$.

A commonly used definition of G_1 is given by choosing† $f(0) = 1$; this is used in § 16 below.‡ Another definiton of G_1 (due to Watson and Lepore§) is obtained by continuing the function f to unphysical values of its argument and choosing $f(-\mu^2) = 1$. It is conjectured that the values of G_1^2 so defined differ by a factor $1+O((m_\pi/M)^2)$. The second definition is used in dispersion relations.

16. Example: The Kroll–Ruderman theorem

This theorem‖ states that at threshold the complete renormalized theory calculation for the photo-production process††

$$h\nu+\mathscr{N} \rightarrow \mathscr{N}+\pi$$

reduces to the second-order perturbation theory result, provided we work only to the lowest order in (m_π/M). This is the analogue of Thirring's result for Compton scattering (cf. the end of § 12).

Ward's relation

The proof of this theorem depends on an extension of Ward's result (194). If $\Sigma^*(p)$ is the sum of all proper self-energy parts for a proton of four-momentum p_μ, then

$$-\frac{1}{2\pi}\frac{\partial\Sigma^*(p)}{\partial p_\mu}$$

is the sum of the vertex parts obtained by inserting an external photon line of zero momentum into *all* charged internal lines of these self-energy parts. In the notation of (262) this gives‡‡

$$\Gamma_\mu(p,p) = \gamma^\mu - \frac{1}{2\pi}\frac{\partial\Sigma^*(p)}{\partial p_\mu}. \tag{265}$$

† More precisely, we require

$$\lim_{p_2\to p_1} \{\bar{u}(p_2)\Gamma_{5c}(p_2, p_1)u(p_1)/\bar{u}(p_2)\gamma^5 u(p_1)\} \rightarrow 1,$$

where $u(p_1)$, $u(p_2)$ are free nucleon spinors. (Note that $\bar{u}(p)\gamma^5 u(p) = 0$.)

‡ For a discussion see G. Källén, loc. cit., and H. A. Bethe and F. de Hoffmann, *Mesons and Fields* (Row, Peterson, Evanston, Ill., 1955), vol. ii. Källén points out that the criterion for a satisfactory definition of G_1 is its self-consistency. The above leads to a large value of G_1^2, which, however, appears to be consistent.

§ K. M. Watson and J. V. Lepore, *Phys. Rev.* **76** (1949) 1157.

‖ N. M. Kroll and M. A. Ruderman, *Phys. Rev.* **93** (1954) 233.

†† $\mathscr{N}$ = nucleon, m_π = pion mass, M = nucleon mass.

‡‡ A. Salam, *Phys. Rev.* **79** (1950) 911.

This relation arises from the fact that the motion of a charged particle in a weak external electromagnetic field is necessarily described by a propagator in which the four-momentum p_μ is replaced† by $\{p_\mu+(e/c)A_\mu^{(e)}\}$; terms linear in $A_\mu^{(e)}$ are proportional to the vertex parts. Comparing powers of e gives (265).‡

The relation can also conveniently be written (cf. (262))

$$\frac{\partial S'_P(p)}{\partial p_\mu} = -2\pi S'_P(p)\Gamma_\mu(p,p)S'_P(p), \tag{266}$$

where the complete proton propagator S'_P is given by the equation§

$$S'_P(p) = S_P(p)+S_P(p)\Sigma^*(p)S'_P(p). \tag{267}$$

For convenience we have written S'_P instead of $S_F^{P\prime}$, etc. Using (190), (265), and (267), it is easy to verify (266).||

The same general argument shows that there is a similar relation between the pion vertex part $V_\mu(p_2, p_1)$ and the charged pion self-energy part $\Delta'_F(p)$; it is††

$$\frac{\partial \Delta'_F(p)}{\partial p_\mu} = -2\pi\Delta'_F(p)V_\mu(p,p)\Delta'_F(p). \tag{268}$$

The matrix element

By similar reasoning and by using (265) it is readily seen that the matrix element for the production of a positive pion from a proton at threshold (neglecting the mass of the outgoing pion) is‡‡

$$M_P^+ = eGA'_\mu(\mathbf{k})\bar{\phi}'(\mathbf{q})\lim_{p\to\bar{p}}\bar{\psi}'_N(\bar{p})\left[\frac{\partial}{\partial p_\mu}\Gamma_5(\bar{p},p)S'_P(p)\right]\{S'_P(p)\}^{-1}\psi'_P(\bar{p}). \tag{269}$$

Here numerical factors have been omitted. $A'(\mathbf{k})$, $\bar{\phi}'(\mathbf{q})$ are operators annihilating a photon and creating a pion, and $\bar{\psi}'_N$, ψ'_P are the nucleon operators. The dashes indicate that all the higher order corrections have been inserted. The factor $\partial\Gamma_5(\bar{p},p)/\partial p_\mu$ inserts a photon line of small momentum in the Γ_5 vertex part, and (266) shows that $\partial S'_P(p)/\partial p_\mu$ inserts a vertex part Γ_μ in the incoming proton line. The interaction of the photon with the outgoing pion has been omitted, because this term vanishes at the threshold. This interaction is given by $V_\mu(q, q-k)$,

† Cf. eqns. (3.5) or (235).

‡ The constant factor of proportionality $(-1/2\pi)$ is given by (190) or (191) which are the simplest examples of this relation.

§ Eqn. (267) is the general form of (206) after performing the mass renormalization.

|| It is useful to remember that S_P, S'_P, Σ^* are functions of (γp).

†† The constant of proportionality $(-1/2\pi)$ is checked by examining the lowest order terms in which $\Delta_F(p) = \{2\pi i(p^2+\mu^2)\}^{-1}$, $V_\mu(p_2, p_1) = i(p_1+p_2)_\mu$.

‡‡ For the present we ignore isotopic spin; it is introduced below.

where V_μ is the photon-pion three-vertex part (cf. (262)); q, k are the pion and photon four-momenta respectively. $V_\nu(q, q-k)$ is a four-vector, so it must be a linear combination of q_ν and k_ν. Because $A_\nu(\mathbf{k})$ is transverse, $k_\nu A_\nu(\mathbf{k})$ must vanish; also, at threshold $\mathbf{q} = 0$ and $q_\nu A_\nu$ becomes $(-q_0 A_0)$, which vanishes because A_0 is zero.

Renormalization

The usual external line renormalization gives (cf. (212), (213))

$$\psi'_P(p) = Z_6^{\frac{1}{2}}\psi_P(p), \quad \bar{\psi}'_N(p) = Z_7^{\frac{1}{2}}\bar{\psi}_N(p), \quad \tilde{\phi}'(\mathbf{q}) = Z_1^{\frac{1}{2}}\tilde{\phi}(\mathbf{q}). \tag{270}$$

Using (262), (263), and (270), we get

$$M_P^+ = e_1 G_1 A_\mu(\mathbf{k})\tilde{\phi}(\mathbf{q}) \lim_{p\to\bar{p}} \bar{\psi}_N(\bar{p})\left[\frac{\partial}{\partial p_\mu}\Gamma_{5c}(\bar{p}, p)S_{Pc}(p)\right]\{S_{Pc}(p)\}^{-1}\psi_P(\bar{p}). \tag{271}$$

Here all quantities are finite, and we have the renormalized coupling constants e_1, G_1. By Lorentz invariance, and with the first definition of G_1 given above, $\Gamma_{5c}(p_2, p_1)$ must be of the form

$$\Gamma_{5c}(p_2, p_1) = \gamma^5(1+F_1)+(i\gamma p_2+\kappa)\gamma^5 F_2+F_3\gamma^5(i\gamma p_1+\kappa)+ \\ +(i\gamma p_2+\kappa)\gamma^5(i\gamma p_1+\kappa)F_4, \tag{272}$$

where F_1,..., F_4 are functions of $(p_1-p_2)^2$, $p_1^2+\kappa^2$, $p_2^2+\kappa^2$; also F_1 vanishes when we substitute

$$p_1 = p_2, \qquad p_1^2+\kappa^2 = 0.$$

Remembering the form† of $S_{Pc}(p)$, it is easy to see that (271) reduces to

$$M_P^+ = -2\pi e_1 G_1 A_\mu(\mathbf{k})\tilde{\phi}(\mathbf{q})\bar{\psi}_N(\bar{p})\gamma^5 S_P(\bar{p})\gamma^\mu\psi_P(\bar{p}). \tag{273}$$

This is the lowest order perturbation theory matrix element.

The production of negative pions from neutrons is obtained on replacing the fermion terms in (269) by

$$\lim_{p\to\bar{p}} \bar{\psi}'_P(\bar{p})\{S'_P(p)\}^{-1}\left[\frac{\partial}{\partial p_\mu} S'_P(p)\Gamma_5(p_1, \bar{p})\right]\psi'_N(\bar{p}).$$

In the limit this gives the matrix element

$$M_N^- = -2\pi e_1 G_1 A_\mu(\mathbf{k})\phi(\mathbf{q})\bar{\psi}_P(\bar{p})\gamma^\mu S_P(\bar{p})\gamma^5\psi_N(\bar{p}). \tag{274}$$

The production of neutral pions from protons is given by using the fermion factors

$$\lim_{p\to\bar{p}} \bar{\psi}'_P(\bar{p})\{S'_P(p)\}^{-1}\left[\frac{\partial}{\partial p_\mu} S'_P(p)\Gamma_5(p, p)S'_P(p)\right]\{S'_P(p)\}^{-1}\psi'_P(\bar{p}).$$

In the limit this vanishes.‡ The production of a neutral pion from a

† $S_{Pc}(p) = S_P(p)+(i\gamma p+\kappa)f_1+(p_2+\kappa^2)f_2$, where f_1 and f_2 are functions of $(p^2+\kappa^2)$ (cf. eqns. (169), (172)).

‡ By symmetry it must contain a factor $\gamma^\mu\gamma^5+\gamma^5\gamma^\mu = 0$.

neutron also vanishes, because this requires the insertion of the external photon line into a closed loop carrying charge.†

Consequences

This theorem has been proved by such general and powerful methods, that the result may be expected to have a range of validity greater than perturbation theory. Finally, we notice that on using the charge-independent interaction (4.131) between pions and nucleons, the matrix elements M_P^+, M_N^- are equal (apart from a change of sign).‡ Hence we expect that near threshold

$$\frac{\sigma(h\nu+N\rightarrow\pi^-+P)}{\sigma(h\nu+P\rightarrow\pi^++N)}=1+O\Big(\frac{m_\pi}{M}\Big).$$

The experimental results indicate that this ratio is about 1·3.§ Another prediction of the theory is that at threshold the cross-sections for producing neutral pions are at the most of order $(m_\pi/M)^2$ relative to those for charged pions; this also agrees with experiment.§|| The value of the coupling constant†† $(G_1^2/4\pi\hbar c^3)$ which is deduced from these experiments is of the order of 12. (For a discussion of the angular momentum selection rules for photo-production of pions see Chapter I, § 21; for isotopic selection rules see Chapter IV, § 13.)

† Compare with the arguments in footnote §, p. 295.

‡ For another derivation of the Kroll–Ruderman theorem see F. Low, *Phys. Rev.* **97** (1955) 1392.

§ For a comparison with experiment and a description of phenomenological theories see K. M. Watson, J. C. Keck, A. V. Tollestrup, and R. L. Walker, *Phys. Rev.* **101** (1956) 1159; M. J. Moravsick, ibid. **105** (1957) 267.

|| Other low-energy limit theorems (including photon scattering, and p-wave pion photo-production) are discussed by A. Klein, *Phys. Rev.* **99** (1955) 998. Both F. E. Low, ibid. **96** (1954) 1428, and M. Gell-Mann and M. L. Goldberger, ibid. 1433, have shown that to the *first order* in the frequency, the scattering of light by spin-½ particles depends only on the mass, charge, and static magnetic moment of the scatterer. This extends the zero frequency result of Thirring (§ 12).

†† Our units differ slightly from the system in which $G^2/4\pi\hbar c$ is a number. See Chapter IV, § 12, for discussion.

VI

HEISENBERG OPERATORS AND PION-NUCLEON SCATTERING

1. Heisenberg and interaction representation operators

In this chapter we examine methods for describing interacting fields which are expected to have a validity extending beyond the simple perturbation theory of Chapter V.† By developing such methods it is hoped to get some understanding of the effects which occur in strongly interacting fields, such as the pion, nucleon, K-meson, and hyperon fields. In some cases it will be necessary to use the results of perturbation theory as a step in the argument; this will only be done when the final result is of such a general form that we may have confidence in its general validity.‡

Heisenberg operators describe the actual interacting fields; they obey the interacting field equations of motion, such as (4.90). Physical states are described by state vectors which are constant in space and time.

In Chapter IV, § 7, it was shown that any Heisenberg field operator $\mathbf{A}(x_\nu)$ is related to an interaction representation operator $A(x_\nu)$ by§

$$\mathbf{A}(x_\nu) = \tilde{U}(t,t_0)A(x_\nu)U(t,t_0), \tag{1}$$

where $x_\nu = (\mathbf{x}, ict)$, and $U(t,t_0)$ obeys (cf. (4.97), (4.100))

$$\left.\begin{aligned} \frac{\partial U(t,t_0)}{\partial t} &= -\frac{i}{\hbar}H_{\text{int}}(t)U(t,t_0) \\ U(t_0,t_0) &= I \end{aligned}\right\}. \tag{2}$$

It follows from (1) and (2) that $A(x_\nu)$ obeys the *free field* equations of motion;‖ also, the operators $\mathbf{A}(x_\nu)$ and $A(x_\nu)$ coincide at time t_0. The interaction representation state vector $|\Phi(t)\rangle$ and the corresponding Heisenberg state vector $|\,\rangle$ are related by

$$|\Phi(t)\rangle = U(t,t_0)|\,\rangle. \tag{3}$$

† The Tamm–Dancoff method, which is in this category, has been described in Chapter IV, § 8.

‡ The Kroll–Ruderman theorem (Chapter V, § 16) may be regarded as an example of such an argument.

§ In this section Heisenberg operators are denoted by bold-face type; interaction representation operators and the operators for non-interacting fields are denoted by italic type.

‖ i.e. the equations of motion obtained by omitting all coupling terms.

The incoming and the outgoing representations

Different values of t_0 give rise to different interaction representations. These various interaction representations are mathematically equivalent; that is, they are obtained from each other by constant unitary transformations.† Here we discuss the three cases $t_0 = 0$, $t_0 \to +\infty$, $t_0 \to -\infty$. The latter two are associated with the incoming and the outgoing solutions of the wave equations.‡ In Chapter V, § 2, the operators $U(t, -\infty)$, $U(t, \infty)$ were defined carefully by using the adiabatic switching process.§ The *incoming representation* is defined by

$$\left.\begin{aligned} \mathbf{A}(x_\nu) &= \tilde{U}(t, -\infty)A_{\text{in}}(x_\nu)U(t, -\infty) \\ |\Psi_{\text{in}}(t)\rangle &= U(t, -\infty)|\,\rangle \end{aligned}\right\}. \tag{4}$$

Similarly the *outgoing representation* is defined by

$$\left.\begin{aligned} \mathbf{A}(x_\nu) &= \tilde{U}(t, \infty)A_{\text{out}}(x_\nu)U(t, \infty) \\ |\Psi_{\text{out}}(t)\rangle &= U(t, \infty)|\,\rangle \end{aligned}\right\}. \tag{5}$$

Because of the adiabatic switching process, eqn. (5.8) shows that

$$U(t, -\infty) \to I \quad \text{as} \quad t \to -\infty. \tag{6}$$

Hence
$$\mathbf{A}(x_\nu) \to A_{\text{in}}(x_\nu) \quad \text{as} \quad t \to -\infty.$$

In the distant past, before the interaction was switched on, the incoming representation coincided with the Heisenberg representation; similarly, in the distant future the outgoing representation coincides with the Heisenberg representation.|| The derivation of the S-matrix expansion in Chapter IV, § 7, used the incoming representation.

Remembering that $|\,\rangle$ is constant,†† we deduce the relation between the incoming and outgoing representations. By (4) and (5),

$$\begin{aligned} |\Psi_{\text{in}}(\infty)\rangle &= U(\infty, -\infty)|\,\rangle \\ &= U(\infty, -\infty)|\Psi_{\text{out}}(\infty)\rangle. \end{aligned}$$

Also,
$$\frac{\partial}{\partial t}\langle\Psi_{\text{in}}(t)|\Psi_{\text{out}}(t)\rangle = 0.$$

Therefore
$$|\Psi_{\text{in}}(t)\rangle = U(\infty, -\infty)|\Psi_{\text{out}}(t)\rangle. \tag{7}$$

Consequently,‡‡

$$A_{\text{out}}(x_\nu) = \tilde{U}(\infty, -\infty)A_{\text{in}}(x_\nu)U(\infty, -\infty). \tag{8}$$

† Let $\mathbf{A}(x_\nu) = \tilde{U}(t, t_1)A_1(x_\nu)U(t, t_1) = \tilde{U}(t, t_2)A_2(x_\nu)U(t, t_2)$, then by Chapter IV, § 7, $A_1(x_\nu) = U(t, t_1)\tilde{U}(t, t_2)A_2(x_\nu)U(t, t_2)\tilde{U}(t, t_1)$. Also, $U(t, t_1)\tilde{U}(t, t_2)$ is a constant operator; it equals $U(t_2, t_1)$ (to see this, use eqn. (4.95)).

‡ The case $t_0 = 0$ is frequently called the *interaction representation* in the literature. That nomenclature is not sufficiently precise.

§ The definitions are eqns. (5.8), (5.24).

|| Similar to (6) we have (eqn. 5.24) $U(t, \infty) \to I$ as $t \to \infty$.

†† This is true even when the interaction is switched on and off.

‡‡ In Chapter V, § 2, it was shown that $U(\infty, -\infty)$ is unitary.

Eqn. (7) states that the S-matrix $(U(\infty, -\infty))$ relates the incoming and outgoing states in any scattering problem; this aspect of S has been discussed in Chapter IV, § 7.†

The use of Green's functions

The incoming and outgoing fields can be written explicitly with the help of the retarded and advanced Green's functions (cf. Appendix). As an example, consider the neutral (pseudo-scalar) pion field interacting with a nucleon field; the equations for the Heisenberg variables are given in (4.90). Adding the renormalization term (5.261), the pion variable obeys‡

$$(\partial_\nu^2-\mu^2)\boldsymbol{\varphi}(x_\nu) = -\mathbf{j}(x_\nu), \tag{9}$$

where

$$\mathbf{j}(x_\nu) = -i\frac{G}{c^2}\bar{\boldsymbol{\psi}}(x_\nu)\gamma^5\boldsymbol{\psi}(x_\nu)+\delta\mu^2\boldsymbol{\varphi}(x_\nu)+\delta\lambda\boldsymbol{\varphi}^3(x_\nu).$$

By (A.44), (A.45), the solution of (9) can be written (cf. (A.19))

$$\boldsymbol{\varphi}(x_\nu) = \phi_{\text{in}}(x_\nu)+\int\limits_{-\infty}^{\infty} d^4x'\,D_{\text{ret}(\mu)}(x_\nu-x'_\nu)\mathbf{j}(x'_\nu), \tag{10}$$

where the operator $\phi_{\text{in}}(x_\nu)$ satisfies the homogeneous equation

$$(\partial_\nu^2-\mu^2)\phi_{\text{in}}(x_\nu) = 0. \tag{11}$$

Because the interaction is switched on gradually, we have $\boldsymbol{\varphi}(x_\nu) \to \phi_{\text{in}}(x_\nu)$ as $t \to -\infty$; therefore $\phi_{\text{in}}(x_\nu)$ defined by (10) is identical with the operator defined by (4):

$$\boldsymbol{\varphi}(x_\nu) = \tilde{U}(t, -\infty)\phi_{\text{in}}(x_\nu)U(t, \infty). \tag{12}$$

The retarded solution of the equation§

$$(\gamma^\mu\partial_\mu+\kappa)\boldsymbol{\psi}(x_\nu) = -\frac{iG}{\hbar c}\gamma^5\boldsymbol{\psi}(x_\nu)\boldsymbol{\varphi}(x_\nu)+\delta\kappa\boldsymbol{\psi}(x_\nu) \tag{13}$$

may be used to define $\psi_{\text{in}}(x_\nu)$; viz.

$$\boldsymbol{\psi}(x_\nu) = \psi_{\text{in}}(x_\nu)+\int\limits_{-\infty}^{\infty} d^4x'\,S_{\text{ret}}(x_\nu-x'_\nu)\left\{\frac{iG}{\hbar c}\gamma^5\boldsymbol{\psi}(x'_\nu)\boldsymbol{\varphi}(x'_\nu)-\delta\kappa\boldsymbol{\psi}(x'_\nu)\right\} \tag{14}$$

(cf. eqn. (A.72)).

The incoming operator $\psi_{\text{in}}(x_\nu)$ obeys the free nucleon field equation (4.8). The retarded Green's function $S_{\text{ret}}(x)$, which vanishes for $x_0 < 0$, is defined by (A.77). The incoming operator $\bar{\psi}_{\text{in}}(x_\nu)$ is defined by using

† Eqn. (8) was derived by C. N. Yang and D. Feldman, *Phys. Rev.* **79** (1950) 972.

‡ μ gives the renormalized pion mass; $\mu^2-\delta\mu^2 = \mu_0^2$ where μ_0 gives the unrenormalized mass For neutral pions the numerical factors differ from (5.261).

§ κ gives the renormalized nucleon mass; $\kappa-\delta\kappa = \kappa_0$ gives the unrenormalized mass.

eqn. (A.86); this involves the Green's function $S_{\text{adv}}(-x)$ (which also vanishes for $x_0 < 0$).

The outgoing operators can be defined in the same way. For example, by (A.21) we have

$$\boldsymbol{\varphi}(x_\nu) = \phi_{\text{out}}(x_\nu) + \int_{-\infty}^{\infty} d^4x'\, D_{\text{adv}(\mu)}(x_\nu - x'_\nu)\mathbf{j}(x'_\nu). \tag{15}$$

Similar equations define $\psi_{\text{out}}(x_\nu)$, $\bar{\psi}_{\text{out}}(x_\nu)$. These definitions are obviously identical with definition (5). Using eqn. (A.12) we have

$$\phi_{\text{out}}(x_\nu) = \phi_{\text{in}}(x_\nu) - \int_{-\infty}^{\infty} d^4x'\, D_{(\mu)}(x_\nu - x'_\nu)\mathbf{j}(x'_\nu). \tag{16}$$

The relation between $\phi_{\text{in}}(x_\nu)$ and $\phi_{\text{out}}(x_\nu)$ is also given by (8); comparing (8) and (16) gives

$$\left.\begin{aligned} [U(\infty,-\infty), \phi_{\text{in}}(x_\nu)] &= U(\infty,-\infty) \int_{-\infty}^{\infty} d^4x'\, D_{(\mu)}(x_\nu - x'_\nu)\mathbf{j}(x'_\nu) \\ [U(\infty,-\infty), \phi_{\text{out}}(x_\nu)] &= \int_{-\infty}^{\infty} d^4x'\, D_{(\mu)}(x_\nu - x'_\nu)\mathbf{j}(x'_\nu) \,.\, U(\infty,-\infty) \end{aligned}\right\}. \tag{17}$$

Similarly,

$$[U(\infty,-\infty), \psi_{\text{in}}(x_\nu)] = U(\infty,-\infty) \int_{-\infty}^{\infty} d^4x'\, S(x_\nu - x'_\nu) \times$$

$$\times \left\{\frac{iG}{\hbar c}\gamma^5 \boldsymbol{\psi}(x'_\nu)\boldsymbol{\varphi}(x'_\nu) - \delta\kappa\boldsymbol{\psi}(x'_\nu)\right\}, \quad \text{etc.} \tag{18}$$

Eqns. (17) can be used to derive the pion-nucleon scattering matrix in terms of Heisenberg operators;† we use them below to interpret the expectation values of the current operator $\mathbf{j}(x)$ (cf. eqn. (40)).

The interaction representation ($t_0 = 0$)

Operators in other interaction representations can readily be expressed in terms of Heisenberg operators by equations like (10), (14), and (15). We consider the interaction representation which coincides‡ with the Heisenberg representation at time $t = 0$; it is obtained by putting $t_0 = 0$ (in (1) and (2)). An identical definition of the interaction representation pion operator $\phi(x_\nu)$ is§

$$\boldsymbol{\varphi}(x_\nu) = \phi(x_\nu) - \int_0^t d^4x'\, D_{(\mu)}(x_\nu - x'_\nu)\mathbf{j}(x'_\nu). \tag{19}$$

† M. Cini and S. Fubini, *Nuovo Cim.* **2** (1955) 192.

‡ The time derivatives of corresponding operators in these two representations are not in general identical at $t = 0$.

§ S. S. Schweber, *Nuovo Cim.* **2** (1955) 397.

This is easily verified, by noticing that for $t > 0$, (19) gives

$$\boldsymbol{\varphi}(x) = \phi(x) + \int_0^\infty d^4x' D_{\text{ret}(\mu)}(x-x')\mathbf{j}(x'),$$

and for $t < 0$,

$$\boldsymbol{\varphi}(x) = \phi(x) + \int_{-\infty}^0 d^4x' D_{\text{adv}(\mu)}(x-x')\mathbf{j}(x').$$

Remembering that D_{ret}, D_{adv} obey (A.52) it follows from (9) that $\phi(x_\nu)$ must obey the homogeneous wave equation (11).† It is easy to verify from (19) that $\boldsymbol{\varphi}(\mathbf{x},0) = \phi(\mathbf{x},0)$; $(\partial/\partial t)\boldsymbol{\varphi}(\mathbf{x},0) = (\partial/\partial t)\phi(\mathbf{x},0)$. Therefore the definitions (19) and (1) (with $t_0 = 0$) are identical. Using (1), an alternative form of (19) is†

$$[U(t,0), \phi(x)] = U(t,0) \int_0^t d^4x' D_{(\mu)}(x-x')\mathbf{j}(x'). \tag{20}$$

It should be emphasized that the relations in this section have been derived *without* the use of perturbation theory. $U(t,0)$, $U(t,\pm\infty)$ are defined by integral equations like (5.8), (5.24); our results are independent of the method used to solve these integral equations.

2. Heisenberg state vectors and matrix elements

The vacuum state

We first show how the incoming and outgoing operators can be used to specify the Heisenberg vacuum state $|0\rangle$. The interaction representation operators defined by (1) and (2) with $t_0 = 0$ will be written $A(x_\nu)$, $\phi(x_\nu)$, $\psi(x_\nu)$, $\bar{\psi}(x_\nu)$, etc.; the state vector in this representation is (cf. (3))

$$|\Phi(t)\rangle = U(t,0)|\,\rangle.$$

Therefore

$$|\,\rangle = U(0,t)|\Phi(t)\rangle.$$

A particularly important case of this relation is given in the limit $t \to -\infty$:

$$|\,\rangle = U(0,-\infty)|\Phi(-\infty)\rangle. \tag{21}$$

$|\Phi(-\infty)\rangle$ described the system before the interaction was switched on, and eqn. (21) shows how the switching-on converts the *bare particle state* $|\Phi(-\infty)\rangle$ into the *real particle state* $|\,\rangle$.‡ In particular,

$$|0\rangle = U(0,-\infty)|\Phi_0\rangle \tag{22}$$

† Eqn. (20) can also be deduced from the perturbation expansion (4.102) for $U(t, 0)$. The commutator $[\phi(x), \phi(x')] = (i\hbar/c)D_{(\mu)}(x-x')$ enables us to write

$$[\phi(x), U(t,0)] = (i\hbar/c) \int_{-\infty}^{\infty} d^4x' \frac{\delta}{\delta\phi(x')} U(t,0) D_{(\mu)}(x-x').$$

Evaluation of the functional derivative gives (20) (cf. p. 304, nn. †, §).

‡ An initial bound state requires a more elaborate treatment.

relates the real vacuum and the bare particle vacuum† $|\Phi_0\rangle$. Similarly,

$$|0\rangle = U(0,\infty)|\Phi_0\rangle. \tag{23}$$

In writing (22) and (23), phase factors (which are unimportant) have been ignored.‡

The relation between any operator $A(x_\nu)$ and $A_{\text{in}}(x_\nu)$ is found by letting $t \to -\infty$ in (1) (with $t_0 = 0$); thus

$$A_{\text{in}}(x_\nu) = \tilde{U}(-\infty,0)A(x_\nu)U(-\infty,0).$$

Using (5.45), $$A_{\text{in}}(x_\nu) = U(0,-\infty)A(x_\nu)\tilde{U}(0,-\infty). \tag{24}$$

Similarly, $$A_{\text{out}}(x_\nu) = U(0,\infty)A(x_\nu)\tilde{U}(0,\infty). \tag{25}$$

The bare particle vacuum state vector $|\Phi_0\rangle$ is constant, and it satisfies relations of the type

$$A^{(+)}(x_\nu)|\Phi_0\rangle = 0 \quad (\text{all } x_\nu).$$

Hence, by (24), the real vacuum $|0\rangle$ for the interacting pion-nucleon fields obeys§

$$\phi_{\text{in}}^{(+)}(x_\nu)|0\rangle = \psi_{\text{in}}^{(+)}(x_\nu)|0\rangle = \bar{\psi}_{\text{in}}^{(+)}(x_\nu)|0\rangle = 0 \quad (\text{all } x_\nu). \tag{26}$$

Similarly, by (25),||

$$\phi_{\text{out}}^{(+)}(x_\nu)|0\rangle = \psi_{\text{out}}^{(+)}(x_\nu)|0\rangle = \bar{\psi}_{\text{out}}^{(+)}(x_\nu)|0\rangle = 0 \quad (\text{all } x_\nu). \tag{27}$$

The physical meaning of (26) and (27) is that there are neither incoming nor outgoing particles in the real vacuum.

Real particle states

The state vector for a real pion $\mathbf{p}$ is (cf. (21))

$$|\Psi(\mathbf{p})\rangle = U(0,-\infty)|\Phi_{\mathbf{p}}(-\infty)\rangle,$$

where $|\Phi_{\mathbf{p}}(-\infty)\rangle$ is the state vector for a bare pion. Because

$$|\Phi_{\mathbf{p}}(-\infty)\rangle = \tilde{a}(\mathbf{p})|\Phi_0\rangle,$$

where $\tilde{a}(\mathbf{p})$ is the bare particle creation operator (eqn. (2.53)), eqn. (24) gives

$$|\Psi(\mathbf{p})\rangle = \tilde{a}_{\text{in}}(\mathbf{p})|0\rangle; \tag{28}$$

here $\tilde{a}_{\text{in}}(\mathbf{p})$ is the creation operator for a pion $\mathbf{p}$ in the incoming representation. Single particle states (as well as the vacuum) are steady states of the total Hamiltonian; therefore we can also write

$$\begin{aligned}|\Psi(\mathbf{p})\rangle &= U(0,\infty)|\Phi_{\mathbf{p}}(\infty)\rangle \\ &= \tilde{a}_{\text{out}}(\mathbf{p})|0\rangle.\end{aligned} \tag{29}$$

† In (22) and (23) we write $|\Phi_0\rangle = |\Phi_0(-\infty)\rangle = |\Phi_0(+\infty)\rangle$.

‡ See M. Gell-Mann and F. Low, *Phys. Rev.* **84** (1951) 350, for details of these phase factors. Note that $|\Phi_0\rangle \neq |\Phi_0(t)\rangle$ for finite t.

§ We use $\tilde{U}(0,\infty)U(0,\infty) = I$, $\tilde{U}(0,-\infty)U(0,-\infty) = I$ (eqns. (5.36), (5.43)) in deriving (26) and (27). These relations are true in general.

|| $\phi_{\text{in}}(x_\nu)$, $\psi_{\text{out}}(x_\nu)$, etc., can be split into positive and negative frequency parts uniquely, because they obey the free field equations (cf. (11)).

It is convenient to express the Heisenberg state vector for a pion of momentum **p** in a form derived from (2.35) and (2.39). Using (26) and (27), we have†

$$\left.\begin{aligned}|\Psi(\mathbf{p})\rangle &= \left(\frac{2\omega_k}{\hbar V}\right)^{\frac{1}{2}} \int\limits_{(t)} d^3\mathbf{x}\exp[i(\mathbf{k}.\mathbf{x}-\omega_k t)]\phi_{\text{in}}(\mathbf{x},t)|0\rangle \\ &= \left(\frac{2\omega_k}{\hbar V}\right)^{\frac{1}{2}} \int\limits_{(t)} d^3\mathbf{x}\exp[i(\mathbf{k}.\mathbf{x}-\omega_k t)]\phi_{\text{out}}(\mathbf{x},t)|0\rangle\end{aligned}\right\}. \tag{30}$$

Here and below, the time t is arbitrary.

Similarly using (4.26) and (4.46), the Heisenberg state vector $|\Psi(\mathbf{p},s,+)\rangle$ for a nucleon with momentum **p** and spin component s is given by‡

$$|\Psi(\mathbf{p},s,+)\rangle = \left(\frac{\omega_k}{V^{\frac{1}{2}}c\kappa}\right) \int\limits_{(t)} d^3\mathbf{x}\exp[i(\mathbf{k}.\mathbf{x}-\omega_k t)]\bar{\psi}_{\text{in}}(\mathbf{x},t)u^{(s)}(\mathbf{k})|0\rangle. \tag{31}$$

The anti-nucleon state $|\Psi(\mathbf{p},s,-)\rangle$ is

$$|\Psi(\mathbf{p},s,-)\rangle = -\left(\frac{\omega_k}{V^{\frac{1}{2}}c\kappa}\right) \int\limits_{(t)} d^3\mathbf{x}\exp[i(\mathbf{k}.\mathbf{x}-\omega_k t)]\bar{v}^{(s)}(\mathbf{k})\psi_{\text{in}}(\mathbf{x},t)|0\rangle. \tag{32}$$

The factor $(\omega_k/c\kappa)$ occurs in (31) and (32) because the spinors $u^{(s)}(\mathbf{k})$, $v^{(s)}(\mathbf{k})$ have been normalized by the scheme (i) of Chapter IV, § 3 (cf. eqns. (4.19), (4.25)). The state vectors (30), (31), (32) have been normalized so that

$$\langle\Psi(\mathbf{p}')|\Psi(\mathbf{p})\rangle = \delta_{\mathbf{p},\mathbf{p}'}; \qquad \langle\Psi(\mathbf{p}',s',+)|\Psi(\mathbf{p},s,+)\rangle = \delta_{\mathbf{p},\mathbf{p}'}\delta_{s,s'}, \quad \text{etc.}$$

This normalization is suitable for discrete values of **p**; if desired, it is very easy to go over to the form which is suitable for continuous values of **p**.

Scattering states

Eqns. (28) to (32) show how real single-particle states can be expressed in terms of the real particle vacuum $|0\rangle$. We now show a similar relationship for the many-particle states which occur in collision problems; it is sufficient to discuss two-pion states. The state vector

$$|\Psi_{\text{in}}(\mathbf{p},\mathbf{p}')\rangle \equiv \tilde{a}_{\text{in}}(\mathbf{p})\tilde{a}_{\text{in}}(\mathbf{p}')|0\rangle$$

can be written

$$|\Psi_{\text{in}}(\mathbf{p},\mathbf{p}')\rangle = U(0,-\infty)\tilde{a}(\mathbf{p})\tilde{a}(\mathbf{p}')|\Phi_0\rangle,$$

where $\tilde{a}(\mathbf{p})$, $\tilde{a}(\mathbf{p}')$ are the interaction representation pion creation opera-

† $\mathbf{p} = \hbar\mathbf{k}$; V is the spatial volume; $\omega_k = c(\mathbf{k}^2+\mu^2)^{\frac{1}{2}}$.
‡ Here $\omega_k = c(\mathbf{k}^2+\kappa^2)^{\frac{1}{2}}$.

tors. Therefore $|\Psi_{\text{in}}(\mathbf{p},\mathbf{p}')\rangle$ is the real state which is produced by switching on the interaction in the bare two-pion state; it is the scattering state consisting of plane wave pions $\mathbf{p}$, $\mathbf{p}'$ plus outgoing spherical waves. $|\Psi_{\text{in}}(\mathbf{p},\mathbf{p}')\rangle$ is a Heisenberg state vector which corresponds to the scattering solutions $|\psi_\alpha^{(+)}\rangle$ of Chapter V, § 1. Similarly,

$$|\Psi_{\text{out}}(\mathbf{q},\mathbf{q}')\rangle \equiv \tilde{a}_{\text{out}}(\mathbf{q})\tilde{a}_{\text{out}}(\mathbf{q}')|0\rangle$$
$$= U(0,\infty)\tilde{a}(\mathbf{q})\tilde{a}(\mathbf{q}')|\Phi_0\rangle$$

is the scattering state having the property that when the interaction is adiabatically switched off, two bare pions $\mathbf{q}$, $\mathbf{q}'$ remain; it corresponds to $|\psi_\beta^{(-)}\rangle$ of Chapter V, § 1. The real vacuum state $|0\rangle$ is also (by (26), (27)) the incoming and outgoing vacuum state. Hence $|\Psi_{\text{in}}(\mathbf{q},\mathbf{q}')\rangle$, $|\Psi_{\text{out}}(\mathbf{q},\mathbf{q}')\rangle$ are related by eqn. (7). Thus the S-matrix element for pion-pion scattering can be written

$$\langle\Psi_{\text{out}}(\mathbf{q},\mathbf{q}')|\Psi_{\text{in}}(\mathbf{p},\mathbf{p}')\rangle = \langle\Psi_{\text{in}}(\mathbf{q},\mathbf{q}')|U(\infty,-\infty)|\Psi_{\text{in}}(\mathbf{p},\mathbf{p}')\rangle.$$

Using the notation of (30), we have (for arbitrary t)

$$|\Psi_{\text{in}}(\mathbf{p},\mathbf{p}')\rangle = \left(\frac{2}{\hbar V}\right)(\omega_k\,\omega_{k'})^{\frac{1}{2}}e^{-i(\omega_k+\omega_{k'})t}\int\limits_{(t)} d^3\mathbf{x}\int d^3\mathbf{x}'\,e^{i(\mathbf{k}\cdot\mathbf{x}+\mathbf{k}'\cdot\mathbf{x}')}\times$$
$$\times\phi_{\text{in}}^{(-)}(\mathbf{x},t)\phi_{\text{in}}^{(-)}(\mathbf{x}',t)|0\rangle. \quad (33)$$

It is obvious how scattering states with more incoming (or outgoing) particles are defined.

A general formula

A more systematic and convenient method of writing state vectors like (30) and (33) has been given by Lehmann, Symanzik, and Zimmermann.† We give the result for the general boson case. Let the function $f(x_\nu)$ be any solution of the wave equation

$$(\partial_\nu^2-\mu^2)f(x_\nu) = 0, \quad (34)$$

which is normalized so that (for all t)

$$\frac{1}{i}\int\limits_{(t)} d^3\mathbf{x}\left(f\frac{\partial f^*}{\partial x_0}-f^*\frac{\partial f}{\partial x_0}\right) = 1 \quad (x_0 = ct). \quad (35)$$

This normalization condition also ensures that $f(x_\nu)$ contains only positive frequency terms. To *any* boson operator $A(x_\nu)$ we relate an operator $A^f(t)$ by

$$A^f(t) = i\left(\frac{c}{\hbar}\right)^{\frac{1}{2}}\int\limits_{(t)} d^3\mathbf{x}\left\{A(x)\frac{\partial f(x)}{\partial x_0}-f(x)\frac{\partial A(x)}{\partial x_0}\right\}. \quad (36)$$

† H. Lehmann, K. Symanzik, and W. Zimmermann, *Nuovo Cim.* **1** (1955) 205.

If $A(x)$ obeys $$(\partial_\nu^2-\mu^2)A(x) = 0,$$

then $$\frac{d}{dt}A^f(t) = 0.$$

In particular, if $A(x)$ is replaced by a Heisenberg operator $\mathbf{A}(x)$, then $A^f(t)$ tends to a constant operator as $t \to \pm\infty$.

Inserting $\phi_{\text{in}}(x)$ in (36) and using

$$f_{\mathbf{k}}(x) = \frac{1}{(2Vk_0)^{\frac{1}{2}}}e^{ik_\mu x_\mu} \quad (k_0 = +(\mathbf{k}^2+\mu^2)^{\frac{1}{2}})$$

gives (cf. (2.34)) $$\phi_{\text{in}}^f = \tilde{a}_{\text{in}}(\mathbf{k}).$$

Eqn. (30) can now be written

$$|\Psi(\mathbf{p})\rangle = \phi_{\text{in}}^f|0\rangle \quad (\mathbf{p} = \hbar\mathbf{k}). \tag{37}$$

This scheme is generalized by using a set of functions $f_\alpha(x_\nu)$ each of which obeys (34). In place of (35) we require

$$\frac{1}{i}\int\limits_{(t)}\left(f_\alpha\frac{\partial f_\beta^*}{\partial x_0}-f_\beta^*\frac{\partial f_\alpha}{\partial x_0}\right)d^3\mathbf{x} = \delta_{\alpha\beta}. \tag{38}$$

The operators defined by (36) using the set $f_\alpha(x)$ are written $A^{f_\alpha}(t)$. It follows that the incoming state vector (33) for two pions can be written†

$$|\Psi_{\text{in}}(\mathbf{p},\mathbf{p}')\rangle = \phi_{\text{in}}^{f\mathbf{p}}\phi_{\text{in}}^{f\mathbf{p}'}|0\rangle. \tag{39 a}$$

Similarly, the outgoing state vector for two pions is

$$|\Psi_{\text{out}}(\mathbf{q},\mathbf{q}')\rangle = \phi_{\text{out}}^{f\mathbf{q}}\phi_{\text{out}}^{f\mathbf{q}'}|0\rangle. \tag{39 b}$$

Incoming and outgoing states with many pions can now be built up in an obvious way.‡ In using (36) and (38) it is not necessary to restrict $f_\alpha(x)$ to plane wave solutions of (34).

The matrix element of $\mathbf{j}(x)$

Now we examine the expectation values of some typical Heisenberg operators. The first example concerns the expectation value of the current operator $\mathbf{j}(x)$ of eqn. (9). Let $|\Psi_q\rangle$, $|\Psi_{q'}\rangle$ be Heisenberg state vectors for single nucleons (cf. (31)).§ Because simple particle states are steady we write $\langle\Psi_{q'}|$ and $|\Psi_{q'}\rangle$, but it is to be understood that states on the right and left are incoming and outgoing respectively.

† If $\mathbf{p} = \mathbf{p}'$ an additional factor $1/\sqrt{2!}$ is to be inserted on the right of (39 a).

‡ Sufficiently careful treatment of the adiabatic process (cf. Chapter V, § 2) could take account of bound states; we shall not require to do this. In summations such as eqn. (98) below, $|n\rangle$ includes all bound states.

§ The notation $|\Psi_q\rangle$ is now more convenient than (31) or (32).

From (27),
$$\langle \Psi_{q'}|\phi^{(-)}_{\text{out}}(x_\nu) = 0.$$
Hence, by (16),
$$\langle \Psi_{q'}|\phi^{(-)}_{\text{in}}(x_\nu)|\Psi_q\rangle = \int\limits_{-\infty}^{\infty} d^4x' D^{(-)}_{(\mu)}(x_\nu - x'_\nu)\langle \Psi_{q'}|\mathbf{j}(x'_\nu)|\Psi_q\rangle. \qquad (40\text{ a})$$

If $|\Psi_{\text{in}}(q,\mathbf{p})\rangle$ is the Heisenberg state vector for a scattering state whose *incoming* part consists of a nucleon q and a pion $\mathbf{p}$, then eqns. (30) and (40 a) give
$$\left.\begin{aligned}\langle \Psi_{q'}|\Psi_{\text{in}}(q,\mathbf{p})\rangle &= i\frac{c}{(2\hbar\omega_k V)^{\frac{1}{2}}}\langle \Psi_{q'}|\mathbf{j}(-\mathbf{k}, -\omega_k/c)|\Psi_q\rangle \\ &= i\frac{c}{(2\hbar\omega_k V)^{\frac{1}{2}}}\int d^4x\, e^{i(\mathbf{k}.\mathbf{x}-\omega_k t)}\langle \Psi_{q'}|\mathbf{j}(x)|\Psi_q\rangle\end{aligned}\right\} \qquad (40\text{ b})$$
where $\mathbf{p} = \hbar\mathbf{k}$, $\omega_k = c(\mathbf{k}^2+\mu^2)^{\frac{1}{2}}$, and
$$\mathbf{j}(x_\nu) = (2\pi)^{-4}\int d^4k\, \mathbf{j}(k_\nu)e^{ik_\nu x_\nu}.$$

In this way we relate the Fourier coefficients of the Heisenberg current $\mathbf{j}(x_\nu)$ to the inner product of two Heisenberg state vectors.

Matrix element of a field amplitude

Our second example is another relation for the Heisenberg operator $\mathbf{j}(x)$. We start by evaluating $\langle \Psi_{q'}|\boldsymbol{\varphi}(x_\nu)|\Psi_q\rangle$, where $\boldsymbol{\varphi}(x_\nu)$ is the Heisenberg pion operator and $|\Psi_q\rangle$, $|\Psi_{q'}\rangle$ are state vectors for real nucleons q, q'. Using (1) (with $t_0 = 0$) gives†
$$\langle \Psi_{q'}|\boldsymbol{\varphi}(x_\nu)|\Psi_q\rangle = \langle \Phi_0|c(q')U(\infty,0)\tilde{U}(t,0)\phi(x_\nu)U(t,0)U(0,-\infty)\tilde{c}(q)|\Phi_0\rangle,$$
where $\tilde{c}(q)$, $\tilde{c}(q')$ are the interaction representation operators for the creation of nucleons q, q' respectively. From (5.41) we have
$$\langle \Psi_{q'}|\boldsymbol{\varphi}(x_\nu)|\Psi_q\rangle = \langle \Phi_0|c(q')U(\infty,t)\phi(x_\nu)U(t,-\infty)\tilde{c}(q)|\Phi_0\rangle. \qquad (41)$$
In order to evaluate (41) we must use perturbation theory; this gives (using eqn. (4.102))
$$\langle \Psi_{q'}|\boldsymbol{\varphi}(x)|\Psi_q\rangle$$
$$= \langle \Phi_0|c(q')\sum_{n=0}^{\infty}\left(\frac{-i}{\hbar c}\right)^n\frac{1}{n!}\int dx_1\ldots dx_n\, T\{\mathscr{H}_1(x_1)\ldots\mathscr{H}_1(x_n)\phi(x)\}\tilde{c}(q)|\Phi_0\rangle, \qquad (42)$$
where $\mathscr{H}_1$ is the pion-nucleon interaction density‡ (cf. (4.131))
$$\mathscr{H}_1(x) = iG\bar{\psi}(x)\gamma^5\psi(x)\phi(x).$$
The terms in (42) can be represented by the graphical notation as in

† The phase factor $\langle \Phi_0(+\infty)|\Phi_0(-\infty)\rangle$ is neglected.

‡ The variables in $\mathscr{H}_1$ are not yet renormalized; the subtraction terms (5.261) should also be included in $\mathscr{H}_1$.

Fig. 32; Fig. 32 (*c*) shows the general nature of the contribution. We calculate the lowest-order contribution (i.e. Fig. 32 (*a*)); it is (cf. (5.127))

$$M_1 = \frac{G}{\hbar c}\int d^4x_1\, e^{i(q-q')x_1/\hbar}\bar{w}(q')\gamma^5 w(q)\langle\Phi_0|T\{\phi(x_1)\phi(x)\}|\Phi_0\rangle,$$

where $w(q)$, $w(q')$ are spinor wave functions for nucleons having energy momenta q, q' respectively.† Using (5.258) and (5.156) gives

$$M_1 = 2\pi(G/c^2)\bar{w}(q')\gamma^5 w(q)\Delta_F(q'-q)e^{i(q-q')x}. \tag{43}$$

Here $\Delta_F(q'-q)$ is the free pion propagator. The matrix element (42) is

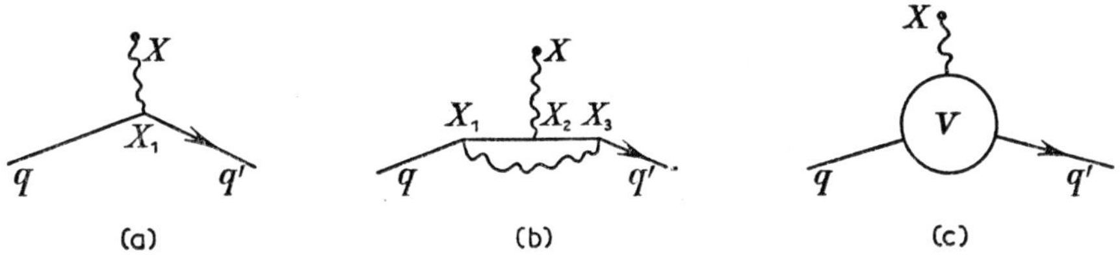

FIG. 32. Contributions to the Heisenberg matrix element (42).

obtained from (43) on replacing Δ_F by Δ'_F, γ^5 by Γ_5, $w(q)$ by $Z_6^{\frac{1}{2}}w(q)$, etc.,‡ using the notation of (5.262); thus

$$\langle\Psi_{q'}|\boldsymbol{\varphi}(x)|\Psi_q\rangle = \frac{2\pi G}{c^2}Z_6\,\bar{w}(q')\Gamma_5(q',q)w(q)\Delta'_F(q'-q)e^{i(q-q')x}.$$

Dividing $\boldsymbol{\varphi}(x)$ by $Z_1^{\frac{1}{2}}$ to get the renormalized operator $\boldsymbol{\varphi}_1(x)$ (cf. (5.270)), and using (5.262), gives

$$\langle\Psi_{q'}|\boldsymbol{\varphi}_1(x)|\Psi_q\rangle = 2\pi(G_1/c^2)\bar{w}(q')\Gamma_{5c}(q',q)w(q)\Delta_c(q'-q)e^{i(q-q')x}. \tag{44}$$

G_1 is the renormalized coupling constant (cf. (5.263)) and all quantities in (44) are finite.

Derivatives of operators

The matrix element of $\mathbf{j}(x)$ can now be deduced using (9); for this purpose we have to find the derivatives of the Heisenberg operators. Invariance of the interacting fields under translations of the coordinates x_μ, and under proper Lorentz transformations, implies the existence of a 4-vector energy-momentum operator P_μ; it satisfies§

$$\frac{\hbar}{i}\partial_\mu \mathbf{A}(x) = [\mathbf{A}(x), P_\mu], \tag{45}$$

where $\mathbf{A}(x)$ is any Heisenberg field variable. Also‖

$$[P_\mu, P_\nu] = 0.$$

† For anti-nucleons there is a change in the sign of M_1.

‡ We make an unimportant simplification by putting $Z_6 = Z_7$ (cf. (5.262)).

§ See Chapter IX, eqn. (39).

‖ Cf. p. 61, n. §.

The adiabatic switching process does not alter the total momentum of a state. Also, it will not alter the total energy of a state, provided we are dealing with a scattering process (for further discussion see Chapter V, § 2). Therefore the scattering states $|\Psi_{\text{in}}(\mathbf{p},\mathbf{p}')\rangle$, etc., and the single-particle states $|\Psi(\mathbf{p})\rangle$, etc., have the same energy-momentum eigenvalues as the corresponding bare particle states.

From (45) we deduce (as the form (44) already shows)

$$\frac{\hbar}{i}\partial_\nu\langle\Psi_{q'}|\boldsymbol{\varphi}(x)|\Psi_q\rangle = \hbar(q-q')_\nu\langle\Psi_{q'}|\boldsymbol{\varphi}(x)|\Psi_q\rangle,$$

where $\hbar q_\nu$, $\hbar q'_\nu$ are the energy momenta of the respective real nucleon states. Applying this relation twice, eqn. (9) gives† the required formula

$$\langle\Psi_{q'}|\mathbf{j}(x)|\Psi_q\rangle = \frac{2\pi G_1}{c^2}Z_1^{\frac{1}{2}}\bar{w}(q')\Gamma_{5c}(q',q)w(q)\{(q'-q)^2+\mu^2\}\Delta_c(q'-q)e^{i(q-q')x}. \tag{46 a}$$

As a simple check on (46 a) we notice that to the lowest order in the renormalized coupling constant G_1 we have (putting $Z_1 = 1$)

$$\langle\Psi_{q'}|\mathbf{j}(x)|\Psi_q\rangle \simeq -i\frac{G_1}{c^2}\bar{w}(q')\gamma^5 w(q)e^{i(q-q')x}. \tag{46 b}$$

This should be compared with the definition of $\mathbf{j}(x)$ in § 1 above.

Feynman amplitudes

Our final example is the vacuum expectation value of the chronological product of two Heisenberg operators; these chronological products are frequently called the *Feynman amplitudes*. We consider $\langle 0|T\{\boldsymbol{\varphi}(x)\boldsymbol{\varphi}(x')\}|0\rangle$. Using (1) (with $t_0 = 0$), a little manipulation gives‡

$$\langle 0|T\{\boldsymbol{\varphi}(x)\boldsymbol{\varphi}(x')\}|0\rangle = \langle\Phi_0|T\{U(\infty,t)\phi(\mathbf{x},t)U(t,t')\phi(\mathbf{x}',t')U(t',-\infty)\}|\Phi_0\rangle. \tag{47}$$

The operator T leaves the terms on the right as they stand for $t > t'$; it exchanges $(\mathbf{x},t)$ with $(\mathbf{x}',t')$ in these terms for $t < t'$. Evaluating (47) by perturbation theory we have

$$\langle 0|T\{\boldsymbol{\varphi}(x)\boldsymbol{\varphi}(x')\}|0\rangle$$
$$= \sum_{n=0}^{\infty}\left(\frac{-i}{\hbar c}\right)^n\frac{1}{n!}\int d^4x_1\ldots\int d^4x_n\,\langle\Phi_0|T\{\mathscr{H}_1(x_1)\ldots\mathscr{H}_1(x_n)\phi(x)\phi(x')\}|\Phi_0\rangle. \tag{48}$$

The expression on the right of (48) equals the bare particle propagator

† F. E. Low, *Phys. Rev.* **97** (1955) 1392.

‡ We use $U(t,0)\tilde{U}(t',0) = U(t,t')$; $U(\infty,0)\tilde{U}(t,0) = U(\infty,t)$, etc. (cf. Chapter V, § 2).

$\langle\Phi_0|T\{\phi(x)\phi(x')\}|\Phi_0\rangle$ together with all its radiative corrections;† hence by (5.262),‡

$$\langle 0|T\{\boldsymbol{\varphi}(x)\boldsymbol{\varphi}(x')\}|0\rangle = \frac{1}{2}\frac{\hbar}{c}\Delta'_F(x-x'). \tag{49}$$

Analogous results hold for other fields. For protons (or neutrons)

$$\langle 0|T\{\bar{\boldsymbol{\psi}}_{\rho'}(x')\boldsymbol{\psi}_{\rho}(x)\}|0\rangle = \tfrac{1}{2}\{S'_F(x-x')\}_{\rho\rho'} \tag{50}$$

(cf. (5.262)). Eqns. (49) and (50) can readily be extended to the case of charged pions interacting with nucleons. Similar results hold in electrodynamics.

Two-body propagators of the form $\langle 0|T\{\boldsymbol{\psi}(x_1)\boldsymbol{\psi}(x_2)\bar{\boldsymbol{\psi}}(x_1)\bar{\boldsymbol{\psi}}(x_2)\}|0\rangle$, etc., can be used to describe the interaction of two real particles.§ These propagators can be the starting-point of a relativistic discussion of the bound states of interacting fields, and they yield the Bethe–Salpeter equation.‖ Unfortunately the practical calculations have several of the disadvantages of perturbation theory.

3. Spectral analysis of Heisenberg variables

Powerful methods of investigating the expectation values of Heisenberg variables have been developed by Källén‡ and Lehmann;†† we use Lehmann's technique. We again consider a neutral pion field $\boldsymbol{\varphi}(x)$ interacting with a nucleon field $\boldsymbol{\psi}(x)$. All dependence on perturbation theory is removed if (49) and (50) are taken as *definitions* of the invariant functions $\Delta'_F(x)$, $S'_F(x)$.

It is more convenient to use the renormalized Heisenberg operators which are given by (5.270) (and by (66) below). We write these operators $\boldsymbol{\varphi}_1(x)$, $\boldsymbol{\psi}_1(x)$, $\bar{\boldsymbol{\psi}}_1(x)$. Using (5.262), it follows that eqns. (49) and (50) define the renormalized propagators $\Delta_{Fc}(x)$, $S_{Fc}(x)$ by

$$\langle 0|T\{\boldsymbol{\varphi}_1(x)\boldsymbol{\varphi}_1(x')\}|0\rangle = \frac{1}{2}\frac{\hbar}{c}\Delta_{Fc}(x-x'), \quad \text{etc.}$$

Similarly, we define invariant functions $\Delta_c(x)$, $S_c(x)$ by the vacuum expectation values (cf. (2.27), (4.17))

$$\left.\begin{aligned} \langle 0|[\boldsymbol{\varphi}_1(x),\boldsymbol{\varphi}_1(x')]|0\rangle &= \frac{i\hbar}{c}\Delta_c(x-x') \\ \langle 0|[\bar{\boldsymbol{\psi}}_{1\beta}(x'),\boldsymbol{\psi}_{1\alpha}(x)]_+|0\rangle &= -iS_{\alpha\beta c}(x-x') \end{aligned}\right\}. \tag{51}$$

Using (45), it is clear that these expectation values must be functions

† Omitting the phase factor $\langle\Phi_0(+\infty)|\Phi_0(-\infty)\rangle$ is equivalent to omitting all contributions from disconnected vacuum loops.

‡ G. Källén, *Helv. phys. Acta*, **25** (1952) 417.

§ M. Gell-Mann and F. Low, *Phys. Rev.* **84** (1951) 350.

‖ E. E. Salpeter and H. A. Bethe, *Phys. Rev.* **84** (1951) 1232.

†† H. Lehmann, *Nuovo Cim.* **11** (1954) 342.

of $(x_\mu - x'_\mu)$.† In the Heisenberg representation there is no statement as simple as $\phi^{(+)}(x)|\Phi_0\rangle = 0$; therefore we make the further *definitions*:

$$\left.\begin{aligned} \langle 0|\boldsymbol{\varphi}_1(x)\boldsymbol{\varphi}_1(x')|0\rangle &= \frac{i\hbar}{c}\Delta_c^{(+)}(x-x') = -\frac{i\hbar}{c}\Delta_c^{(-)}(x'-x) \\ \langle 0|\bar{\boldsymbol{\psi}}_{1\beta}(x')\boldsymbol{\psi}_{1\alpha}(x)|0\rangle &= -iS_{\alpha\beta c}^{(-)}(x-x') \\ \langle 0|\boldsymbol{\psi}_{1\alpha}(x)\bar{\boldsymbol{\psi}}_{1\beta}(x')|0\rangle &= -iS_{\alpha\beta c}^{(+)}(x-x') \end{aligned}\right\}. \tag{52}$$

The *linear* relations between the functions Δ_{Fc}, Δ_c, $\Delta_c^{(+)}$, $\Delta_c^{(-)}$ are the same as the relations between the corresponding free particle singular functions Δ_F, Δ, $\Delta^{(+)}$, $\Delta^{(-)}$ (cf. Appendix);‡ the same is true for the functions S_{Fc}, etc.

The expansion

Consider a complete set $|\Psi_k\rangle$ of Heisenberg state vectors such that

$$P_\mu|\Psi_k\rangle = \hbar k_\mu|\Psi_k\rangle. \tag{53}$$

Assuming that the vacuum $|0\rangle$ has the least energy,§ we let this be zero energy; for all other $|\Psi_k\rangle$ we have $k_0 > 0$. It follows from Lorentz invariance that $k_\mu^2 < 0$ for all $|\Psi_k\rangle$ (except $|0\rangle$).‖ Because

$$\sum_k |\Psi_k\rangle\langle\Psi_k| = I,$$

we have

$$\begin{aligned} \langle 0|\boldsymbol{\varphi}_1(x)\boldsymbol{\varphi}_1(x')|0\rangle &= \sum_k \langle 0|\boldsymbol{\varphi}_1(x)|\Psi_k\rangle\langle\Psi_k|\boldsymbol{\varphi}_1(x')|0\rangle \\ &= \sum_k |a_{0k}|^2 e^{ik(x-x')}, \end{aligned} \tag{54}$$

where a_{0k} is a complex number.†† Thus, by (52),

$$\left.\begin{aligned} \Delta_c^{(+)}(x) &= -\frac{i}{(2\pi)^3}\int_{-\infty}^{\infty} d^4k\, e^{ik_\mu x_\mu}\theta(k)\rho(-k^2) \\ \text{where}\qquad \rho(-k^2) &= \frac{c}{\hbar}(2\pi)^3 \sum_{(k)} |a_{0k}|^2 \end{aligned}\right\}. \tag{55}$$

$\sum_{(k)}$ denotes the summation over all states $|\Psi_k\rangle$ having the eigenvalue k_μ. $\Delta_c^{(+)}(x)$ must be a Lorentz invariant, therefore $\rho(-k^2)$ is an invariant. Also, by (55),

$$\rho(-k^2) \geqslant 0 \quad (-k^2 \geqslant 0). \tag{56}$$

† If $\mathbf{A}(x)$, $\mathbf{B}(x')$ are any Heisenberg operators, (45) gives

$$(\partial/\partial x_\mu + \partial/\partial x'_\mu)\langle 0|\mathbf{A}(x)\mathbf{B}(x')|0\rangle = 0$$

on using $P_\mu|0\rangle = 0$.

‡ The functions Δ_F, etc., are written D_F, etc., in Chapter II and the Appendix.

§ Stability of the vacuum requires that it has the least energy.

‖ To have $k_\mu^2 > 0$ would require imaginary experimental mass.

†† $a_{0k} = \langle 0|\boldsymbol{\varphi}_1(0)|\Psi_k\rangle$; in deriving (54) we use the fact that $\boldsymbol{\varphi}$ is Hermitian.

Writing $$\rho(-k^2) = \int\limits_0^\infty \rho(m^2)\delta(k^2+m^2)d(m^2),$$

and using (A.66) to define the free pion function $\Delta^{(+)}_{(m)}(x)$ for a particle of rest mass† m, we get

$$\Delta_c^{(+)}(x) = \int\limits_0^\infty d(m^2)\rho(m^2)\Delta_m^{(+)}(x). \tag{57}$$

An identical spectral form obviously applies to Δ_c, Δ_{Fc}, etc., for example

$$\Delta_{Fc}(x) = \int\limits_0^\infty d(m^2)\rho(m^2)\Delta_{F(m)}(x), \tag{58}$$

where $\Delta_{F(m)}(x)$ is given by (A.53). In the momentum representation (cf. (5.155))

$$\left.\begin{aligned} \Delta_{Fc}(k) &= \int\limits_0^\infty d(m^2)\rho(m^2)\Delta_{F(m)}(k) \\ &= \frac{1}{2\pi i}\int\limits_0^\infty d(m^2)\,\frac{\rho(m^2)}{k^2+m^2-i\epsilon} \end{aligned}\right\}. \tag{59}$$

For a non-interacting field of mass μ, $\rho(m^2) = \delta(m^2-\mu^2)$. In general, discrete eigenvalues of P_μ^2 give stable particles, and they correspond to δ-functions in $\rho(m^2)$. If only one stable particle of mass μ is associated with the field $\boldsymbol{\varphi}(x)$, then

$$\rho(m^2) = \delta(m^2-\mu^2)+\sigma(m^2),$$

where $\sigma(m^2)$ contains no δ-functions, and in addition $\sigma(m^2)$ vanishes for $m^2 < 4\mu^2$, because, by (54), $\sigma(m^2)$ for a pion must arise from states containing at least two pions.‡

The singularities

These powerful formulae (57) to (59) lead directly to several important results. For example, they show that the behaviour of the function $\Delta_c(x)$ on the light cone is at least as singular as $\Delta(x)$. From (A.49) the singular part of $\Delta_{(m)}(x)$ is $-(1/2\pi)\epsilon(x)\delta(x_\mu^2)$. Hence

$$\Delta_c(x) = -\frac{1}{2\pi}\epsilon(x)\delta(x_\mu^2)\int\limits_0^\infty d(m^2)\rho(m^2)+(\text{less singular terms}).$$

If $\int\limits_0^\infty d(m^2)\rho(m^2)$ does not converge, $\Delta_c(x)$ is more singular than $\Delta(x)$§

† The associated rest mass is actually $(m\hbar/c)$.

‡ H. Lehmann, p. 313, n. ††. A nucleon pair gives larger values of m^2.

§ Certainly $\int\limits_0^\infty \rho(m^2)d(m^2) > 1$. For a more detailed examination of the singularities see M. Gell-Mann and F. Low, *Phys. Rev.* **95** (1954) 1301.

(cf. eqn. (70) below). Similar results hold for the other singular functions $\Delta_c^{(+)}$, Δ_{Fc}, etc. Eqns. (57) to (59) are also used below to derive important relations for the renormalization constants.

The nucleon field

For the nucleon field we can write

$$\left.\begin{aligned}\langle 0|\psi_{1\alpha}(x)\bar{\psi}_{1\beta}(x')|0\rangle &= \sum_k \langle 0|\psi_{1\alpha}(x)|\Psi_k\rangle\langle\Psi_k|\bar{\psi}_{1\beta}(x')|0\rangle \\ &= \sum_k c_{0k}^{\alpha}\,\bar{c}_{0k}^{\beta}\,e^{ik(x-x')}\end{aligned}\right\}, \tag{60}$$

where $c_{0k}^{\alpha} = \langle 0|\psi_{1\alpha}(0)|\Psi_k\rangle$ is a spinor, and $\bar{c}_{0k} = \tilde{c}_{0k}\gamma^4$. Now we introduce real invariant functions $\rho_1(-k^2)$, $\rho_2(-k^2)$ such that

$$\rho_1(-k^2)\{i\gamma k-\surd(-k^2)\}_{\alpha\beta}+\rho_2(-k^2)\,\delta_{\alpha\beta} = -(2\pi)^3\sum_{(k)} c_{0k}^{\alpha}\,\bar{c}_{0k}^{\beta}. \tag{61}$$

Using (52), (60), (61), gives

$$S_c^{(+)}(x) = \int_0^{\infty} d(m^2)\{\rho_1(m^2)S_{(m)}^{(+)}(x)+\rho_2(m^2)D_{(m)}^{(+)}(x)\}. \tag{62}$$

Here $$S_{(m)}^{(+)}(x) = (\gamma^{\mu}\partial_{\mu}-m)D_{(m)}^{(+)}(x)$$

(cf. eqn. (A.92)). Similar relations hold for the other singular nucleon functions,† e.g.

$$S_{Fc}(x) = \int_0^{\infty} d(m^2)\{\rho_1(m^2)S_{F(m)}(x)+\rho_2(m^2)D_{F(m)}(x)\}. \tag{63}$$

Defining a spinor $f \equiv i(\gamma k)c_{0k}$, eqn. (61) gives

$$(2\pi)^3\sum_{(k)} \text{spur}(\tilde{f}f) = 4k_0(-k^2)\rho_1(-k^2).$$

Therefore $$\rho_1(-k^2) \geqslant 0 \quad (-k^2 \geqslant 0). \tag{64}$$

It can also be shown that‡

$$0 \leqslant \rho_2(m^2) \leqslant 2m\rho_1(m^2) \quad (m > 0). \tag{65}$$

For a free nucleon field, $\rho_1(m^2) = \delta(m^2-\kappa^2)$, $\rho_2(m^2) = 0$. We can now deduce the form of the most singular parts of $S_c(x)$, $S_{Fc}(x)$, etc., by the method which was used for $\Delta_c(x)$, $\Delta_{Fc}(x)$ above.

The renormalization constants

We use these spectral expansions to find properties of the renormalization constants in a renormalizable theory. The example chosen is a neutral pion field interacting with a nucleon field; the method could

† We use $(S_c^{(-)}(x))_T = -C^{-1}S_c^{(+)}(-x)C$, where C is the charge conjugation matrix.

‡ Using $g = (i\gamma k-\lambda)c_{0k}$, where λ is real, (61) gives

$$(m-\lambda)^2\rho_1(m^2)+2\lambda\rho_2(m^2) \geqslant 0.$$

Minimizing w.r.t. λ we have $\rho_2(2m\rho_1-\rho_2) \geqslant 0$; eqn. (65) follows.

readily be applied to any other renormalizable theory. The notation of (5.262), (5.263) is used, and we ignore any difference between proton and neutron propagators (this implies $Z_6 = Z_7$). The renormalized Heisenberg variables $\boldsymbol{\psi}_1(x)$, $\boldsymbol{\varphi}_1(x)$ are defined by

$$\boldsymbol{\psi}(x) = Z_6^{\frac{1}{2}}\boldsymbol{\psi}_1(x), \quad \bar{\boldsymbol{\psi}}(x) = Z_6^{\frac{1}{2}}\bar{\boldsymbol{\psi}}_1(x), \quad \boldsymbol{\varphi}(x) = Z_1^{\frac{1}{2}}\boldsymbol{\varphi}_1(x). \tag{66}$$

The equations of motion for the renormalized variables are (cf. (9), (13))

$$\left.\begin{aligned} (\partial_\nu^2-\mu^2)\boldsymbol{\varphi}_1(x) &= \frac{iG_1}{c^2}Z_1^{-1}Z_5\bar{\boldsymbol{\psi}}_1\gamma^5\boldsymbol{\psi}_1-\delta\mu^2\boldsymbol{\varphi}_1-\delta\lambda Z_1\boldsymbol{\varphi}_1^3 \\ (\gamma^\nu\partial_\nu+\kappa)\boldsymbol{\psi}_1(x) &= -\frac{iG_1}{\hbar c}Z_5\,Z_6^{-1}\boldsymbol{\psi}_1\boldsymbol{\varphi}_1+\delta\kappa\boldsymbol{\psi}_1 \end{aligned}\right\}, \tag{67}$$

where G_1 is the renormalized coupling constant,† μ and κ are the renormalized masses.

The renormalized operators also obey the relations (51), (52). From (51) and (57)

$$\langle 0|[\dot{\boldsymbol{\varphi}}_1(\mathbf{x},0),\boldsymbol{\varphi}_1(\mathbf{x}',0)]|0\rangle = \frac{\hbar}{i}\delta^3(\mathbf{x}-\mathbf{x}')\int\limits_0^\infty d(m^2)\rho(m^2). \tag{68}$$

The basic commutation relations for simultaneous Heisenberg operators (cf. eqn. (4.89)) lead to

$$[\dot{\boldsymbol{\varphi}}_1(\mathbf{x},0),\boldsymbol{\varphi}_1(\mathbf{x}',0)] = \frac{\hbar}{i}Z_1^{-1}\delta^3(\mathbf{x}-\mathbf{x}'). \tag{69}$$

Comparing (68), (69) gives

$$Z_1^{-1} = \int\limits_0^\infty d(m^2)\rho(m^2). \tag{70}$$

Similarly, from the nucleon equations (62), (66), and (4.89), we get

$$Z_6^{-1} = \int\limits_0^\infty d(m^2)\rho_1(m^2). \tag{71}$$

Real pions and nucleons must be given by the theory, hence ρ and ρ_1 must contain at least one δ-function, and the integrals on the right of (70), (71) are greater than unity. Consequently‡

$$0 \leqslant Z_1 < 1; \qquad 0 \leqslant Z_6 < 1. \tag{72}$$

† $G_1 = Z_1^{\frac{1}{2}}Z_5^{-1}Z_6 G$. The notation of Lehmann (loc. cit.) would replace our Z_1, Z_5, Z_6 by Z_3, Z_1, Z_2 respectively.

‡ Such formulae were first published by G. Källén, *Helv. phys. Acta*, **25** (1952) 417. He states that the first derivation was by J. Schwinger. In quantum electrodynamics the analogue of the second inequality (72) need not hold.

Using the equations of motion (67), the mass correction terms $\delta\mu^2$, $\delta\kappa$ can also be expressed in terms of the spectral functions† ρ, ρ_1, ρ_2.

Physical interpretation

The physical meaning of (72) is seen from (5.212), (5.213). These formulae relate the real pion and real nucleon states $|\Psi(\mathbf{p})\rangle$, $|\Psi(\mathbf{p},s,+)\rangle$ to the corresponding bare pion and bare nucleon states $|\Phi(\mathbf{p})\rangle$, $|\Phi(\mathbf{p},s,+)\rangle$. We have‡

$$|\langle\Psi(\mathbf{p})|\Phi(\mathbf{p})\rangle|^2 = Z_1, \qquad |\langle\Psi(\mathbf{p},s,+)|\Phi(\mathbf{p},s,+)\rangle|^2 = Z_6. \tag{73}$$

Eqns. (72) merely state that the projection of $|\Psi(\mathbf{p})\rangle$ on $|\Phi(\mathbf{p})\rangle$ should be of less than unit magnitude, etc.§

It has been shown by Lee that it is possible to construct a renormalizable theory in which inequalities similar to (72) are not satisfied.‡ In Lee's example the renormalization constant $Z \to -\infty$. This would make nonsense of the physical interpretation (73), and it suggests that it may not be possible to start with a *real* unrenormalized coupling constant G and deduce a *real* renormalized constant G_1.‖

The spectral analysis has also been used to show†† that the vertex function $\Gamma_5(p_1,p_2)$ tends to zero for large transfers of momenta $(p_1-p_2)_\mu$, while p_1, p_2 have free particle values.

4. Pion-nucleon scattering

In Chapter IV, § 14, it was pointed out that the pseudo-vector interaction (4.151) gave a simpler physical picture of the emission and absorption of pions at low energy than the pseudo-scalar interaction (4.152). However, in Chapter V, § 15, we saw that the pseudo-scalar interaction could be consistently renormalized whereas the pseudo-vector interaction could not; the Tamm–Dancoff method (Chapter IV, § 8) has been used with pseudo-scalar coupling to calculate pion-nucleon scattering up to pion kinetic energy of 250 MeV (lab.).‡‡ Unfortunately, this method is complicated in application, and it does not readily give a simple description of the scattering process.

† The relations are (cf. H. Lehmann, loc. cit.)

$$\delta\mu^2 = -Z_1\int\limits_0^\infty (m^2-\mu^2)\rho(m^2)\,d(m^2); \quad \delta\kappa = Z_6\int\limits_0^\infty \{(\kappa-m)\rho_1(m^2)+\rho_2(m^2)\}\,d(m^2).$$

By (72), $\delta\mu^2 < 0$.

‡ T. D. Lee, *Phys. Rev.* **95** (1954) 1329.

§ For a discussion on the finiteness of the renormalization constants see G. Källén, *K. danske vidensk. Selsk.* **27** (1953), No. 12.

‖ For further discussion and references see W. Pauli, Pisa Conference Rep., *Suppl. Nuovo Cim.* **2** (1956) 703.

†† H. Lehmann, K. Symanzik, and W. Zimmermann, *Nuovo Cim.* **2** (1955) 425.

‡‡ F. J. Dyson *et al.*, *Phys. Rev.* **95** (1954) 1644; see also n. †, p. 191.

Here we shall use the method of Low and Chew† which is based on general Heisenberg operator manipulations similar to those in §§ 1, 2 above; the method can be adapted to the pseudo-vector interaction, and it gives a very good description of pion-nucleon scattering in the energy region where p-waves are predominant and nucleon recoil is not important. Some account of the s-wave scattering will also be given; however, we shall not discuss scattering in the GeV region or when inelastic processes become important. Any adequate theoretical description of scattering in the GeV region would involve K-meson forces as well as pion-nucleon and pion-pion forces.

First, we must give a brief survey of the experimental results.‡ Fig. 33 shows the total cross-sections $\sigma(\pi^+, P)$, $\sigma(\pi^-, P)$ for the scattering of positive and negative pions by protons, up to pion energies of about 1·8 GeV (lab.). The region of the resonance near 200 MeV is also shown in Fig. 34. The maxima in the cross-sections around 0·7 GeV and 1·0 GeV (c.m.) in Fig. 33 are associated with inelastic pion scattering in which one or more pions are created; for a discussion of these inelastic processes the reader is referred to the paper by Cool *et al.*‡

Isotopic spin

It was pointed out in Chapter IV, § 12, that the pion-nucleon scattering phenomena obey the law of conservation of isotopic spin.§ A nucleon $\mathcal{N}$ with isotopic spin $\frac{1}{2}$ and a pion π with isotopic spin 1, can form isotopic state vectors $|T, T_3\rangle$ where the total isotopic spin is $T = \frac{1}{2}$ or $\frac{3}{2}$. Thus, using eqns. (3.50), (3.51), the state vectors $|\pi\mathcal{N}\rangle$ are written

$$\left.\begin{aligned}
&|\pi^+P\rangle = |T=\tfrac{3}{2},\, T_3=\tfrac{3}{2}\rangle; \qquad |\pi^-N\rangle = |T=\tfrac{3}{2},\, T_3=-\tfrac{3}{2}\rangle;\\
&|\pi^0P\rangle = \sqrt{\frac{2}{3}}\,|T=\tfrac{3}{2},\, T_3=\tfrac{1}{2}\rangle - \frac{1}{\sqrt{3}}\,|T=\tfrac{1}{2},\, T_3=\tfrac{1}{2}\rangle;\\
&|\pi^+N\rangle = \frac{1}{\sqrt{3}}\,|T=\tfrac{3}{2},\, T_3=\tfrac{1}{2}\rangle + \sqrt{\frac{2}{3}}\,|T=\tfrac{1}{2},\, T_3=\tfrac{1}{2}\rangle;\\
&|\pi^-P\rangle = \frac{1}{\sqrt{3}}\,|T=\tfrac{3}{2},\, T_3=-\tfrac{1}{2}\rangle - \sqrt{\frac{2}{3}}\,|T=\tfrac{1}{2},\, T_3=-\tfrac{1}{2}\rangle;\\
&|\pi^0N\rangle = \sqrt{\frac{2}{3}}\,|T=\tfrac{3}{2},\, T_3=-\tfrac{1}{2}\rangle + \frac{1}{\sqrt{3}}\,|T=\tfrac{1}{2},\, T_3=-\tfrac{1}{2}\rangle.
\end{aligned}\right\} \quad (74)$$

† F. E. Low, *Phys. Rev.* **97** (1955) 1392; G. F. Chew and F. E. Low, ibid. **107** (1956) 1570, 1579.

‡ For an account of the total cross-sections see S. J. Lindenbaum and L. C. L. Yuan, *Phys. Rev.* **100** (1955) 306; R. Cool, O. Piccioni, and D. Clark, ibid. **103** (1956) 1082; A. L. Mukhin *et al.*, CERN Symposium (Geneva, 1956), vol. ii.

§ The Coulomb interaction and the $(\pi^\pm - \pi^0)$ mass difference can cause deviations from charge independence at small angles or at energies below 30 MeV.

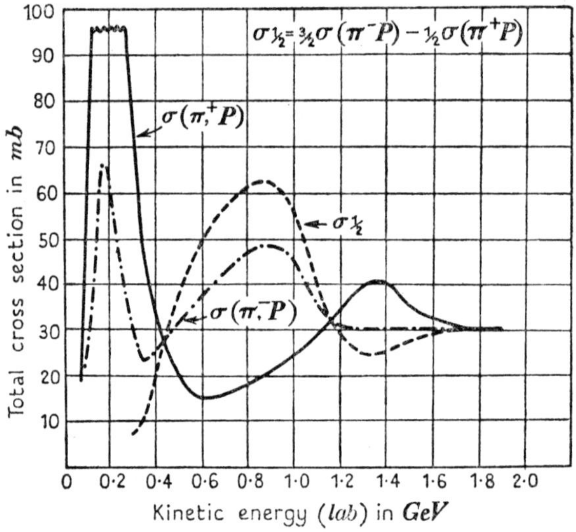

(a)

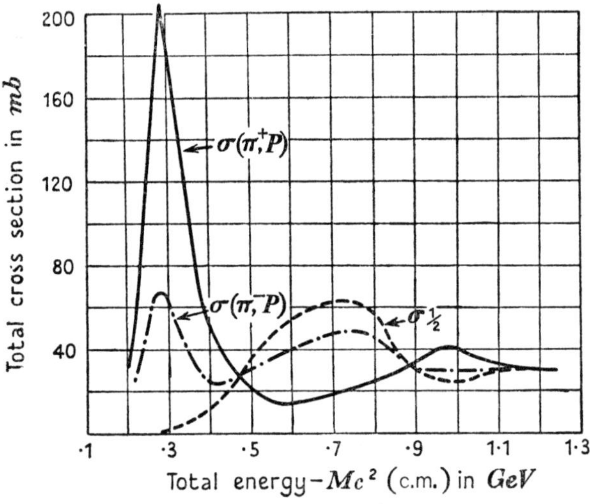

(b)

FIG. 33 (a) and (b). The total cross-sections $\sigma(\pi^+, P)$ and $\sigma(\pi^-, P)$ deduced from all experimental data. In (a) and (b) the cross-sections are expressed as functions of the laboratory and the centre of mass energies respectively. $\sigma_{\frac{1}{2}}$ is obtained by assuming charge independence (Cool, Piccioni, and Clark, loc. cit.).

Conservation of isotopic spin implies that there are only two independent scattering matrix elements $M(\frac{3}{2})$, $M(\frac{1}{2})$ for elastic (or charge exchange) scattering between initial and final states in which the nucleon and pion have given momenta and given (ordinary) spin.

Eqns. (74) now give the following relations between the scattering matrix elements:

$$\left.\begin{aligned} \langle\pi^+P|M|\pi^+P\rangle &= \langle\pi^-N|M|\pi^-N\rangle = M(\tfrac{3}{2}) \\ \langle\pi^-P|M|\pi^-P\rangle &= \tfrac{1}{3}M(\tfrac{3}{2})+\tfrac{2}{3}M(\tfrac{1}{2}) \\ \langle\pi^0N|M|\pi^-P\rangle &= \frac{\sqrt{2}}{3}\{M(\tfrac{3}{2})-M(\tfrac{1}{2})\} \end{aligned}\right\}. \tag{75}$$

The last line in (75) gives the charge exchange matrix element. Suppose

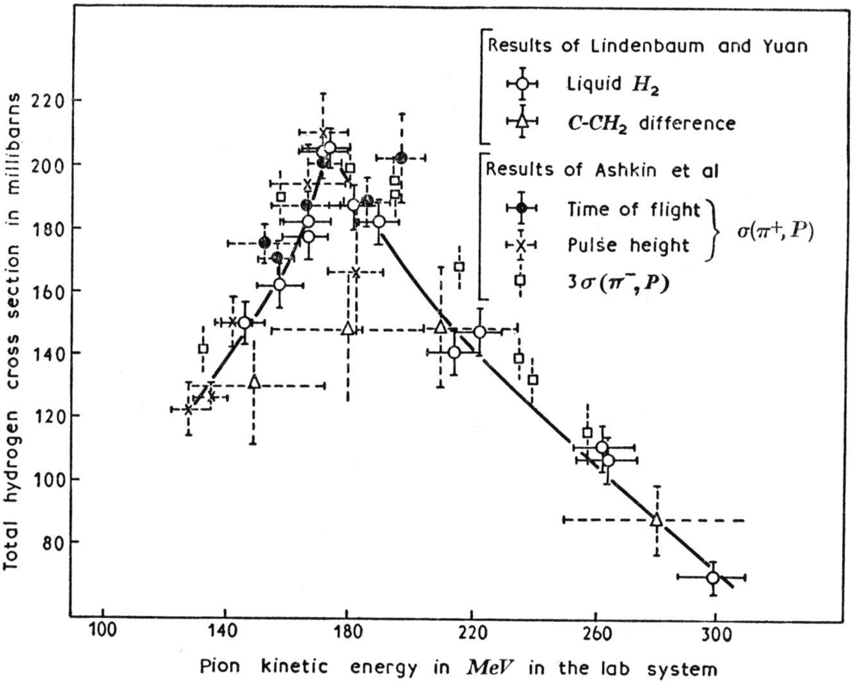

FIG. 34. The total cross-section measurements $\sigma(\pi^+, P)$ by Lindenbaum and Yuan (loc. cit.) in the region of the first resonance. Results of J. Ashkin *et. al.* (*Phys. Rev.* **105** (1955) 724) for $\sigma(\pi^+, P)$ and $\sigma(\pi^-, P)$ are also shown.

we sum the transition probability or differential cross-section over the different configurations of charge which are possible in a final state $|f\rangle$ having given momenta and spin values; the state $|f\rangle$ can describe either elastic or inelastic scattering. In this sum there will be no interference between states of different total isotopic spin T, and some simple relations follow. For example, $|\pi^-P\rangle\langle\pi^-P|$ can then be replaced by

$$\tfrac{1}{3}|T=\tfrac{3}{2},\ T_3=-\tfrac{1}{2}\rangle\langle T=\tfrac{3}{2},\ T_3=-\tfrac{1}{2}|+$$
$$+\tfrac{2}{3}|T=\tfrac{1}{2},\ T_3=-\tfrac{1}{2}\rangle\langle T=\tfrac{1}{2},\ T_3=-\tfrac{1}{2}|.$$

Hence (cf. Fig. 33) the total cross-section $\sigma(\frac{1}{2})$ for $T = \frac{1}{2}$ scattering is given by
$$\sigma(\tfrac{1}{2}) = \tfrac{3}{2}\sigma(\pi^-, P) - \tfrac{1}{2}\sigma(\pi^+, P).$$

From Fig. 34 it is seen that near the first maximum in the total cross-section, $3\sigma(\pi^-, P)$ is very little greater than $\sigma(\pi^+, P)$; therefore this resonance (or nucleon isobar) effect is in a $T = \frac{3}{2}$ state. Also, it follows that the $T = \frac{1}{2}$ scattering is small below pion (kinetic) energy of 250 MeV (lab.). The suggestion that there might be a $T = \frac{3}{2}$ resonance was first made by Pauli and Dancoff on the basis of strong coupling theory.† Brueckner‡ showed that the peak could be fitted by a single level resonance formula of the type
$$\sigma(\pi^+, P) = \frac{2\pi}{k^2}\frac{\Gamma^2}{(E-E_0)^2 + \frac{1}{4}\Gamma^2}, \tag{76}$$
where E, k are the energy and propagation vector of the pion (in the c.m. system), Γ is the width, and $E_0 = 125$ MeV (c.m.s.) is the 'resonant' pion (kinetic) energy.

Angular distribution in elastic scattering

The angular distribution of the elastic scattering can readily be examined if we adapt the analysis of Chapter III, § 8, for the scattering of a fermion by a spherically symmetric centre of force. It is convenient to use the non-relativistic approximation for the nucleon, so its spin is described by the Pauli matrix $\boldsymbol{\sigma}$. The scattering matrix§ for either isotopic spin state is of the form (cf. eqn. (8.38))
$$M = f(\theta) + (\boldsymbol{\sigma}.\mathbf{n})g(\theta) = \begin{pmatrix} f(\theta) & -ig(\theta)e^{-i\phi} \\ ig(\theta)e^{i\phi} & f(\theta) \end{pmatrix},$$
where (θ, ϕ) is the direction of scattering and $\mathbf{n}$ is the normal to the plane of scattering. Also (cf. eqns. (3.73), (8.39)),
$$\left.\begin{aligned} f(\theta) &= \frac{1}{k}\sum_{l=0}^{\infty} P_l(\cos\theta)\{(l+1)A_{l,l+\frac{1}{2}} + lA_{l,l-\frac{1}{2}}\} \\ g(\theta) &= \frac{i}{k}\sum_{l=1}^{\infty} P_l^1(\cos\theta)\{A_{l,l+\frac{1}{2}} - A_{l,l-\frac{1}{2}}\} \end{aligned}\right\}, \tag{77}$$
where
$$A_{lJ} = e^{i\eta_{lJ}}\sin\eta_{lJ};$$
η_{lJ} are the elastic scattering phase angles (there is a phase η_{lJ} for each value of T). We work in the centre of mass system.

† W. Pauli and S. M. Dancoff, *Phys. Rev.* **62** (1942) 85; the great width of the resonance peak shows that the isobar has an extremely short life.

‡ K. A. Brueckner, *Phys. Rev.* **86** (1952) 206; see also M. Gell-Mann and K. M. Watson, *Ann. Rev. Nuclear Sci.* (Annual Reviews Inc., Stanford, Cal., 1954), vol iv.

§ The elastic scattering matrix M is a real multiple of matrix $\mathbf{T}$ in Chapter V, § 1. The normalization is such that $f(\theta)e^{ikr}/r$ and $g(\theta)e^{ikr}/r$, are the direct and spin-flip outgoing waves corresponding to an incident wave $e^{i\mathbf{k}\cdot\mathbf{x}}$.

Assuming that it is sufficient to consider s-waves and p-waves for the energies shown in Fig. 34 (cf. Chapter VIII, § 10, for a discussion of this point), the differential cross-section† (for a state of definite isotopic spin) is

$$Q\,d\Omega = \{|f(\theta)|^2+|g(\theta)|^2\}\,d\Omega.$$

This can be written‡

$$Q\,d\Omega = \frac{d\Omega}{k^2}\{|A_{0\frac{1}{2}}+(A_{1\frac{1}{2}}+2A_{1\frac{3}{2}})\cos\theta|^2+|A_{1\frac{3}{2}}-A_{1\frac{1}{2}}|^2\sin^2\theta\}. \tag{78 a}$$

It is convenient to use the notation

$$\left.\begin{array}{llll} \eta_{0\frac{1}{2}} = \alpha_3, & \eta_{1\frac{1}{2}} = \alpha_{31}, & \eta_{1\frac{3}{2}} = \alpha_{33} & \text{for } T = \frac{3}{2} \\ \eta_{0\frac{1}{2}} = \alpha_1, & \eta_{1\frac{1}{2}} = \alpha_{11}, & \eta_{1\frac{3}{2}} = \alpha_{13} & \text{for } T = \frac{1}{2} \end{array}\right\}. \tag{78 b}$$

Then the total cross-section for $T = \frac{3}{2}$ becomes

$$\sigma(\pi^+, P) = \frac{8\pi}{k^2}\{\tfrac{1}{2}\sin^2\alpha_3+\tfrac{1}{2}\sin^2\alpha_{31}+\sin^2\alpha_{33}\}. \tag{79}$$

Brueckner (loc. cit.) suggested that the resonance (76) appears in the state ($T = \frac{3}{2}$, $J = \frac{3}{2}$); in that case $\sin^2\alpha_{33}$ is unity at the resonance. There is no reason to expect that either $\sin\alpha_3$ or $\sin\alpha_{31}$ is large; hence for $E = E_0$ we expect $\sigma_{\max}(\pi^+, P) \simeq (8\pi/k^2)$. The peak of the curve in Fig. 34 has this value.§ We shall see that the theory of Chew and Low explains why a resonance occurs in the $(\frac{3}{2}, \frac{3}{2})$ state but does not occur in the other p-states.

s-Wave scattering

At low energies ($E_n \lesssim 40$ MeV) the scattering is predominantly in the s-states, and it is given by the phases α_1, α_3. Let the separation of the pion and the nucleon be r. The wave function $\psi(r)$ for the s-state relative motion (at low energies) obeys a Schrödinger equation; for $r > b$, where $b \simeq (\hbar/m_\pi c)$ is the range‖ of the pion-nucleon interaction, we have

$$r\psi(r) \sim \sin(kr+\delta),$$

where δ is constant. For small k,

$$r\psi(r) \sim \sin\delta\{1+kr\cot\delta\}. \tag{80}$$

For $k = 0$, the Schrödinger equation has a solution which for $r > b$ has the form†† $r\psi(r) \sim C(1+r/a)$ (C, a are constants). Thus, from (80),

† The notation is identical with Chapter III, § 9.

‡ For the observed angular distribution of the $T = \frac{1}{2}$, $T = \frac{3}{2}$ elastic scattering in the p-wave region see J. Ashkin, J. P. Blaser, F. Feiner, and M. O. Stern, *Phys. Rev.* **101** (1956) 1149; **105** (1957) 724.

§ It is easy to show from eqn. (77) that the maximum elastic cross-section *for a single state* (J, T) is $\sigma_M(J) = (2\pi/k^2)(2J+1)$. In general $\sigma_M(J) = (2\pi/k^2)(2J+1)(\sigma_E/\sigma_T)$, where σ_E, σ_T are the elastic and total cross-sections.

‖ We neglect any Coulomb force.

†† The sign of a here is the reverse of that used in nuclear physics.

$k \cot \delta \to 1/a$ as $k \to 0$. Further, it is easy to show† that for small k,

$$k \cot \delta = \frac{1}{a} + \tfrac{1}{2} r_0 k^2 + O(k^4), \tag{81}$$

where the constant r_0 is called the *effective range*; r_0 is of the order of the range of the pion-nucleon interaction. The constant a is called the *scattering length*. From (75), (77), and (81) the total cross-sections have the following low-energy limiting values:‡

$$\left.\begin{aligned} \sigma(\pi^+, P) &= 4\pi |a_3|^2 \\ \sigma(\pi^-, P \to \pi^-, P) &= 4\pi |\tfrac{2}{3} a_1 + \tfrac{1}{3} a_3|^2 \end{aligned}\right\}. \tag{82}$$

a_1 and a_3 are the scattering lengths in the pure isotopic states $T = \frac{1}{2}$, $T = \frac{3}{2}$ respectively. Similarly from (75), the low-energy value of charge-exchange scattering is§

$$\sigma(\pi^-, P \to \pi^0, N) = \frac{8\pi}{9} |a_1 - a_3|^2 \left(\frac{v_0}{v_-}\right). \tag{83}$$

Accepted values of the scattering lengths are‖

$$a_3 = -0{\cdot}11, \quad a_1 = 0{\cdot}17 \quad (\text{in units of } \hbar/m_\pi c = 1{\cdot}4 \times 10^{-13}\,\text{cm}). \tag{84}$$

The differential cross-sections determine the relative but not the absolute signs of the phase shifts.†† The absolute sign is found by examining Coulomb interference effects. For example, at 120 MeV, (π^+, P) scattering shows strong destructive interference at angles below 20°. Because the $(T = \frac{3}{2}, J = \frac{3}{2})$ state is predominant at this energy, it follows‡‡ that $\alpha_{33} > 0$ corresponding to an attractive interaction.

5. The scattering matrix

First we find the S-matrix element for pion scattering in the neutral pion theory given by eqn. (9) above; the derivation uses a powerful technique which makes it unnecessary to specify the form of the interaction current $\mathbf{j}(x)$. We then generalize to charged pions, and derive

† See J. M. Blatt and V. F. Weisskopf, *Theoretical Nuclear Physics* (J. Wiley, New York, 1952), ch. 2.

‡ For a careful calculation of the low-energy cross-sections including Coulomb effects, see L. van Hove, *Phys. Rev.* **88** (1952) 1358; see also F. T. Solmitz, ibid. **94** (1954) 1799.

§ Because of the mass difference $(m_{\pi_-} - m_{\pi^0}) = 8{\cdot}8 m_e$ an additional factor (v_0/v_-) appears on the right of (83) (cf. Chapter III, p. 137). This is only important at very low energies. (v_0, v_- are the pion velocities.)

‖ D. E. Nagel, R. H. Hildebrand, and R. J. Plano, *Phys. Rev.* **105** (1957) 718; J. Orear, *Nuovo Cim.* **4** (1956) 856. In addition to (82) and (83), the shift in the energy levels of π-mesic atoms is proportional to $\{(A-Z)a_N + Za_P\}$, where a_N, a_P are the scattering lengths of π^- on neutrons and protons. For $A \simeq 2Z$ this gives $\frac{2}{3}Z(a_1 + 2a_3)$. In (83), $\sigma(\pi^- \to \pi^0)$ is deduced from the Panofsky ratio; see H A. Bethe and F. de Hoffmann, *Mesons and Fields* (Row, Peterson, Evanston, Ill., 1955), vol. ii, § 33 f.

†† For other ambiguities in the phases see H. A. Bethe and F. de Hoffmann, loc. cit.

‡‡ J. Orear, *Phys. Rev.* **96** (1954) 1417.

an integral equation for the S-matrix element. Denoting the initial nucleon and pion by p, q respectively and the final nucleon and pion by p', q' we have, by § 2 and eqns. (36), (39),

$$\langle p',q'|S|p,q\rangle = \langle\Psi_{\text{out}}(p',q')|\Psi_{\text{in}}(p,q)\rangle$$
$$= (-i)\lim_{x_0\to+\infty}\langle\Psi_{\text{out}}(p')|\int_{(x_0)} d^3\mathbf{x}\,\boldsymbol{\varphi}(x)\,\overleftrightarrow{\partial}_{x_0} f^*_{\mathbf{q}'}(x)\,|\Psi_{\text{in}}(p,q)\rangle, \tag{85}$$

where $f_{\mathbf{q}'}(x) = e^{iq'_\nu x_\nu}/(2\mathscr{E}_{q'})^{\frac{1}{2}}$, and $\mathscr{E}_{q'}$ is the energy of the pion $\mathbf{q}'$.† Also

$$f\,\overleftrightarrow{\partial}_{x_0} g \equiv f\frac{\partial g}{\partial x_0} - \frac{\partial f}{\partial x_0}g.$$

Here, and for the remainder of this chapter, we shall generally put $\hbar = c = 1$, for convenience, and we also normalize to unit spatial volume. Wherever necessary, $\hbar$, c and the normalizing volume V can be easily reintroduced. We write

$$\int_{(x_0\to+\infty)} d^3\mathbf{x}\,\boldsymbol{\varphi}(x)\,\overleftrightarrow{\partial}_{x_0} f^*_{\mathbf{q}'}(x)$$
$$= \int_{(x_0\to-\infty)} d^3\mathbf{x}\,\boldsymbol{\varphi}(x)\,\overleftrightarrow{\partial}_{x_0} f^*_{\mathbf{q}'}(x) + \int_{-\infty}^{\infty} d^4x\frac{\partial}{\partial x_0}\{\boldsymbol{\varphi}(x)\,\overleftrightarrow{\partial}_{x_0} f^*_{\mathbf{q}'}(x)\}.$$

Now‡

$$\frac{\partial}{\partial x_0}\{\boldsymbol{\varphi}(x)\,\overleftrightarrow{\partial}_{x_0} f^*_{\mathbf{q}'}(x)\} = \boldsymbol{\varphi}(x)[\nabla^2 f^*_{\mathbf{q}'}(x) - \mu^2 f^*_{\mathbf{q}'}(x)] - \frac{\partial^2\boldsymbol{\varphi}(x)}{\partial x_0^2} f^*_{\mathbf{q}'}(x),$$

and spatial integration by parts gives

$$\langle p',q'|S|p,q\rangle = (-i)\langle\Psi_{\text{out}}(p')|\int_{-\infty}^{\infty} d^4x\, f^*_{\mathbf{q}'}(x)(\partial_\nu^2 - \mu^2)\boldsymbol{\varphi}(x)\,|\Psi_{\text{in}}(p,q)\rangle -$$
$$-i\lim_{x_0\to-\infty}\langle\Psi_{\text{out}}(p')|\int_{(x_0)} d^3\mathbf{x}\,\boldsymbol{\varphi}(x)\,\overleftrightarrow{\partial}_{x_0} f^*_{\mathbf{q}'}(x)\,|\Psi_{\text{in}}(p,q)\rangle.$$

The real nucleon state $|\Psi_{\text{out}}(p')\rangle$ is a steady state, and we may write $|\Psi_{\text{out}}(p')\rangle = |\Psi_{\text{in}}(p')\rangle = |\Psi(p')\rangle$; using (36), (37) gives§

$$\langle p',q'|S|p,q\rangle = \langle\Psi_{\text{in}}(p',q')|\Psi_{\text{in}}(p,q)\rangle +$$
$$+ i\langle\Psi(p')|\int_{-\infty}^{\infty} d^4x\, f^*_{\mathbf{q}'}(x)\mathbf{j}(x)|\Psi_{\text{in}}(p,q)\rangle. \tag{86 a}$$

This relation should be compared with (40 b) above.

The Heisenberg energy momentum operator P_μ (cf. (45)) enables us to write‖

$$\mathbf{j}(x) = e^{-iP_\mu x_\mu}\mathbf{j}(0)e^{iP_\mu x_\mu}. \tag{86 b}$$

† $\boldsymbol{\varphi}(x)$ is the Heisenberg operator for the neutral pion field. (Also $\mathscr{E}_{q'} \equiv q'_0$).

‡ Using $(\partial_\nu^2 - \mu^2)f_{\mathbf{q}'}(x) = 0$ (cf. eqn. (34)).

§ H. Lehmann, K. Symanzik, and W. Zimmermann, *Nuovo Cim.* **1** (1955) 205; F. E. Low, *Phys. Rev.* **97** (1955) 1392.

‖ This expression and its application in (87) are valid so long as the initial state is a collision state (cf. the discussion in Chapter V, § 2).

Using this, eqn. (86 a) becomes

$$\langle p',q'|S|p,q\rangle$$
$$= I+(2\pi)^4 i\delta^{(4)}(p+q-p'-q')f^*_{\mathbf{q}'}(0)\langle\Psi(p')|\mathbf{j}(0)|\Psi_{\text{in}}(p,q)\rangle, \tag{87}$$

where I is the unit matrix, p, q are the energy momenta of the incoming nucleon and pion, etc. Comparing with Chapter V, § 1, it is seen that the second term on the right of (87) is the matrix $(-T) = S-I$. Using (5.26) gives the *scattering matrix* element for unit volume,

$$\langle p',q'|\mathbf{T}|p,q\rangle = -(2\mathscr{E}_{q'})^{-\frac{1}{2}}\langle\Psi(p')|\mathbf{j}(0)|\Psi_{\text{in}}(p,q)\rangle, \tag{88}$$

where $\mathscr{E}_{q'} = q'_0$ is the energy of the outgoing pion.

Further reduction of the matrix element

The matrix element on the right of (88) can now be reduced to a matrix element between real nucleon states. By (36) and (37),

$$\langle\Psi(p')|\mathbf{j}(0)|\Psi_{\text{in}}(p,q)\rangle = i\int\limits_{(x_0\to-\infty)} d^3\mathbf{x}\langle\Psi(p')|\mathbf{j}(0)\boldsymbol{\varphi}(x)|\Psi(p)\rangle\,\overleftrightarrow{\partial}_{x_0} f_{\mathbf{q}}(x)$$
$$= -i\int\limits_{-\infty}^{\infty} d^4x\frac{\partial}{\partial x_0}[\langle\Psi(p')|T\{\mathbf{j}(0)\boldsymbol{\varphi}(x)\}|\Psi(p)\rangle\,\overleftrightarrow{\partial}_{x_0} f_{\mathbf{q}}(x)]$$
$$+i\int\limits_{(x_0\to+\infty)} d^3\mathbf{x}\langle\Psi(p')|\boldsymbol{\varphi}(x)\mathbf{j}(0)|\Psi(p)\rangle\,\overleftrightarrow{\partial}_{x_0} f_{\mathbf{q}}(x). \tag{89}$$

By (37), the last integral gives $\langle\Psi(p')|\phi^{(-)}_{\text{out}}(x)\mathbf{j}(0)|\Psi(p)\rangle$; using (29) and remembering that the outgoing pion and nucleon operators commute, this term vanishes (by (27)). The chronological operator is necessary in the first term on the right of (89) if the second term is to vanish. Eqn. (89) becomes (on spatial integration by parts)†

$$\langle\Psi(p')|\mathbf{j}(0)|\Psi_{\text{in}}(p,q)\rangle = -i\int\limits_{-\infty}^{\infty} d^4x\, f_{\mathbf{q}}(x)(\partial_\nu^2-\mu^2)\times$$
$$\times\langle\Psi(p')|T\{\mathbf{j}(0)\boldsymbol{\varphi}(x)\}|\Psi(p)\rangle$$
$$= i\int\limits_{-\infty}^{\infty} d^4x\, f_{\mathbf{q}}(x)\langle\Psi(p')|T\{\mathbf{j}(0)\mathbf{j}(x)\}|\Psi(p)\rangle+$$
$$+i\int\limits_{(x_0=0)} d^3\mathbf{x}\, f_{\mathbf{q}}(x)\,\overleftrightarrow{\partial}_{x_0}\langle\Psi(p')|[\boldsymbol{\varphi}(x),\mathbf{j}(0)]|\Psi(p)\rangle. \tag{90}$$

The last term in (90) comes from the derivative of the change in order of $\mathbf{j}(0)$ and $\boldsymbol{\varphi}(x)$ occurring at $x_0 = 0$.

We *assume* that at a *space-like separation* the Heisenberg operators have the same commutators as the non-interacting fields (cf. (4.82), (4.83)); it follows that for the particular form of $\mathbf{j}(x)$ given in eqn. (9),

† F. E. Low, *Phys. Rev.* **97** (1955) 1392. A derivation based on eqns. (17) above has been given by M. Cini and S. Fubini, *Nuovo Cim.* **2** (1955) 192; see also ibid. page 860.

only the renormalization term containing $\delta\lambda$ will contribute to the last integral in (90) (assuming $p \neq p'$).

The $\delta\lambda$ term in (9) arises from a pion-pion point interaction; in general the last integral in (90) will contribute if the interaction current $\mathbf{j}(0)$ contains the square or higher powers of the pion field amplitude. This is the case where there is a direct pion-pion scattering term in the Lagrangian (or more complicated terms); it also occurs if we use a phenomenological interaction of the form $\boldsymbol{\varphi}\boldsymbol{\varphi}\bar{\boldsymbol{\psi}}\boldsymbol{\psi}$ (cf. eqn. (4.156)) to describe s-wave pion scattering.† Apart from the s-phases, a good description of pion-nucleon scattering up to about 400 MeV is obtained using the pseudo-vector interaction (4.151) alone;‡ we shall therefore, from eqn. (94) onwards, ignore the last term in (90).§

Charged and neutral pions

For charged and neutral pions having an isotopic invariant interaction with nucleons, we use the three Hermitian pion field operators $\boldsymbol{\varphi}_\alpha(x)$ $(\alpha = 1,2,3)$ (cf. Chapter II, § 8), and the current $\mathbf{j}(x)$ is replaced by the components $\mathbf{j}_\alpha(x)$ of an isotopic vector. Eqn. (9) becomes

$$(\partial_\nu^2-\mu^2)\boldsymbol{\varphi}_\alpha(x) = -\mathbf{j}_\alpha(x) \quad (\alpha = 1,2,3).$$

As an example, for the pseudo-scalar interaction we have

$$\mathbf{j}_\alpha(x) = -iG\bar{\boldsymbol{\psi}}(x)\gamma^5\tau_\alpha\boldsymbol{\psi}(x)+\delta\mu^2\boldsymbol{\varphi}_\alpha(x)+\delta\lambda\boldsymbol{\varphi}_\alpha(\mathbf{x})\{\boldsymbol{\varphi}_{\alpha'}(x)\boldsymbol{\varphi}_{\alpha'}(x)\},$$

where the notation of Chapter IV, § 12, is used. The scattering matrix (88) is now replaced by $\langle p';q',\alpha'|\mathbf{T}|p;q,\alpha\rangle$, where (q,α), (q',α') are the initial and final pion states.‖ Eqns. (88) and (90) become

$$\left.\begin{aligned}
&\langle p';\, q',\alpha'|\mathbf{T}|p;\, q,\alpha\rangle \\
&\quad = -(2\mathscr{E}_{q'})^{-\frac{1}{2}}\langle\Psi(p')|\mathbf{j}_{\alpha'}(0)|\Psi_{\text{in}}(p;\, q,\alpha)\rangle, \\
&\langle\Psi(p')|\mathbf{j}_{\alpha'}(0)|\Psi_{\text{in}}(p;\, q,\alpha)\rangle \\
&\quad = i\int_{-\infty}^{\infty} d^4x\, f_{\mathbf{q}}(x)\langle\Psi(p')|T\{\mathbf{j}_{\alpha'}(0)\mathbf{j}_\alpha(x)\}|\Psi(p)\rangle + \\
&\qquad +i\int_{(x_0=0)} d^3\mathbf{x}\, f_{\mathbf{q}}(x)\overleftrightarrow{\partial}_{x_0}\langle\Psi(p')|\,[\boldsymbol{\varphi}_\alpha(x),\mathbf{j}_{\alpha'}(0)]\,|\Psi(p)\rangle
\end{aligned}\right\}. \tag{91a}$$

This completes the generalization to charged and neutral pions.

† For the analysis in this case see S. R. Drell, M. H. Friedman, and F. Zachariasen, *Phys. Rev.* **104** (1956) 236.

‡ It has been suggested that π–π interactions are important in the 1 GeV region—for a discussion see R. Cool, O. Piccioni, and D. Clark, *Phys. Rev.* **103** (1956) 1082.

§ See, however, § 8.

‖ The notation of Chapter II, § 7, shows that a state containing a positive pion is given by $|q,+\rangle = (1/\sqrt{2})\{|q,1\rangle+i|q,2\rangle\}$; a negative pion state is $|q,-\rangle = (1/\sqrt{2})\{|q,1\rangle-i|q,2\rangle\}$. Using these, the scattering matrix is expressed in terms of π^+ and π^- states.

The crossing relation

Instead of (91 a) we can write

$$\langle p';\, q',\alpha'|\mathbf{T}|p;\, q,\alpha\rangle = -(2\mathscr{E}_q)^{-\frac{1}{2}}\langle\Psi_{\text{out}}(p';\, q',\alpha')|\mathbf{j}_\alpha(0)|\Psi(p)\rangle. \quad (91\,\text{b})$$

The same method of evaluation gives

$$\langle\Psi_{\text{out}}(p';\, q',\alpha)|\mathbf{j}_\alpha(0)|\Psi(p)\rangle$$

$$= -i\int\limits_{-\infty}^{\infty} d^4x\, f^*_{\mathbf{q}'}(x)(\partial_\nu^2-\mu^2)\langle\Psi(p')|T\{\mathbf{j}_\alpha(0)\boldsymbol{\varphi}_{\alpha'}(x)\}|\Psi(p)\rangle. \quad (92)$$

Comparing (92) and (90) we have the formal relation

$$\langle p';\, q',\alpha'|\mathbf{T}|p;\, q,\alpha\rangle = \langle p';\, -q,\alpha|\mathbf{T}|p;\, -q',\alpha'\rangle. \quad (93)$$

This *crossing relation*† can only have physical meaning when $q \to 0$, $q' \to 0$; this is only possible when the mass of the pion is negligible. In this case we get

$$\langle p;\, 0,\alpha'|\mathbf{T}|p;\, 0,\alpha\rangle = \langle p;\, 0,\alpha|\mathbf{T}|p;\, 0,\alpha'\rangle;$$

hence at zero energy $\mathbf{T}$ is symmetric in the isotopic indices; $\mathbf{T}$ must therefore be a multiple of $\delta_{\alpha\alpha'}$, so it is independent of isotopic spin to order (μ/M).‡ Because of the somewhat violent approximation, this gives little useful information about the low-energy phase shifts. As we shall see in the next section, the real value of the crossing relation is the information which it gives about formal extensions (e.g. analytic continuation) of the scattering matrix into regions of negative pion energy.

The integral equation

The result of (86 a) and (91 a) can be written (ignoring the last integral in (91 a))

$$\langle p';\, q',\alpha'|(S-I)|p;\, q,\alpha\rangle$$

$$= -(4\mathscr{E}_q\mathscr{E}_{q'})^{-\frac{1}{2}}\int\limits_{-\infty}^{\infty} d^4x \int\limits_{-\infty}^{\infty} d^4y\, e^{i(qy-q'x)}\langle\Psi(p')|T\{\mathbf{j}_{\alpha'}(x)\mathbf{j}_\alpha(y)\}|\Psi(p)\rangle. \quad (94)$$

The spatial integrals are evaluated by using the operator

$$\mathbf{J}_{\mathbf{q}}(y_0) = \int d^3\mathbf{y}\; e^{i\mathbf{q}.\mathbf{y}}\,\mathbf{j}_\alpha(\mathbf{y}, y_0). \quad (95)$$

By (86 b) the matrix element of $\mathbf{J}_{\mathbf{q}}(y_0)$ between states $|\mathbf{P}_1\rangle$, $|\mathbf{P}_2\rangle$ having

† M. Gell-Mann and M. L. Goldberger in *Proc. Fourth Ann. Rochester Conf.* (University of Rochester Press, 1954). In perturbation theory the crossing relation comes from exchanging the free pion lines representing the ingoing and outgoing pions.

‡ M = nucleon mass. The result follows from eqn. (133) below.

total momentum $\mathbf{P}_1$, $\mathbf{P}_2$, respectively, is

$$\langle \mathbf{P}_1 | \mathbf{J}_{\mathbf{q}}(y_0) | \mathbf{P}_2 \rangle = \delta_{\mathbf{P}_1, \mathbf{P}_2+\mathbf{q}}\, \mathbf{j}_\alpha(0, y_0), \tag{96}$$

where $\delta_{\mathbf{P}_1,\mathbf{P}_2+\mathbf{q}}$ equals unity if $\mathbf{P}_1 = \mathbf{P}_2+\mathbf{q}$, and is zero otherwise.

Similarly,

$$\langle \mathbf{P}_1 | \mathbf{\tilde{J}}_{\mathbf{q}'}(x_0) | \mathbf{P}_2 \rangle = \delta_{\mathbf{P}_1, \mathbf{P}_2-\mathbf{q}'}\, \mathbf{j}_{\alpha'}(0, x_0).$$

Thus we have†

$$\langle p'; q', \alpha' | (S-I) | p; q, \alpha \rangle = -(4\mathscr{E}_q \mathscr{E}_{q'})^{-\frac{1}{2}} \int\limits_{-\infty}^{\infty} dx_0 \int\limits_{-\infty}^{\infty} dy_0\, e^{i(\mathscr{E}_{q'}x_0 - \mathscr{E}_q y_0)} \times$$
$$\times \Bigg[\theta(x_0-y_0) \sum_{\substack{(n)\\(\mathbf{p}_n=\mathbf{p}+\mathbf{q})}} \langle \Psi(p') | \mathbf{j}_{\alpha'}(0, x_0) | n \rangle \langle n | \mathbf{j}_\alpha(0, y_0) | \Psi(p) \rangle +$$
$$+\theta(y_0-x_0) \sum_{\substack{(n)\\(\mathbf{p}_n=\mathbf{p}'-\mathbf{q})}} \langle \Psi(p') | \mathbf{j}_\alpha(0, y_0) | n \rangle \langle n | \mathbf{j}_{\alpha'}(0, x_0) | \Psi(p) \rangle \Bigg]. \tag{97}$$

Here $\sum_{(n)}$ denotes the summation over *all* Heisenberg states which have the total momentum $\mathbf{p}_n = \mathbf{p}+\mathbf{q}$ and $\mathbf{p}_n = \mathbf{p}'-\mathbf{q}$ respectively. The time dependence of $\mathbf{j}_{\alpha'}(0, x_0)$, $\mathbf{j}_\alpha(0, y_0)$ is given by (86 b). Substituting and integrating (and using (5.26)) gives‡

$$\langle p'; q', \alpha' | \mathbf{T} | p; q, \alpha \rangle = (4\mathscr{E}_q \mathscr{E}_{q'})^{-\frac{1}{2}} \times$$
$$\times \left\{ \sum_{\substack{(n)\\(\mathbf{p}_n=\mathbf{p}+\mathbf{q})}} \frac{\langle \Psi(p') | \mathbf{j}_{\alpha'}(0) | n \rangle \langle n | \mathbf{j}_\alpha(0) | \Psi(p) \rangle}{E_{p'} + \mathscr{E}_{q'} - E_n + i\eta} + \right.$$
$$\left. + \sum_{\substack{(n)\\(\mathbf{p}_n=\mathbf{p}'-\mathbf{q})}} \frac{\langle \Psi(p') | \mathbf{j}_\alpha(0) | n \rangle \langle n | \mathbf{j}_{\alpha'}(0) | \Psi(p) \rangle}{E_{p'} - \mathscr{E}_q - E_n + i\eta} \right\}. \tag{98}$$

E_n, E_p, $E_{p'}$ are the energies of the states $|n\rangle$, $|\Psi(p)\rangle$, $|\Psi(p')\rangle$ respectively, and η is an infinitesimal positive number. The derivation of (98) can readily be extended to include the last integral on the right of (91 a).

Eqn. (98) is one of a family of integral equations for the matrix elements of the current $\mathbf{j}_\alpha(0)$ between Heisenberg states.§ As it stands (98) gives the scattering matrix in terms of the interaction current $\mathbf{j}_\alpha(0)$. Although (98) looks like the result of second-order perturbation theory, it is actually very different, because $\mathbf{j}_\alpha(0)$ is a Heisenberg operator and because $|n\rangle$ can be *any* Heisenberg state of total momentum $(\mathbf{p}+\mathbf{q})$ or $(\mathbf{p}'-\mathbf{q})$, respectively. The summation includes summing over E_n.

† We use $\sum |n\rangle\langle n| = I$, where the sum is over *all* Heisenberg states.
‡ F. E. Low, *Phys. Rev.* **97** (1955) 1392.
§ M. Cini and S. Fubini, *Nuovo Cim.* **2** (1955) 192.

6. The theory of Chew and Low

Chew and Low† use eqn. (98) to develop a theory of the p-wave interactions of pions with a static nucleon. A pseudo-vector interaction based on (4.151) is used, and it is necessary to cut off the interaction at high pion momenta if we are to get finite results. A very important feature of their method is that the techniques used are of a general character; it is therefore hoped that the most important results will also hold in any more sophisticated realistic theory. For the present, no more satisfactory method is known.

The pseudo-vector interaction without recoil

We start with the interaction‡

$$H_{(\mathrm{p.v.})} = \frac{f}{\mu}\int d^3\mathbf{x} \sum_{\alpha=1}^{3} (\bar{\boldsymbol{\psi}}\boldsymbol{\sigma}\tau_\alpha\boldsymbol{\psi}.\mathrm{grad}\,\boldsymbol{\varphi}_\alpha).$$

Integrating by parts and using the Heisenberg equations of motion (45), gives the interaction current

$$\mathbf{j}_\alpha(x) = \frac{f}{\mu}\mathrm{div}\{\bar{\boldsymbol{\psi}}(x)\boldsymbol{\sigma}\tau_\alpha\boldsymbol{\psi}(x)\}. \tag{99}$$

For convenience we shall put $\mu = 1$ for the rest of this section. The matrix elements appearing in (98) are evaluated by using (45):

$$\begin{aligned}\langle\Psi(p')|\mathrm{div}(\bar{\boldsymbol{\psi}}\boldsymbol{\sigma}\boldsymbol{\psi})|n\rangle &= i\sum_{j=1}^{3}\langle\Psi(p')|\,[\bar{\boldsymbol{\psi}}\sigma_j\boldsymbol{\psi}, P_j]\,|n\rangle \\ &= i(\mathbf{p}_n-\mathbf{p}').\langle\Psi(p')|\bar{\boldsymbol{\psi}}\boldsymbol{\sigma}\boldsymbol{\psi}|n\rangle,\end{aligned} \tag{100}$$

where $\mathbf{p}'$, $\mathbf{p}_n$ are the momenta of the states $|\Psi(p')\rangle$, $|n\rangle$.

Substituting (99) and (100) into (98) would give a scattering theory which included nucleon recoil. Here we shall use the approximation appropriate for a very heavy nucleon, i.e. we *neglect* nucleon recoil and anti-nucleon-nucleon pairs. The real nucleon now becomes a fixed source; it is given by a state vector $|\Psi_0\rangle$ which describes any of the four possible states (two spin values and two isotopic spin values). The complete set of states $|n\rangle$ consists of the states $|\Psi_0\rangle$ together with states describing one or more pions in interaction with the nucleon. Neglecting nucleon recoil implies that the factor $(\mathbf{p}_n-\mathbf{p}')$ in (100) is to be replaced by the difference in the pion momentum between states $|n\rangle$ and $|\Psi_0\rangle$.

† G. F. Chew and F. E. Low, *Phys. Rev.* **101** (1956) 1570; G. C. Wick, *Rev. Mod. Phys.* **27** (1955) 339. See also L. Sartori and V. Watagin, *Nuovo Cim.* **12** (1954) 145; S. F. Edwards and P. T. Matthews, *Phil. Mag.* **2** (1957) 176.

‡ The pseudo-vector coupling constant f is related to the pseudo-scalar coupling constant G by $f/\mu = G/2M$ by the equivalence theorem (Chapter IV, § 14).

We now return to eqn. (94). Because recoil is neglected and we are working with a static nucleon, the spatial integration no longer gives the overall conservation of momentum. The factor $\exp[i(\mathbf{q}.\mathbf{y}-\mathbf{q}'.\mathbf{x})]$ in the integrand shows the transfer in pion momentum which must be produced by $\mathbf{j}_{\alpha'}(x)$ and $\mathbf{j}_{\alpha}(y)$. From (99) and (100) it follows that we have to make replacements like

$$\left.\begin{aligned} e^{-iq'x}\langle\Psi(p')|\mathbf{j}_{\alpha'}(x)|n\rangle &\rightarrow if\langle\Psi_0|(\boldsymbol{\sigma}.\mathbf{q}')\tau_{\alpha'}|n\rangle e^{-i(E_n-M+\mathscr{E}_{q'})x_0} \\ e^{iqy}\langle n|\mathbf{j}_{\alpha}(y)|\Psi(p)\rangle &\rightarrow -if\langle n|(\boldsymbol{\sigma}.\mathbf{q})\tau_{\alpha}|\Psi_0\rangle e^{i(E_n-M-\mathscr{E}_q)y_0} \end{aligned}\right\}. \tag{101}$$

The spatial integration in (94) is now trivial.

The integral equation

For the complete set of states $|n\rangle$, we use the single nucleon states $|\Psi_0\rangle$, plus all scattering states which consist of plane wave pions and *ingoing* spherical wave pions. In accord with the notation of Chapter V, § 1, this complete set is written $|\Psi_n^{(-)}\rangle$. ($|\Psi_{\text{out}}(\mathbf{q},\mathbf{q}')\rangle$ of page 308 above belongs to this set.) In order to get finite results it is necessary to use a cut-off factor $v(q)$; the terms $(\boldsymbol{\sigma}.\mathbf{q})$, $(\boldsymbol{\sigma}.\mathbf{q}')$ in (101) are to be replaced by $(\boldsymbol{\sigma}.\mathbf{q})v(q)$, $(\boldsymbol{\sigma}.\mathbf{q}')v(q')$ respectively. We define

$$\left.\begin{aligned} v(q) &= 1 \quad (\mathscr{E}_q < \omega_{\text{max}}) \\ v(q) &= 0 \quad (\mathscr{E}_q > \omega_{\text{max}}) \end{aligned}\right\}.$$

ω_{max} is to be much larger than the range of pion energies in which we are interested. It will appear that ω_{max} is of the order of the nucleon mass.

Now we write eqn. (98) in the static nucleon theory. We take the (observed) energy M of $|\Psi_0\rangle$ to be the zero of the energy scale. It is convenient to define

$$\left.\begin{aligned} V_q &= if(\boldsymbol{\sigma}.\mathbf{q})\tau_q v(q)(2\mathscr{E}_q)^{-\frac{1}{2}} \\ T_q(n) &= \langle\Psi_n^{(-)}|V_q|\Psi_0\rangle \end{aligned}\right\}; \tag{102}$$

here q is used to denote the isotopic state of the pion as well as its momentum. Writing $|\Psi_{q'}^{(-)}\rangle = |\Psi_{\text{out}}(q')\rangle$, the scattering matrix is (by (91 b))

$$\langle q'|\mathbf{T}|q\rangle = T_q(q').$$

Eqn. (98) now becomes

$$T_q(q') = -\sum_n \left\{\frac{\tilde{T}_{q'}(n)T_q(n)}{E_n-\mathscr{E}_q-i\eta}+\frac{\tilde{T}_q(n)T_{q'}(n)}{E_n+\mathscr{E}_{q'}}\right\}, \tag{103}$$

where, by energy conservation, $\mathscr{E}_q = \mathscr{E}_{q'}$. The summation is over all the states $|\Psi_n^{(-)}\rangle$; the small imaginary term plays no role in the second denominator and is omitted. It should be noted that although $T_q(q')$

refers to the energy shell ($\mathscr{E}_q = \mathscr{E}_{q'}$), the general term appearing on the right of (103) does not refer to the energy shell (in general $E_n \neq \mathscr{E}_q$).

The matrix function

Chew and Low† study the properties of (103) by introducing the matrix function $t_{qp}(z)$ of a complex variable z, viz.

$$t_{qp}(z) = -\sum_n \left\{\frac{\tilde{T}_p(n)T_q(n)}{E_n - z} + \frac{\tilde{T}_q(n)T_p(n)}{E_n + z}\right\} \quad (\text{with } \mathscr{E}_p = \mathscr{E}_q). \tag{104 a}$$

As $z \to \mathscr{E}_p + i\eta$, $t_{qp}(z) \to T_q(p)$. The crossing theorem (93) is expressed by the general relation‡

$$t_{qp}(z) = t_{pq}(-z) \tag{104 b}$$

(the two terms on the right of (104 a) exchange roles under crossing).

The sum in (103) includes the term $|\Psi_n^{(-)}\rangle = |\Psi_0\rangle$; this gives a simple pole of $t_{qp}(z)$ at $z = 0$ having the residue $\{\tilde{T}_p(0)T_q(0) - \tilde{T}_q(0)T_p(0)\}$. Also $T_q(0) = \langle\Psi_0^{(\beta)}|V_q|\Psi_0^{(\beta')}\rangle$, where β, β' denote the state (spin and charge) of the nucleon.

At this point, by using (102), we can define the *renormalized* coupling constant f_1 through the relation

$$f\langle\Psi_0^{(\beta)}|\sigma_i\tau_\alpha|\Psi_0^{(\beta')}\rangle = f_1\langle\Phi_0^{(\beta)}|\sigma_i\tau_\alpha|\Phi_0^{(\beta')}\rangle. \tag{105}$$

Here $|\Phi_0^{(\beta)}\rangle$, $|\Phi_0^{(\beta')}\rangle$ are the state vectors for the non-interacting nucleon. This definition of f_1 is possible because invariance under rotations and isotopic rotations requires the two matrix elements in (105) to have a constant ratio. We substitute (105) into the residue at $z = 0$ and retain f_1 explicitly in that term; thus the renormalized coupling constant appears in the zero-pion term.§ This definition has been shown‖ to be appropriate for treating the threshold photo-production of pions in the sense of the Kroll–Ruderman theorem (Chapter V, § 16).

The one-pion approximation

As $z \to \infty$, we expect that $t_{qp}(z)$ behaves as $(1/z)$. In addition to the pole at $z = 0$, it follows from (104 a) that $t_{qp}(z)$ has branch points at

† G. F. Chew and F. E. Low, loc. cit.

‡ By (102), the momentum reversal $\mathbf{p} \to -\mathbf{p}$, $\mathbf{q} \to -\mathbf{q}$ is trivial.

§ Even though a cut-off $\omega_{\max}$ is being used, it is necessary to renormalize f, because the real nucleon and the bare nucleon are not identical; the use of f_1 should give more consistent results. Further details of the renormalization are given by T. D. Lee, *Phys. Rev.* **95** (1954) 1329.

‖ A theory of threshold photo-production which is consistent with the above p-wave scattering theory has been given by G. F. Chew and F. E. Low, *Phys. Rev.* **101** (1956) 1579.

$z = \pm\mu$, and cuts along the real axis from μ to ∞, and from $-\mu$ to $-\infty$. Using these general properties, it is possible† to find a solution for $t_{qp}(z)$ in the one-pion approximation, i.e. when the summation over n in (104 a) is restricted to the states $|\Psi_0\rangle$ and the single-pion states $|\Psi_{\text{out}}(\mathbf{q}')\rangle$. This restriction implies that inelastic processes may be neglected. In this case, the unitary condition for $\mathbf{T}$ (eqn. (5.31)) shows that the scattering can be described by the usual pion-nucleon scattering phases (cf. § 4 above).

A little manipulation shows that the relation between the scattering matrix and the phases $\alpha_\gamma(\mathscr{E}_p)$ is given by (cf. the notation (78 b))

$$t_{qp}(z) = -\frac{2\pi}{\mathscr{E}_p}\sum_{(\gamma)} P_\gamma(p,q)h_\gamma(z) \quad (\mathscr{E}_p < \omega_{\max}),$$

where‡

$$\lim_{z\to\mathscr{E}_p+i\eta} h_\gamma(z) = \frac{1}{|\mathbf{p}|^3}e^{i\alpha_\gamma(\mathscr{E}_p)}\sin\{\alpha_\gamma(\mathscr{E}_p)\}. \tag{106}$$

The index $\gamma = (2T, 2J)$ denotes the four states of total angular momentum and isotopic spin J and T, and $P_\gamma(p,q)$ are the projection operators for these states, viz.

$$P_{11} = \tfrac{1}{3}\tau_p\tau_q(\boldsymbol{\sigma}.\mathbf{p})(\boldsymbol{\sigma}.\mathbf{q}), \quad P_{13} = \tfrac{1}{3}\tau_p\tau_q\{3(\mathbf{p}.\mathbf{q})-(\boldsymbol{\sigma}.\mathbf{p})(\boldsymbol{\sigma}.\mathbf{q})\},$$

$$P_{31} = (\delta_{pq}-\tfrac{1}{3}\tau_p\tau_q)(\boldsymbol{\sigma}.\mathbf{p})(\boldsymbol{\sigma}.\mathbf{q}), \quad P_{33} = (\delta_{pq}-\tfrac{1}{3}\tau_p\tau_q)\{3(\mathbf{p}.\mathbf{q})-(\boldsymbol{\sigma}.\mathbf{p})(\boldsymbol{\sigma}.\mathbf{q})\}. \tag{107}$$

The interaction (102) could equally well have been written in the form $V_{ij} = if\sigma_i\tau_j|\mathbf{q}|v(q)(2\mathscr{E}_q)^{-\frac{1}{2}}$, where i, j are coordinate indices in configuration space and isotopic space respectively; it follows by symmetry that, for p-wave pions interacting with nucleons through (102), the role of angular momentum and isotopic spin can be exchanged.§ This implies

$$\alpha_{31} = \alpha_{13}; \quad \text{i.e. } h_{(31)} = h_{(13)}.$$

From (106) and (107) it follows that $h_\gamma(z)$ has a simple pole at $z = 0$ with residue λ_γ; where, for $\gamma = (1,1)$, $(1,3)$, $(3,3)$, $\lambda_\gamma = -\frac{8}{3}f_1^2$, $-\frac{2}{3}f_1^2$, $\frac{4}{3}f_1^2$, respectively.

About the function $t_{qp}(z)$ (or $h_\gamma(z)$) we know the position of the singularities, the residue of the simple pole at the origin, and the crossing theorem;|| in addition, the discontinuity in $h_\gamma(z)$ across the cuts can be expressed simply. Chew and Low† show that these conditions

† See p. 330, n. †. Note also that $h_\gamma(z) \sim 1/z$ as $z \to \infty$.
‡ Here $\mathscr{E}_p = \mathscr{E}_q$.
§ Cf. F. H. Harlow and B. A. Jacobsohn, *Phys. Rev.* **93** (1954) 333.
|| The crossing theorem does not have quite the simple form (104 b) for $h_\gamma(z)$.

are satisfied by functions $h_\gamma(z)$, where

$$\frac{\lambda_\gamma}{zh_\gamma(z)} = 1-\frac{z}{\pi}\lambda_\gamma \int\limits_1^\infty \frac{d\mathscr{E}_q}{\mathscr{E}_q^2}\frac{|\mathbf{q}|^3v^2(q)}{\mathscr{E}_q-z}-\frac{z}{\pi}\int\limits_1^\infty \frac{d\mathscr{E}_q\, G_\gamma(\mathscr{E}_q)v^2(p)}{\mathscr{E}_q+z}. \tag{108}$$

Here $G_\gamma(\mathscr{E}_q)$ is a differentiable weight function. For the present purpose it is not necessary to discuss how $G_\gamma(\mathscr{E}_q)$ is determined.

The effective range approximation

An important result now follows. We let $z \to \mathscr{E}_p+i\eta$, and take the real part of (108). It is then reasonable to assume that the integrals

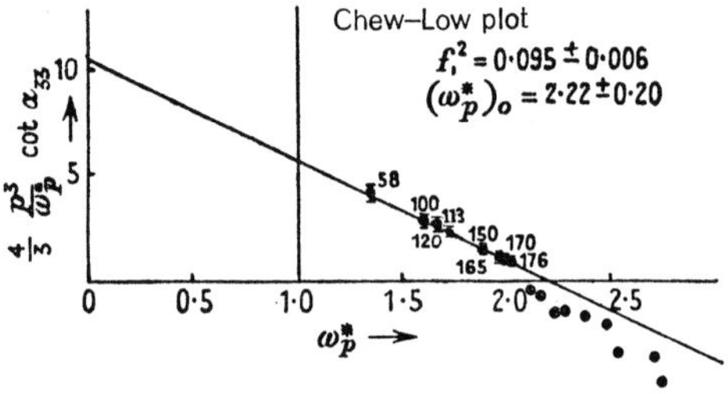

FIG. 35. The effective range analysis based on (π^+, P) scattering up to energies just above the first resonance. The physical region is $\omega_p^* \geqslant 1$. The intercept with $\omega_p^* = 0$ gives f_1^{-2}; the other intercept is the resonance.†

on the right of (108) vary slowly with $\mathscr{E}_p$ for small values of $\mathscr{E}_p/\omega_{\max}$.‡ By (106) this gives

$$\lambda_\gamma \frac{|\mathbf{p}|^3}{\mathscr{E}_p}\cot\{\alpha_\gamma(\mathscr{E}_p)\} = 1-\mathscr{E}_p\, r_\gamma(\mathscr{E}_p), \tag{109}$$

where $r_\gamma(\mathscr{E}_p)$ is almost constant for small $\mathscr{E}_p$. In analogy with eqn. (81) for the s-wave phases, this may be called the *effective range approximation*. In particular, it can be shown that

$$\tfrac{4}{3}f_1^2\frac{|\mathbf{p}|^3}{\mathscr{E}_p}\cot\{\alpha_{33}(\mathscr{E}_p)\} \simeq 1-\mathscr{E}_p\, r_3, \tag{110}$$

where r_3 is a *positive* constant. A cut-off $\omega_{\max}$ at about the nucleon rest mass gives the resonance ($\cot\alpha_{33} = 0$) at the correct energy. The theory predicts that α_{11} and $\alpha_{13} = \alpha_{31}$ should be small and negative. Fig. 35 shows how well the experimental values of α_{33} fit the formula (110); as a modification, to take some account of nucleon recoil, $\mathscr{E}_p$ is

† For further discussion and experimental results see J. Ashkin, J. P. Blaser, F. Feiner, and M. O. Stern, *Phys. Rev.* **105** (1955) 724 (where references to earlier work are given). See also G. F. Chew, *Encyclopedia of Physics* (Springer, Berlin, 1959), vol. xliii.

‡ This is borne out by the form of $G_\gamma(\mathscr{E}_q)$ for small $\mathscr{E}_q$ (cf. p. 330, n. †).

replaced by ω_p^* which includes the proton's kinetic energy (c.m.s.):

$$\omega_p^* = \mathscr{E}_p + \mathbf{p}^2/2M.$$

The experimental data† here show that $f_1^2 = 0{\cdot}095 \pm 0{\cdot}005$.

Comments

It has been suggested‡ that (108) is not the unique solution $h_\gamma(z)$. The solution (108) has no zeros of $h_\gamma(z)$ for real z, but other solutions may occur which have zeros on the real axis. The solution above, however, has the advantage that it is the analytic continuation of the perturbation theory solution;§ it is therefore expected to be the physically significant solution.

From the unitary property (Chapter V, § 2) it is easy, in the present approximation, to obtain sum rules for the total cross-sections in terms of the renormalized and the unrenormalized coupling constants.||

In addition to photo-production of pions, the method of Chew and Low has been applied to study the structure of the nucleon,†† and inelastic pion scattering.‡‡ Pion scattering and photo-production at low energies have been examined by a similar theory§§ which, as well as a pseudo-vector interaction, uses a phenomenological s-state interaction,|||| designed to give the correct isotopic dependence of α_1 and α_3 (eqn. (84)).

7. Dispersion relations (general)

It has just been shown that important general properties of pion-nucleon scattering result from the p-wave character of the interaction. Now we shall see how the powerful methods of *dispersion theory*††† give important results for pion-nucleon scattering assuming only that the pion-nucleon and pion-pion interactions are local.‡‡‡

The refractive index

In optics a dispersion relation is an integral relation connecting the real and imaginary parts of the refractive index $n(\omega)$; in other words,

† G. Puppi and A. Stanghellini, *Nuovo Cim.* **5** (1957) 1305.

‡ L. Castillejo, R. H. Dalitz, and F. J. Dyson, *Phys. Rev.* **101** (1956) 453.

§ For further discussion see R. Haag, *Nuovo Cim.* **5** (1957) 203.

|| M. Cini and S. Fubini, *Nuovo Cim.* **3** (1956) 764; also G. F. Chew and F. E. Low, loc. cit.

†† G. Salzman, *Phys. Rev.* **105** (1957) 1076 (where full references are given).

‡‡ J. Franklin, *Phys. Rev.* **105** (1957) 1101.

§§ S. D. Drell, M. H. Friedman, and F. Zachariasen, *Phys. Rev.* **104** (1956) 236.

|||| Cf. Chapter IV, § 14.

††† For the general discussion of dispersion relations, the author is much indebted to Prof. H. A. Bethe's Rouse Ball Lecture given at Cambridge in 1956.

‡‡‡ In a *local* interaction, field variables at the same space-time point are coupled. Because of the cut-off, the Chew–Low theory is, in effect, non-local.

it relates the refractive and the absorptive parts of $n(\omega)$. We shall show that there are analogous relations between the real and the imaginary parts of the scattering matrix for elementary particle collisions. First we consider a simple model of the optical case which shows the fundamental relation between dispersion relations and causality.

Classically, the refractive index of an optical medium can be described in terms of optical electrons (of charge e and mass m) which are bound in the atoms so that they have a natural period ω_0. Under the influence of an applied electric field $\mathbf{E}e^{-i\omega t}$, the displacement of the electron $\mathbf{x}(t)$ obeys

$$m(\ddot{\mathbf{x}}+\gamma\dot{\mathbf{x}}+\omega_0^2\mathbf{x}) = e\mathbf{E}e^{-i\omega t}.$$

γ is a *positive* damping constant which must necessarily be present. The motion of the electron gives rise to a refractive index $n(\omega)$, where

$$n^2-1 = \frac{Ne^2}{m}\frac{1}{\omega_0^2-\omega^2-i\gamma\omega} \tag{111}$$

(N is the number of atoms/c.c.).

If the atom contains electrons having several natural frequencies ω_k, then (111) becomes

$$n^2-1 = \frac{Ne^2}{m}\sum_k g_k\frac{1}{\omega_k^2-\omega^2-i\gamma_k\omega}, \tag{112}$$

where $\gamma_k > 0$ (all k), and g_k are constants. Using (1.40) (which holds when $|n-1|$ is small) and writing $f(\omega)$ for the forward scattering amplitude at frequency ω, we have

$$f(\omega) = \sum_k d_k\frac{\omega^2}{\omega_k^2-\omega^2-i\gamma_k\omega}, \tag{113}$$

where d_k are constants.

A dispersion relation

The poles of $f(\omega)$ regarded as a function of a complex variable ω, occur at $\omega = -\frac{1}{2}i\gamma_k\pm(\omega_k^2-\frac{1}{4}\gamma_k^2)^{\frac{1}{2}}$. Because $\omega_k^2 > \frac{1}{4}\gamma_k^2$ (all k),† the poles of $f(\omega)$ are all in the lower half-plane ($\operatorname{im}\omega < 0$). It is easy to prove the relation‡

$$P\int_{-\infty}^{\infty}\frac{d\omega'}{(\omega'-\alpha)(\omega'-\omega)} = \begin{Bmatrix}\dfrac{-\pi i}{\omega-\alpha}, & \operatorname{im}\alpha > 0\\[2ex] \dfrac{\pi i}{\omega-\alpha}, & \operatorname{im}\alpha < 0\end{Bmatrix}, \tag{114}$$

† This is the condition for $\ddot{\mathbf{x}}+\gamma_k\dot{\mathbf{x}}+\omega_k^2\mathbf{x} = 0$ to describe damped oscillations (as distinct from a periodic motion). This condition is not necessary.

‡ The principal value integral is the mean of the integrations along two straight lines a little above and a little below the real axis.

where α is a complex number, ω is real, and P denotes the principal value integration along the real axis. Remembering that $f(\omega)/\omega^2$ is a sum of terms like $1/(\omega-x_k+iy_k)$, where $y_k > 0$, it follows directly from (114) that (for real ω)

$$\left.\begin{aligned} P\int\limits_{-\infty}^{\infty} \frac{1}{\omega'-\omega}\frac{\mathrm{re}f(\omega')}{\omega'^2}\,d\omega' &= -\frac{\pi}{\omega^2}\mathrm{im}f(\omega) \\ P\int\limits_{-\infty}^{\infty} \frac{1}{\omega'-\omega}\frac{\mathrm{im}f(\omega')}{\omega'^2}\,d\omega' &= \frac{\pi}{\omega^2}\mathrm{re}f(\omega) \end{aligned}\right\}. \tag{115}$$

Real functions like $\mathrm{re}f(\omega')/\omega'^2$, $\mathrm{im}f(\omega')/\omega'^2$ which obey (115) are called *Hilbert transforms*, or *conjugate functions*.†

Eqns. (115) are converted into useful form by noting that (113) gives

$$\left.\begin{aligned} \mathrm{re}\,f(\omega) &= \mathrm{re}\,f(-\omega) \\ \mathrm{im}\,f(\omega) &= -\mathrm{im}\,f(-\omega) \end{aligned}\right\}; \tag{116}$$

hence we get the *dispersion relations*:

$$\left.\begin{aligned} P\int\limits_{0}^{\infty} \frac{\omega}{\omega'^2-\omega^2}\frac{\mathrm{re}\,f(\omega')}{\omega'^2}\,d\omega' &= -\frac{\pi}{2\omega^2}\mathrm{im}\,f(\omega) \\ P\int\limits_{0}^{\infty} \frac{\omega'}{\omega'^2-\omega^2}\frac{\mathrm{im}f(\omega')}{\omega'^2}\,d\omega' &= \frac{\pi}{2\omega^2}\mathrm{re}f(\omega) \end{aligned}\right\}. \tag{117}$$

Using (1.35) ($\mathrm{im}f(\omega) = \omega\sigma_{\mathrm{tot}}(\omega)/4\pi$), the second eqn. (117) relates $\mathrm{re}f(\omega)$ to an integral over $\sigma_{\mathrm{tot}}(\omega)$, the total cross-section for scattering and absorption of light by an atom.

The derivation of (117) depends essentially on the poles of $f(\omega)/\omega^2$ being in the lower half-plane; hence other dispersion relations exist. For example, subtracting from the second equation in (117) its value for $\omega = 0$, we get another dispersion relation. This device of using‡ $\{f(\omega)-f(0)\}$ increases the convergence of the integrals. Dispersion relations like (117) have been derived by various authors in classical and in quantum electrodynamics.§ Sum rules for the total cross-section $\sigma_{\mathrm{tot}}(\omega)$ are deduced if we know $f(0)$ and $\mathrm{re}f(\infty)$.‖

† The theory of such functions is given by E. C. Titchmarsh, *The Theory of Fourier Integrals* (Clarendon Press, 1937), ch. 5.

‡ $\mathrm{im}f(0) = 0$, because $\sigma_{\mathrm{tot}}(0)$ is finite.

§ R. Kronig, *J. Opt. Soc. Amer.* **12** (1926) 547; H. A. Kramers, *Atti. Congr. intern. fisici, Como*, **2** (1927) 545; M. Gell-Mann, M. L. Goldberger, and W. E. Thirring, *Phys. Rev.* **95** (1954) 1612.

‖ Several applications to sum rules are given by M. Gell-Mann *et al.*, loc. cit.

Causality

The relation between the dispersion relations and causality can be seen as follows. Suppose the incident wave train is

$$A(x_3, t) = \frac{1}{(2\pi)^{\frac{1}{2}}} \int_{-\infty}^{\infty} d\omega\, a(\omega) e^{i\omega(x_3 - t)}. \tag{118}$$

A single atom placed at the origin produces a scattered wave at distance r (in the forward direction):

$$G(r, t) = \frac{1}{(2\pi)^{\frac{1}{2}} r} \int_{-\infty}^{\infty} d\omega\, f(\omega) a(\omega) e^{i\omega(r-t)}, \tag{119}$$

where $f(\omega)$ is the forward scattering amplitude. Provided $a(\omega)$ has no poles in the region $\mathrm{im}\,\omega > 0$, then†

$$A(0, t) = 0 \quad \text{for } t < 0;$$

that is, the incident wave train does not reach the scattering atom before time $t = 0$. Causality requires that the scattered wave (119) is zero for $(t-r) < 0$. Because of the very general character of $a(\omega)$, this implies that $f(\omega)$ has no poles in the region $\mathrm{im}\,\omega > 0$. This proof does not depend on assuming any particular form (such as (113)) for $f(\omega)$. Hence, in general, relations similar to (115) hold; therefore causality implies that $f(\omega)$ obeys dispersion relations.

The argument which has just been given may be put in a much more general form.‡ Suppose an input signal $A(t)$ reaches a linear system§ (e.g. an atom, a nucleus, a radio amplifier), then the output signal $G(t)$ is of the form

$$G(t) = \frac{1}{(2\pi)^{\frac{1}{2}}} \int_{-\infty}^{\infty} F(t-t') A(t')\, dt', \tag{120}$$

where causality requires that

$$F(t) = 0, \quad \text{for } t < 0. \tag{121}$$

By (120), the Fourier transforms $g(\omega)$, $a(\omega)$, $f(\omega)$ of $G(t)$, $A(t)$, $F(t)$, respectively, are related by (cf. (119))

$$g(\omega) = f(\omega) a(\omega).$$

If

$$\int_{-\infty}^{\infty} |f(\omega)|^2\, d\omega$$

† The integral (118) for $A(0, t)$ is evaluated by residues; the contour may be completed for $t < 0$ by the infinite semicircle in $\mathrm{im}\,\omega > 0$.

‡ J. S. Toll, *Phys. Rev.* **104** (1956) 1760.

§ The output is to be a linear function (or a linear functional) of the input.

converges, there is a theorem† which states that (121) implies

$$\left.\begin{aligned} \operatorname{im} f(\omega) &= -\frac{1}{\pi} P \int\limits_{-\infty}^{\infty} \frac{\operatorname{re} f(\omega')}{\omega'-\omega}\, d\omega' \\ \operatorname{re} f(\omega) &= \frac{1}{\pi} P \int\limits_{-\infty}^{\infty} \frac{\operatorname{im} f(\omega')}{\omega'-\omega}\, d\omega' \end{aligned}\right\}. \qquad (122)$$

for all real ω. This is the basis of classical dispersion relations‡ which are applicable to a wide range of phenomena.§

8. Dispersion relations for pion-nucleon scattering

We now show how to derive dispersion relations‖ for elastic pion-nucleon scattering.†† The starting-point is the relation (92) giving the matrix $\mathbf{T}$ for the scattering of charged or neutral pions by nucleons. For $\mathscr{E}_q > \mu$, $\langle p'; q', \alpha'|\mathbf{T}|p; q, \alpha\rangle$ may be replaced by‡‡

$$\langle p'; q', \alpha'|\mathbf{M}|p; q, \alpha\rangle = -i(4\mathscr{E}_q \mathscr{E}_{q'})^{-\frac{1}{2}} \int\limits_{-\infty}^{\infty} d^4x\, e^{-iq'x} \times$$
$$\times \{\theta(x_0)\langle\Psi(p')|\,[\mathbf{j}_{\alpha'}(x), \mathbf{j}_\alpha(0)]\,|\Psi(p)\rangle +$$
$$+\delta(x_0)\langle\Psi(p')|\,[\dot{\boldsymbol{\varphi}}_{\alpha'}(x), \mathbf{j}_\alpha(0)]\,|\Psi(p)\rangle\}. \qquad (123)$$

The equivalence of (92) and (123) (for $\mathscr{E}_q \equiv q_0 > 0$) follows from (97) and (98). In the second denominator on the right of (98) the expression $(E_{p'} - \mathscr{E}_q - E_n)$ cannot vanish. The interaction current $\mathbf{j}$ must obey the conservation law of nucleons; hence the least value of $E_n^2 - (E_{p'} - \mathscr{E}_q)^2$ which can occur is§§

$$M^2 + (\mathbf{p}'-\mathbf{q})^2 - \{\sqrt{(M^2+\mathbf{p}'^2)} - \sqrt{(\mu^2+\mathbf{q}^2)}\}^2$$
$$= -\mu^2 + 2\{\sqrt{(M^2+\mathbf{p}'^2)}\sqrt{(\mu^2+\mathbf{q}^2)} - (\mathbf{p}'.\mathbf{q})\} > 0.$$

† E. C. Titchmarsh, *Theory of Fourier Integrals* (Clarendon Press, 1937), theorem 95, p. 128.

‡ For a more general discussion (and less restrictive conditions on $f(\omega)$) see J. S. Toll, loc. cit.

§ See p. 337, n. §. R. N. Euwema and J. A. Wheeler, *Phys. Rev.* **103** (1956) 803, relate the dispersive and the absorptive parts of vacuum polarization (cf. Chapter V, § 13). The absorptive part (giving real charge separation) is easily evaluated to the lowest order.

‖ A simple use of causality for s-wave scattering of Schrödinger waves gives the condition $d\delta(k)/dk > -a$, where $\delta(k)$ is the scattering phase, and a is the radius of the scatterer (E. P. Wigner, *Phys. Rev.* **98** (1955) 145).

†† The method is due to M. L. Goldberger, *Phys. Rev.* **99** (1955) 979.

‡‡ In writing (123) we have assumed that $\mathbf{j}_\alpha$ does not depend on $\dot{\boldsymbol{\varphi}}_\alpha$—this assumption simplifies the algebra, but it is not essential.

§§ The inequality follows on noting that the final expression is Lorentz invariant, and choosing a frame in which $\mathbf{q} = 0$. Other states $|n\rangle$ containing pions give larger values of E_n.

It follows that the denominator can be replaced by $(E_{p'}-\mathscr{E}_q-E_n-i\eta)$ without error; this is equivalent to replacing $\theta(y_0-x_0)$ in the second term in (97) by $-\theta(x_0-y_0)$. Hence (91 a) and (123) are equal† (for $\mathscr{E}_q > 0$).

The causality assumption is that the commutators in (123) vanish for $x_\mu^2 > 0$. It follows that the matrix $(4|\mathscr{E}_q\mathscr{E}_{q'}|)^{\frac{1}{2}}\mathbf{M}$ is the Fourier transform of a function which vanishes outside the forward light cone; therefore we expect the components of $(4|\mathscr{E}_q\mathscr{E}_{q'}|)^{\frac{1}{2}}\mathbf{M}$ to obey dispersion relations like (122).

Forward scattering

We now show how the dispersion relations for *forward scattering* are deduced. In this case it is convenient to use the laboratory system with $\mathbf{q} = \mathbf{q}'$ and $\mathbf{p} = \mathbf{p}' = 0$; α, α' indicate the charge state of the initial and final pions and p, p' denote the remaining nucleon quantum numbers. (The pion energy will now be written q_0.)

It is necessary to find the *dispersive* and the *absorptive* parts of $\mathbf{M}$. The absorptive part A comes from the integral (over E_n) around the poles in (98); the dispersive part D is given by the remaining principal value integration. Intermediate states $|n\rangle$ for which energy is conserved give the absorptive part, all other states $|n\rangle$ give the dispersive part. This definition agrees with the separation of the S-matrix element in Chapter V, §§ 1, 2, into real (absorptive) and virtual (dispersive) processes. The absorptive part A is a measure of the number of pions which are removed from the forward beam (by elastic or inelastic scattering). We write (123) as a function of q_0 $(= q_0')$:

$$2|q_0|\langle p';\mathbf{q},\alpha|\mathbf{M}|p;\mathbf{q},\alpha\rangle \equiv M_{\alpha'\alpha}(q_0;p',p) \quad (\mathbf{p}' = \mathbf{p} = 0).$$

The absorptive and dispersive parts are given by

$$M_{\alpha'\alpha}(q_0;p',p) = D_{\alpha'\alpha}(q_0;p',p)+iA_{\alpha'\alpha}(q_0;p',p), \tag{124}$$

with‡

$$\left.\begin{aligned} A_{\alpha'\alpha}&(q_0;p',p)\\ &= -\tfrac{1}{2}\int\limits_{-\infty}^{\infty} d^4x\, e^{-iqx}\langle\Psi(p')|\,[\mathbf{j}_{\alpha'}(x),\mathbf{j}_\alpha(0)]\,|\Psi(p)\rangle,\\ D_{\alpha'\alpha}&(q_0;p',p)\\ &= -\tfrac{1}{2}i\int\limits_{-\infty}^{\infty} d^4x\, e^{-iqx}\{\epsilon(x_0)\langle\Psi(p')|\,[\mathbf{j}_{\alpha'}(x),\mathbf{j}_\alpha(0)]\,|\Psi(p)\rangle+\\ &\qquad\qquad +2\delta(x_0)\langle\Psi(p')|\,[\dot{\boldsymbol{\varphi}}_\alpha(x),\mathbf{j}_\alpha(0)]\,|\Psi(p)\rangle\}\end{aligned}\right\}. \tag{125}$$

† The term $[\dot{\boldsymbol{\varphi}},\mathbf{j}]$ is unaltered by these manipulations.

‡ We use $2\theta(x_0) = 1+\epsilon(x_0)$. The term $[\dot{\boldsymbol{\varphi}}_{\alpha'}(x),\mathbf{j}_\alpha(0)]$ gives an infinitesimal contribution on the energy shell.

The negative frequencies

The dispersion relations involve $M_{\alpha'\alpha}(-q_0; p', p)$ which is obtained from (124), (125) on changing the sign of q_0 in the integrand. It should be noted that here, and in other extensions to negative q_0, the momentum $\mathbf{q}$ changes sign.† The definition (91 a) of $\mathbf{T}$ is similarly extended to negative frequencies by changing the sign of $\mathbf{T}$ in the integrand. Writing (for $|q_0| > \mu$)

$$2|q_0|\langle p'; \mathbf{q}, \alpha'|\mathbf{T}|p; \mathbf{q}, \alpha\rangle \equiv T_{\alpha'\alpha}(q_0; p', p) \quad (\mathbf{p}' = \mathbf{p} = 0),$$

it is easy to verify that‡ (cf. (124))

$$T_{\alpha'\alpha}(q_0; p', p) = D_{\alpha'\alpha}(q_0; p', p) + i\epsilon(q_0)A_{\alpha'\alpha}(q_0; p', p). \tag{126}$$

The derivation of the dispersion relations is simplified if we take account of various symmetry properties of $M_{\alpha'\alpha}(q_0; p', p)$. From (125) we get

$$A_{\alpha'\alpha}(q_0; p', p)^* = \tfrac{1}{2}\int\limits_{-\infty}^{\infty} d^4x\, e^{iqx}\langle\Psi(p)|[\mathbf{j}_{\alpha'}(x), \mathbf{j}_{\alpha}(0)]|\Psi(p')\rangle. \tag{127}$$

The strong interactions are parity conserving; hence as the nucleons p, p' have the same parity, the commutator in (127) can be replaced by

$$P[\mathbf{j}_{\alpha'}(\mathbf{x}, x_0), \mathbf{j}_{\alpha}(0)]P^{-1} = [\mathbf{j}_{\alpha'}(-\mathbf{x}, x_0), \mathbf{j}_{\alpha}(0)].$$

Substituting in (127) gives

$$\left.\begin{aligned} A_{\alpha'\alpha}(q_0; p', p)^* &= -A_{\alpha'\alpha}(-q_0; p, p') \\ \text{similarly,}\quad D_{\alpha'\alpha}(q_0; p', p)^* &= D_{\alpha'\alpha}(-q_0; p, p') \end{aligned}\right\}. \tag{128}$$

Substituting $x_\mu \to -x_\mu$ in (125) and using the translation invariance

$$\langle\Psi(p')|[\mathbf{j}_{\alpha'}(0), \mathbf{j}_{\alpha}(-x)]|\Psi(p)\rangle = \langle\Psi(p')|[\mathbf{j}_{\alpha'}(x), \mathbf{j}_{\alpha}(0)]|\Psi(p)\rangle,$$

$$\left.\begin{aligned} \text{we get}\quad A_{\alpha'\alpha}(q_0; p', p) &= -A_{\alpha\alpha'}(-q_0; p', p) \\ \text{similarly,§}\quad D_{\alpha'\alpha}(q_0; p', p) &= D_{\alpha\alpha'}(-q_0; p', p) \end{aligned}\right\} \quad (\textit{crossing}). \tag{129}$$

Further symmetry properties

It is convenient to write

$$\left.\begin{aligned} A_{\alpha'\alpha}(q_0; p', p) &= A^{(1)}_{\alpha'\alpha}(q_0; p', p) + iA^{(2)}_{\alpha'\alpha}(q_0; p', p) \\ D_{\alpha'\alpha}(q_0; p', p) &= D^{(1)}_{\alpha'\alpha}(q_0; p', p) + iD^{(2)}_{\alpha'\alpha}(q_0; p', p) \end{aligned}\right\}, \tag{130}$$

† The q_0 plane is cut from $-\mu$ to μ. Thus $\mathbf{q} = \boldsymbol{\epsilon} q(q_0)$ where $\boldsymbol{\epsilon}$ is a unit vector and $q = -(q_0^2-\mu^2)^{\frac{1}{2}}$ for $q_0 < -\mu$; $q = i(\mu^2-q_0^2)^{\frac{1}{2}}$ for $-\mu < q_0 < \mu$. In general

$$q^*(-q_0^*) = -q(q_0).$$

‡ Eqn. (126) is true in general. For $\mathscr{E}_q < -\mu$ the denominator $(E_p+\mathscr{E}_q-E_n+i\eta)$ of the first term in (98) can be replaced by $(E_p+\mathscr{E}_q-E_n-i\eta)$; this is equivalent to replacing $\theta(x_0-y_0)$ in the first term in (97) by $-\theta(y_0-x_0)$. The result agrees with (125).

§ In deriving the relation for $D_{\alpha'\alpha}$, the last commutator in (125) is expressed in the form

$$-\tfrac{1}{2}i\int d^4x\,\delta(x_0)\{e^{iqx}[\dot{\boldsymbol{\varphi}}_{\alpha}(x), \mathbf{j}_{\alpha'}(0)] + e^{-iqx}[\dot{\boldsymbol{\varphi}}_{\alpha'}(x), \mathbf{j}_{\alpha}(0)]\}.$$

where $A^{(1)}_{\alpha'\alpha}$, $D^{(1)}_{\alpha'\alpha}$ are symmetric, and $A^{(2)}_{\alpha'\alpha}$, $D^{(2)}_{\alpha'\alpha}$ are anti-symmetric in the pion charge indices α', α. It follows from (129) that $D^{(1)}$ and $A^{(2)}$ are *even* functions of q_0, while $D^{(2)}$ and $A^{(1)}$ are *odd* functions of q_0. Eqn. (128) then shows that all four matrices are Hermitian with respect to the nucleon indices p, p'; in particular, for $p = p'$ they are real. Hence $D^{(j)}_{\alpha'\alpha}(q_0;\, p,\, p')+D^{(j)}_{\alpha'\alpha}(q_0;\, p',\, p)$ and $A^{(j)}_{\alpha'\alpha}(q_0;\, p,\, p')+A^{(j)}_{\alpha'\alpha}(q_0;\, p',\, p)$ $(j = 1, 2)$ are the real and imaginary parts of functions whose Fourier transforms (with respect to q_0) vanish for $x_0 < 0$. The same is true for $\{D^{(j)}_{\alpha'\alpha}(q_0;\, p, p')-D^{(j)}_{\alpha'\alpha}(q_0;\, p', p)\}/i$ and $\{A^{(j)}_{\alpha'\alpha}(q_0;\, p, p')-A^{(j)}_{\alpha'\alpha}(q_0;\, p', p)\}/i$. Ignoring for the present any difficulties arising from the *unphysical region* $0 \leqslant |q_0| < \mu$, this implies the dispersion relations (cf. (122))

$$D^{(1)}_{\alpha'\alpha}(q_0;\, p', p) = \frac{1}{\pi} P \int\limits_{-\infty}^{\infty} d\omega \frac{A^{(1)}_{\alpha'\alpha}(\omega;\, p', p)}{\omega - q_0} = \frac{2}{\pi} P \int\limits_{0}^{\infty} d\omega \frac{\omega A^{(1)}_{\alpha'\alpha}(\omega;\, p', p)}{\omega^2 - q_0^2},$$

$$D^{(2)}_{\alpha'\alpha}(q_0;\, p', p) = \frac{1}{\pi} P \int\limits_{-\infty}^{\infty} d\omega \frac{A^{(2)}_{\alpha'\alpha}(\omega;\, p', p)}{\omega - q_0} = \frac{2q_0}{\pi} P \int\limits_{0}^{\infty} d\omega \frac{A^{(2)}_{\alpha'\alpha}(\omega;\, p', p)}{\omega^2 - q_0^2}.$$

The subtraction device is used to improve the convergence, giving (for example)†

$$\left.\begin{aligned} &D^{(1)}_{\alpha'\alpha}(q_0;\, p', p) - D^{(1)}_{\alpha'\alpha}(\mu;\, p', p) \\ &\qquad = \frac{2\mathbf{q}^2}{\pi} P \int\limits_{0}^{\infty} d\omega \frac{\omega A^{(1)}_{\alpha'\alpha}(\omega;\, p', p)}{(\omega^2 - q_0^2)(\omega^2 - \mu^2)} \\ &D^{(2)}_{\alpha'\alpha}(q_0;\, p', p) - \frac{q_0}{\pi} D^{(2)}_{\alpha'\alpha}(\mu;\, p', p) \\ &\qquad = \frac{2q_0\mathbf{q}^2}{\pi} P \int\limits_{0}^{\infty} d\omega \frac{A^{(2)}_{\alpha'\alpha}(\omega;\, p', p)}{(\omega^2 - q_0^2)(\omega^2 - \mu^2)} \end{aligned}\right\}. \tag{131}$$

Mathematical comments

Various steps in this derivation require careful discussion in a rigorous treatment. The term containing $\delta(x_0)$ occurring in the Fourier transform of $D_{\alpha'\alpha}$ (eqn. (125)) does not cause difficulty; it does not contribute if the final relations are sufficiently convergent.‡

A serious difficulty is the appearance of an exponential factor $\exp[\pm(\mathbf{n}.\mathbf{x})(\mu^2 - q_0^2)^{\frac{1}{2}}]$ in the unphysical region ($\mathbf{n}$ is a unit vector); the spatial integrals in (125) do not converge for $|q_0| < \mu$. In a rigorous‡ treatment it is necessary to integrate over time before completing the

† M. L. Goldberger, *Phys. Rev.* **99** (1955) 979.
‡ R. Oehme, *Phys. Rev.* **100** (1955) 1503; K. Symanzik, ibid. **105** (1957) 743.

spatial integration; eqns. (131) can then be derived after considerable labour.

Before evaluating (131) we must know the absorptive parts for the unphysical range $0 < \omega < \mu$. Integrating the first eqn. (125) gives

$$A_{\alpha'\alpha}(q_0; p', p)$$
$$= -8\pi^4 \sum_n \{\langle\Psi(p')|\mathbf{j}_{\alpha'}(0)|n\rangle\langle n|\mathbf{j}_\alpha(0)|\Psi(p)\rangle\delta^3(\mathbf{p}_n-\mathbf{q})\delta(M+q_0-E_n)-$$
$$-\langle\Psi(p')|\mathbf{j}_\alpha(0)|n\rangle\langle n|\mathbf{j}_{\alpha'}(0)|\Psi(p)\rangle\delta^3(\mathbf{p}_n+\mathbf{q})\delta(E_n-M+q_0)\}. \quad (132)$$

For $0 < q_0 < \mu$, only those real particle states (frequently called 'bound states') having $M < E_n < M+\mu$ can contribute to the absorptive part. The relation $q_0^2 = \mu^2+\mathbf{q}^2$ requires $\mathbf{q}$ to be imaginary in this region, and we shall see that only the single nucleon state can contribute. Here, in effect, we are making an analytic continuation. It is convenient to alter the notation before evaluating this term.

Isotopic spin notation†

By (126) and (130), $T_{\alpha'\alpha}$ can be written

$$T_{\alpha'\alpha} = T^{(1)}_{\alpha'\alpha}+iT^{(2)}_{\alpha'\alpha},$$

where $T^{(1)}_{\alpha'\alpha}$ and $T^{(2)}_{\alpha'\alpha}$ are symmetric and anti-symmetric in the pion indices α', α. Charge independence requires that when $T^{(1)}_{\alpha'\alpha}$, $iT^{(2)}_{\alpha'\alpha}$ are written as matrices in the nucleon isotopic space, they have the forms $\delta_{\alpha'\alpha}T^{(1)}$, $\tau_{\alpha'}\tau_\alpha T^{(2)}$, respectively;‡ so

$$T_{\alpha'\alpha} = \delta_{\alpha'\alpha}T^{(1)}+\tfrac{1}{2}[\tau_{\alpha'},\tau_\alpha]T^{(2)}. \quad (133)$$

Remembering that $\tilde{\phi}^{(-)} = 2^{-\frac{1}{2}}(\phi_1^{(-)}+i\phi_2^{(-)})$ and $\phi^{(-)} = 2^{-\frac{1}{2}}(\phi_1^{(-)}-i\phi_2^{(-)})$ create positive and negative pions respectively (Chapter II, § 7), it is easy to see that the scattering matrix for $\pi^+ \to \pi^+$ is

$$\tfrac{1}{2}(T_{11}+T_{22})-\tfrac{1}{2}i(T_{21}-T_{12}) = T^{(1)}-\tau_3 T^{(2)}.$$

For $\pi^- \to \pi^-$ the scattering matrix is $(T^{(1)}+\tau_3T^{(2)})$. Letting $T_+(q_0)$, $T_-(q_0)$ denote the scattering matrices for π^+ and π^- on protons, we have

$$\left.\begin{aligned} T_+(q_0) &= T^{(1)}(q_0)-T^{(2)}(q_0) \\ T_-(q_0) &= T^{(1)}(q_0)+T^{(2)}(q_0) \end{aligned}\right\}. \quad (134)$$

Relations analogous to (126) now define dispersive and absorptive parts $D_\pm(q_0)$, $A_\pm(q_0)$ for the scattering of charged pions by protons.

† It is convenient but *not* necessary to use charge independence to get (137).

‡ $T^{(1)}$, $T^{(2)}$ are matrices in ordinary spin space. $T^{(1)}$ gives no isotopic spin-flip and $T^{(2)}$ gives isotopic spin-flip.

The bound state contribution

Writing $\mathbf{j}_{\pm} = (1/\sqrt{2})(\mathbf{j}_1 \pm i\mathbf{j}_2)$, the 'bound state' contribution for coherent forward scattering is deduced from (132); it is†

$$A_{\pm}(\omega) = -\pi \sum_{\substack{n \\ (\mathbf{p}_n = -\mathbf{q})}} |\langle n|\mathbf{j}_{\mp}(0)|\Psi(p)\rangle|^2 \delta(M-\omega-E_n). \tag{135}$$

By charge conservation, only $\mathbf{j}_-(0)$ contributes, and $|n\rangle$ then represents a neutron. Any other states contributing to (132) must lie in the continuum range $\omega > \mu$. The absorption of the incident pion by the nucleon ordinarily violates energy conservation, but the process can occur in the unphysical range $0 < q_0 < \mu$. The conditions

$$E_n = (M^2+\mathbf{q}^2)^{\frac{1}{2}}, \quad E_n = M-q_0, \quad q_0 = (\mu^2+\mathbf{q}^2)^{\frac{1}{2}}.$$

are satisfied by $q_0 = (\mu^2/2M)$, $E_n = M-(\mu^2/2M)$. Thus

$$\left.\begin{aligned} A_+(\omega) &= -\pi|\langle n|\mathbf{j}_-(0)|\Psi(p)\rangle|^2\delta(\omega-\mu^2/2M) \\ A_-(\omega) &= 0 \end{aligned}\right\} \quad (0 \leqslant \omega < \mu). \tag{136}$$

We cannot get any more detailed information about $A_+(\omega)$ $(\omega < \mu)$ without considering a specific interaction. Using the pseudo-scalar interaction (eqn. (4.131)) eqn. (46 a) gives

$$\langle n|\mathbf{j}_-(0)|\Psi(p)\rangle = -iG_1(\boldsymbol{\sigma}.\mathbf{q}')/(2^{\frac{1}{2}}M);$$

G_1 is the renormalized (Watson–Lepore) coupling constant,‡ and

$$\mathbf{q}'^2 = (\mu^2/2M)^2-\mu^2.$$

Using this virtual matrix element and (131), (133), (134), we have the final form of the dispersion relations for the forward coherent scattering of charged pions:§

$$\left.\begin{aligned} D_+(q_0)-\tfrac{1}{2}\Big(1+\frac{q_0}{\mu}\Big)D_+(\mu)-\tfrac{1}{2}\Big(1-\frac{q_0}{\mu}\Big)D_-(\mu) \\ = 2\frac{f_1^2}{\mu^2}\frac{\mathbf{q}^2}{q_0-\mu^2/2M}+\frac{\mathbf{q}^2}{4\pi^2}\int\limits_{\mu}^{\infty}\frac{d\omega}{k}\Big[\frac{\sigma_+(\omega)}{\omega-q_0}+\frac{\sigma_-(\omega)}{\omega+q_0}\Big] \\ D_-(q_0)-\tfrac{1}{2}\Big(1+\frac{q_0}{\mu}\Big)D_-(\mu)-\tfrac{1}{2}\Big(1-\frac{q_0}{\mu}\Big)D_+(\mu) \\ = -2\frac{f_1^2}{\mu^2}\frac{\mathbf{q}^2}{q_0+\mu^2/2M}+\frac{\mathbf{q}^2}{4\pi^2}\int\limits_{\mu}^{\infty}\frac{d\omega}{k}\Big[\frac{\sigma_-(\omega)}{\omega-q_0}+\frac{\sigma_+(\omega)}{\omega+q_0}\Big] \end{aligned}\right\}. \tag{137}$$

Here $\mathbf{k}^2+\mu^2 = \omega^2$, and $f_1 = (\mu G_1/2M)$ is the effective renormalized

† We normalize to unit volume. ‡ In Heaviside units.

§ M. L. Goldberger, H. Miyazawa, and R. Oehme, *Phys. Rev.* **99** (1955) 988.

pseudo-vector coupling constant (cf. Chapter IV, § 14). The optical theorem (Chapter I, § 7) has been used to substitute

$$A_{\pm}(\omega) = \frac{k}{4\pi}\sigma_{\pm}(\omega) \quad (\omega > \mu), \tag{138}$$

where $\sigma_{\pm}(\omega)$ are the *total* cross-sections for π^+ and π^- striking protons.

In (137) and (138) we have made a slight change in the definition of $D_{\pm}(\omega)$ and $A_{\pm}(\omega)$; these are now the real and the imaginary parts of the elastic scattering amplitudes $f_{\pm}(\theta = 0, \omega)_{\text{lab}}$. For forward scattering eqn. (5.73) holds in any reference system. Using

$$(E_{\text{tot}})_{\text{lab}} = M+(\mathbf{q}^2+\mu^2)^{\frac{1}{2}}$$

it follows from eqn. (126), and the state vector normalization as defined in § 2 above, that†

$$f_{\pm}(\theta = 0, q_0)_{\text{lab}} = -\frac{1}{4\pi}T_{\pm}(q_0) \quad (j = 1, 2).$$

The factor $(4\pi)^{-1}$ is absorbed in the coupling constant f_1^2 in (137); the latter is now in Gaussian units.‡

The dispersion relations (137) have been used to examine the phase shifts, and in particular to prove that the phase shift α_{33} passes through 90° in the region of 180 MeV (lab.) pion energy.§ We substitute

$$D_{+}(\mu) = \left(1+\frac{\mu}{M}\right)a_3, \qquad D_{-}(\mu) = \left(1+\frac{\mu}{M}\right)(\tfrac{2}{3}a_1+\tfrac{1}{3}a_3),$$

where a_1 and a_3 are the s-wave scattering lengths. The relation||

$$\{f_{\pm}(0, q_0)/|\mathbf{q}|\}_{\text{lab}} = \{f_{\pm}(0, q_0)/|\mathbf{q}|\}_{\text{c.m.}}$$

gives $$D_{+}(q_0) = \frac{|\mathbf{q}_{\text{lab}}|}{2|\mathbf{q}_{\text{c.m.}}|^2}\{\sin 2\alpha_3+\sin 2\alpha_{31}+2\sin 2\alpha_{33}+...\}$$

and $$D_{-}(q_0) = \tfrac{1}{3}D_{+}(q_0)+\tfrac{2}{3}D_{1}(q_0),$$

with $$D_{1}(q_0) = \frac{|\mathbf{q}_{\text{lab}}|}{2|\mathbf{q}_{\text{c.m.}}|^2}\{\sin 2\alpha_1+\sin 2\alpha_{11}+2\sin 2\alpha_{13}+...\}.$$

In this calculation the coupling constant is taken as $f_1^2 = 0{\cdot}095$ (cf.

† State vector normalization gives an extra factor $(2\pi)^{-3}$ on the right of (5.73); then

$$f(\theta = 0, q_0)_{\text{c.m.}} = -\frac{1}{2\pi}\frac{(E_{\pi}.E_N)_{\text{c.m.}}}{(E_{\text{tot}})_{\text{c.m.}}}\langle\mathbf{q}|\mathbf{T}|\mathbf{q}\rangle.$$

The Lorentz transformation of $\mathbf{T}$ (Chapter V, p. 236, n. §) to the laboratory system gives the result.

‡ This can be checked by perturbation theory.

§ H. L. Anderson, W. C. Davidon, and U. F. Kruse, *Phys. Rev.* **100** (1955) 339; see also U. Haber-Schaim, ibid. **104** (1956) 1113.

|| This follows, either from footnote † above on using $|\mathbf{q}|_{\text{lab}} = |\mathbf{q}|_{\text{c.m.}}(E_{\text{tot}})_{\text{c.m.}}/M$, or from the invariance of σ_{tot} in (138) under Lorentz transformations along $\mathbf{k}$.

§ 6 above), and the experimental values of the *total* cross-sections $\sigma_{\pm}(\omega)$ (cf. § 4 above) are inserted in the integrals. It is assumed that the contributions to the integrals from the region $\omega > 2$ GeV are small.

A direct experimental check of (137) has been made by Puppi and Stanghellini.† They extrapolate the differential cross-section to $\theta = 0$; then $\{|f_{\pm}(\theta = 0, q_0)|^2 - (q_{\text{lab}}\,\sigma_{\pm}/4\pi)^2\}^{\frac{1}{2}}$ gives $D_{\pm}(q_0)$. For (π^+, P) scattering eqn. (137) is shown to be in good agreement with experiment up to (pion kinetic) energy 350 MeV. For (π^-, P) scattering a careful analysis‡ of the data up to 350 MeV shows little disagreement. A non-local or a non-causal interaction could give disagreement.

The scattering amplitude for nuclear spin-flip ($g(\theta)$ of eqn. (77)) vanishes in the forward direction. However, it is possible to find dispersion relations for $\{\partial g(\theta)/\partial\theta\}_{\theta=0}$ by very similar methods.§ These relations have been used to remove the Yang–Fermi ambiguity concerning the sign of $(\alpha_{31} - \alpha_{33})$.|| Dispersion relations for the scattering of pions†† through finite angles have been derived by various authors.‡‡ A rigorous derivation in the latter case has been given by N. Bogolubov.§§

This completes our survey of typical methods which have been comparatively successful in treating the strong pion-nucleon interaction. There are several very important pion-nucleon phenomena which appear to be beyond the scope of the present methods; in particular there is no convincing discussion of the scattering in the energy region about 1 GeV where inelastic processes become very important. Broadly speaking there is no theory of pion interactions which has anything like the scope and the accuracy of quantum electrodynamics.

† G. Puppi and A. Stanghellini, *Nuovo Cim.* **5** (1957) 1305.

‡ J. Hamilton, *Phys. Rev.* **110** (1958) 1134; H.-Y. Chiu and J. Hamilton, *Phys. Rev. Letters* **1** (1958) 146.

§ This has been done by R. Oehme, *Phys. Rev.* **100** (1955) 1503.

|| W. C. Davidon and M. L. Goldberger, *Phys. Rev.* **104** (1956) 1119; W. Gilbert and G. R. Screaton, ibid. 1758.

†† The connexion between dispersion relations and the p-wave fixed source theory of § 6 has been discussed by G. F. Chew, M. L. Goldberger, F. E. Low, and Y. Nambu, *Phys. Rev.* **106** (1957) 1337.

‡‡ M. L. Goldberger, M. Gell-Mann, and J. Polkinghorne, *Proc. Sixth Ann. Rochester Conf.* (Interscience, New York, 1956); A. Salam and W. Gilbert, *Nuovo Cim.* **3** (1956) 607; R. H. Capps and G. Takeda, *Phys. Rev.* **103** (1956) 1877.

§§ See N. N. Bogolubov and V. S. Vladimirov, *Izv. Akad. Nauk SSSR, Ser. Mat.* **22** (1958) 15. See also H. J. Bremermann, R. Oehme, and J. G. Taylor, *Phys. Rev.* **109** (1958) 2178.

VII

SELECTION RULES

1. The parity of π-mesons; the decay of κ-mesons

THE selection rules for angular momentum have been discussed in Chapter I. In Chapter III the breakdown of parity conservation for weak interactions (slow particle decays) was mentioned; for strong interactions, including electromagnetic effects, there is no evidence of parity violation. Before discussing other important selection rules we give some typical examples of the application of angular momentum and parity conservation to elementary particles. The direct experimental evidence† for the pseudo-scalar nature of pions is a good example.

The parity of pions

The spin of the positive pion π^+ was shown to be zero‡ by using the principle of detailed balance§ to compare the rate of the pion production process

$$P+P \rightarrow D+\pi^+,$$

with the inverse process in which π^+ is absorbed by deuterium and two protons are produced,

$$\pi^+ + D \rightarrow P+P.$$

Charge symmetry requires π^- and π^+ to have the same spin.|| Assuming the pion has zero spin, the existence of the process††

$$\pi^- + D \rightarrow N+N \tag{1}$$

for *stopped* π^-, shows that charged pions have negative parity.‡‡ It can be shown that π^- is captured in a Bohr s-orbit.§§ Because the ground

† Of course the theory of pion-nucleon interactions as given in Chapter VI and Chapter IV (§ 14) is very strong indirect evidence.

‡ W. F. Cartwright, C. Richman, M. N. Whitehead, and H. A. Wilcox, *Phys. Rev.* **91** (1953) 677. For spin S, σ(prod.)/σ(abs.) is proportional to $(2S+1)$.

§ This principle is discussed by J. M. Blatt and V. F. Weisskopf, *Theoretical Nuclear Physics* (J. Wiley, New York, 1952), ch. 10.

|| Charge conjugation commutes with spatial rotations.

†† Process (1) was observed directly by W. Chinowsky and J. Steinberger, *Phys. Rev.* **95** (1954) 1561.

‡‡ π^+ and π^- must have the same parity because of the symmetric roles they play in pion-nucleon scattering. For boson fields this is to be expected; charge conjugation only involves taking the complex conjugate (cf. Chapter IV, § 12).

§§ For a discussion see H. A. Bethe and F. de Hoffmann, *Mesons and Fields* (Row, Peterson, Evanston, Ill., 1955), vol. ii, p. 15.

state of the deuteron is ${}^3S_1$, the total angular momentum of the two neutrons is $J = 1$. The Pauli principle does not allow the neutrons to be in the ${}^3S_1$, ${}^1P_1$, or ${}^3D_1$ states of relative motion; this is because exchanging the positions of the neutrons is equivalent to the parity operation. The neutrons must be in the ${}^3P_1$ state, therefore π^- has negative intrinsic parity.†

The neutral pion

The neutral pion π^0 decays into two γ-rays with a lifetime of less than 1×10^{-15} sec.‡ The existence of this decay process proves that π^0 cannot have unit spin.§ Let us suppose a meson of spin 1 decays into two γ-rays, and assume that the γ-rays have momenta $\mathbf{p}$ and $-\mathbf{p}$. The component of angular momentum of each γ-ray along $\mathbf{p}$ can only be $\hbar$ or $-\hbar$; therefore the component of the total angular momentum along $\mathbf{p}$ can only be $2\hbar$, 0 (twice), $-2\hbar$. It follows that the meson has *zero* component of angular momentum along $\mathbf{p}$. Its wave function has the angular form $Y_1^{(0)}(\theta,\phi) \sim \cos\theta$, where $\theta = 0$ is the direction $\mathbf{p}$; therefore rotation through 180° about an axis perpendicular to $\mathbf{p}$ will reverse the sign of the meson wave function. The same rotation merely exchanges the two γ-rays, hence it leaves their wave function unaltered. Thus a spin-1 particle cannot have a 2γ decay mode. The simplest assumption (which fits charge independence, etc.) is that π^0 has zero spin.

The capture reaction

$$\pi^- + D \rightarrow N + N + \pi^0 \tag{2}$$

for stopped π^- appears to be fairly strongly forbidden.‖ This is strong evidence for the pseudo-scalar nature of π^0. The Pauli principle allows the two neutrons to be in a ${}^1S_0$, ${}^3P$, ${}^1D_2$,... state of relative motion; the pion can move in a state of definite angular momentum relative to the centre of mass of the two neutrons. The total angular momentum is again $J = 1$. If π^0 had positive parity it could be in a p-state and the neutrons in the ${}^1S_0$ state; in that case the reaction (2) would certainly occur. If π^0 has negative parity, it will be in a p-state and the neutrons are in a ${}^3P$ state. Because there is little kinetic energy available,†† the overlap between this ${}^3P$ state and the deuteron is very small; in this case the reaction is forbidden.

† We can only determine the parity of $\pi^\pm$ relative to that of proton and neutron.

‡ G. Harris, J. Orear, and S. Taylor, *Phys. Rev.* **106** (1957) 327; they measure the lifetime by using the rare alternative decay $\pi^0 \rightarrow e^+ + e^- + \gamma$.

§ C. N. Yang, *Phys. Rev.* **77** (1950) 242.

‖ W. Chinowsky and J. Steinberger, *Phys. Rev.* **100** (1955) 1476.

†† $m_{\pi^-} - m_{\pi^0} = 8{\cdot}8 m_e \simeq 4{\cdot}5$ MeV; the deuteron binding energy is 2·2 MeV.

Parity and the γ-rays

The decay of π^0 into γ-rays is so fast that it must be produced by a strong interaction. We assume therefore that parity is conserved and examine the consequences for the γ-rays. The γ-rays, which have momenta $\mathbf{p}_1 = \mathbf{p}$, $\mathbf{p}_2 = -\mathbf{p}$, can be in either of the states $|\psi_a\rangle$, $|\psi_b\rangle$ shown in Fig. 36 (*a*), (*b*); $\mathbf{S}_1$, $\mathbf{S}_2$ are the spins of the photons. Spatial inversion P changes the sign of the momenta but leaves the spins unaltered.† Applying inversion to $|\psi_a\rangle$ and exchanging the two photons gives $|\psi_b\rangle$; thus $P|\psi_a\rangle = |\psi_b\rangle$, similarly $P|\psi_b\rangle = |\psi_a\rangle$. Therefore the state $(|\psi_a\rangle+|\psi_b\rangle)$ has even parity, and $(|\psi_a\rangle-|\psi_b\rangle)$ has odd parity.

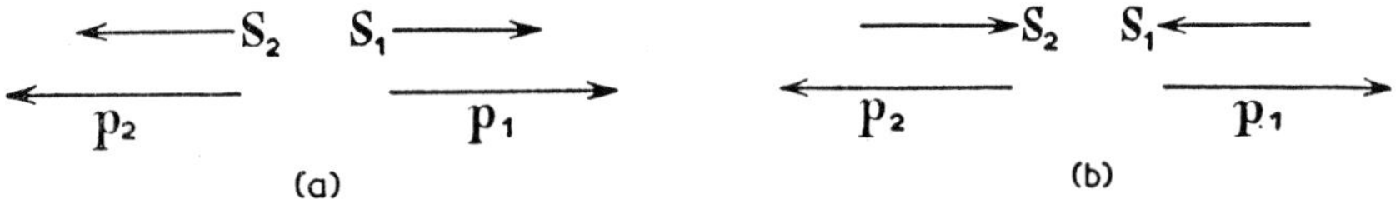

FIG. 36. Both (*a*) and (*b*) are two-photon states having zero total momentum and total spin. Spatial inversion changes (*a*) into (*b*), and vice versa.

Let $\mathbf{A}^{(1)}$, $\mathbf{A}^{(2)}$ be the operators creating the first and second photons. Taking the O_3 axis along $\mathbf{p}$, the states $|\psi_a\rangle$, $|\psi_b\rangle$ are multiples of‡

$$(A_1^{(1)}+iA_2^{(1)})(A_1^{(2)}-iA_2^{(2)})|0\rangle, \qquad (A_1^{(1)}-iA_2^{(1)})(A_1^{(2)}+iA_2^{(2)})|0\rangle,$$

respectively. From these state vectors we can form states of even and odd parity $\mathbf{A}^{(1)}.\mathbf{A}^{(2)}|0\rangle$ and $(\mathbf{A}^{(2)}\times\mathbf{A}^{(1)}.\mathbf{p})|0\rangle$ respectively. The potential operator $\mathbf{A}$ is parallel to the polarization of the created photon; it follows that the two γ-rays from the decay of π^0 have perpendicular polarization. A scalar particle would give parallel polarization of the two γ-rays (i.e. the state $\mathbf{A}^{(1)}.\mathbf{A}^{(2)}|0\rangle$).

An interesting example of these rules is the decay of the $^1S_0$ state of positronium. As was seen in Chapter IV, § 5, this state annihilates to give two γ-rays; because the electron and the positron in the S-state have opposite parities (Chapter III, § 6) the γ-rays must have perpendicular polarization.

K-meson decays

The K-meson decays $(K_{\pi 2}, K_{\pi 3}, K_{\mu 2}, K_{\mu 3}, K_{e3})$§ arise from a particle which in each case has a mass of about|| $966m_e$. It is reasonable to

† Spin vectors being angular momenta are axial vectors.

‡ Cf. Chapter I, § 14.

§ $K_{\pi 2} \rightarrow 2\pi$, $K_{\pi 3} \rightarrow 3\pi$, $K_{\mu 2} \rightarrow \mu+\nu$, $K_{\mu 3} \rightarrow \mu+\pi+\nu$, $K_{e3} \rightarrow e+\pi+\nu$. The particles labelled ν are unidentified, but they are assumed to be neutrinos.

|| W. H. Barkas *et al.*, *Phys. Rev.* **105** (1957) 1417; J. R. Peterson, ibid. 693.

assume that the $K_{\mu 2}$, $K_{\mu 3}$, K_{e3} are alternative modes of decay of the $K_{\pi 2}$ or $K_{\pi 3}$ mesons. Therefore we assume that the K-mesons are bosons.† We now consider whether the selection rules would allow us to regard all these decays as different decay modes of a *single* K-meson. It is simplest to discuss the $K_{\pi 2}$ (or θ-meson) and the $K_{\pi 3}$ (or τ-meson) modes. Both

$$\tau^{\pm} \to \pi^{\pm}+\pi^{+}+\pi^{-}, \qquad \tau'^{+} \to \pi^{+}+\pi^{0}+\pi^{0}$$

and

$$\theta^{\pm} \to \pi^{\pm}+\pi^{0} \tag{3 a}$$

have been observed.‡§ A neutral particle which decays by the mode

$$\theta^{0} \to \pi^{+}+\pi^{-} \tag{3 b}$$

is well established; it also has an alternative mode of decay $\theta^0 \to \pi^0+\pi^0$.‡ ||

The neutral decay mode $\theta^0 \to 2\pi^0$ would not be possible if θ^0 had odd spin; the wave function of two identical bosons must be symmetric under exchange of the particles, and this is not possible in a state of odd relative angular momentum.

The K-meson decays are weak processes (for charged K the mean lifetimes are about 10^{-8} sec, and for θ^0 about 10^{-10} sec). We might therefore expect parity conservation to be violated. For the moment we examine the consequences of parity conservation. The decays (3 a) and (3 b) then restrict the spin and parity values of θ to 0^+, 1^-, 2^+,....

Parity conservation will not allow τ to be 0^+. Consider τ^+; let the relative angular momentum of the two π^+ be L, and the angular momentum of π^- relative to the centre of mass of the two π^+ be l. Obviously L must be even, and the parity of τ is $(-1)^{l+1}$. Spin $J = 0$ can only occur if $l = L$, so we have a 0^- τ-meson. This argument does not exclude a 1^- τ-meson, but if we wish to preserve parity and allow for the mode $\theta^0 \to 2\pi^0$, the simplest *single particle* which would obey the selection rules is a 2^+ K-meson. However, analysis†† of experimental data for τ^+ mesons, using simple considerations,‡‡ shows that τ is a 0^- mode. Hence K has spin 0 and K-decay violates parity. Other evidence for this is the longitudinal polarization of μ^+ in $K_{\mu 2}$ decay.§§

† The disintegration products of a boson do not include an odd number of fermions.
‡ See *Proc. Seventh Rochester Conf.* (Interscience, New York, 1957).
§ W. Birge *et al.*, *Nuovo Cim.* **4** (1956) 834.
|| S. L. Ridgway, D. Berley, and G. B. Collins, *Phys. Rev.* **104** (1956) 513.
†† R. P. Haddock, *Nuovo Cim.* **4** (1956) 240.
‡‡ For example, the presence of slow π^- in τ^+ decay would tend to suggest $l = 0$.
§§ C. A. Coombes *et al.*, *Phys. Rev.* **108** (1957) 1348.

2. Anti-nucleon annihilation

Charge conjugation was used in Chapter IV, § 5, to give selection rules for the annihilation of positronium. A similar method could be used to obtain selection rules for the annihilation of anti-nucleons by nucleons; it is however more convenient and more systematic to assume that anti-nucleon annihilation conserves isotopic spin as well as the charge conjugation eigenvalue.†

The annihilation of an anti-nucleon in a nucleus generally produces pions.‡ On the average there are four to five pions created, and in a few cases K-mesons have also been seen. Most of the selection rules we derive are only of value when a small number (two or three) pions are produced and when annihilation takes place in a state of definite angular momentum (the latter is the case for the annihilation of a *stopped* anti-proton).§ It is reasonable to assume that in a nucleus the annihilation process occurs between the anti-nucleon and a single nucleon.§

As we saw in Chapter IV, § 11, the total isotopic spin of a nucleon and an anti-nucleon can be zero or unity. For each value, there are isotopic state vectors which are symmetric or anti-symmetric for particle exchange; we label these isotopic spin states $T' = 0^s,\ 0^a,\ 1^s,\ 1^a$ (cf. eqns. (4.127), (4.128)).

Charge conjugation

Let u_P, u_N, $u_{\bar{P}}$, $u_{\bar{N}}$ be state vectors for a proton, neutron, anti-proton, anti-neutron, respectively, having the same momentum and spin. The charge conjugation operator U as defined in Chapter IV, § 5 (especially eqns. (4.74), (4.75)), gives

$$U\begin{pmatrix} u_P \\ u_N \end{pmatrix} = \begin{pmatrix} u_{\bar{P}} \\ u_{\bar{N}} \end{pmatrix}, \qquad U\begin{pmatrix} u_{\bar{P}} \\ u_{\bar{N}} \end{pmatrix} = \begin{pmatrix} u_P \\ u_N \end{pmatrix}. \tag{4}$$

The charge conjugation operator U exchanges positive and negative pions; therefore it obeys

$$U\phi U^{-1} = \tilde{\phi}, \qquad U\tilde{\phi}U^{-1} = \phi, \tag{5}$$

where ϕ, $\tilde{\phi}$ are the pion field operators defined in Chapter II, § 7. By (5), the unitary operator U exchanges the creation (or destruction) operators for positive and negative pions (cf. eqn. (2.114)). The neutral

† The selection rules when isotopic spin is not conserved are discussed on p. 354.
‡ W. H. Barkas *et al.*, *Phys. Rev.* **105** (1957) 1037.
§ See H. A. Bethe and J. Hamilton, *Nuovo Cim.* **4** (1956) 1, for further discussion.

pion has the same charge conjugation properties as the two γ-rays into which it annihilates.† From (4.73):

$$UA_\mu(x_\nu)U^{-1} = -A_\mu(x_\nu);$$

it follows that

$$U\phi_3(x_\nu)U^{-1} = \phi_3(x_\nu), \tag{6}$$

where ϕ_3 is the neutral pion field operator. Thus the neutral pion is its own anti-particle; it has the charge conjugation eigenvalue‡

$$U' = +1.$$

In addition to charge conjugation we use the unitary operator R which produces a rotation of 180° about the O_1 axis in isotopic spin space. For the pion field this rotation§ gives

$$R\phi_1(x_\nu)R^{-1} = \phi_1(x_\nu), \quad R\phi_2(x_\nu)R^{-1} = -\phi_2(x_\nu),$$
$$R\phi_3(x_\nu)R^{-1} = -\phi_3(x_\nu).$$

Hence, by (2.100),

$$R\phi(x_\nu)R^{-1} = \tilde{\phi}(x_\nu), \quad R\tilde{\phi}(x_\nu)R^{-1} = \phi(x_\nu), \quad R\phi_3(x_\nu)R^{-1} = -\phi_3(x_\nu). \tag{7}$$

The form of R for the nucleon field is deduced from the fact that the 2×2 matrix $\frac{1}{2}\tau_1$ is the generator for infinitesimal rotations about the O_1 axis;|| hence the transformation of the nucleon operator $\psi(x_\nu)$ and its Hermitian conjugate $\tilde{\psi}(x_\nu)$ is

$$\left.\begin{aligned} R\psi(x_\nu)R^{-1} &= i\tau_1\psi(x_\nu) \\ R\tilde{\psi}(x_\nu)R^{-1} &= -i\tilde{\psi}(x_\nu)\tau_1 \end{aligned}\right\}; \tag{8}$$

here we have used $\exp(\frac{1}{2}i\pi\tau_1) = i\tau_1$. It follows from (4.26) that the state vectors u_P, etc., obey††

$$R\begin{pmatrix} u_P \\ u_N \end{pmatrix} = -i\begin{pmatrix} u_N \\ u_P \end{pmatrix}, \qquad R\begin{pmatrix} u_{\bar{P}} \\ u_{\bar{N}} \end{pmatrix} = i\begin{pmatrix} u_{\bar{N}} \\ u_{\bar{P}} \end{pmatrix}. \tag{9}$$

Obviously the operator R is closely related to the charge symmetry operation in the theory of nuclear forces (see Chapter IV, § 12).

† π^0 annihilation is a fast process; we expect charge conjugation to be valid.

‡ It follows that so long as charge conjugation is not violated, π^0 cannot decay into an odd number of γ-rays.

§ Isotopic space for pions is discussed in Chapter II, § 8.

|| Cf. Chapter IV, § 11.

†† The minus sign in the second term of (9) occurs because the pair (u_P, u_N) is *covariant* with $(u_{\bar{N}}, -u_{\bar{P}})$ for isotopic space rotations. Cf. eqn. (4.125).

The operator W

Our selection rules are obtained by using the operator† $W = U.R$. Clearly

$$\left.\begin{aligned} W\phi(x_\nu)W^{-1} = \phi(x_\nu), \quad W\tilde{\phi}(x_\nu)W^{-1} = \tilde{\phi}(x_\nu), \\ W\phi_3(x_\nu)W^{-1} = -\phi_3(x_\nu) \end{aligned}\right\} \tag{10}$$

and

$$W\begin{pmatrix} u_P \\ u_N \end{pmatrix} = -i\begin{pmatrix} u_{\bar{N}} \\ u_{\bar{P}} \end{pmatrix}, \qquad W\begin{pmatrix} u_{\bar{P}} \\ u_{\bar{N}} \end{pmatrix} = i\begin{pmatrix} u_N \\ u_P \end{pmatrix}. \tag{11}$$

Charge is associated with gauge transformations of the type $\phi \rightarrow e^{i\alpha}\phi$, $\tilde{\phi} \rightarrow e^{-i\alpha}\tilde{\phi}$; that is, charge is related to rotations in one sense about the O_3 isotopic axis. Charge conjugation reverses the sense of the rotation; hence it is given by reflection in any plane containing the O_3 isotopic axis. In particular, with the representation given by (5) and (6) above, U corresponds to reflection in the plane O_{13}. It follows that the operator W describes reflection in the plane O_{12} in isotopic space.

From its geometrical property we deduce that $W^2 = 1$, and that W commutes with T_3, the generator of infinitesimal rotations about the axis O_3; also, W anti-commutes with T_1 and T_2, the generators of infinitesimal rotations about the axes O_1 and O_2. (These statements are readily verified using (10) and (11).)

The eigenvalues of W are $W' = \pm 1$. If we can find a state $|a\rangle$ which is an eigenstate of W and of T_3, with eigenvalues W', T_3' respectively, then the states $(T_1 \pm iT_2)|a\rangle$ are eigenstates of W and T_3 having the eigenvalues $(-W')$ and $(T_3' \pm 1)$ respectively. Consequently, all the information given by W for a set of eigenstates of $\mathbf{T}^2$ $(-T' \leqslant T_3' \leqslant T')$ is contained in the eigenvalue of W for the eigenstate $T_3' = 0$ of this set.‡

By (10) the eigenvalue of W for a pion state is $(-1)^{n_{\pi^0}}$, where n_{π^0} is the number of neutral pions. Also, for nucleon–anti-nucleon pair states we have, by (11),

$$W(u_P^{(1)}u_{\bar{P}}^{(2)} \pm u_N^{(1)}u_{\bar{N}}^{(2)}) = u_N^{(1)}u_{\bar{N}}^{(2)} \pm u_P^{(1)}u_{\bar{P}}^{(2)},$$

where the superscripts 1 and 2 label the particles. It follows from (4.128) that for the $T' = 0^s$, 0^a states, the eigenvalues are $W' = +1$, -1 respectively. Similarly for $T_3' = 0$, $T' = 1^s$ and $T' = 1^a$ we have $W' = -1$ and $+1$ respectively. In general $W' = (-1)^{T'+L+S}$.

† This, or a similar method, has been used by D. Amati and B. Vitate, *Nuovo Cim.* **2** (1955) 719; H. A. Bethe and J. Hamilton, loc. cit.; T. D. Lee and C. N. Yang, *Nuovo Cim.* **3** (1956) 749. The last authors write G for W.

‡ See the appendix to the paper by H. A. Bethe and J. Hamilton, loc. cit.

The selection rules

The selection rules follow directly. In a pion state with $T'_3 = 0$ the number of charged pions is even, or zero. Therefore the state $T' = 0^s$ and the three states $T' = 1^a$ ($T'_3 = -1, 0, 1$) must give an *even* number of pions on annihilation. Similarly, the state $T' = 0^a$ and the three states $T' = 1^s$ ($T'_3 = -1, 0, 1$) must give an *odd* number of pions.

Suppose the nucleon-anti-nucleon pair is in an eigenstate of angular momentum J. By the Pauli principle the $T' = 0^s$, 1^s states can only be ${}^1S_0$, ${}^3P$, ${}^1D_2$, ${}^3F$,...; while $T' = 0^a$, 1^a can only be ${}^3S_1$, ${}^1P_1$, ${}^3D$, ${}^1F_3$,.... From Chapter I, § 11, we see that, for two pions, the isotopic state $T' = 0$ must be symmetric in the pion spatial coordinates, while the $T' = 1$ states are anti-symmetric in these coordinates. Hence for two-pion states, $T' = 0$ gives even J and even parity, while $T' = 1$ gives odd J and odd parity. Remembering that the intrinsic parity of the nucleon is opposite to that of the anti-nucleon, it follows that two-pion annihilation can only occur from the states

$$T' = 0^s\colon \quad {}^3P_{0,2},\ {}^3F_{2,4},\ldots;$$
$$T' = 1^a\colon \quad {}^3S_1,\ {}^3D_{1,3},\ldots.$$

In applying this rule we notice that if a proton P and an anti-proton $\bar{P}$ move around each other in a Bohr orbit, by (4.127) the isotopic component of the state vector is of the form

$$|\bar{P}P\rangle = \frac{1}{\sqrt{2}}|T'{=}0\rangle - \frac{1}{\sqrt{2}}|T'{=}1,\ T'_3{=}0\rangle. \tag{12}$$

If, for example, they are in a ${}^3P$-state, the pure isotopic states appearing in (12) must be $T' = 0^s$ and $T' = 1^s$, $T'_3 = 0$.

For annihilation leading to three-pion states the selection rules are not so restrictive. If the nucleon–anti-nucleon pair are in an S- or a P-state, three-pion annihilation can occur from†

$$T' = 0^a\colon \quad {}^3S_1,\ {}^1P_1; \qquad T' = 1^s\colon \quad {}^1S_0,\ {}^3P_{1,2}.$$

Finally we notice that even if it turns out that isotopic spin is not a good quantum number for the annihilation process, the conservation of charge conjugation, angular momentum, and parity gives a very restrictive set of selection rules. For example, it is easy to verify that two-pion annihilation cannot occur for a nucleon–anti-nucleon pair in the ${}^1S_0$, ${}^1P_1$, ${}^3P_1$,... states.‡

† ${}^3P_0$ does not occur because we cannot form a pseudo-scalar out of the momenta $\mathbf{p}_1$, $\mathbf{p}_2$, $\mathbf{p}_3$ of the three pions where $\mathbf{p}_1+\mathbf{p}_2+\mathbf{p}_3 = 0$ (c.m.s.).

‡ For a comprehensive list of selection rules see L. Michel, *Nuovo Cim.* **10** (1953) 319; T. D. Lee and C. N. Yang, ibid. **3** (1956) 749.

3. Time reversal

The propagation equations for fields, for example Maxwell's equations and Dirac's equation, do not require that time should go forward rather than backward; in fact, corresponding to each solution which goes forward in time there will be a solution going backward in time. Apart from the boundary conditions which are imposed, there appears to be no preference in elementary particle physics for motion forward rather than backward in time. The laws of elementary particle physics therefore show certain invariance properties under time reversal, or time reflection. We now examine the scope of these invariance properties and their consequences.

Wigner time reversal

This type of time reversal is an extension of time reversal as applied to a classical dynamical system. It yields a number of important results in quantum theory. For a classical system, under time reversal, the space-time coordinates of a particle obey

$$\mathbf{x}' = \mathbf{x}, \qquad t' = -t.$$

Consequently the velocity of any particle is reversed and we have

$$\mathbf{v}' = -\mathbf{v}, \quad \mathbf{p}' = -\mathbf{p}, \quad \mathbf{L}' = -\mathbf{L}, \tag{13}$$

where $\mathbf{v}$, $\mathbf{p}$, $\mathbf{L}$ are the velocity, momentum, and angular momentum. Relations (13) mean that when time is reversed, the particle (or particles) move along the same path in the opposite direction.†

In the presence of an electromagnetic field it is necessary that both terms in $\{\mathbf{p}+(e/c)\mathbf{A}\}$ should change sign together; otherwise we cannot preserve the vector properties. This determines the form of $\mathbf{A}(\mathbf{x},t)$ under time reversal which is required to preserve our interpretation of (13). In Wigner's time reversal it is assumed that the charge e is invariant. It follows that for the electromagnetic field

$$\mathbf{A}'(\mathbf{x},t) = -\mathbf{A}(\mathbf{x},-t), \qquad \phi'(\mathbf{x},t) = \phi(\mathbf{x},-t). \tag{14}$$

The second expression in (14) is deduced from Poisson's equation. Both relations (14) are consistent with

$$\mathbf{j}'(\mathbf{x},t) = -\mathbf{j}(\mathbf{x},-t), \qquad \rho'(\mathbf{x},t) = \rho(\mathbf{x},-t). \tag{15}$$

The 4-vectors $(\mathbf{A},\phi)$, $(\mathbf{j},\rho)$ transform in the opposite way to $(\mathbf{x},t)$ under time reversal. By (14), the electric and magnetic field strengths obey

$$\mathbf{E}'(\mathbf{x},t) = \mathbf{E}(\mathbf{x},-t), \qquad \mathbf{H}'(\mathbf{x},t) = -\mathbf{H}(\mathbf{x},-t). \tag{16}$$

The consistency of (15) and (16) shows how a system of particles can

† More precisely, $\mathbf{v}'(t) = -\mathbf{v}(-t)$, etc.

have the reversed motion under the influence of their *mutual* electric and magnetic effects. In other words, the motion of the system cannot be used to distinguish the positive from the negative time direction. Eqns. (16) show that if *external* fields are present, it is necessary to change the sign of the external magnetic field to obtain the reversed motion.

It is shown in § 5 that invariance under Wigner time reversal (like invariance under charge conjugation) may break down in elementary particle processes which violate parity conservation. So far as is known these invariance properties hold in all strong interactions (including electromagnetic interactions). For the remainder of this section we assume invariance under time reversal, that is $H' = H$ where H is the Hamiltonian of the interacting system. In Chapter VIII, § 7 (see also Chapter VIII, § 6) time-reversal invariance is used to eliminate certain terms in the nucleon-nucleon scattering matrix. (Elastic scattering proceeds backward in time at the same rate as it goes forward, provided we reverse the spin directions.)

Time reversal in wave mechanics

Wigner† has shown the form of time reversal in wave mechanics. He discusses an atomic system without external magnetic fields, so that $H' = H$. The Schrödinger equation for this system should not distinguish between the forward and the backward time directions.‡

The usual wave function $\psi(t)$ for such a system and its time reverse $\psi'(t')$ obey, respectively,

$$i\hbar\frac{\partial\psi(t)}{\partial t} = H\psi(t); \qquad -i\hbar\frac{\partial\psi'(t')}{\partial t'} = H\psi'(t'). \tag{17}$$

The solution of the second equation is related to the complex conjugate of the first equation. Let $\mathscr{K}_0$ be the operator which takes the complex conjugate of all terms to its right. Clearly $\mathscr{K}_0^2 = 1$; $\mathscr{K}_0$ is not a linear operator.§ The corresponding solutions of (17) are connected by

$$\psi'(t) = \mathscr{K}\psi(t), \tag{18}$$

where $\mathscr{K} = V\mathscr{K}_0$, and the constant unitary operator V is chosen so that

$$\mathscr{K}^{-1}H\mathscr{K} = H. \tag{19}$$

† E. P. Wigner, *Nachr. Ges. Wiss. Göttingen* (1932), p. 546.

‡ The non-relativistic Hamiltonian for several particles,

$$H = \sum \frac{1}{2m_j}\left\{\mathbf{p}_j + \frac{e_j}{c}\mathbf{A}(\mathbf{x}_j, t)\right\}^2 - \sum e_j\,\phi(\mathbf{x}_j, t),$$

is a simple example. By (13) and (14), $H' = H$.

§ Because $\mathscr{K}_0(a\psi_1 + b\psi_2) = a^*\mathscr{K}_0\psi_1 + b^*\mathscr{K}_0\psi_2$, where a, b are constants.

Corresponding to (18), the time reverse A' of any dynamical variable A is

$$A' = \mathscr{K}^{-1}A\mathscr{K}. \tag{20}$$

For spinless particles interacting through scalar potentials, H is a *real* operator,† and (19) is satisfied by $V = I$. Using the representation in which the coordinates are diagonal, we also see that $V = I$ gives the relations (13).‡ For particles with spin, V must be chosen carefully. Consider an electron which is described by the two-component Pauli wave functions. The spin $\boldsymbol{\sigma}$ must behave like an angular momentum under time reversal; thus

$$\boldsymbol{\sigma}' = -\boldsymbol{\sigma} = \mathscr{K}^{-1}\boldsymbol{\sigma}\mathscr{K}. \tag{21}$$

Using the representation (3.34) we see that $\mathscr{K} = \sigma_2\mathscr{K}_0$ satisfies (21).§

A simple consequence is that if invariance under time reversal is assumed, elementary particles cannot possess electric dipole moments.‖ Such a dipole moment must be of the form $d\boldsymbol{\sigma}$, where d is the dipole strength and $\boldsymbol{\sigma}$ is the spin of the particle. It gives an interaction energy $d(\boldsymbol{\sigma}.\mathbf{E})$ in an electric field; by (21) and (16) this changes sign on time reversal.†† Hence d must be zero.

Real and imaginary Hermitian operators

Hermitian operators A and B, such that

$$A' = A, \qquad B' = -B,$$

are called *real* and *imaginary* operators, respectively. Wigner deduces an important result from (19) and (20): the sum of the expectation values of any imaginary Hermitian operator over all eigenstates of the Hamiltonian which have the same eigenvalue E must vanish. Suppose ψ_k is an eigenstate of H, then, by (19), $\mathscr{K}\psi_k$ is also an eigenstate of H having the same eigenvalue. If $\psi_k \neq \mathscr{K}\psi_k$, we can write

$$\psi_k = u_k + iv_k, \qquad \mathscr{K}\psi_k = u_k - iv_k, \tag{22}$$

where $$u_k = \tfrac{1}{2}(\psi_k + \mathscr{K}\psi_k), \qquad v_k = \frac{1}{2i}(\psi_k - \mathscr{K}\psi_k).$$

We must have $\mathscr{K}^2 = 1$, hence‡‡

$$\mathscr{K}u_k = u_k, \qquad \mathscr{K}v_k = v_k. \tag{23a}$$

† For example, in the non-relativistic case,

$$H = \sum_j (\hbar^2/2m_j)\nabla_j^2 + \sum_{j,k} v_{jk}.$$

‡ $\mathscr{K}_0^{-1}\mathbf{p}\mathscr{K}_0 = \mathscr{K}_0(\hbar/i)\,\text{grad}\,\mathscr{K}_0 = -\mathbf{p}$.

§ $\mathscr{K} = \sigma_2\mathscr{K}_0$ also satisfies (19) because $\boldsymbol{\sigma}$ can only appear in H together with a function (e.g. $\mathbf{H}$) which changes sign on reversing time.

‖ L. Landau, *Nuclear Phys.* **3** (1957) 127.

†† Of course, invariance under space inversion gives the same result.

‡‡ For an odd number of fermions, $\mathscr{K}^2 = -1$, and another is used (p. 358).

The sum of the expectation values of B over all states having the eigenvalue E is therefore

$$\sum_{(E)} (\psi_k^* B\psi_k) = 2\sum_k \{(u_k^* Bu_k)+(v_k^* Bv_k)\}. \tag{23 b}$$

By (23 a) and (20),

$$\begin{aligned}(u_k^* Bu_k) &= \{(\mathscr{K}u_k)^* B\mathscr{K}u_k\} = -\{(\mathscr{K}u_k)^*\mathscr{K}Bu_k\}\\ &= -\{(\mathscr{K}_0 u_k)^*\mathscr{K}_0 Bu_k\} = -\{(Bu_k)^* u_k\}\\ &= -(u_k^* Bu_k).\end{aligned}$$

The last step uses the Hermitian property of B. It follows that (23 b) vanishes, and the theorem is proved.† We deduce that the sum of the expectation values of momentum, angular momentum component, electron spin, etc., over all states of a system which have the same energy E will vanish. A similar theorem holds for the sum of the expectation values of any imaginary Hermitian operator B over all eigenstates of any real Hermitian operator A which have the same eigenvalue A'; for example, A could be the total angular momentum $\mathbf{J}^2$, and B the current density operator $\mathbf{j}(\mathbf{x})$.

Angular momentum (standing wave) eigenstates

The time reversal of the eigenstates of angular momentum gives important results. The method we shall use is applicable to any system (atoms, nuclei, or elementary particles) provided the Hamiltonian is invariant under time reversal; for convenience the language of wave mechanics is used. Let $\psi_J^{(M)}$ be an eigenstate of the Hamiltonian H, the the total angular momentum $\mathbf{J}^2$, and its component J_3, with eigenvalues E, $J(J+1)$, and M respectively. From (20) we have

$$\mathbf{J} = -\mathscr{K}^{-1}\mathbf{J}\mathscr{K}. \tag{24}$$

Eqns. (19) and (24) show that $\mathscr{K}\psi_J^{(M)}$ is an eigenstate of the same three operators, having the eigenvalues E, $J(J+1)$, and $(-M)$ respectively. Hence $\mathscr{K}\psi_J^{(M)}$ is a constant multiple of $\psi_J^{(-M)}$; if the normalization of $\psi_J^{(M)}$ and $\psi_J^{(-M)}$ is the same, this constant must have modulus unity. It is only the angular component of $\psi_J^{(M)}$ which is altered by applying $\mathscr{K}$. The radial part of these eigenstates is a standing wave.

Let us consider the case of a spinless particle. Then $\mathscr{K} = \mathscr{K}_0$, and the angular momentum component is $Y_l^{(m)}(\theta,\phi)$. By (1.47),

$$\mathscr{K}_0 Y_l^{(m)} = (-1)^m Y_l^{(-m)}. \tag{25}$$

† For $\mathscr{K}^2 = -1$, we use

$$(\psi_k^* B\psi_k) = ((\mathscr{K}B\psi_k)^*\mathscr{K}\psi_k) = -((B\mathscr{K}\psi_k)^*\mathscr{K}\psi_k) = -((\mathscr{K}\psi_k)^* B\mathscr{K}\psi_k).$$

Summing over ψ_k the result follows.

For an electron, $\mathscr{K} = \sigma_2 \mathscr{K}_0$ (in the representation (3.34)). Let $u(\sigma_3')$ be the spin eigenfunction for spin component $\frac{1}{2}\hbar\sigma_3'$ ($\sigma_3' = \pm 1$). Now

$$\mathscr{K} Y_l^{(m)}(\theta,\phi)u(\sigma_3') = (-1)^m Y_l^{(-m)}(\theta,\phi)\,\sigma_2\,u(\sigma_3')$$
$$= (i)^{(2m+\sigma_3')} Y_l^{(-m)}(\theta,\phi)u(-\sigma_3'). \quad (26)$$

Here the phases of the spin functions are chosen so that $\mathscr{K}_0\,u(\sigma_3') = u(\sigma_3')$. Thus in both these cases the phases *can be chosen* so that

$$\psi_J^{(M)\prime} = \mathscr{K}\psi_J^{(M)} = i^{2M}\psi_J^{(-M)}. \quad (27)$$

In any problem† the phases of the angular and spin components (or the phases of the state vectors) can be chosen so that (27) is true.‡

The reaction matrix

Eqn. (27) enables us to prove an important property of the reaction matrix **K** (Chapter V, § 3). If the free particle Hamiltonian H_0 and the interaction H_{int} are invariant under time reversal, it follows from (5.67) that the reaction matrix **K** is invariant under time reversal, i.e.

$$\mathscr{K}^{-1}\mathbf{K}\mathscr{K} = \mathbf{K}. \quad (28)$$

Let $\psi_{\alpha J}^{(M)}$ be the eigenstates of the *free particle* Hamiltonian H_0; α denotes the remaining quantum numbers. The matrix **K** may be written in terms of these stationary eigenstates, thus

$$\mathbf{K} = \sum_M \sum_{\alpha,\alpha'} \langle\alpha|\mathbf{K}|\alpha'\rangle \psi_{\alpha J}^{(M)}\psi_{\alpha' J}^{(M)*} \quad (29)$$

(we consider only the sub-matrix referring to total angular momentum J). Using (27), (28), and (29), we get

$$\langle\alpha|\mathbf{K}|\alpha'\rangle^* = \langle\alpha|\mathbf{K}|\alpha'\rangle.$$

Because **K** is Hermitian it follows§ that in the representation given by (27), $\langle\alpha|\mathbf{K}|\alpha'\rangle$ is *real and symmetric*.

This property can be used to give important information about the off-diagonal elements of the scattering matrix **T**. Consider the photo-production of pions near threshold in a state of definite angular momentum. Labelling the first row and column by the γ-ray-nucleon state and the second by the pion-nucleon state, the reaction matrix has the form (cf. eqn. (5.64))

$$\mathbf{K} = \begin{pmatrix} 0 & \gamma \\ \gamma & -\frac{1}{\pi}\tan\delta \end{pmatrix}, \quad (30)$$

† It is easy to build up the more complicated cases from the results (25) and (26).

‡ E. P. Wigner, loc. cit. See also R. G. Sachs, *Phys. Rev.* **87** (1952) 1100.

§ K. M. Watson, *Phys. Rev.* **95** (1954) 228. See also E. Fermi, *Suppl. Nuovo Cim.* **1** (1955) 17; M. Gell-Mann and K. M. Watson, *Ann. Rev. Nuclear Sci.* **4** (Annual Reviews Inc., Stanford, Cal., 1954).

where γ, δ are real, and δ is the pion-nucleon scattering phase for the values of energy and angular momentum concerned.† Near threshold γ is small; using (cf. (5.62))

$$\mathbf{T} = \mathbf{K} - i\pi\mathbf{K}\mathbf{T},$$

in the same standing wave representation, gives (on neglecting γ^2)

$$\mathbf{T} = \begin{pmatrix} 0 & \gamma e^{i\delta}\cos\delta \\ \gamma e^{i\delta}\cos\delta & -\frac{1}{\pi}e^{i\delta}\sin\delta \end{pmatrix}. \tag{31}$$

The method on p. 78 shows $\mathbf{T}$ has the same form for *outgoing* final waves. The off-diagonal terms in (31) give the photo-production amplitude. So long as γ is small, this amplitude is of the form $e^{i\delta}\times$(real quantity); Watson has made considerable use of this property.‡

This property of $\mathbf{K}$ has also been used to relate the amplitude for the production of pions in a nucleon-nucleon collision to the difference of two nucleon-nucleon scattering phases. Cf. Chapter VIII, § 10, p. 420.

4. Time reversal for quantized fields

For a relativistic quantized field theory it is more natural to use a different form of time reversal which we call *strong reflection* (SR for short). In SR,

$$x'_\mu = -x_\mu, \quad j'_\mu(x'_\nu) = -j_\mu(x_\nu), \quad P'_\mu = P_\mu, \tag{32}$$

where j_μ and P_μ are the charge-current density and the energy-momentum 4-vectors respectively. Eqn. (32) shows that the sign of all charges is reversed in SR; the condition $P'_\mu = P_\mu$ is necessary if we are to keep the energy positive.

Strong reflection

The transformation SR is a consequence of invariance under *proper* Lorentz transformations. In the notation of Chapter I, § 1, proper Lorentz transformations obey

$$\det(a_{\mu\nu}) = +1, \tag{33 a}$$

and

$$a_{44} > 0. \tag{33 b}$$

† γ-ray scattering by the nucleon is neglected, and for simplicity of argument we do not consider charge exchange scattering. The argument is easily extended to the general case. (Note that $\mathbf{T}$ is symmetric because $\mathbf{K}$ is symmetric.)

‡ K. M. Watson, *Phys. Rev.* **95** (1954) 228. See also E. Fermi, p. 359, n. §.

§ A similar method has been used to discuss hyperon and K-meson decays. G. Takeda, *Phys. Rev.* **101** (1956) 1547.

Consider any classical field tensor $T_{\mu_1\ldots\mu_n}$ of rank n, and apply the proper Lorentz transformation

$$\left.\begin{aligned} x'_\mu &= a_{\mu\nu}x_\nu \\ a_{11} = a_{22} = -1, \quad a_{33} &= a_{44} = \cosh\theta \\ a_{34} = -a_{43} &= i\sinh\theta \end{aligned}\right\}. \tag{34}$$

where†

Then $$T'_{\mu_1\cdots\mu_n}(x'_\nu) = a_{\mu_1\lambda_1}\ldots a_{\mu_n\lambda_n}T_{\lambda_1\ldots\lambda_n}(x_\nu),$$

so $T'(x'_\nu)$ and x'_ν are functions of $\cosh\theta$ and $\sinh\theta$. They can be expressed by absolutely convergent power series in θ. Hence we can replace θ by the pure imaginary value $i\phi$; condition (33 a) (but not (33 b)) is still satisfied. Choosing $\theta = i\pi$ gives‡

$$x'_\mu = -x_\mu, \qquad T'_{\mu_1\ldots\mu_n}(x') = (-1)^n T_{\mu_1\ldots\mu_n}(x). \tag{35}$$

The equations of motion are Lorentz covariant: it follows§ that if $T_{\mu_1\ldots\mu_n}(x_\nu)$ is a solution of the equations, then $(-1)^n T_{\mu_1\ldots\mu_n}(-x_\nu)$ is also a solution. Hence a relativistic classical boson field theory is invariant under the operation SR. A somewhat more complicated proof of invariance under SR is necessary in the fermion case; this has been given by several authors.||

In relativistic quantized field theory, eqn. (35) is still valid when we use the Heisenberg representation. The invariance of relativistic quantized theories under SR follows;|| however, there are several matters which require careful discussion.

The interpretation of the transformed operators is deduced from the equations of motion. Any Heisenberg variable f obeys

$$\frac{\partial f}{\partial x_\mu} = \frac{i}{\hbar}[f, P_\mu]. \tag{36}$$

No *linear* transformation of f can preserve this equation under SR (eqn. (32)), because the left-hand side must change sign relative to the right-hand side when we reverse the sign of x_μ. This difficulty is avoided†† if, after making the operation SR, each state vector $|\psi'_a\rangle$ is replaced by its complex conjugate $|\psi'_a\rangle^*$. This is equivalent to replacing each Hermitian operator by its transpose.‡‡ It is much more convenient to adopt the equivalent rule that after SR each operator formula is to

† All other $a_{\mu\nu}$ vanish.

‡ J. S. Bell, *Proc. Roy. Soc.* A, **231** (1955) 479.

§ We have $$\frac{\partial}{\partial x'_{\mu_1}} T'_{\mu_1\ldots\mu_n}(x'_\nu) = (-1)^{n-1}\frac{\partial}{\partial x_{\mu_1}} T_{\mu_1\ldots\mu_n}(x_\nu), \quad \text{etc.}$$

|| G. Lüders, *K. danske vidensk. Selsk.* **28** (1954), No. 5; also the article by W. Pauli in *Niels Bohr and the Development of Physics* (Pergamon, London, 1955).

†† J. Schwinger, *Phys. Rev.* **82** (1951) 914.

‡‡ $\langle\psi'_b|A'|\psi'_a\rangle^* = \langle\psi'_a|A'_T|\psi'_b\rangle$ (T denotes the transpose).

be read from right to left instead of from left to right.† This compensates for the change of sign in (36) when f and x_μ are replaced by f' and x'_μ. This rule is used here.

SR for field operators

The SR transform of the field operators is deduced from the Lorentz transformation properties. For the electromagnetic field (because $A_\mu(x)$ is a 4-vector)

$$A'_\mu(x_\lambda) = -A_\mu(-x_\lambda), \quad \mathbf{E}'(x_\lambda) = \mathbf{E}(-x_\lambda), \quad \mathbf{H}'(x_\lambda) = \mathbf{H}(-x_\lambda). \tag{37}$$

For the pseudo-scalar pion fields‡

$$\tilde{\phi}'(x_\lambda) = \tilde{\phi}(-x_\lambda), \quad \phi'(x_\lambda) = \phi(-x_\lambda), \quad \phi'_3(x_\lambda) = \phi_3(-x_\lambda). \tag{38}$$

From (2.114) it is seen that under SR the creation of a positive pion is replaced by the destruction of a negative pion, and so on. The relations (2.112)

$$[Q, \phi(x)] = -e\phi(x), \qquad [Q, \tilde{\phi}(x)] = +e\tilde{\phi}(x) \tag{39}$$

are preserved, together with $Q' = -Q$, by the device of reading the formula *backwards*.

For the Dirac field we note that the relations analogous to (39) (eqns. (4.32)) show that $\psi(x)$, $\bar{\psi}(x)$ must be constant (matrix) multiples of $\psi(-x)$, $\bar{\psi}(-x)$. The Lorentz transformation properties of Dirac spinors are given in Chapter III, § 2. It follows from (3.14) that under *proper* Lorentz transformations, the properties of $\gamma^5\psi(-x_\lambda)$ and of $\psi(x_\lambda)$ are identical.§ Thus we can write

$$\left.\begin{aligned} \psi'(x_\lambda) &= \alpha\gamma^5\psi(-x_\lambda) \\ \bar{\psi}'(x_\lambda) &= -\alpha^*\bar{\psi}(-x_\lambda)\gamma^5 \end{aligned}\right\}, \tag{40}$$

where α is a constant number. It is usual to choose $\alpha = 1$, or $\alpha = i$.‖

An important result follows from (40). In order that the four-current (Chapter IV, § 5)††

$$j_\mu(x) = \tfrac{1}{2}iec\{\bar{\psi}(x)\gamma^\mu\psi(x) - \psi_T(x)\gamma^\mu_T\bar{\psi}_T(x)\} \tag{41}$$

should obey (32), it is necessary that $\psi(x)$ and $\bar{\psi}(x)$ obey anti-commutation relations, rather than commutation relations‡‡ (in deriving this result we must remember to read the formula for $j'_\mu(x')$ backwards).

Similarly, we find the transform of any covariant Hermitian operator of the form

$$J(x) = \tfrac{1}{2}\{\bar{\psi}(x)O\psi(x) - \psi_T(x)O_T\bar{\psi}_T(x)\}$$

† W. Pauli, loc. cit.

‡ Note that eqn. (33 a) holds.

§ For rest mass $\kappa = 0$ there may be special solutions (cf. Chapter III, § 16).

‖ $\alpha = i$ is necessary for the Majorana particle (Chapter III, § 13).

†† Subscript T denotes the *transpose*.

‡‡ For a discussion on the relation between time reversal and the spin-statistics connexion see J. Schwinger, *Phys. Rev.* **82** (1951) 914. The spin-statistics connexion is discussed by W. Pauli, ibid. **85** (1940) 716; also W. Pauli and F. Belinfante, *Physica*, **7** (1940) 177.

under SR. For $O = I$, $i\gamma^5$, $i[\gamma^k, \gamma^l]$, $\gamma^5[\gamma^k, \gamma^l]$ ($k \neq l$) we have $J'(x) = +J(-x)$; for $O = i\gamma^\mu$, $i\gamma^5\gamma^\mu$, $J'(x) = -J(-x)$.

The transformation SR can be regarded as the product of the operations: charge conjugation C, Wigner time reversal T, and space inversion P. We write (SR) $= CTP$; the operations C, P, T can occur in any order. C changes the sign of the charge, but leaves space-time unaltered; T reverses the time, but not the charge; and P is the inversion $\mathbf{x}' = -\mathbf{x}$. Of these transformations, SR is the most important, because, as we have seen, any Lorentz invariant local quantum field theory is invariant under SR.

Time reversal T for field theories

Finally we notice the form of Wigner time reversal T for field variables. It is necessary to read all operator formulae backwards after making the transformation, if we are to preserve a positive Hamiltonian in (36). For Hermitian operators this transposition is equivalent to taking the complex conjugate; therefore the present method agrees with eqn. (20) which Wigner used for Hermitian operators (or observables). In Wigner time reversal (T), creation operators are to be replaced by destruction operators for the *same* particle, and vice versa; it follows that both boson and fermion field amplitudes are to be replaced by their Hermitian conjugates, e.g. for pions,

$$\phi'(\mathbf{x}, t) = (\text{const})\bar{\phi}(\mathbf{x}, -t), \quad \text{etc.}$$

As an example we consider the fermion fields. We have

$$\bar{\psi}'(\mathbf{x}, t) = \psi_T(\mathbf{x}, -t)\Omega, \qquad \psi'(\mathbf{x}, t) = \Omega^{-1}\bar{\psi}_T(\mathbf{x}, -t),$$

where the constant matrix Ω has to be chosen to give (15). This requires

$$\Omega\gamma^4\Omega^{-1} = \gamma_T^4, \qquad \Omega\gamma^k\Omega^{-1} = -\gamma_T^k \quad (k = 1, 2, 3). \tag{42}$$

Eqns. (42) are satisfied by

$$\Omega = C^{-1}\gamma^5\gamma^4, \tag{43}$$

where C is the 4×4 charge conjugation matrix of Chapter III, § 11.

The β-decay interaction

This transformation T can be used to examine the β-decay interaction (3.102) between four fermion fields. Let us consider the operator product $A \equiv (\bar{\psi}_P O \psi_N)$, where O is any product of the γ-matrices multiplied by a *real* number.† Under T it becomes

$$A' = (\psi_P \Omega O \Omega^{-1} \bar{\psi}_N).$$

† $O = 1$, γ^μ, $\gamma^\mu\gamma^\nu$, $\gamma^5\gamma^\mu$, γ^5.

We show that, when read backwards, this term is equal to the Hermitian conjugate of A, i.e.

$$\tilde{A} = (\bar{\psi}_N \gamma^4 \tilde{O} \gamma^4 \psi_P).$$

For this, we must prove

$$(\Omega O \Omega^{-1})_T = \gamma^4 \tilde{O} \gamma^4. \tag{44}$$

From (43) and (3.84),

$$(\Omega O \Omega^{-1})_T = \gamma^4 \gamma^5 (C^{-1} O C)_T \gamma^5 \gamma^4.$$

Using (3.63) again, it is easy to verify that

$$(C^{-1} O C)_T = \gamma^5 \tilde{O} \gamma^5;$$

thus (44) is true.

It follows that if the β-decay interaction (3.102) is to be invariant under T, all the coefficients C, C' must be *real*.† For example, the parity violating vector interaction is

$$H'_\nu = C'_\nu (\bar{\psi}_P \gamma^\mu \psi_N)(\bar{\psi}_e \gamma^\mu \gamma^5 \psi_\nu) + (\text{Hermitian conjugate}).$$

Thus $TH'_\nu T^{-1} = H_\nu$ implies that C'_ν is real.

5. The *CTP* theorem

As we saw in § 4, the product of the operations C, T, P (in any order commutes with the Hamiltonian H of any relativistic local field theory.

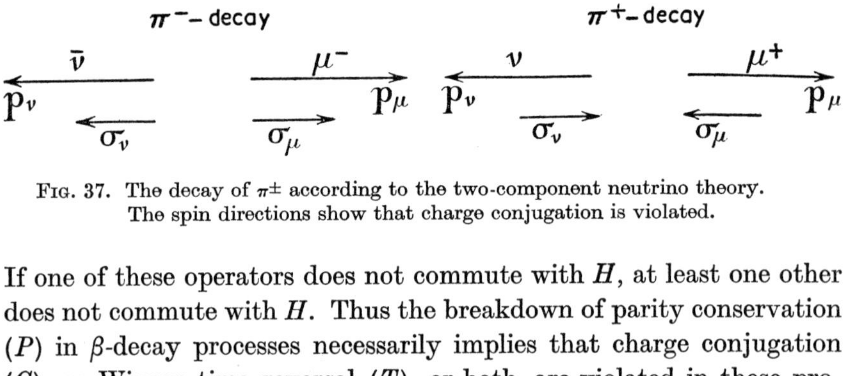

FIG. 37. The decay of $\pi^\pm$ according to the two-component neutrino theory. The spin directions show that charge conjugation is violated.

If one of these operators does not commute with H, at least one other does not commute with H. Thus the breakdown of parity conservation (P) in β-decay processes necessarily implies that charge conjugation (C), or Wigner time reversal (T), or both, are violated in these processes.‡

As an example, the two-component neutrino theory (Chapter III, § 16), which is not invariant under P, leads to the description of charged pion decay which is shown in Fig. 37.§ The initial states (π^+ and π^-)

† H. A. Tolhoek and S. R. de Groot, *Phys. Rev.* **84** (1951) 151. Strictly, all C, C' are real apart from a *common* phase factor which can appear through (43) when different fields are present.

‡ For parity violation experiments see Chapter III, § 15.

§ We have assumed the conservation of leptons in Figure 37.

are charge conjugates. Charge conjugation should not reverse the spins in the final states, therefore the process violates charge conjugation.

We now consider interesting deductions which can be made from the conservation of CTP in cases in which all of C, T, and P are not conserved. For example, applying SR to a particle at rest, it is clear that the mass of a *stable* particle must in any case, equal the mass of the anti-particle.

The decay of charge conjugate particles

A more subtle example is a theorem† which shows that the identical lifetimes of the π^+ and π^- mesons and of the μ^+ and μ^- mesons does not imply that these decay processes are invariant under charge conjugation. Suppose the Hamiltonian H of a system is of the form $H = H_s+H_w$, where both terms are Lorentz invariant, and H_s is invariant under C, T, and P. The decay of a particle A proceeds through H_w; it is assumed that we need calculate only to the *lowest* order in H_w. The theorem states that if A and its anti-particle $\bar{A}$ do not decay into identical particles, their lifetimes are equal, even if H_w is not invariant under C.

The proof we give follows that of Lee *et al.*† Let final states after the decays of A and $\bar{A}$ be B and $\bar{B}$ respectively. As we saw in § 3 above, the Wigner time-reversal operator‡ is of the form $T = V\mathscr{K}_0$, where V is unitary, and $\mathscr{K}_0$ is the operation of taking the complex conjugate. The decay matrix element is $\langle B|H_w|A\rangle$. Now§

$$\langle B|H_w|A\rangle^* = \langle \mathscr{K}_0 B|\mathscr{K}_0 H_w \mathscr{K}_0|\mathscr{K}_0 A\rangle$$
$$= \langle TB|TH_w T^{-1}|TA\rangle. \tag{45 a}$$

This is evaluated using (27). We assume that A is at rest and has zero spin, and that B is a standing wave eigenstate of H_s, so that

$$T|A\rangle = |A\rangle, \qquad T|B\rangle = |B\rangle. \tag{45 b}$$

It is clear in (47) that this restriction to zero spin is unimportant.

We can always write $H_w = H_1+H_2$, where||

$$P^{-1}H_1 P = H_1, \qquad P^{-1}H_2 P = -H_2. \tag{46}$$

Because H_w commutes with CTP, we get

$$\langle B|H_w|A\rangle^* = \langle B|C^{-1}H_1 C|A\rangle - \langle B|C^{-1}H_2 C|A\rangle$$
$$= \langle \bar{B}|H_1|\bar{A}\rangle - \langle \bar{B}|H_2|\bar{A}\rangle. \tag{47}$$

However, $$\langle \bar{B}|H_w|\bar{A}\rangle = \langle \bar{B}|H_1|\bar{A}\rangle + \langle \bar{B}|H_2|\bar{A}\rangle. \tag{48}$$

† T. D. Lee, R. Oehme, and C. N. Yang, *Phys. Rev.* **106** (1957) 340.
‡ We write $T \equiv \mathscr{K}$. § In the last step the unitary property of V is used.
|| $2H_1 = H_w+PH_w P^{-1}$, $2H_2 = H_w-PH_w P^{-1}$.

The interactions H_1 and H_2 lead to states $\bar{B}$ of opposite parity which do not interfere in the calculation of the lifetimes.† Taking the square modulus of $\langle B|H_w|A\rangle$ and $\langle \bar{B}|H_w|\bar{A}\rangle$ and summing over the states B, $\bar{B}$, (47) and (48) show that A and $\bar{A}$ have equal lifetimes.

The CTP theorem makes possible another comparison between π^+ and π^- decay. Under CPT,‡ $\mathbf{p} \to \mathbf{p}$, $\boldsymbol{\sigma} \to -\boldsymbol{\sigma}$, $Q \to -Q$. Therefore the angular distributions of e^+ and e^- in the decays $\pi^+ \to \mu^+ \to e^+$ and $\pi^- \to \mu^- \to e^-$ (from pions at rest) are identical.§ The expectation values of the components of the spins of the particles along their momenta change sign on going from the π^+ to the π^- case.

Charge conjugation and parity interference experiments

It is easy to deduce other theorems if the weak interaction H_w commutes with *one* of C, P, or T. If H_w commutes with C, we prove that in the decay of A no interference of the type discussed in Chapter 3, § 15, can occur between the parity conserving and the parity non-conserving parts of H_w, provided the decay products in the final state do not interact.‖

The proof is direct if we use the notation above. C must commute†† with H_1 and H_2. If the spin of A is zero, we have in place of (47)

$$\langle B|H_1|A\rangle^* = \langle B|H_1|A\rangle, \qquad \langle B|H_2|A\rangle^* = -\langle B|H_2|A\rangle. \tag{49}$$

Hence the H_1 matrix element is real, and that for H_2 is pure imaginary; therefore no interference between the two terms can occur. If the decaying particle has spin J, we denote initial and final states with the spin component M by A_M, B_M. In place of (49) we get

$$\langle B_M|H_1|A_M\rangle^* = \langle B_{-M}|H_1|A_{-M}\rangle = \langle B_M|H_1|A_M\rangle.$$

The last step follows from rotation invariance. A similar result holds for H_2; hence there is no interference. The parity interference observed in $\pi \to \mu$ decay and in $\mu \to e$ decay proves that in *both* processes charge conjugation is violated (cf. Chapter III, § 15).

If the particles in the final state do interact, this theorem does not hold. This is the case for the β-decay of the nucleus in which the β-particle is created in the Coulomb field of the nucleus. The final states B must be *stationary* states of H_s if (45 b) is to hold; eqn. (5.51) indicates the form of the representative of a stationary state for the relative

† Of course, interference can occur in the angular distributions of the decay products.

‡ Under P, $\mathbf{p} \to -\mathbf{p}$, $\boldsymbol{\sigma} \to \boldsymbol{\sigma}$; under T, $\mathbf{p} \to -\mathbf{p}$, $\boldsymbol{\sigma} \to -\boldsymbol{\sigma}$; under C, $Q \to -Q$, $\mathbf{p} \to \mathbf{p}$, $\boldsymbol{\sigma} \to \boldsymbol{\sigma}$.

§ T. D. Lee and C. N. Yang, *Phys. Rev.* **105** (1957) 1671.

‖ T. D. Lee, R. Oehme, and C. N. Yang, loc. cit.

†† Because P and C commute.

motion of two particles. We must, however, calculate the matrix element for an *outgoing* final state. Eqns. (2.95) and (2.96) show that this outgoing state is obtained if we use the integral

$$\int |B\rangle \frac{dE_B}{E_B - E_A - i\epsilon} \langle B|H_w|A\rangle$$

over E_B. E_A and E_B are the energies of states A and B, and ϵ is a small positive quantity. If the particles in the final states are free, the matrix elements for these outgoing states have the same relative phase as is given by (49) (cf. eqn. (5.52)). If the particles in B are not free, there will in general be a relative phase difference between the outgoing state matrix elements different from that given by (49); essentially this is because H_1 and H_2 lead to states of different parity, and different orbital angular momentum and scattering phase shifts.

In the expression (3.117) for the parity interference in β-decay, the term independent of Z would vanish if H_w and C were to commute. The Z-dependent term shows the effect of the Coulomb field. If H_w were to commute with T, eqn. (45 a) shows that both $\langle B|H_1|A\rangle$ and $\langle B|H_2|A\rangle$ would be *real*. Then, to the lowest order in the Coulomb interaction, the difference between the outgoing and the stationary states gives a correction which is out of phase. It follows that the Z-dependent term in (3.117) will vanish† if H_w commutes with T.

6. Hyperons and K-mesons

It is desirable to mention briefly the selection rule associated with the attribute or 'strangeness' quantum number S. Unfortunately the significance of this quantum number is not as yet particularly well understood, although this empirical selection rule is of great importance. The K-mesons were discussed in § 1 above. The hyperons are: a neutral particle Λ^0 with mass $2{,}182m_e$; the charged and neutral particles Σ^+, Σ^0, Σ^-, with $m_{\Sigma^+} \simeq 2{,}328m_e$, and the cascade particle Ξ^- with mass $2{,}585m_e$.‡ The Σ^+ and Σ^- hyperons are *not* anti-particles; in fact they have a mass difference§‖ $(m_{\Sigma^-} - m_{\Sigma^+}) = (14 \pm 2)m_e$. The mass of the Σ^0 hyperon is given‖ as $m_{\Sigma^0} = (2{,}329 \pm 3)m_e$. It is believed on theoretical grounds†† that the Ξ^- hyperon has a companion Ξ^0. If we call any

† A general proof has been given by T. D. Lee, R. Oehme, and C. N. Yang, loc. cit.

‡ See the Table of particles on p. 471.

§ W. F. Fry *et al.*, *Phys. Rev.* **104** (1956) 270. See also W. H. Barkas *et al.*, ibid. **105** (1957) 1417.

‖ R. Plano, N. Samios, M. Schwartz, and J. Steinberger, *Nuovo Cim.* **5** (1957) 216. F. Eisler *et al.*, *Phys. Rev.* **110** (1958) 226.

†† See below.

hyperon or nucleon a *baryon*, or heavy particle, the present experimental evidence shows that the number of baryons is conserved.† It is assumed‡ that there is a strict conservation law:

$$N \equiv (\text{no. of baryons}) - (\text{no. of anti-baryons}) = \text{constant}. \qquad (50)$$

The hyperons and K-mesons are produced at a rate which is almost comparable with pion-nucleon processes at the same energy. However, most of these particles have metastability; their lifetimes are mostly extremely long by nuclear standards (i.e. long compared with 10^{-20} sec to 10^{-22} sec). The Λ^0 and the charged hyperons§ have lives of the order of 10^{-10} sec; similarly, the K-mesons are long lived (cf. p. 350 above). This metastability is inconsistent with the existence of strong interactions between hyperons (or K-mesons) and the more familiar particles: nucleons, pions, and photons; the laws of physics which we have discussed so far would suggest lifetimes of the order of 10^{-20} sec.†

Associated production

The copious production of K-mesons and hyperons can be reconciled with their metastability if we introduce†‡ a new quantum number S, which we call the *attribute*. It is easy to define S, so that the proposed conservation law for S permits the *associated* production of hyperons and K-mesons, e.g.

$$(\text{pion}) + (\text{nucleon}) \rightarrow (\text{hyperon}) + (K\text{-meson}).$$

Hyperon or K-meson decay violates the conservation of S, and can only occur very slowly, just as forbidden transitions in atomic spectra are very slow.

Gell-Mann‡ has related the attribute to the idea that the hyperons and K-mesons form isotopic spin multiplets. It is suggested that the Λ^0 hyperon has isotopic spin $T = 0$, while Σ^+, Σ^0, Σ^- are the components $T_3 = 1, 0, -1$ of an isotopic spin triplet $T = 1$. This idea is a natural extension of the nucleon concept. Gell-Mann also suggests that Ξ^- and Ξ^0 are the components $T_3 = -\frac{1}{2}, \frac{1}{2}$ of a doublet|| $T = \frac{1}{2}$. The attribute S is defined by the relation between the charge and the T_3 component of isotopic spin (cf. (4.114))

$$Q/e = T_3 + \tfrac{1}{2}N + \tfrac{1}{2}S, \qquad (51)$$

† M. Gell-Mann and A. Pais, *Proc. 1954 Glasgow Conf.* (Pergamon, London, 1955), p. 342.

‡ M. Gell-Mann, *Suppl. Nuovo Cim.* **4** (1956) 848.

§ Σ^0 appears to have a very short life; the fast process $\Sigma^0 \rightarrow \Lambda^0 + \gamma$ is allowed by the scheme given below.

|| This allows Ξ^- to be metastable against decay to Λ^0.

where N is given by (50). Thus for nucleons, $S = 0$; for the Λ and Σ hyperons, $S = -1$; for the Ξ hyperon(s), $S = -2$.

The selection rule

Putting $N = 0$, the definition (51) gives $S = 0$ for pions. We assume that the selection rule for strong (or allowed) interactions is

$$\Delta S = 0. \tag{52}$$

Thus all the ordinary nucleon-nucleon and pion-nucleon processes are allowed. In addition it is assumed that electromagnetic transitions do not violate (52). γ-rays, electrons, muons, and neutrinos have $S = 0$.

The associated production process†

$$\mathcal{N}+\pi \rightarrow \Lambda^0+K^0 \tag{53}$$

occurs readily.‡ The existence of this process, and similar production processes for the other hyperons, shows that§ the hyperons must be fermions. The process (53) is allowed if we assign $S = +1$ to the K^0 meson. Because K^0 is not a baryon we put $N = 0$ in (51) and get $T_3 = -\frac{1}{2}$ for K^0.

The decay of the K^0 meson to pions, or lighter particles, violates (52), hence it is a very slow process. Similarly, the selection rule (52) implies that the decay of a hyperon (giving a nucleon and a pion, or a nucleon and photons, etc.) is a very slow process. An exception‖ is $\Sigma^0 \rightarrow \Lambda^0+\gamma$, which is allowed, and is presumed to be fast. Before completing the assignment of S for K-mesons we notice that on going over to anti-particles, Q, T_3, and N all change sign; hence by (51) the sign of S is reversed for anti-particles.††

Although the production process (53) is well known, the process

$$\mathcal{N}+\mathcal{N} \rightarrow \Lambda^0+\Lambda^0 \tag{54}$$

apparently does not occur.‡ If K^0 were identical with its anti-particle $\bar{K}^0$, (51) would imply that (54) should also occur;‡‡ hence it is assumed§§ that K^0 and $\bar{K}^0$ are distinct. The simplest suggestion is that the pair K^+, K^0 form an isotopic doublet ($T = \frac{1}{2}$) with $S = +1$, while the

† $\mathcal{N} \equiv$ nucleon. K^0 is the neutral K meson with $S = +1$; the older notation is θ^0.

‡ For discussion of the experimental evidence and for references see R. W. Thompson, *Suppl. Nuovo Cim.* **4** (1956) 642.

§ We know that K^0 is a boson (§ 1, above).

‖ Energy conservation prevents $\Sigma \rightarrow \Lambda^0+\pi$. $\Delta S = 1$ for $\Xi^- \rightarrow \Lambda^0+\pi^-$.

†† Charge conjugation is assumed to be valid for all strong interactions.

‡‡ Process (53) implies the strong virtual process $\mathcal{N} \rightarrow \Lambda^0+K^0$ or $K^0 \rightarrow \mathcal{N}+\bar{\Lambda}^0$. Charge conjugation gives $\bar{K}^0 \rightarrow \bar{\mathcal{N}}+\Lambda^0$. If $K^0 = \bar{K}^0$, then (54) follows.

§§ See M. Gell-Mann, loc. cit.

anti-particles $\bar{K}^0$, K^- form another doublet with $S = -1$. The resulting scheme is shown in Table 3.

This scheme explains a variety of important phenomena. For example, just over the threshold K^+ particles are produced in pion-nucleon collisions but K^- particles are not produced until a much higher pion energy is reached. K^+ can be produced together with hyperons, but K^- (with $S = -1$) can only be produced in a (K^-, K^+) pair. The threshold for the second process is much higher than that for the first. The K^- mesons interact strongly with nuclei, producing hyperons and pions;† the K^+ mesons can only be scattered (possibly with charge exchange) by a nucleus.

TABLE 3

The Isotopic Multiplet Scheme

Particles and charge + 0 −	Isotopic spin T_3	Isotopic spin T	Attribute S
Baryons			
P, N	$\frac{1}{2}, -\frac{1}{2}$	$\frac{1}{2}$	0
Λ^0	0	0	−1
Σ^+ Σ^0 Σ^-	1, 0, −1	1	−1
Ξ^0 Ξ^-	$\frac{1}{2}, -\frac{1}{2}$	$\frac{1}{2}$	−2
Mesons			
π^+ π^0 π^-	1, 0, −1	1	0
K^+ K^0	$\frac{1}{2}, -\frac{1}{2}$	$\frac{1}{2}$	1
$\bar{K}^0$ K^-	$\frac{1}{2}, -\frac{1}{2}$	$\frac{1}{2}$	−1

Decay of neutral K-mesons

The fact that K^0 and its anti-particle $\bar{K}^0$ are distinct may lead to somewhat complicated behaviour in the decay of these particles. We shall *assume* that the decay interaction is invariant under the operation product $L \equiv CP$.‡ The particles K^0, $\bar{K}^0$ are not themselves eigenstates of the charge conjugation operator C; the eigenstates of L are the neutral particles K_1^0 and K_2^0 whose state vectors are

$$\left.\begin{aligned} |K_1^0\rangle &= \frac{1}{\sqrt{2}}\{|K^0\rangle + \eta|\bar{K}^0\rangle\} \\ |K_2^0\rangle &= \frac{1}{\sqrt{2}}\{|K^0\rangle - \eta|\bar{K}^0\rangle\} \end{aligned}\right\} \quad (\eta = \pm 1). \tag{55}$$

We choose η so that K_1^0 and K_2^0 have eigenvalues $L' = +1, -1$ respec-

† See D. M. Haskin, T. Bowen, and M. Shein, *Phys. Rev.* **103** (1956) 1512, for discussion and references.

‡ M. Gell-Mann and A. Pais, *Phys. Rev.* **97** (1955) 1387; A. Pais and O. Piccioni, *Phys. Rev.* **100** (1955) 1487; R. Gatto, ibid. **106** (1957) 168.

tively. The relation of K_1^0 and K_2^0 to K^0 and $\bar{K}^0$ is similar to the relation between photons having circular polarization and photons having plane polarization.

Invariance under the operation CP implies that K_1^0 and K_2^0 have different lifetimes and different decay modes. The 2π mode (i.e. θ^0) can only arise from K_1^0 because it has the eigenvalue $L' = 1$. This is because the operations C and P *both* exchange the pions. However K_2^0, but not K_1^0, can give a 3π mode in which the pions are in s-states. Thus the 3π mode is strongly inhibited for K_1^0. Experiments show that there are indeed two neutral K lifetimes,† $0{\cdot}95\times10^{-10}$ sec (K_1^0) and $0{\cdot}9\times10^{-7}$ sec (K_2^0).

Suppose we produce a beam of neutral K-mesons. By a suitable choice of the energy of the incident pions, we can ensure that the K-mesons coming from the target are all K^0 (i.e. $S = +1$). Within a short distance of flight the K_1^0 component will annihilate ($K_1^0 \to \pi^+ + \pi^-$);‡ the beam now contains only the K_2^0 component.§ The K_2^0 component may move through several metres before it decays. There is much evidence† for a long-lived neutral K-meson; its decay modes (π^+, π^-, π^0), ($\pi^\pm, \mu^\mp, \nu$), ($\pi^\pm, e^\mp, \nu$) are in agreement with what would be expected for K_2^0 on comparing with the $\tau^\pm$, $K_{\mu3}$, K_{e3} modes of $K^\pm$.

Suppose we were to insert a target of dense matter in the K_2^0 beam before it decays. In interactions with nuclei, $\bar{K}^0$ is expected to be strongly absorbed by hyperon production; K^0 is not absorbed. Hence that part of the K_2^0 beam which strikes a nucleus will reappear on the other side of the nucleus as a K^0 beam of reduced intensity.|| Thus we would expect the somewhat striking phenomenon that a neutral K-meson beam which started with $S = +1$ particles could show phenomena associated with $S = -1$ particles after free flight of several metres.††

Another simple deduction is that if $T = CP$ is invariant, the observed rates of decay of the long-lived component into (π^+, e^-, ν) and (π^-, e^+, ν) will be equal. Assuming that we cannot observe the spin of the fermions, the operation CP converts a final state (π^+, e^-, ν) into the corresponding state (π^-, e^+, ν). The same is true for the ($\pi^\pm, \mu^\mp, \nu$) modes.

† J. A. Kadyk *et al.*, *Phys. Rev.* **105** (1957) 1862; K. Lande *et al.*, ibid. 1925; M. Bardon *et al.*, ibid. **110** (1958), 780.

‡ By eqn. (55) $|K^0\rangle = 2^{-\frac{1}{2}}\{|K_1^0\rangle + |K_2^0\rangle\}$.

§ A good analogy is the passage of an initially plane polarized beam of light through a filter which absorbs all the right-handed circularly polarized component and passes all the left-handed component.

|| A simple analogy is the absorption, from a circularly polarized beam, of radiation polarized in one plane only.

†† We have not mentioned the effects which arise from the small difference in the masses of K_1^0 and K_2^0. See K. M. Case, *Phys. Rev.* **103** (1956) 1449.

If it is not legitimate to assume that the decay interactions are invariant under the operation CP then these neutral K decay phenomena may be more complicated.†

7. Furry's theorem; the universal fermion interaction

As was seen in Chapter V, § 9, Furry's theorem is a consequence of charge conjugation. If it is assumed that the theorem is valid for those matrix elements which relate to strongly interacting fields, further selection rules can be deduced. These are not absolute selection rules; they depend on a knowledge of the types of interaction which are involved.‡ As an example we consider the decay of the charged pion.§

If ψ is a fermion operator and ψ_c its charge conjugate, then

$$\left.\begin{aligned} \bar{\psi}_c \Omega \psi_c &= \bar{\psi}\Omega\psi \quad \text{for} \quad \Omega = 1,\ \gamma^5\gamma^\mu,\ \gamma^5 \\ \bar{\psi}_c \Omega \psi_c &= -\bar{\psi}\Omega\psi \quad \text{for} \quad \Omega = \gamma^\mu,\ \gamma^\mu\gamma^\nu \quad (\mu \neq \nu) \end{aligned}\right\}$$

(cf. eqns. (4.77)). In other words, charge conjugation leaves S, A, and P matrix elements unaltered, and reverses the sign of V and T matrix elements.‖ Thus Furry's theorem states that closed fermion loops which contain an odd number of V and T interactions must vanish.

By virtual dissociation a charged pion gives

$$\pi^+ \rightarrow P+\bar{N}. \tag{56}$$

The virtual nucleon–anti-nucleon pair may lead to several decay modes for the pion. The β-decay process (3.103) shows that

$$\pi^+ \rightarrow e^+ + \nu \tag{57}$$

may occur. The observed muon capture‡ process

$$P+\mu^- \rightarrow N+\nu \tag{58}$$

gives the observed decay

$$\pi^+ \rightarrow \mu^+ + \nu. \tag{59}$$

The experimental results show that (57) is about 10^{-4} times as frequent as (59).

Consider the four-fermion interactions (cf. (3.102))

$$\left.\begin{aligned} C_\Omega(\bar{\psi}_P \Omega\psi_N)(\bar{\psi}_e \Omega\psi_\nu) + C'_\Omega(\bar{\psi}_P \Omega\psi_N)(\bar{\psi}_e \Omega\gamma^5\psi_\nu) \\ D_\Omega(\bar{\psi}_P \Omega\psi_N)(\bar{\psi}_\mu \Omega\psi_\nu) + D'_\Omega(\bar{\psi}_P \Omega\psi_N)(\bar{\psi}_\mu \Omega\gamma^5\psi_\nu) \end{aligned}\right\} + \text{h.c.} \tag{60}$$

which may be used to describe the β-decay process and process (58). Furry's theorem applied to the closed nucleon loop, shows that (57)

† This situation is analysed by T. D. Lee, R. Oehme, and C. N. Yang, *Phys. Rev.* **106** (1957) 340.

‡ For a review of the selection rules and a discussion of universal four-fermion interactions see the article by M. Gell-Mann and A. H. Rosenfeld in *Ann. Rev. Nuclear Sci.* **7** (Annual Reviews Inc., Stanford, Cal., 1957).

§ See S. B. Treiman and H. W. Wyld, *Phys. Rev.* **101** (1956) 1552; G. Morpurgo, *Nuovo Cim.* **5** (1957) 1159.

‖ S = scalar, V = vector, T = tensor, A = axial vector, P = pseudo-vector.

and (59) cannot occur for the cases in which Ω is V or T. Here we have assumed that the strong interaction (56) is pseudoscalar. Simple calculations also show that to the first and third orders in the pion-nucleon interaction, the matrix elements for (57) and (59) vanish† when $\Omega = S$. It is true to any order.‡

If the four-fermion interaction is to be a universal property of matter, the coupling constants C_Ω and C'_Ω (cf. (3.102)) for the matrix elements in the first line of (60) must equal those in the second line.§ The interaction term $\Omega = P$ must be excluded because it gives much too large a branching ratio of (57) to (59). With the other interaction (i.e. $\Omega = A$) a small ratio can be obtained|| which agrees with the observed value.†† Because we cannot adequately calculate the strong part (56) of these pion decays, no good estimate of the absolute rates can be given.

The universal interaction can account for the muon's decay (3.110). The interaction used is

$$(\bar{\psi}_e \Omega \psi_\mu)(\bar{\psi}_\nu \Omega \psi_\nu). \tag{61}$$

Assuming also the two-component neutrino theory (Chapter III, § 16), only $\Omega = V$ and $\Omega = A$ do not vanish in (61) (cf. eqn. (3.114)). Our discussion of β-decay in Chapter III, § 16, showed that the pair of interactions (V, A) must be predominant. Muon decay using (61) also obliges us to choose (V, A). The muon decay interaction becomes (cf. (3.102))

$$2\{\bar{\psi}_e(C_V+\gamma^5 C_A)\gamma^\lambda \psi_\mu\}(\bar{\psi}_\nu \gamma^\lambda \psi_\nu). \tag{62}$$

It follows from β-decay theory (Chapter III, § 17) that $|C_V| \simeq |C_A|$. Also, we believe $C_A \simeq -C_V$, so the positrons occurring in μ^+ decay will have longitudinal polarization $(+v_e/c)$ irrespective of the muon spin or the neutrino momenta. Electrons in μ^- decay will have longitudinal polarization $(-v_e/c)$. The observed longitudinal polarization of the positrons in μ^+ decay is positive.‡‡

From (62) the muon lifetime is easily calculated. Taking $C_A = -C_V$ and using the value of C_V from O^{14} β-decay (p. 158) gives the observed lifetime $(2{\cdot}2\times 10^{-6}$ sec) to within 2 per cent.

Feynman and Gell-Mann§§ suggest that $C_A = -C_V$ in all four-fermion interactions, such as (62), where there are no strong virtual processes. In (60) the strong pion-nucleon interaction could give corrections, so that

† Trace $\{\gamma^5 S_F(p_1) S_F(p_2)\} = 0$, etc. ‡ See p. 372, n. ‡.

§ We assume the correspondence $PNe\nu \rightarrow PN\mu\nu$.

|| M. A. Ruderman and R. J. Finkelstein, *Phys. Rev.* **76** (1949) 1458.

†† T. Fazzini *et al.*, *Phys. Rev. Letters* **1** (1958) 247; G. Impeduglia *et al.*, ibid. 249.

‡‡ G. Culligan *et al.*, *Nature* **180** (1957) 751.

§§ R. P. Feynman and M. Gell-Mann, *Phys. Rev.* **109** (1958) 553. See also G. Sudarshan and R. E. Marshak, ibid. 1860.

for β-decay $C_A \simeq -1{\cdot}2C_V$ (eqn. (3.118)). The excellent agreement between the values of C_V in β-decay and muon decay suggests C_V is a universal constant. This is possible if the vector part of the universal interaction is like a *conserved* 'current' for which C_V plays the role of 'charge'. Such a current can be constructed if we add a small pion contribution to the universal interaction.†

The four interacting fields consist of two pairs, either or both of which may be baryons or leptons. One member of each pair is charged and one is neutral. In the note below it is shown that when $C_A = -C_V$ the order of writing the fields is unimportant.

Finally we notice that this suggestion of Feynman and Gell-Mann also accounts for the parity violation which occurs in K-meson and hyperon decays. K-meson decay was discussed in § 1. In the decay of the Λ^0 hyperon ($\Lambda^0 \to P+\pi^-$) it is observed that the momentum of the pion shows a strong up–down asymmetry‡ relative to the plane in which the Λ^0 and the K-meson are produced ($\pi^-+P \to \Lambda^0+K^0$).

The universal interaction is used in the form

$$C_V\{\bar\psi_P\gamma^\lambda(1+\gamma^5)\psi_\Lambda\}\{\bar\psi_N\gamma^\lambda(1+\gamma^5)\psi_P\}+\text{h.c.}, \tag{63}$$

where C_V is the same constant as above. This (or similar) weak interactions acting together with the strong pion-nucleon and K-meson-hyperon interactions can explain the observed strange particle decays.† Unfortunately, calculations of the lifetimes are necessarily rough because of the virtual processes which have to estimated.

This weak universal fermion interaction therefore appears to have considerable success in accounting for the main features of all the 'slow' decays and for parity violation.

Note. The rearrangement of the anti-commuting operators in (61) is as follows. Let

$$J_1 = \bar\psi_1\psi_2\bar\psi_3\psi_4,\quad J_2 = \bar\psi_1\gamma^\mu\psi_2\bar\psi_3\gamma^\mu\psi_4,\quad J_3 = \bar\psi_1\sigma^{\mu\nu}\psi_2\bar\psi_3\sigma^{\mu\nu}\psi_4,$$

$$J_4 = -\bar\psi_1\gamma^\mu\gamma^5\psi_2\bar\psi_3\gamma^\mu\gamma^5\psi_4,\quad J_5 = \bar\psi_1\gamma^5\psi_2\bar\psi_3\gamma^5\psi_4;\quad J_1' = \bar\psi_1\psi_4\bar\psi_3\psi_2,\quad \text{etc.}$$

Then it can be shown that§

$$J_i' = -\sum_{j=1}^{5} b_{ij}J_j \quad \text{where} \quad 4b_{ij} = \begin{pmatrix} 1 & 1 & 1 & 1 & 1 \\ 4 & -2 & 0 & 2 & -4 \\ 6 & 0 & -2 & 0 & 6 \\ 4 & 2 & 0 & -2 & 4 \\ 1 & -1 & 1 & -1 & 1 \end{pmatrix}.$$

The same relations hold if we replace ψ_2 by $\gamma^5\psi_2$, etc. Notice that

$$J_2'-J_4' = J_2-J_4,$$

i.e. $C_A = -C_V$ becomes $C_A' = -C_V'$ with $C_V' = C_V$.

† R. P. Feynman and M. Gell-Mann, *Phys. Rev.* **109** (1958) 553.

‡ F. Eisler *et al.*, *Phys. Rev.* **108** (1957) 1353; F. S. Crawford *et al.*, ibid. 1102. For longitudinal polarization of the proton in Λ^0 decay see E. Boldt *et al.*, *Phys. Rev. Letters*, **1** (1937) 256.

§ M. Fierz, *Z. Phys.* **104** (1937) 553.

VIII

POLARIZATION ANALYSIS

1. A beam of particles of spin $\frac{1}{2}$

The density matrix

SUPPOSE that individual elementary particles, atoms, or nuclei are in completely specified eigenstates $|\alpha_m\rangle$ ($m = 1, 2, \ldots$). We assume that in a beam of such particles there is no interference between individual particles, and that the probability of an individual particle being in the state $|\alpha_m\rangle$ is p_m. Clearly, $p_m > 0$ and

$$\sum_m p_m = 1. \tag{1}$$

Let $|\beta_n\rangle$ be any other complete set of eigenstates which can be used to represent the set $|\alpha_m\rangle$, so that

$$|\alpha_m\rangle = \sum_n |\beta_n\rangle\langle\beta_n|\alpha_m\rangle. \tag{2}$$

The density matrix† $\boldsymbol{\rho}$ is defined in the $|\beta_n\rangle$ system by

$$\langle\beta_n|\boldsymbol{\rho}|\beta_{n'}\rangle = \sum_m \langle\beta_n|\alpha_m\rangle p_m \langle\alpha_m|\beta_{n'}\rangle. \tag{3}$$

It follows from (3) that $\boldsymbol{\rho}$ is Hermitian, i.e.

$$\langle\beta_n|\boldsymbol{\rho}|\beta_{n'}\rangle = \langle\beta_{n'}|\boldsymbol{\rho}|\beta_n\rangle^*,$$

because $\langle\beta_n|\alpha_m\rangle^* = \langle\alpha_m|\beta_n\rangle$. Eqn. (1) may be written in terms of $\boldsymbol{\rho}$, as

$$\sum_n \langle\beta_n|\boldsymbol{\rho}|\beta_n\rangle = \mathrm{tr}(\boldsymbol{\rho}) = 1, \tag{4}$$

on using the property $\quad \sum_n |\beta_n\rangle\langle\beta_n| = I.$

Here I is the identity matrix in the space of $|\beta_n\rangle$ and tr is the *trace* (i.e. the diagonal sum).

The average of the expectation value of any operator O is

$$\langle O\rangle = \sum_m p_m\langle\alpha_m|O|\alpha_m\rangle, \tag{5}$$

and using (2) and (3) this may be written‡

$$\begin{aligned}\langle O\rangle &= \sum_m\sum_n\sum_{n'} p_m\langle\alpha_m|\beta_n\rangle\langle\beta_n|O|\beta_{n'}\rangle\langle\beta_{n'}|\alpha_m\rangle \\ &= \sum_n\sum_{n'} \langle\beta_{n'}|\boldsymbol{\rho}|\beta_n\rangle\langle\beta_n|O|\beta_{n'}\rangle \\ &= \sum_{n'} \langle\beta_{n'}|\boldsymbol{\rho}O|\beta_{n'}\rangle,\end{aligned}$$

or $\quad \langle O\rangle = \mathrm{tr}(\boldsymbol{\rho}O). \tag{6}$

† J. von Neumann, *Nachr. Ges. Wiss. Göttingen* (1927), p. 245. A simple account is given by P. A. M. Dirac, *Quantum Mechanics* (Clarendon Press, 3rd edn., 1947), ch. 6.

‡ It is useful to remember that $\mathrm{tr}(AB) = \mathrm{tr}(BA)$, but in general $\mathrm{tr}(ABC) \neq \mathrm{tr}(ACB)$.

The properties of the density matrix which we have given are sufficient for the application to polarization experiments.†

Basic spin states

We consider a beam of fermions of spin $\frac{1}{2}$, each having momentum **p**. It is necessary first to remember the spin properties of a single fermion. The spin eigenstates are $|+\frac{1}{2}\rangle$ and $|-\frac{1}{2}\rangle$ corresponding to the spin being, respectively, parallel and anti-parallel to **p**. Basic orthogonal spin states $|\alpha_m\rangle$ for the individual particle of momentum **p** can be written

$$\left.\begin{aligned} |\alpha_1\rangle &= a|+\tfrac{1}{2}\rangle + b|-\tfrac{1}{2}\rangle \\ |\alpha_2\rangle &= b^*|+\tfrac{1}{2}\rangle - a^*|-\tfrac{1}{2}\rangle \end{aligned}\right\}, \tag{7}$$

where a, b are complex numbers. Eqns. (3.40) to (3.41 b) show how to find the spin orientation associated with these states. For example, with $a = b = 2^{-\frac{1}{2}}$, the expectation values of the components of the spin S vanish except for one direction perpendicular to **p**. For these basic states $|\alpha_1\rangle$, $|\alpha_2\rangle$ the non-vanishing components equal $+\frac{1}{2}\hbar mc^2/E$ and $-\frac{1}{2}\hbar mc^2/E$ respectively. In the non-relativistic approximation we say that for the basic states, the spin has the values $\pm\frac{1}{2}\hbar$ in this direction.

Eqns. (7) give the most general basic states $|\alpha_m\rangle$ for our beam. We assume that the probability of an individual fermion being in the states $|\alpha_1\rangle$, $|\alpha_2\rangle$ is p_1 and p_2 respectively. Clearly,

$$p_1 + p_2 = 1. \tag{8}$$

The density matrix (3) is found by evaluating

$$\sum_{m=1}^{2} |\alpha_m\rangle p_m \langle\alpha_m|.$$

Using (7), this becomes

$$|+\tfrac{1}{2}\rangle\langle+\tfrac{1}{2}|(a^*ap_1 + b^*bp_2) + |-\tfrac{1}{2}\rangle\langle-\tfrac{1}{2}|(a^*ap_2 + b^*bp_1) + \\ + |+\tfrac{1}{2}\rangle\langle-\tfrac{1}{2}|(p_1 - p_2)ab^* + |-\tfrac{1}{2}\rangle\langle+\tfrac{1}{2}|(p_1 - p_2)a^*b \tag{9}$$

or, in matrix form for the representation given by the state vectors $|\pm\frac{1}{2}\rangle$,

$$\boldsymbol{\rho} = \begin{pmatrix} a^*ap_1 + b^*bp_2 & ab^*(p_1 - p_2) \\ a^*b(p_1 - p_2) & a^*ap_2 + b^*bp_1 \end{pmatrix}. \tag{10}$$

Because $|a|^2 + |b|^2 = 1$, and on account of (8), it follows that the

† For an early paper on the use of the density matrix to describe the polarization of electron beams see H. A. Tolhoek and S. R. de Groot, *Physica*, **17** (1951) 1–16 and 17–32.

Hermitian matrix (10) has unit trace. In the same representation we define the matrices† σ_1', σ_2', σ_3' by

$$\sigma_1' = \begin{pmatrix} 0 & 1 \\ 1 & 0 \end{pmatrix}, \qquad \sigma_2' = \begin{pmatrix} 0 & -i \\ i & 0 \end{pmatrix}, \qquad \sigma_3' = \begin{pmatrix} 1 & 0 \\ 0 & -1 \end{pmatrix}. \tag{11}$$

The polarization (relativistic case)

These matrices are sufficient to describe all Hermitian 2×2 matrices which have zero trace. Therefore there are three real numbers P_1, P_2, P_3, such that (10) can be written in the form

$$\boldsymbol{\rho} = \tfrac{1}{2}\{I+(\boldsymbol{\sigma}'.\mathbf{P})\}, \tag{12}$$

where $$\boldsymbol{\sigma}'.\mathbf{P} = \sigma_1' P_1+\sigma_2' P_2+\sigma_3' P_3.$$

The notation $(\boldsymbol{\sigma}'.\mathbf{P})$ is used for convenience and is not intended to imply that $\mathbf{P}$ is in general an axial vector. The values of the numbers P_i are

$$\left.\begin{aligned} P_1 = (p_1-p_2)(ab^*+a^*b), \qquad P_2 = (p_1-p_2)i(ab^*-a^*b) \\ P_3 = (p_1-p_2)(a^*a-b^*b) \end{aligned}\right\}. \tag{13}$$

It follows that $$\mathbf{P}^2 = P_1^2+P_2^2+P_3^2 = (p_1-p_2)^2; \tag{14}$$

so, by (8), $$0 \leqslant \mathbf{P}^2 \leqslant 1. \tag{15}$$

Comparing (7) with (3.39) to (3.41 b) shows that the expectation values $\langle\alpha_m|S_i|\alpha_m\rangle$ $(m = 1, 2)$ for the components of spin of an individual fermion, in the state $|\alpha_m\rangle$, obey the relation

$$\langle\alpha_1|S_i|\alpha_1\rangle = -\langle\alpha_2|S_i|\alpha_2\rangle \quad (i = 1, 2, 3).$$

Choosing an orthogonal axes system with O_3 pointing along the momentum $\mathbf{p}$, we express P_1, P_2, P_3 (given by eqns. (13)) in terms of these expectation values of the spin components S_i. Clearly

$$\left.\begin{aligned} \tfrac{1}{2}\hbar P_1 &= \{p_1\langle\alpha_1|S_1|\alpha_2\rangle+p_2\langle\alpha_2|S_1|\alpha_2\rangle\}E/mc^2 \\ \tfrac{1}{2}\hbar P_2 &= \{p_1\langle\alpha_1|S_2|\alpha_2\rangle+p_2\langle\alpha_2|S_2|\alpha_2\rangle\}E/mc^2 \\ \tfrac{1}{2}\hbar P_3 &= \{p_1\langle\alpha_1|S_3|\alpha_2\rangle+p_2\langle\alpha_2|S_3|\alpha_2\rangle\} \end{aligned}\right\}. \tag{16}$$

Thus the P_i $(i = 1, 2, 3)$ are related to the average spin expectation value for the beam (cf. eqn. (5)):

$$\left.\begin{aligned} \tfrac{1}{2}\hbar P_1 &= \frac{E}{mc^2}\langle S_1\rangle \\ \tfrac{1}{2}\hbar P_2 &= \frac{E}{mc^2}\langle S_2\rangle \\ \tfrac{1}{2}\hbar P_3 &= \langle S_3\rangle \end{aligned}\right\} \quad (E = c(\mathbf{p}^2+m^2c^2)^{\frac{1}{2}}). \tag{17}$$

† The Pauli matrices σ_1, σ_2, σ_3 introduced in Chapter III, § 5, were associated with the representation (3.33) and they acted on *components* u_1 and u_2 of the complete Dirac state vector or wave function. The present matrices σ_1', σ_2', σ_3' act on the exact state vectors $|\pm\frac{1}{2}\rangle$ for particles of fixed momentum $\mathbf{p}$ having spin $\pm\frac{1}{2}\hbar$ in the direction of $\mathbf{p}$.

The transformation properties of the P_i ($i = 1, 2, 3$) under changes of the coordinate axes are deduced from (17). The components $\langle S_i \rangle$ form an axial vector; (P_i) is not an axial vector (except in the case $E = mc^2$). (P_i) is unaltered by spatial inversion; under a rotation through an angle ϕ about the momentum $\mathbf{p}$, the transformed values (P_i') are

$$\left.\begin{aligned} P_1' &= P_1 \cos\phi + P_2 \sin\phi \\ P_2' &= P_2 \cos\phi - P_1 \sin\phi \\ P_3' &= P_3 \end{aligned}\right\}.$$

(P_i) is called the *polarization* of the beam. Having three independent quantities—a magnitude $(p_1 - p_2)$, and a direction (given by a, b in (7))—it is sufficiently general to describe any beam of particles of spin $\frac{1}{2}$. The direction mentioned is that in which we choose to measure the spin of individual particles. The description is sufficient because we can only measure the component of spin in *one* direction at one time (or, by one measuring device).

An *unpolarized* beam has $(P_i) = 0$, and by (17) its spin average $\langle S_i \rangle$ vanishes. A completely polarized beam has $\mathbf{P}^2 = 1$. Eqn. (17) shows that while $\langle S_3 \rangle$, the average spin component in the direction of $\mathbf{p}$, can be as great (in magnitude) as $(\frac{1}{2}\hbar)$, the average of either of the perpendicular components $\langle S_1 \rangle$ or $\langle S_2 \rangle$ cannot have a greater value than $(mc^2/E)\frac{1}{2}\hbar$. Thus for a beam of extremely relativistic particles these perpendicular components must be very small.† In any case, if one of the components P_i is unity, the average spin in the other orthogonal directions must vanish.

The polarization vector (non-relativistic case)

Whenever it is possible to replace E/mc^2 by unity (i.e. to neglect terms in $(p/mc)^2$) eqns. (17) reduce to

$$\tfrac{1}{2}\hbar P_i = \langle S_i \rangle \quad (i = 1, 2, 3) \tag{18}$$

and $\mathbf{P} = (P_i)$ is in this case the *polarization vector* (it is an axial vector). Using the representation (3.33) and remembering that $S_1 = \frac{1}{2}\hbar\sigma^{23}$, etc., it is clear from (3.35) and (3.37) that, to the same order of approximation, we may neglect the components u_2 of the wave function in computing the expectation value of $\mathbf{S}$ (u_1 is to be neglected for antifermions). Without further error, $\langle \mathbf{S} \rangle$ can be replaced by $\frac{1}{2}\hbar\langle \boldsymbol{\sigma} \rangle$, where

† This is related to the corresponding property for the spin expectation value of a single particle. In (3.41 a) we have $|(\tilde{\psi} S_1 \psi)| \leqslant \frac{1}{2}\hbar mc^2/E$ because $|a^*b + ab^*| \leqslant 1$.

$\langle \boldsymbol{\sigma} \rangle$ is the average of the expectation values of the Pauli spin operators σ_i ($i = 1, 2, 3$) given in (3.34). Hence (18) is replaced by†

$$\mathbf{P} = \langle \boldsymbol{\sigma} \rangle, \tag{19}$$

giving the non-relativistic form of the polarization. As was pointed out in Chapter III, § 10, extremely relativistic particles are not polarized by scattering in an electric field (such as the field of a nucleus); therefore polarization experiments are, in general, carried out in energy ranges for which (19) is a fairly good approximation.‡ In this case any two orthogonal vectors in the space of the component u_1 of representation (3.33) can be our basic vectors $|\alpha_m\rangle$, and $\boldsymbol{\rho}$ has the simple form

$$\boldsymbol{\rho} = \tfrac{1}{2}\{I + (\boldsymbol{\sigma}.\mathbf{P})\} \tag{20}$$

(σ_i are the Pauli matrices (3.34)).

2. Scattering of polarized beams of spin-$\frac{1}{2}$ particles by spin-0 targets

The scattering matrix

The elastic scattering of spin-$\frac{1}{2}$ fermions by a spherically symmetrical target (e.g. the scattering of protons by a zero-spin nucleus) can be described by a 2×2 scattering matrix M.§ Consider a beam of particles all having momentum $\hbar\mathbf{k}_i$ which are incident on the scatterer, or on an assembly of such scatterers. Suppose an individual particle is scattered so that its momentum is $\hbar\mathbf{k}_f$; the matrix M relates its initial spin state $|I\rangle$ to its spin state after scattering $|F\rangle$. If $|\lambda_m\rangle$ ($m = 1, 2$) are two basic (orthogonal) spin states, the representatives $\langle \lambda_m | I \rangle$, $\langle \lambda_m | F \rangle$ satisfy

$$\langle \lambda_m | F \rangle = \sum_{m'=1}^{2} M_{mm'} \langle \lambda_{m'} | I \rangle \quad (m = 1, 2). \tag{21}$$

It is convenient to normalize M so that the total|| differential cross-sections $Q\,d\Omega$ for scattering (from a given initial spin state) into a solid angle $d\Omega$ about $\mathbf{k}_f$ are given by the diagonal elements of

$$Q\,d\Omega = \tilde{M}M\,d\Omega. \tag{22}$$

† In general, by (6) and (12) we have $P_i = \langle \sigma_i' \rangle$. It is only in the non-relativistic approximation that σ_i' has a simple physical meaning, and can be equated with σ_i.

‡ The validity of this approximation for electron beams is considered by H. Mendlowitz and K. M. Case, *Phys. Rev.* **97** (1955) 33. These authors also discuss the effect of electric and magnetic fields on polarized electron beams.

§ See Chapter V, §§ 1–3, for a discussion of the scattering matrix. It is convenient to write M rather than $\mathbf{T}$ in the present chapter.

|| By 'total' we mean the sum over both spin values of the scattered particle.

The density matrix $\boldsymbol{\rho}_{\text{out}}$

The polarization properties of the incident beam are described by a density matrix $\boldsymbol{\rho}_{\text{in}}$ (cf. (12)). If the incident beam is described in terms of normalized pure spin states $|I_m\rangle$ ($m = 1, 2$) we have (cf. (3))

$$\boldsymbol{\rho}_{\text{in}} = \sum_{m=1}^{2} |I_m\rangle p_m \langle I_m|.$$

Scattering is described by (21); it does not introduce any randomness. The pure states $|I_m\rangle$ become pure states $|F_m\rangle$ ($m = 1, 2$); hence the scattered beam (in direction $\mathbf{k}_f$) is described by the density matrix

$$\boldsymbol{\rho}_{\text{out}} = \sum_{m=1}^{2} |F_m\rangle p_m \langle F_m|. \tag{23}$$

Using (21) we have
$$\boldsymbol{\rho}_{\text{out}} = M\boldsymbol{\rho}_{\text{in}}\tilde{M}. \tag{24}$$

Eqn. (24)† may be used in any spin representation; it shows how the statistical mixture in the scattered beam in the direction $\mathbf{k}_f$ is related to the statistical mixture in the incident beam.‡ The density matrix $\boldsymbol{\rho}_{\text{out}}$ given by (24) is not normalized to unity as would be required by (1) or (4). However, it is convenient to use (24) for $\boldsymbol{\rho}_{\text{out}}$, because with this form the differential cross-section $Q\,d\Omega$ for scattering of the beam into the solid angle $d\Omega$ about $\mathbf{k}_f$ is given by

$$Q = \text{tr}(\boldsymbol{\rho}_{\text{out}}) = \text{tr}(\boldsymbol{\rho}_{\text{in}}\tilde{M}M). \tag{25}$$

Assuming that $\text{tr}(\boldsymbol{\rho}_{\text{in}}) = 1$, eqn. (25) follows by using (22) and (6). The average of any operator O for the scattered beam is

$$\langle O\rangle_{\text{out}} = \frac{\text{tr}\langle\boldsymbol{\rho}_{\text{out}}\,O\rangle}{\text{tr}\langle\boldsymbol{\rho}_{\text{out}}\rangle}. \tag{26}$$

$\boldsymbol{\rho}_{\text{out}}/\text{tr}(\boldsymbol{\rho}_{\text{out}})$ is the normalized density matrix. So far the discussion of $\boldsymbol{\rho}_{\text{out}}$ has been quite general. As we showed in § 1, it is sufficient for a wide variety of cases to use the approximation given by (18) or (19) in which the polarization $\mathbf{P}$ is the average of the Pauli spin operator $\boldsymbol{\sigma}$. In what follows we use this approximation, but if it were necessary the exact eqns. (17) for (P_i) could be substituted.

Using the representation (3.33) and ignoring the small component u_2 of the wave function (which at the most gives second-order corrections) the scattering matrix M becomes a 2×2 matrix in the space of the two-component vector u_1. The most general form would be

$$M = f+g(\sigma_1 n_1+\sigma_2 n_2+\sigma_3 n_3),$$

† See L. Wolfenstein and J. Askin, *Phys. Rev.* **85** (1952) 947; R. H. Dalitz, *Proc. Phys. Soc.* A, **65** (1952) 175.

‡ Eqn. (23) was given in another form by Tolhoek and de Groot, loc. cit.

where σ_i are the Pauli matrices (3.34) and f, g, n_i are numbers (f, g may be complex). M must be independent of the Euclidean axis system which is used, and because $\boldsymbol{\sigma}$ is an axial vector, it follows that M has to be of the form

$$M = f + g(\boldsymbol{\sigma}.\mathbf{n}), \tag{27}$$

where $\mathbf{n}$ is a unit axial vector, and f and g are scalars. In deriving (27) it is assumed that the scattering is invariant under spatial inversion; this certainly appears to be valid for the strong nucleon-nucleon and nucleon-nucleus interactions, and for the electromagnetic interactions. M describes elastic scattering from the direction $\mathbf{k}_i$ into the direction $\mathbf{k}_f$, and the only unit axial vector which is a function of these polar vectors is

$$\mathbf{n} = (\mathbf{k}_i \times \mathbf{k}_f)/|\mathbf{k}_i \times \mathbf{k}_f|. \tag{28}$$

f and g may be functions of the scalar $(\mathbf{k}_i . \mathbf{k}_f)$ and of the energy of the particles.

3. The double-scattering experiment

Now we can discuss the double-scattering experiment shown in Fig. 38. The total cross-section for scattering at A into the direction AB is

$$Q\,d\Omega = \mathrm{tr}(\boldsymbol{\rho}_{\mathrm{in}} \tilde{M} M)\,d\Omega.$$

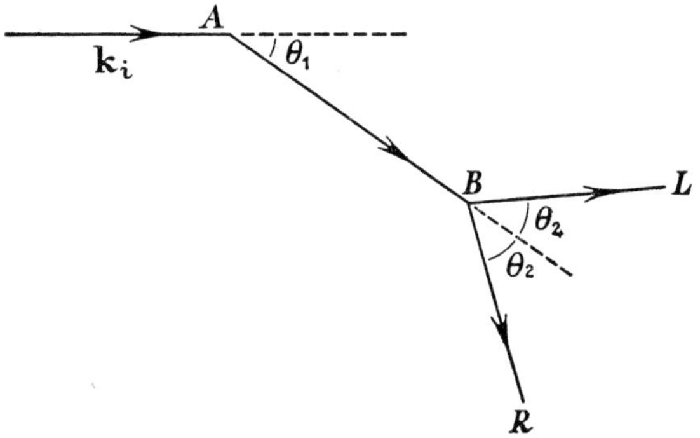

FIG. 38. The double-scattering experiment.

If $\mathbf{P}^{(1)}$ is the polarization of the incident beam, (20) gives

$$Q = \tfrac{1}{2}\{\mathrm{tr}(\tilde{M}M) + \mathrm{tr}(M\boldsymbol{\sigma}\tilde{M}).\mathbf{P}^{(1)}\}. \tag{29}$$

The polarization $\mathbf{P}^{(2)}$ of the beam AB is given by (24) and (26):

$$\mathbf{P}^{(2)} = \langle \boldsymbol{\sigma}_{\mathrm{out}} \rangle = \frac{\mathrm{tr}(\tilde{M}\boldsymbol{\sigma}M) + \mathrm{tr}\{\boldsymbol{\sigma}M(\boldsymbol{\sigma}.\mathbf{P}^{(1)})\tilde{M}\}}{\mathrm{tr}(\tilde{M}M) + \mathrm{tr}(M\boldsymbol{\sigma}\tilde{M}).\mathbf{P}^{(1)}}. \tag{30}$$

For an unpolarized incident beam, $\mathbf{P}^{(1)} = 0$, and

$$Q = \tfrac{1}{2}\mathrm{tr}(\tilde{M}M), \qquad \mathbf{P}^{(2)} = \mathrm{tr}(\tilde{M}\boldsymbol{\sigma}M)/\mathrm{tr}(\tilde{M}M). \tag{31}$$

Using (27) for M gives

$$\left.\begin{aligned} Q &= |f|^2+|g|^2 \\ \mathbf{P}^{(2)} &= \mathbf{n}\,\frac{2\,\mathrm{re}(f^*g)}{|f|^2+|g|^2} = \mathbf{n}P^{(2)} \end{aligned}\right\}, \tag{32}$$

where re denotes the real part. The polarization produced by scattering an unpolarized beam on a spin zero target is therefore perpendicular to the plane containing the incident and the scattered beams. Forward (or backward) scattering ($\theta_1 = 0$) cannot give polarization, because in that case (27) reduces to $M = f$. To obtain appreciable polarization it is in general necessary to work at fairly large scattering angles θ.

Detection of the polarization

The polarization $\mathbf{P}^{(2)}$ produced by the scattering at A may be detected by a second scattering at B.† Let the scattering matrix for the second scattering, through the angle θ_2, be M' (which is of the same form (27)). We use the vector

$$\mathrm{tr}(M'\boldsymbol{\sigma}\tilde{M}')/\mathrm{tr}(\tilde{M}'M') = \mathbf{P}^{(3)} = P^{(3)}\mathbf{n}'. \tag{33}$$

Clearly, $\mathbf{P}^{(3)}$ *is given by* (32) on inserting the new values of f and g, and $\mathbf{n}'$ is the unit normal to the plane in which the second scattering occurs.‡ The cross-section $Q'\,d\Omega$ for the second scattering is given by (29):

$$Q' = \tfrac{1}{2}\mathrm{tr}(\tilde{M}'M')\{1+(\mathbf{P}^{(3)}.\mathbf{P}^{(2)})\}, \tag{34}$$

where $\mathbf{P}^{(2)}$ is the polarization of the beam incident at B.

We may write

$$Q' = \bar{Q}'\{1+P^{(3)}P^{(2)}\cos\phi\} \tag{35}$$

when, by (32) and (33), ϕ is the angle between the planes of scattering at A and B. We call $A = P^{(3)}P^{(2)}\cos\phi$ the *asymmetry* of scattering; by (15), $|A| \leqslant 1$. If Q'_L, Q'_R denote the cross-sections for scattering into the directions L and R respectively (see Fig. 38), where AB and the directions L and R lie in a plane, then

$$A = \frac{Q'_R-Q'_L}{Q'_R+Q'_L}. \tag{36}$$

Choosing the two scattering angles to be equal ($\theta_1 = \theta_2$), a single measurement of A will give the absolute value of the polarization $P^{(2)}$.

† This was first suggested (for electron scattering) by N. F. Mott, *Proc. Roy. Soc.* A, **124** (1929) 425.

‡ Because $\mathrm{tr}(M'\boldsymbol{\sigma}\tilde{M}')$ and $\mathrm{tr}(\tilde{M}'\boldsymbol{\sigma}M')$ are equal for M' given by (27), it follows from (31) that $\mathbf{P}^{(3)}$ is the polarization that would be produced in an unpolarized beam by the scattering at B. Then with $\theta_1 = \theta_2$, (35) gives the polarization directly.

Because the experiment can only determine cross-sections, the sign of $P^{(2)}$ cannot be found from a double-scattering experiment.

A double-scattering experiment for 400 keV electrons on gold was successfully carried out by Shull *et al.*† The scattering is mainly due to the electric field of the nucleus, so the scatterer has spherical symmetry.‡ An asymmetry A of about 6 per cent was found, and this is in reasonable agreement§ with the computations of Mott's formulae made by Bartlett and Watson.||

4. Polarization of nucleons on scattering by nuclei

Polarized beams of thermal neutrons were originally produced by scattering in iron under an applied magnetic field.†† Double-scattering experiments on high-energy protons are now successfully performed using reasonably intense cyclotron beams.‡‡ An idea of the order of magnitude of the results of these experiments is given by Fig. 39 for the scattering of polarized protons on helium.§§ The polarized beams of protons used in these experiments were produced by a first target of beryllium placed inside the cyclotron in a beam of 340 MeV protons. The asymmetry A (eqn. (36)) gave the polarization $P(\theta)$ of the second scattering, because the polarization of the beam incident on the second target was already determined.

The experimental set-up is simplified by applying a magnetic field along the beam between the first and second targets. Instead of varying the azimuthal angle, variation of the magnetic field rotates the polarization distribution.|||| This does not distort the polarization distribution.

Nucleon-nucleus forces

The polarization of nucleons scattered by a nucleus gives information about the forces between the nucleon and the nucleus. We confine the

† C. G. Shull, C. T. Chase, and F. E. Myers, *Phys. Rev.* **63** (1943) 29.

‡ The polarization relations in the bremsstrahlung process have been examined by R. L. Gluckstern, M. H. Hall, and G. Breit, *Phys. Rev.* **90** (1953) 1026.

§ For a critical discussion of the difficulties and errors caused by multiple scattering, etc., see G. Goertzel and R. T. Cox, *Phys. Rev.* **63** (1943) 37. A comprehensive review of electron polarization is given by H. A. Tolhoek, *Rev. Mod. Phys.* **28** (1956) 277.

|| J. H. Bartlett and R. E. Watson, *Phys. Rev.* **56** (1939) 612. Extensive calculations for a number of nuclei have been made by N. Sherman, *Phys. Rev.* **103** (1956) 1601; see also H. N. Yadov, *Proc. Phys. Soc.* A, **68** (1955) 348.

†† F. Bloch, *Phys. Rev.* **50** (1936) 259; see also D. J. Hughes, J. R. Wallace, and R. H. Holtzmann, ibid. **73** (1948) 1277.

‡‡ For a survey, see the article by L. Wolfenstein in *Ann. Rev. Nuclear Sci.* **6** (Annual Reviews, Inc., Stanford, Cal., 1956).

§§ O. Chamberlain, *et al.*, *Phys. Rev.* **96** (1954) 807; **102** (1956) 1659.

|||| M. J. Brinkworth and B. Rose, *Nuovo Cim.* **3** (1956) 195.

discussion to the case in which the nucleus can be regarded as spherically symmetric; this is an adequate first approximation. In any case, if the nuclei in the target are unpolarized, the information we can derive will not give any angular structure in the nucleon-nucleus interaction.

The shell model of the nucleus, if it is to be satisfactory, requires,

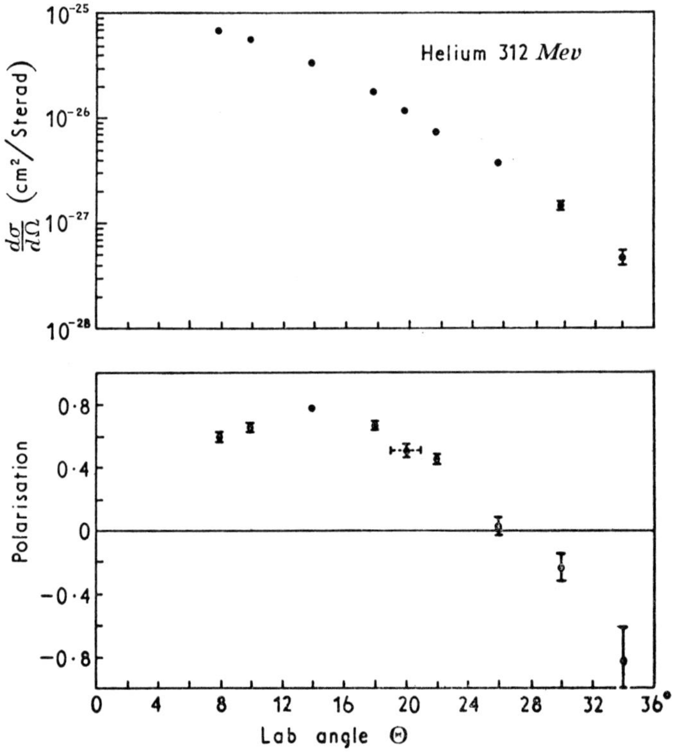

FIG. 39. The differential cross-section and the polarization for the scattering of 312 MeV (lab.) protons on helium.†

in addition to a central potential, a spin-orbital interaction between a nucleon and the nucleus. This may be written in the form (cf. p. 128)

$$-\gamma\frac{1}{2M^2c^2}(\mathbf{S}.\mathbf{L})\frac{1}{r}\frac{dV(r)}{dr}, \tag{37}$$

where M is the mass of the nucleon, r its distance from the centre of the nucleus, **S** its spin, and **L** its orbital angular momentum. $V(r)$ is the potential energy of the nucleon in the nucleus and γ is a positive‡ constant which must have a value about 30, if the separation of nuclear

† Chamberlain *et al.*, *Phys. Rev.* **102** (1956) 1659.

‡ The Thomas term (p. 128) would only give γ of the order of unity.

levels is to be given correctly by the shell model.† It was seen in Chapter V, § 4, that an interaction of the form (37) results from applying multiple scattering theory to the nucleon-nucleus encounter.

The scattered wave

With a nucleon-nucleus interaction consisting of a central potential and the spin-orbital interaction (37), the total angular momentum **J** of the scattered nucleon is conserved, and the analysis leading to (3.73) gives the scattered wave. The scattering matrix M is given by the expression (27) in which $f(\theta)$ and $g(\theta)$ are functions of the angle θ between the incident and the scattered beams.‡ In Fig. 40 the axes O_1, O_2 are orthogonal to O_3, which is in the direction of the incident beam. ON is the projection of the scattered beam on to the plane O_{12}. The unit vector **n** (eqn. (28)), which is in the plane O_{12}, is perpendicular to ON. By (27) we now have

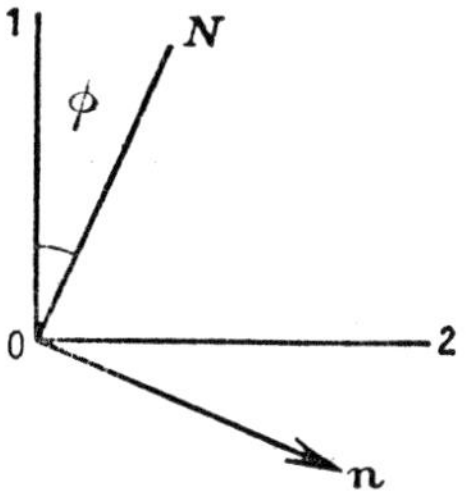

FIG. 40. The incident beam is along the axis O_3. **n** is the perpendicular to the scattering plane.

$$M = \begin{pmatrix} f(\theta) & -ig(\theta)e^{-i\phi} \\ ig(\theta)e^{i\phi} & f(\theta) \end{pmatrix}. \tag{38}$$

The form of a scattered fermion wave has been given by formula (3.73). There $u''_1(m' = \pm\frac{1}{2})$ is the scattered wave originating from an incident wave (of unit density) having a spin component $m'\hbar = \pm\frac{1}{2}\hbar$ along the direction of motion. If the differential cross-section $Q\,d\Omega$ is to be given by (22), we have only to drop the factor (e^{ikr}/r) in (3.73) (as well as N which is unity in this approximation); thus (cf. (6.77))

$$\left.\begin{aligned} f(\theta) &= \frac{1}{k}\sum_{l=0}^{\infty} P_l(\cos\theta)\{(l+1)A_l^+ + lA_l^-\} \\ g(\theta) &= \frac{i}{k}\sum_{l=1}^{\infty} P_l^1(\cos\theta)\{A_l^+ - A_l^-\} \end{aligned}\right\}. \tag{39}$$

Here $$A_l^+ = \frac{e^{2i\eta_{l,l+\frac{1}{2}}}-1}{2i}, \qquad A_l^- = \frac{e^{2i\eta_{l,l-\frac{1}{2}}}-1}{2i}. \tag{40}$$

The differential cross-section Q and the polarization $P^{(2)}$ are now given

† For a discussion of the shell model, see M. Goeppert-Mayer and J. H. D. Jensen, *Elementary Theory of Nuclear Shell Structure* (J. Wiley, New York, 1955).

‡ In deriving (3.73) either we can neglect the recoil of the nucleus, or we can work in the centre of mass system.

by (32). Using formula (1.56) it is possible to write

$$P^{(2)}.Q = \frac{1}{k^2}\sum_{L=1}^{\infty} c_L P_L^1(\cos\theta). \tag{41}$$

The coefficient c_L is a function of the $A_l^{\pm}$, thus,

$$c_L = -\sum_{l,l'} \mathrm{im}[\{(l+1)A_l^+ + lA_l^-\}^*(A_{l'}^+ - A_{l'}^-)](ll'00|L0)(ll'01|L1)\times$$
$$\times\left(\frac{l'(l'+1)}{L(L+1)}\right)^{\frac{1}{2}} \quad (|l-l'| \leqslant L \leqslant l+l'), \tag{42}$$

where the centre factors are Clebsch–Gordan coefficients. It is possible by using (41) and (42) to obtain information about the phases $\eta_{l,l\pm\frac{1}{2}}$, if the angular dependence of the polarization $P^{(2)}$ and the differential cross-section Q is known.† The effect of Coulomb repulsion can be allowed for by the usual methods. In calculating the scattering and polarization of nucleons by a nucleus, it is desirable to add an imaginary term to the central potential to allow for the inelastic scattering and absorption of nucleons by the nucleus.‡ The results of a calculation of $Q\,d\Omega$ and $P^{(2)}$ are shown in Fig. 41. The data refer to the scattering of 287 MeV protons on Al. Further details of the exact calculations are to be found in the literature.§

The Born approximation

A general idea of how the polarization may be expected to vary with the angle of scattering has been given by Fermi using the Born approximation.‖ In this analysis the nucleon-nucleus interaction for nucleons of a few hundred MeV is given by

$$V_1(r)+iV_2(r)-\gamma\frac{1}{2M^2c^2}(\mathbf{S}.\mathbf{L})\frac{1}{r}\frac{dV_1(r)}{dr}. \tag{43}$$

Fermi uses a square well potential,

$$V_1+iV_2 = \begin{cases} -(B+iB_A) & (r<R), \\ 0 & (r>R), \end{cases} \tag{44}$$

where B, B_A are real and positive, and R is the radius of the nucleus.

† For the general theory, see N. F. Mott and H. S. W. Massey, *Theory of Atomic Collisions* (Clarendon Press, 2nd edn., 1949). Details of the application to polarization problems are given by R. M. Sternheimer, *Phys. Rev.* **97** (1955) 1314, and S. Ohnuma and D. Feldman, ibid. **102** (1956) 1641.

‡ The complex potential was used by H. A. Bethe (*Phys. Rev.* **57** (1940) 1125).

§ See B. J. Malenka, ibid. **95** (1954) 522; R. M. Sternheimer, loc. cit.; S. Fernbach, W. Heckrotte, and J. V. Lepore, *Phys. Rev.* **97** (1955) 1059.

‖ E. Fermi, *Nuovo Cim.* **11** (1954) 407. It has been shown by H. S. Köhler (*Nucl. Phys.* **1** (1956) 433) and I. I. Levintov (*Dokl. Akad. Nauk SSSR.* **107** (1956) 240) that the Born approximation gives the *polarization* very accurately for scattering by a heavy nucleus.

The value of B_A is deduced from the nuclear absorption cross-section for the nucleons; if λ is the absorption mean free path in the nucleus, then (cf. (5.91))

$$B_A = \hbar v/2\lambda,$$

where v is the velocity of the nucleon. As an example of the orders of magnitude, for 300 MeV protons scattered by carbon we could use†

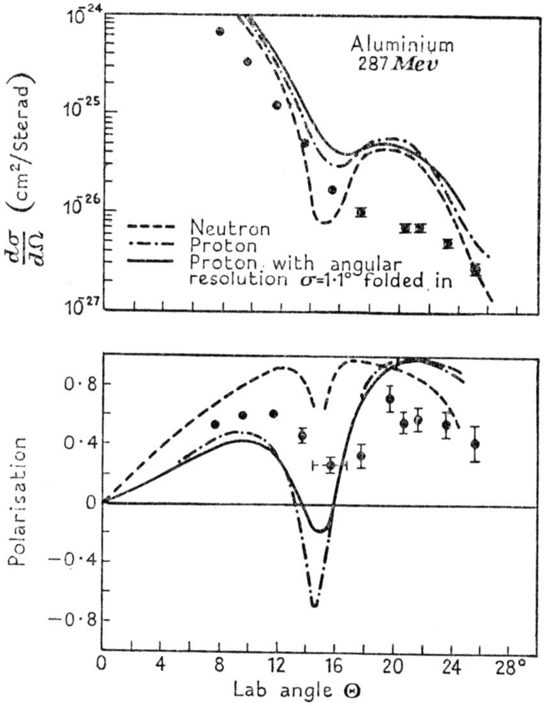

FIG. 41. Aluminium differential cross-section and polarization at 287 MeV (lab.). The graphs shown represent the theoretical curves of Fernbach Heckrotte, and Lepore (loc. cit.) for the scattering of neutrons and protons from aluminium and a graph for protons with the experimental angular resolution folded in. Proton experimental values are shown.

$B = 18$ MeV, $B_A = 16$ MeV. The spin-orbital coupling in (43) now gives a δ-function interaction at the surface of the nucleus.

Evaluating the matrix elements of (43) for transitions between plane wave functions, the scattering matrix (38) is given by

$$\left.\begin{aligned} f(\theta) &= -\frac{2M}{\hbar^2}(B+iB_A)R^3F(q) \\ g(\theta) &= -\frac{i\gamma}{Mc^2}BR^3k^2\sin\theta F(q) \end{aligned}\right\}, \tag{45}$$

† These calculations agree with $\gamma \simeq 25$. More accurate estimates suggest that at 300 MeV, γ has decreased to about 10 (H. A. Bethe, *Ann. Phys.* **3** (1958) 190).

where θ is the angle of scattering, $q = 2kR\sin\frac{1}{2}\theta$, and

$$F(q) = \left(\frac{\sin q}{q^3} - \frac{\cos q}{q^2}\right). \tag{46}$$

$\hbar k$ is the momentum of the incident nucleon.

The function $F(q)$ has the value $\frac{1}{3}$ for $q = 0$, and it behaves like a diffraction amplitude. It vanishes at the other roots of $\tan q = q$ (which, very roughly, are $q = \pm 3\pi/2, \pm 5\pi/2, \pm 7\pi/2,...$), and the maximum value of $|F(q)|$ between each pair of zeros decreases quickly as we go away from $q = 0$. By (32), the differential cross-section $Q\,d\Omega$, calculated by the Born approximation, will vanish at the zeros of $F(q)$. The polarization $P^{(2)}(\theta)$ does not contain $F(q)$, and is a smoothly varying function of $\sin\theta$. For 300 MeV protons incident on nuclei in the range from carbon to iron, the first diffraction zero decreases from around 20° to 12°. For protons of greater energy these angles will be less.

The cross-section given by the exact calculation will not vanish at the zeros of $F(q)$; instead we expect a diffraction minimum in Q. The exact calculation will in general lead to functions $f(\theta)$, $g(\theta)$ having *distinct* zeros in the neighbourhood of the zeros of $F(q)$; therefore it may occur that the polarization $P^{(2)}(\theta)$ shows an oscillation near the minimum in the cross-section. Notice that the first Born approximation gives *no polarization* if the central potential is real.

The sign of the polarization

The sign of the constant γ in the spin-orbital interaction (37) determines the sign of the polarization $P^{(2)}$. It follows from (35) that a double-scattering experiment can only determine the magnitude of $P^{(2)}$. Brinkworth and Rose† have determined the sign of γ by slowing down a 135 MeV polarized proton beam scattered from carbon. When the energy has been reduced to between 4 MeV and 9 MeV, scattering by helium gives the sign of the polarization of the beam. This is because the phase shifts for the scattering of protons by helium at these energies are known; knowing the sign of $P^{(3)}$ in (35), comparison of left and right scattering determines the sign of $P^{(2)}$. The sign of γ as determined by Brinkworth and Rose agrees with the sign required by the shell model; a similar experiment by Marshall and Marshall on 435 MeV protons scattered by beryllium gives the same result.†

The sign of the polarization may also be determined by interference

† M. J. Brinkworth and B. Rose, *Nuovo Cim.* **3** (1956) 195; L. Marshall and J. Marshall, *Phys. Rev.* **98** (1955) 1398.

in small-angle scattering arising from electromagnetic effects,† or by a triple-scattering experiment (see § 9 below).

5. Polarized beams of unit spin particles (non-relativistic)

We now show how to describe the polarization of a beam of particles of unit spin.‡ The particles may be elementary, or they may be nuclei. A beam of spin-$\frac{1}{2}$ particles which are not in a definite spin state can be described by a polarization vector which is the average spin value for the beam; for particles having spin greater than $\frac{1}{2}$ the specification of polarization is more complicated. As an example we consider a beam of deuterons.§

The spin of the deuteron is described by the operators S_i ($i = 1, 2, 3$) which obey the relations (cf. Chapter I, § 14)

$$S_1 S_2 - S_2 S_1 = i\hbar S_3 \quad \text{(and cyclic permutations)}, \tag{47}$$

and $$\mathbf{S}^2 = 2\hbar^2, \quad \text{where } \mathbf{S}^2 = S_1^2 + S_2^2 + S_3^2.$$

These operators have eigenvalues $\pm\hbar$, 0. We can represent them in terms of the eigenvectors $|+\rangle$, $|0\rangle$, $|-\rangle$ of the operator S_3 having eigenvalues $+\hbar$, 0, $-\hbar$, respectively. In this representation

$$\left.\begin{aligned} S_1 = \frac{\hbar}{\sqrt{2}}\begin{pmatrix} 0 & 1 & 0 \\ 1 & 0 & 1 \\ 0 & 1 & 0 \end{pmatrix}, \qquad S_2 = \frac{\hbar}{\sqrt{2}}\begin{pmatrix} 0 & -i & 0 \\ i & 0 & -i \\ 0 & i & 0 \end{pmatrix} \\ S_3 = \hbar\begin{pmatrix} 1 & 0 & 0 \\ 0 & 0 & 0 \\ 0 & 0 & -1 \end{pmatrix} \end{aligned}\right\}. \tag{48}$$

The basic spin states

For basic spin states we can use $|+\rangle$, $|0\rangle$, $|-\rangle$, or alternatively, we can use a general set of three orthogonal state vectors $|\alpha_m\rangle$ ($m = 1, 2, 3$), which are related to the former set by a unitary transformation. This transformation is expressed

$$\begin{pmatrix} \langle\alpha_1| \\ \langle\alpha_2| \\ \langle\alpha_3| \end{pmatrix} = \tilde{R}\begin{pmatrix} \langle+1| \\ \langle 0| \\ \langle -1| \end{pmatrix}, \tag{49}$$

where R is a 3×3 unitary matrix. Here we have written the sets of state vectors as a column vector. The Hermitian transpose of (49) is

$$(|\alpha_1\rangle, |\alpha_2\rangle, |\alpha_3\rangle) = (|+1\rangle, |0\rangle, |-1\rangle)R. \tag{50}$$

† For protons on C see W. Heckrotte, *Phys. Rev.* **101** (1956) 1406, for neutrons on uranium, see R. G. Voss and R. Wilson, *Phil. Mag.* **1** (1956) 175.

‡ The analysis is applicable to any assembly of particles: for example it may be used to describe the incomplete information resulting from an angular correlation experiment.

§ Deuteron polarization is discussed by W. Lakin, *Phys. Rev.* 98 (1955) 139.

The state vectors $|\alpha_m\rangle$ are eigenstates of the component of spin in some arbitrary direction. We do not discuss whether it is possible simultaneously to specify the spin (in an arbitrary direction) and the particle's momentum. We saw when dealing with spin-$\frac{1}{2}$ particles (§ 1) that in the relativistic case the expectation value of the spin could not be as great as $\frac{1}{2}\hbar$ in a direction perpendicular to the momentum; for the non-relativistic case this difficulty did not arise. Here it will be assumed that in a non-relativistic approximation we can freely choose any direction for the spin.

The same matrix R as occurs in (50) will transform the eigenstates of unit *orbital* angular momentum, referred to the original O_3 axis, into eigenstates of angular momentum referred to a new axis; in other words R relates the functions $Y_1^{(m)}(\theta,\phi)$ to the new values $Y_1^{(m)}(\theta',\phi')$ which they assume under a rotation of the axes:

$$Y_1^{(m')}(\theta',\phi') = \sum_{m=-1}^{1} R_{mm'} Y_1^{(m)}(\theta,\phi). \tag{51}$$

Remembering that, apart from a constant factor, we may replace $Y_1^{(m)}(\theta,\phi)$ by the variables

$$-\frac{1}{\sqrt{2}}(x_1+ix_2)/r, \quad x_3/r, \quad \frac{1}{\sqrt{2}}(x_1-ix_2)/r \quad (m = +1,0,-1), \tag{52}$$

it is easy to find the form of R for any given rotation of the axes.

Analysis of the density matrix

A pure spin state of the deuteron is given by some eigenstate of the form $|\alpha_m\rangle$. If the beam of deuterons is not in a pure state, it can be described statistically by the density matrix $\boldsymbol{\rho}$ given by (3). We assume that the probabilities for the individual particle being in the states $|\alpha_1\rangle$, $|\alpha_2\rangle$, $|\alpha_3\rangle$ are p_1, p_2, p_3 respectively, where $\sum_{m=1}^{3} p_m = 1$. Using (3) we see that in terms of the representation given by $|+\rangle$, $|0\rangle$, $|-\rangle$, $\boldsymbol{\rho}$ has the form

$$\boldsymbol{\rho} = R\begin{pmatrix} p_1 & 0 & 0 \\ 0 & p_2 & 0 \\ 0 & 0 & p_3 \end{pmatrix}\tilde{R}. \tag{53}$$

Clearly $\operatorname{tr}\boldsymbol{\rho} = 1$, and $\boldsymbol{\rho}$ is Hermitian. Hence $\boldsymbol{\rho}$ has eight independent components. For spin-$\frac{1}{2}$ particles, the density matrix $\boldsymbol{\rho}$ (eqn. (12)) had only three independent components, so that the three components of the expectation of the spin were sufficient to describe the beam; for particles of unit spin the expectation of the spin is not sufficient to determine $\boldsymbol{\rho}$. We now examine how $\boldsymbol{\rho}$ is specified.

The coefficients of $\boldsymbol{\rho}$ in (53) are bilinear in the matrix elements $R_{mm'}$ and their complex conjugates. Consider the behaviour of these coefficients for different rotations of the coordinate axes system. Using (51) and (52), and keeping (θ, ϕ) fixed on the right-hand side of (51), it is clear that as the rotation of the axes system varies, the components $R_{m'm}$ vary like linear combinations of the components (x_i) of a vector. Therefore, under rotations of the coordinate axes the components of $\boldsymbol{\rho}$ given in (53) will vary like linear combinations of the components $x_i^{(1)}x_j^{(2)}$ $(i,j = 1,2,3)$ of a second-rank tensor (here $(x_i^{(1)})$ and $(x_j^{(2)})$ are chosen to be distinct vectors).

The irreducible tensors

The nine tensor components $x_i^{(1)}x_j^{(2)}$ $(i,j = 1,2,3)$ can be combined (linearly) into sets which transform exclusively into themselves; these sets form the *irreducible*† tensors T_{ij}. We have three types:‡

$$\left.\begin{array}{ll} \text{(i) the scalar:} & \delta_{ij}(\mathbf{x}^{(1)}.\mathbf{x}^{(2)}) = \delta_{ij}\sum_{k=1}^{3} x_k^{(1)}x_k^{(2)}; \\ \text{(ii) the axial vector:} & x_i^{(1)}x_j^{(2)} - x_j^{(1)}x_i^{(2)}; \\ \text{(iii) the second-rank irreducible tensor:} & \\ & x_i^{(1)}x_j^{(2)} + x_j^{(1)}x_i^{(2)} - \tfrac{2}{3}\delta_{ij}(\mathbf{x}^{(1)}.\mathbf{x}^{(2)}). \end{array}\right\} \quad (54)$$

Both (ii) and (iii) must have zero trace§ (i.e. $\sum_i T_{ii} = 0$).

The irreducible tensors (i), (ii), (iii) have 1, 3, 5 independent components, respectively, so the analysis of the tensor $x_i^{(1)}x_j^{(2)}$ is complete. We conclude from (54) that the matrix $\boldsymbol{\rho}$ can be expressed as the sum of nine linearly independent 3×3 matrices. The first (i.e. (i)) is the identity matrix, the next three (i.e. (ii)) are matrices which under a rotation of the axes transform like an axial vector, while the last five (i.e. (iii)) transform like the independent components of a second rank irreducible tensor. The scalar is determined by $\operatorname{tr}\boldsymbol{\rho} = 1$.

It is convenient to use the notation of angular momentum analysis to write these matrices (or linear combinations of those within each set) as Ω_{JM} $(-J \leqslant M \leqslant J)$, where the matrices Ω_{JM} transform under any rotation of the axes like the spherical harmonics $Y_J^{(M)}$. The sets

† Cf. G. Racah, *Phys. Rev.* **62** (1942) 442.

‡ It is important to notice that (i), (ii), and (iii) are 3×3 tensors. The rank r of an irreducible tensor is deduced from the number $(2r+1)$ of independent components of the tensor. The ranks of (i), (ii), (iii) are 0, 1, 2 respectively.

§ The trace is necessarily a scalar; if it did not vanish, this linear combination of the components T_{ij} would transform into itself. In that case T_{ij} would not be irreducible.

(i), (ii), (iii) give $J = 0, 1, 2$ respectively. It is clear that $\mathrm{tr}(\Omega_{JM}) = 0$ for $J > 0$ (only the scalar has non-zero trace); it follows that

$$\mathrm{tr}(\Omega_{JM}\tilde{\Omega}_{J'M'}) = 0, \quad \text{for } J \neq J',\ M \neq M'. \tag{55}$$

This is because the product $\Omega_{JM}\tilde{\Omega}_{J'M'}$ is a 3×3 matrix which can be expressed† as a sum of matrices $\Omega_{J'',(M-M')}$ where $|J-J'| \leqslant J'' \leqslant J+J'$. Only if $J = J'$ and $M = M'$ can any matrix in this sum have non-zero trace.

We make use of (55) to normalize the matrices Ω_{JM}, so that

$$\mathrm{tr}(\Omega_{JM}\tilde{\Omega}_{J'M'}) = 3\delta_{JJ'}\delta_{MM'}. \tag{56}$$

Instead of working with (54) we can conveniently write down the irreducible matrices Ω_{JM} with the aid of the spin matrices (48). Using the dimensionless matrices S_i $(i = 1, 2, 3)$ $(\hbar = 1)$, and remembering that $\mathbf{S}$ transforms like an axial vector, it is easy to see that (56) is satisfied by the 3×3 matrices:

$$\left.\begin{array}{c} \Omega_{00} = I; \quad \Omega_{1,0} = \sqrt{\tfrac{3}{2}}S_3, \quad \Omega_{1,\pm 1} = \mp\tfrac{1}{2}\sqrt{3}(S_1 \pm iS_2); \\ \Omega_{2,0} = \tfrac{1}{2}\sqrt{2}(3S_3^2-2), \quad \Omega_{2,\pm 1} = \mp\tfrac{1}{2}\sqrt{3}\{(S_1\pm iS_2)S_3+S_3(S_1\pm iS_2)\}, \\ \Omega_{2,\pm 2} = \tfrac{1}{2}\sqrt{3}(S_1\pm iS_2)^2. \quad (\text{Notice, } \Omega_{J,-M} = (-1)^M\tilde{\Omega}_{JM}.) \end{array}\right\} \tag{57}$$

The forms of Ω_{00}, Ω_{1M} are obvious. The set Ω_{2M} is found by using

$$\Omega_{2M} = (\text{const.})\left(\sum_i S_i \frac{\partial}{\partial x_i^{(1)}}\right)\left(\sum_j S_j \frac{\partial}{\partial x_j^{(2)}}\right)\mathscr{Y}_2^{(M)}(\mathbf{x}^{(1)}, \mathbf{x}^{(2)}), \tag{58}$$

where‡

$$\mathscr{Y}_2^{(M)}(\mathbf{x}^{(1)}, \mathbf{x}^{(2)}) = \sum_{m',m''} (11m'm''|2M)Y_1^{(m')}(\mathbf{x}^{(1)})Y_1^{(m'')}(\mathbf{x}^{(2)}) \tag{59}$$

is the spherical harmonic of the type $(2, M)$ formed from spherical harmonics associated with the directions $\mathbf{x}^{(1)}$, $\mathbf{x}^{(2)}$. The operator acting on $\mathscr{Y}_2^{(M)}(\mathbf{x}^{(1)}, \mathbf{x}^{(2)})$ in (58) is obviously invariant, therefore we get Ω_{2M}.

The canonical form of the density matrix

Relation (56) makes it very easy to write down $\boldsymbol{\rho}$. Using (6) we have

$$\boldsymbol{\rho} = \tfrac{1}{3}\sum_{J,M} \langle\Omega_{JM}\rangle\tilde{\Omega}_{JM}. \tag{60}$$

This gives $\mathrm{tr}(\boldsymbol{\rho}) = 1$. It follows that the polarization properties of the deuteron beam are specified by the five parameters $\langle\Omega_{2M}\rangle$, in addition to the spin averages given by $\langle\Omega_{1M}\rangle$. Physically, this is to be expected,§ because the deuteron interacts with external fields through its magnetic moment (an axial vector), and its electric quadrupole moment

† This follows because $\Omega_{JM}\tilde{\Omega}_{J'M'}$ transforms like $Y_J^{(M)}Y_{J'}^{(-M')}$ and eqn. (1.50) can be used.

‡ Cf. Chapter I, § 10, p. 23.

§ U. Fano, *Phys. Rev.* **90** (1953) 577.

(a symmetric second-rank tensor). The polarization is described by the average spin $\langle S_i \rangle$, and by the polarization ellipsoid

$$\tfrac{1}{2}\sum_{ij} \langle S_i S_j + S_j S_i \rangle x_i x_j = 1. \tag{61}$$

All expectation values $\langle \Omega_{JM} \rangle$ vanish (except $\langle \Omega_{00} \rangle$ which is unity) for an unpolarized beam. In this case the spin average vanishes and the polarization ellipsoid becomes a sphere.†

We deduce from (3) (or (53)) that

$$\mathrm{tr}(\rho^2) = \sum_{m=1}^{3} p_m^2.$$

Therefore, for a completely polarized beam (a beam having one p_m unity and the others zero), $\mathrm{tr}(\rho^2)$ attains its maximum value of unity. Using (56) and (60) this gives

$$\sum_{JM}' |\langle \Omega_{JM} \rangle|^2 \leqslant 2, \tag{62}$$

where the summation $\sum'$ excludes the term $J = 0$, $M = 0$. Equality occurs in (62) only for a completely polarized beam.

6. Double scattering of deuterons

We illustrate this description of deuteron polarization by showing how an elastic scattering experiment may be used to produce, or detect, the polarization. If a deuteron beam having polarization $\langle \Omega_{JM} \rangle_{(1)}$ is incident on a scatterer with zero spin (or an unpolarized assembly of scatterers),‡ the scattering can be described by a 3×3 scattering matrix M which is defined by a relation similar to (21). The density matrix $\rho_{(2)}$ for the scattered beam is given in terms of the density matrix of the incident beam $\rho_{(1)}$ by (cf. (24))

$$\rho_{(2)} = M \rho_{(1)} \tilde{M}. \tag{63}$$

The differential cross-section for scattering into a given element of solid angle $d\Omega$ is

$$Q_{(2)}\, d\Omega = \mathrm{tr}(\rho_{(2)})\, d\Omega,$$

and the polarization of the scattered beam is given by

$$Q_{(2)} \langle \Omega_{JM} \rangle_{(2)} = \mathrm{tr}(M \rho_{(1)} \tilde{M} \Omega_{JM}). \tag{64}$$

Using (60) this becomes

$$Q_{(2)} \langle \Omega_{JM} \rangle_{(2)} = \tfrac{1}{3} \sum_{J'M'} \langle \Omega_{J'M'} \rangle_{(1)} \mathrm{tr}(M \tilde{\Omega}_{J'M'} \tilde{M} \Omega_{JM}). \tag{65}$$

† Using $\sum_i S_i^2 = 2$, together with (57), we see that for an unpolarized beam

$$\langle S_i S_j + S_j S_i \rangle = \tfrac{4}{3}\delta_{ij}.$$

‡ An unpolarized assembly of scatterers behaves as if the scatterers had no spin. Bilinear expressions ($M\tilde{M}$, etc.) in the scattering matrix M have to be averaged over all the spin states of the scatterer in this case (cf. pp. 396–7).

Here we consider only the case of an unpolarized incident deuteron beam. Then

$$\langle\Omega_{J'M'}\rangle_{(1)} = 0 \quad (J' \neq 0),$$

so the polarization of the scattered beam is

$$Q_{(2)}\langle\Omega_{JM}\rangle_{(2)} = \tfrac{1}{3}\mathrm{tr}(M\tilde{M}\Omega_{JM}). \tag{66}$$

The form of the scattering matrix

Because $M\tilde{M}$ has to be invariant under rotations and inversion, it must have the form†

$$M\tilde{M} = A_0 + \sum_{M=-2}^{2}\{A_1 Y_2^{(M)}(\mathbf{k}^{(1)}) + A_2 Y_2^{(M)}(\mathbf{k}^{(2)})\}\tilde{\Omega}_{2M} + \\ + A_3 \sum_{M=-2}^{2} \mathscr{Y}_2^{(M)}(\mathbf{k}^{(1)},\mathbf{k}^{(2)})\tilde{\Omega}_{2M} + A_4 \sum_{M=-1}^{1} Y_1^{(M)}(\mathbf{k}^{(1)}\times\mathbf{k}^{(2)})\tilde{\Omega}_{1M}. \tag{67}$$

$Y_l^{(m)}(\mathbf{k})$ is the spherical harmonic of order (l, m) associated with the *direction* $\mathbf{k}$, and $\mathscr{Y}_2^{(M)}(\mathbf{k}^{(1)},\mathbf{k}^{(2)})$ is the spherical harmonic of order $(2, M)$ formed as in (59); $\mathbf{k}^{(1)}$, $\mathbf{k}^{(2)}$ are the initial and final deuteron propagation vectors. The *real numbers* $A_0,\ldots, A_4$ depend only on $\mathbf{k}^{(1)}.\mathbf{k}^{(2)}$, $(\mathbf{k}^{(1)})^2$, $(\mathbf{k}^{(2)})^2$.

Using (56) and (66) we find

$$\left.\begin{aligned} Q_{(2)} = A_0, \qquad Q_{(2)}\langle\Omega_{1M}\rangle_{(2)} &= A_4 Y_1^{(M)}(\mathbf{k}^{(1)}\times\mathbf{k}^{(2)}) \\ Q_2\langle\Omega_{2M}\rangle_{(2)} = A_1 Y_2^{(M)}(\mathbf{k}^{(1)}) + A_2 Y_2^{(M)}(\mathbf{k}^{(2)}) &+ A_3 \mathscr{Y}_2^{(M)}(\mathbf{k}^{(1)},\mathbf{k}^{(2)}) \end{aligned}\right\}. \tag{68}$$

Choosing the O_3 axis along $\mathbf{k}^{(1)}\times\mathbf{k}^{(2)}$ ensures that $\langle\Omega_{JM}\rangle_{(2)}$ $(J = 1, 2)$ vanishes for $M = \pm 1$. The spin is therefore polarized perpendicular to the plane of scattering, and the polarization quadric has a principal axis in the same direction O_3. (This follows from (57) on using $\langle\Omega_{2,1}\rangle_{(2)} = \langle\Omega_{2,-1}\rangle_{(2)} = 0$, to show that $\langle S_1 S_3 + S_3 S_1\rangle_{(2)}$ and $\langle S_2 S_3 + S_3 S_2\rangle_{(2)}$ vanish.)

Detection of the polarization

The polarization produced by the scattering (or otherwise) can be detected by a second (elastic) scattering. The second scattering determines the differential cross-section $Q_{(3)}$ at various azimuthal angles (cf. Fig. 42). Eqn. (65) shows that

$$Q_{(3)} = \tfrac{1}{3}\sum_{J'M'} \langle\Omega_{J'M'}\rangle_{(2)}\,\mathrm{tr}(\tilde{M}M\tilde{\Omega}_{J'M'}). \tag{69}$$

Comparison of this formula with (66) can be made, provided we know the relation‡ between $\tilde{M}M$ and $M\tilde{M}$. Assuming that the elastic scattering is unaltered by Wigner time reversal,§ we have

$$M' = M \tag{70}$$

† Cf. W. Lakin, p. 389, n. §. Reflection invariance forbids $Y_1^{(M)}(\mathbf{k}^{(1)})$ and $Y_1^{(M)}(\mathbf{k}^{(2)})$.

‡ Cf. W. Lakin, loc. cit. The method is due to L. Wolfenstein and J. Ashkin, *Phys. Rev.* **85** (1952) 947; R. H. Dalitz, *Proc. Phys. Soc.* A, **65** (1952) 175.

§ Cf. Chapter VII, § 3.

where M' is the time reverse of M. Under time reversal the order of operator products is reversed so

$$(\tilde{M}M)' = M\tilde{M}; \tag{71}$$

also
$$\mathbf{k}^{(1)} \to -\mathbf{k}^{(2)}, \quad \mathbf{k}^{(2)} \to -\mathbf{k}^{(1)}, \quad \mathbf{S} \to -\mathbf{S}. \tag{72}$$

Hence $\Omega_{1M} \to -\Omega_{1M}$, $\Omega_{2M} \to \Omega_{2M}$. It follows from (67) and (71) that

$$\tilde{M}M = A_0 + \sum_{M=-2}^{2} \{A_2 Y_2^{(M)}(\mathbf{k}^{(1)}) + A_1 Y_2^{(M)}(\mathbf{k}^{(2)}) + A_3 \mathscr{Y}_2^{(M)}(\mathbf{k}^{(1)}, \mathbf{k}^{(2)})\}\tilde{\Omega}_{2M} + \\ + A_4 \sum_{M=-1}^{1} Y_1^{(M)}(\mathbf{k}^{(1)} \times \mathbf{k}^{(2)})\tilde{\Omega}_{1M}. \tag{73}$$

For calculating the double-scattering differential cross-section it is

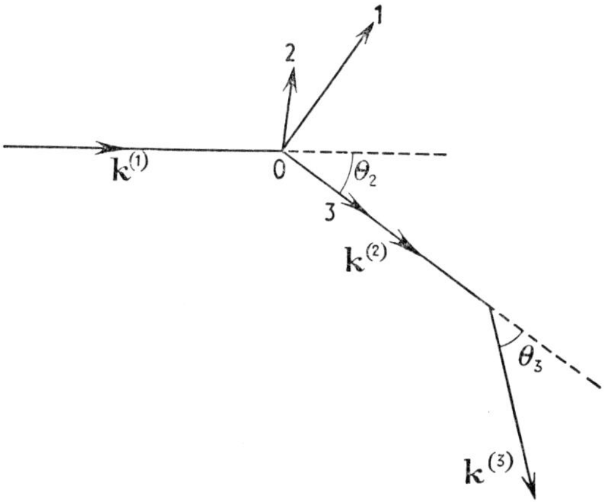

FIG. 42. The propagation vectors $\mathbf{k}^{(1)}$, $\mathbf{k}^{(2)}$, $\mathbf{k}^{(3)}$ in double scattering.

convenient to choose the O_2 axis perpendicular to the plane of the first scattering and the O_3 axis along the first scattered beam. We suppose the second scattering is in the direction $\mathbf{k}^{(3)}$; ϕ is the angle between the two scattering planes.

The polarization after the first scattering is denoted by $\langle\Omega_{2M}\rangle_{(2)}$. Using (56) and (69), the cross-section for the second scattering is

$$Q_{(3)} = A_0 + \sum_{M=-2}^{2} \{A_2 Y_2^{(M)}(\mathbf{k}^{(2)}) + A_1 Y_2^{(M)}(\mathbf{k}^{(3)}) + A_3 \mathscr{Y}_2^{(M)}(\mathbf{k}^{(2)}, \mathbf{k}^{(3)})\}\langle\Omega_{2M}\rangle_{(2)}^{*} + \\ + A_4 \sum_{M=-1}^{1} Y_1^{(M)}(\mathbf{k}^{(2)} \times \mathbf{k}^{(3)})\langle\Omega_{1M}\rangle_{(2)}^{*}. \tag{74}$$

$A_0,\ldots, A_4$ are the same real functions as in (67). In the chosen axes system $Y_2^{(M)}(\mathbf{k}^{(2)})$ $(M \neq 0)$, $\mathscr{Y}_2^{(\pm 2)}(\mathbf{k}^{(2)}, \mathbf{k}^{(3)})$, and $Y_1^{(0)}(\mathbf{k}^{(2)} \times \mathbf{k}^{(3)})$ all vanish.†

† In this coordinate system

$$\mathscr{Y}_2^{(0)}(\mathbf{k}^{(2)}, \mathbf{k}^{(3)}) = \frac{1}{\sqrt{(2\pi)}} Y_1^{(0)}(\mathbf{k}^{(3)}), \quad \text{and} \quad \mathscr{Y}_2^{(1)}(\mathbf{k}^{(2)}, \mathbf{k}^{(3)}) = \sqrt{\left(\frac{3}{8\pi}\right)} Y_1^{(1)}(\mathbf{k}^{(3)}).$$

Also $\langle\Omega_{2M}\rangle_{(2)}$ is real, and $\langle\Omega_{1M}\rangle_{(2)}$ is pure imaginary; this follows from (68) because $\mathbf{k}^{(1)}$ lies in the plane $\phi = \pi$.

In particular the double scattering of a deuteron on identical nuclei for which the two scattering angles are identical ($\theta_2 = \theta_3$) will have the cross-section†

$$Q_{(3)} = Q_{(2)}\{1+\langle\Omega_{20}\rangle_{(2)}^2+2(-\langle\Omega_{21}\rangle^2+|\langle\Omega_{11}\rangle|^2)\cos\phi+2\langle\Omega_{22}\rangle^2\cos 2\phi\}, \quad (75)$$

where ϕ is the angle between the two scattering planes. It should be noted that the part of the cross-section which is independent of ϕ is greater than the corresponding value ($Q_{(2)}$) for the scattering of an unpolarized beam. The double-scattering experiments are not sufficient to determine the polarization $\langle\Omega_{JM}\rangle$; formula (75) does not yield both $\langle\Omega_{21}\rangle$ and $\langle\Omega_{11}\rangle$.

The double scattering by various nuclei of deuterons having energies between 95 MeV and 165 MeV has been observed;† it is found that the term in $\cos\phi$ (eqn. (75)) is large but there is little evidence either of the term varying as $\cos 2\phi$, or of the increase in the part of the cross-section which is independent of the azimuthal angle.

7. Polarization in nucleon-nucleon collisions

General polarization analysis (non-relativistic)

We have discussed the scattering of beams of particles by spin zero targets. The analysis has to be modified when the target particles have spin; as an example‡ we consider the scattering of a beam of nucleons by an assembly of targets whose spin is s. For scattering from given initial momenta to given final momenta, the scattering matrix M is a $2(2s+1)\times 2(2s+1)$ matrix. The density matrix $\boldsymbol{\rho}_i$ for the system before scattering has to describe the spin distributions both of the nucleon beam and of the target assembly; therefore $\boldsymbol{\rho}_i$ has $\{2(2s+1)\}^2$ independent components. We can express $\boldsymbol{\rho}_i$ as a sum of $\{2(2s+1)\}^2$ linearly independent Hermitian matrices§ Ω_μ (cf. the arguments in § 5). Also we can write (cf. (60))

$$\boldsymbol{\rho}_i = \frac{1}{2(2s+1)} \sum_{\mu=1}^{4(2s+1)^2} \langle\Omega_\mu\rangle_{(i)}\Omega_\mu, \quad (76)$$

where the real numbers $\langle\Omega_\mu\rangle_i$ describe the polarization of the initial

† J. Baldwin, *et al.*, *Phys. Rev.* **103** (1956) 1502.

‡ The general case of a beam of particles of spin s' being scattered by an assembly of targets having spin s is discussed by R. Oehme, *Phys. Rev.* **98** (1955) 147.

§ Each Ω_μ is a $2(2s+1)\times 2(2s+1)$ matrix. For proof of the existence of such a basic set of matrices Ω_μ obeying (77) see U. Fano, *Phys. Rev.* **90** (1953) 577.

ensemble. In writing (76) it has been assumed that the Ω_μ obey (cf. (56))

$$\mathrm{tr}(\Omega_\mu \Omega_\nu) = 2(2s+1)\delta_{\mu\nu}. \tag{77}$$

After scattering, the polarization of the nucleons and the target is given by

$$\boldsymbol{\rho}_f = M\boldsymbol{\rho}_i \tilde{M}. \tag{78}$$

The polarization coefficients after scattering, $\langle\Omega_\mu\rangle_{(f)}$, clearly obey

$$\langle\Omega_\mu\rangle_{(f)} = \mathrm{tr}(\boldsymbol{\rho}_f \Omega_\mu)/\mathrm{tr}(\boldsymbol{\rho}_f). \tag{79}$$

It should be noted that this analysis can be applied to processes other than elastic scattering. For example, the polarization relations in $p+p \rightarrow D+\pi^+$ are discussed in § 10 below by the same method; in this case the spin space after the reaction is not identical with the spin space of the initial ensemble.

For elastic nucleon-nucleon scattering the sixteen Hermitian matrices Ω_μ obeying (77) are the 4×4 matrices

$$\sigma_i^{(1)}.\sigma_j^{(2)}, \quad \sigma_i^{(1)}.I^{(2)}, \quad I^{(1)}.\sigma_j^{(2)}, \quad I^{(1)}.I^{(2)} \quad (i,j = 1,2,3),$$

where superscripts refer to the nucleons, and $\boldsymbol{\sigma}$, I are the 2×2 spin matrices and identity respectively. Let superscript 2 refer to the target nucleon. If the target nucleons are unpolarized, $\langle\boldsymbol{\sigma}^{(2)}\rangle_{(i)}$ will vanish, $\langle I^{(2)}\rangle$ gives 2, and (76) will become

$$\boldsymbol{\rho}_i = \tfrac{1}{2}\{I+\boldsymbol{\sigma}^{(1)}.\langle\boldsymbol{\sigma}^{(1)}\rangle_{(i)}\}. \tag{80}$$

It is clear that for the scattering of nucleons by targets of any spin s, the initial density matrix must reduce to (80) if the targets are unpolarized. The matrices in (80) are in the spin space of the incident nucleon.

Scattering of nucleons by unpolarized nucleons

From eqn. (80) it follows that the differential cross-section for the elastic scattering of a polarized nucleon beam by unpolarized nucleons is given by (29); similarly, the polarization produced is given by (30).† The left-right asymmetry in double scattering can be used to find the polarization, by means of eqn. (34), provided we can show that

$$\mathrm{tr}(M\boldsymbol{\sigma}^{(1)}\tilde{M}) = \mathrm{tr}(\tilde{M}\boldsymbol{\sigma}^{(1)}M), \tag{81}$$

where $\boldsymbol{\sigma}^{(1)}$ is the spin of one nucleon. Here, and in (29) and (30), tr means that we successively make the diagonal summation over the spin states of both nucleons. We now prove (81).

† For a discussion of the effect of inelastic scattering on the nucleon polarization, see K. Nishimura and M. Ruderman, *Phys. Rev.* **106** (1957) 558.

Let $\mathbf{k}$, $\mathbf{k}'$ be the initial and final momenta of one of the nucleons in the centre of mass system, and let $\boldsymbol{\sigma}^{(1)}$, $\boldsymbol{\sigma}^{(2)}$ be the spin operators of the two nucleons. If the scattering matrix M is to be invariant under rotations and spatial inversion,† it must be a sum of the independent quantities

$$1;\quad \boldsymbol{\sigma}^{(1)}.\boldsymbol{\sigma}^{(2)};\quad (\boldsymbol{\sigma}^{(1)}+\boldsymbol{\sigma}^{(2)}).\mathbf{n},\quad (\boldsymbol{\sigma}^{(1)}-\boldsymbol{\sigma}^{(2)}).\mathbf{n};\quad (\boldsymbol{\sigma}^{(1)}\times\boldsymbol{\sigma}^{(2)}.\mathbf{n});$$
$$(\boldsymbol{\sigma}^{(1)}.\mathbf{K})(\boldsymbol{\sigma}^{(2)}.\mathbf{K});\quad (\boldsymbol{\sigma}^{(1)}.\mathbf{n})(\boldsymbol{\sigma}^{(2)}.\mathbf{n});\quad (\boldsymbol{\sigma}^{(1)}.\mathbf{K})(\boldsymbol{\sigma}^{(2)}.\mathbf{R})+(\boldsymbol{\sigma}^{(1)}.\mathbf{R})(\boldsymbol{\sigma}^{(2)}.\mathbf{K}), \tag{82}$$

where $\mathbf{K} = \mathbf{k}'-\mathbf{k}$, $\mathbf{n} = \mathbf{k}\times\mathbf{k}'$, $\mathbf{R} = \mathbf{k}'+\mathbf{k}$. Invariance of M under Wigner time reversal ($\mathbf{k}\rightarrow-\mathbf{k}', \mathbf{k}'\rightarrow-\mathbf{k}, \boldsymbol{\sigma}\rightarrow-\boldsymbol{\sigma}$) excludes $(\boldsymbol{\sigma}^{(1)}\times\boldsymbol{\sigma}^{(2)}.\mathbf{n})$ and $[(\boldsymbol{\sigma}^{(1)}.\mathbf{K})(\boldsymbol{\sigma}^{(2)}.\mathbf{R})+(\boldsymbol{\sigma}^{(1)}.\mathbf{R})(\boldsymbol{\sigma}^{(2)}.\mathbf{K})]$. Therefore, assuming spatial inversion and time reversal are both conserved, the most general form is‡

$$M = A+B(\boldsymbol{\sigma}^{(1)}.\mathbf{R})(\boldsymbol{\sigma}^{(2)}.\mathbf{R})+C\{(\boldsymbol{\sigma}^{(1)}+\boldsymbol{\sigma}^{(2)}).\mathbf{n}\}+D\{(\boldsymbol{\sigma}^{(1)}-\boldsymbol{\sigma}^{(2)}).\mathbf{n}\}+$$
$$+E(\boldsymbol{\sigma}^{(1)}.\mathbf{K})(\boldsymbol{\sigma}^{(2)}.\mathbf{K})+F(\boldsymbol{\sigma}^{(1)}.\mathbf{n})(\boldsymbol{\sigma}^{(2)}.\mathbf{n}); \tag{83}$$

here A,..., F are functions of the energies and the scattering angle.

Most terms in $\tilde{M}M$ contain $\boldsymbol{\sigma}^{(2)}$ linearly;§ those which do not are

$$2\,\mathrm{re}\{A^*(C+D)\}(\boldsymbol{\sigma}^{(1)}.\mathbf{n})+2\,\mathrm{re}\{F^*(C-D)\}(\boldsymbol{\sigma}^{(1)}.\mathbf{n}),$$

and multiples of the identity matrix. The same is true for $M\tilde{M}$. Because $\mathrm{tr}(\boldsymbol{\sigma}^{(2)})$ vanishes, it follows that (81) holds for nucleon-nucleon scattering. We also deduce from (30) that when an unpolarized nucleon beam strikes unpolarized nucleons, the polarization of the scattered beam is

$$\mathbf{P}^{(2)} = \mathbf{n}\,4\,\mathrm{re}\{(A^*+F^*)C+(A^*-F^*)D\}/Q, \tag{84}$$

where Q is the differential cross-section.

Wolfenstein and Ashkin‡ have shown that (81) holds for the *elastic* scattering of a nucleon by a scatterer of arbitrary spin s. They notice that the traces of all the matrices in the spin spaces of the incident and target particles, $\sigma_i\times\Omega_\lambda(s)$ and $I\times\Omega_\lambda(s)$, vanish except for the identity $I\times I(s)$. The most general form of the $2(2s+1)\times 2(2s+1)$ scattering matrix is

$$M = A+B(\boldsymbol{\sigma}.\mathbf{n})+C(\boldsymbol{\sigma}.\mathbf{K})+D(\boldsymbol{\sigma}.\mathbf{P}), \tag{85}$$

where $\mathbf{P} = \mathbf{n}\times\mathbf{K}$, and A, B, C, D are linear combinations of the complete set of matrices $\Omega_\lambda(s)$ in the spin space of the target. Because of the spatial invariance requirement, A and B have to be scalars, while

† If a beam of protons polarized parallel to O_3 is scattered, the scattered intensities are equal in any two directions which are images in the O_{12} plane (O. Chamberlain, E. Segré, R. D. Tripp, and T. Ypsilantis, *Phys. Rev.* **93** (1954) 1430).

‡ L. Wolfenstein and J. Ashkin, *Phys. Rev.* **85** (1952) 947; R. H. Dalitz, *Proc. Phys. Soc.* A, **65** (1952) 175. Here $(\boldsymbol{\sigma}^{(1)}.\mathbf{R})(\boldsymbol{\sigma}^{(2)}.\mathbf{R})$ replaces $(\boldsymbol{\sigma}^{(1)}.\boldsymbol{\sigma}^{(2)})$.

§ Notice that $\mathbf{K}$, $\mathbf{R}$, $\mathbf{n}$ are orthogonal.

C and D must be pseudo-scalars.† Under time inversion, A, B, and D are unaltered, and C must change sign. Now we evaluate

$$\mathrm{tr}\{(\tilde{M}M-M\tilde{M})\boldsymbol{\sigma}\}$$

using (85). We need only consider‡ the terms containing commutators of the nucleon spin $\boldsymbol{\sigma}$, i.e. the three commutators like

$$[(\boldsymbol{\sigma}.\mathbf{n}), (\boldsymbol{\sigma}.\mathbf{K})] = 2i(\boldsymbol{\sigma}.\mathbf{n}\times\mathbf{K}). \tag{86}$$

The coefficients of these commutators are $(\tilde{B}C-B\tilde{C})$, $(\tilde{C}D-C\tilde{D})$, $(\tilde{D}B-D\tilde{B})$. These coefficients must (if they are to contribute), be multiples of $I(s)$, and they can therefore only be functions of $\mathbf{k}$, $\mathbf{k}'$. It is easy to see that no such function of $\mathbf{k}$, $\mathbf{k}'$ has the correct transformation properties,§ hence eqn. (81) is true for a target of arbitrary spin.

Isotopic spin

We shall show how nucleon-nucleon scattering can be analysed in the energy region in which relativistic effects and inelastic scattering can be neglected; that is, up to several hundred MeV. As was discussed in Chapter IV, § 12, the nucleon-nucleon interaction is charge independent (apart from the Coulomb interaction in p–p scattering which can be neglected except for low energies and small-angle scattering).

Since the total isotopic spin is a good quantum number, there are two independent scattering matrix elements for scattering in the $T = 0$ and $T = 1$ state; we write them as $M(0)$ and $M(1)$ respectively. The scattering matrix $M(1)$ is determined by proton-proton (p–p) scattering. Any proton-neutron state $|PN\rangle$ can be written

$$|PN\rangle = \frac{1}{\sqrt{2}}|T{=}0\rangle+\frac{1}{\sqrt{2}}|T{=}1, T_3{=}0\rangle. \tag{87}$$

The scattering matrix for the transition in which the proton and neutron have initial momenta and spins‖ λ_1 and λ_2, respectively, and final momenta and spins λ_1' and λ_2', respectively, is written $\langle\lambda_1',\lambda_2'|M|\lambda_1,\lambda_2\rangle$. Thus for proton-neutron scattering eqn. (87) gives

$$\langle\lambda_1',\lambda_2'|M|\lambda_1,\lambda_2\rangle = \tfrac{1}{2}\langle\lambda_1',\lambda_2'|M(1)|\lambda_1,\lambda_2\rangle+\tfrac{1}{2}\langle\lambda_1',\lambda_2'|M(0)|\lambda_1,\lambda_2\rangle. \tag{88}$$

† $\mathbf{P}$ is a polar vector; also $\mathbf{P}$ changes sign under time inversion.

‡ This is because commutators of the type $\tilde{A}A-A\tilde{A}$, $\tilde{A}B-B\tilde{A}$, etc., either vanish, or else are equal to a sum of matrices $\Omega_\lambda(s)$ other than the unit matrix $I(s)$. (To prove this, notice that $\mathrm{tr}(\tilde{A}B-B\tilde{A}) = \mathrm{tr}(\tilde{A}B)-\mathrm{tr}(B\tilde{A}) = 0$ for finite matrices.) The traces of $\Omega_\lambda(s)$ vanish, except for $I(s)$.

§ BC, BD are pseudo-scalars and CD is a scalar. No pesudo-scalar can be formed from $\mathbf{k}$, $\mathbf{k}'$. The scalars are $\mathbf{K}^2$ and $\mathbf{R}^2$; both are unaltered by time reversal, whereas CD changes sign on time reversal.

‖ $\lambda_1 \equiv (\mathbf{p}_1, s_1)$, where $\mathbf{p}_1$, s_1 are the momentum and spin of the incident proton, etc.

The $T = 1$ state vector is symmetric for proton-neutron exchange, and the $T = 0$ state vector is anti-symmetric. Therefore

$$\langle\lambda_2',\lambda_1'|M|\lambda_2,\lambda_1\rangle = \tfrac{1}{2}\langle\lambda_1',\lambda_2'|M(1)|\lambda_1,\lambda_2\rangle - \tfrac{1}{2}\langle\lambda_1',\lambda_2'|M(0)|\lambda_1,\lambda_2\rangle. \quad (89)$$

Eqn. (89) is obtained from (88) by exchanging the momenta and spins of the proton and neutron in the final state. Therefore the $M(0)$ component of the scattering matrix is

$$\langle\lambda_1',\lambda_2'|M(0)|\lambda_1,\lambda_2\rangle = \langle\lambda_1',\lambda_2'|M|\lambda_1,\lambda_2\rangle - \langle\lambda_2',\lambda_1'|M|\lambda_1,\lambda_2\rangle. \quad (90)$$

It is for many purposes more convenient to use the identity

$$\tilde{M}(0)M(0) = \tfrac{1}{2}\{\tilde{M}(0)+\tilde{M}(1)\}\{M(0)+M(1)\}+ \\ +\tfrac{1}{2}\{\tilde{M}(0)-\tilde{M}(1)\}\{M(0)-M(1)\}-M(1)M(1)$$

to express the differential cross-section $Q(T = 0)$ for the $T = 0$ process in terms of the $T = 1$ cross-section $Q(T = 1)$, and the cross-section $Q(\lambda_1',\lambda_2';\,\lambda_1,\lambda_2)$ for proton-neutron scattering, viz.†

$$Q(T{=}0) = 2Q(\lambda_1',\lambda_2';\,\lambda_1,\lambda_2)+2Q(\lambda_2',\lambda_1';\,\lambda_1,\lambda_2)-Q(T{=}1). \quad (91)$$

In the second term on the right, the momenta and spins of the proton and neutron in the final state are exchanged. Using (91) the polarization produced in the $T = 0$ state is readily deduced from (p–p) and (p–n) double-scattering experiments.

Angular momentum

The total spin of the colliding nucleons

$$\mathbf{S} = \tfrac{1}{2}(\boldsymbol{\sigma}^{(1)}+\boldsymbol{\sigma}^{(2)})$$

has the eigenvalues $S' = 0$ and 1 only. The Pauli principle restricts the orbital angular momentum eigenvalues which occur. In p–p states, $S' = 0$ and 1 can only occur respectively with even and odd angular momentum values L. In p–n states the same is true for the $T = 1$ component; in the $T = 0$ component, $S' = 0$ and 1 only occur with odd and even L, respectively.

In the expression (83) for the scattering matrix M, the only term which is not symmetric in the spins of the two nucleons is $(\boldsymbol{\sigma}^{(1)}-\boldsymbol{\sigma}^{(2)}).\mathbf{n}$; therefore this is the only term in M which does not commute with $\mathbf{S}^2$. The polarization $\mathbf{P}^{(2)}$ and $\mathbf{P}^{(\text{rec})}$ of the scattered and the recoil nucleon (when an unpolarized beam is scattered by unpolarized nucleons) can only differ‡ if $D \neq 0$ in (83). This is because

$$\mathbf{P}^{(2)}-\mathbf{P}^{(\text{rec})} = \text{tr}\{(\boldsymbol{\sigma}^{(1)}-\boldsymbol{\sigma}^{(2)})M\tilde{M}\}/\text{tr}(MM);$$

the numerator vanishes if M is symmetric in $\boldsymbol{\sigma}^{(1)}$, $\boldsymbol{\sigma}^{(2)}$.

† L. Wolfenstein, *Phys. Rev.* **101** (1956) 427.

‡ R. H. Dalitz, loc. cit.

The coefficient D cannot be non-zero in p–p scattering. On exchanging the two nucleons, $\mathbf{n}$ is unaltered (in the c.m.s.), therefore $(\boldsymbol{\sigma}^{(1)}-\boldsymbol{\sigma}^{(2)}).\mathbf{n}$ changes the permutation character of the state vector. For p–p scattering, M must be symmetric in the two nucleons.

If the interaction is charge independent, the corresponding D in (83) must also vanish in p–n scattering, this is because the $T = 0$, 1 components do not mix under the interaction.

8. Calculation of the polarization in nucleon-nucleon scattering

Phenomenological potentials

The observed polarization in nucleon-nucleon scattering gives considerable information about the scattering phase shifts and about phenomenological potentials which may be used to describe the nucleon-nucleon interactions. There is no satisfactory derivation of a nucleon-nucleon interaction from field theory; however, partially successful attempts have been made by Lévy and Gartenhaus.† Here we do not attempt to discuss these derivations.

A variety of phenomenological potentials‡ have been used to fit the data up to around 250 MeV; it is hardly reasonable to expect a phenomenological potential to be of value at much higher energies. Figs. 43, 44 give an idea of the order of magnitude of the cross-sections and polarization and the success of some of the phenomenological potentials.

Here we shall merely discuss the relation between the symmetry properties of the assumed nucleon-nucleon potential, and the methods used to calculate the polarization. The simplest potential is

$$[A(r)+B(r)(\boldsymbol{\sigma}^{(1)}.\boldsymbol{\sigma}^{(2)})]F, \tag{92}$$

where $A(r)$, $B(r)$ are functions of the nucleon separation r; A and B will be different for the two isotopic spin values. F may be constant, or it may involve the operator P_x which exchanges the positions of the two nucleons. Serber used the form

$$F = \tfrac{1}{2}(1+P_x). \tag{93}$$

The operator (93) annihilates odd parity state vectors, so there is no scattering in odd parity states; this has been used to explain the symmetry about 90° in p–n scattering around 100 MeV.

† M. M. Lévy, *Phys. Rev.* **88** (1952) 72; S. Gartenhaus, ibid. **100** (1955) 900.

‡ See, for example, J. L. Gammel, R. S. Christian, and R. M. Thaler, *Phys. Rev.* **105** (1957) 311; J. M. Gammel and R. M. Thaler, ibid. **107** (1957) 1337; P. S. Signell and R. E. Marshak, ibid. **106** (1957) 832.

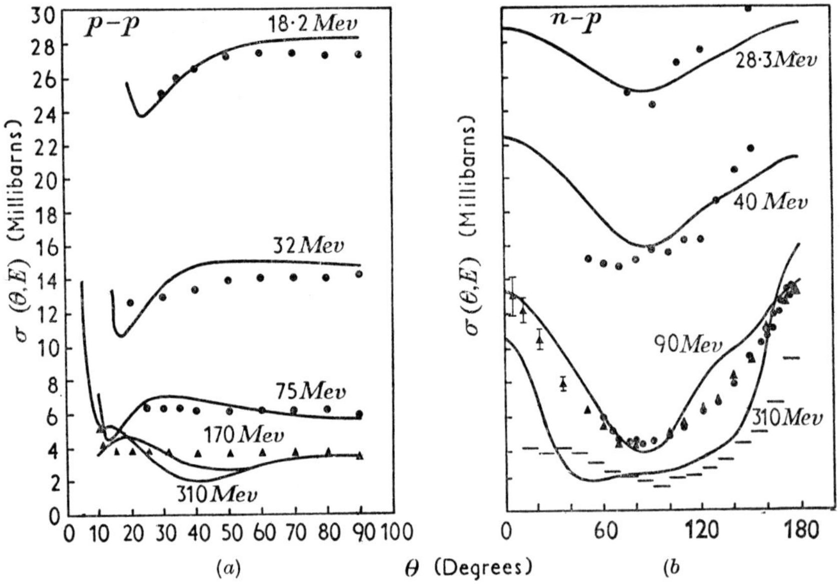

FIG. 43. (*a*) and (*b*) show experimental values and theoretical curves for the (*p*–*p*) and (*n*–*p*) differential cross-sections respectively, in the c.m. system at various lab. energies. The curves are deduced from the first phenomenological potential of Gammel *et al.* (loc. cit.); this involves a hard core and a tensor force.

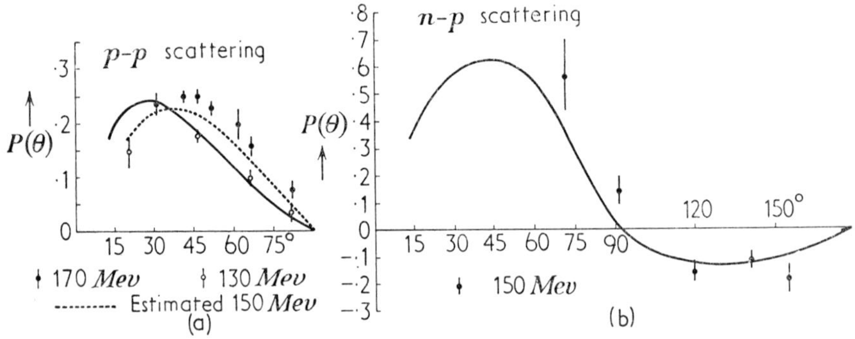

FIG. 44. (*a*) and (*b*) show experimental values and theoretical curves for the polarization $P(\theta)$ in (*p*–*p*) and (*n*–*p*) scattering respectively at 150 MeV (c.m.). The theoretical curves are deduced from the phenomenological potential of Signell and Marshak (loc. cit.) which includes a spin-orbital interaction.

The total spin $\mathbf{S}$ satisfies ($\hbar = 1$)

$$\mathbf{S}^2 = \tfrac{3}{2}+\tfrac{1}{2}(\boldsymbol{\sigma}^{(1)}.\boldsymbol{\sigma}^{(2)}); \tag{94}$$

therefore the potential (92) does not mix the states $S' = 0$, $S' = 1$. Further, the scattering must be identical for the three components $S'_3 = 1, 0, -1$ of the state $S' = 1$; hence the potential (92) cannot give rise to any polarization.

Non-central interactions

The simplest non-central interactions are the tensor interaction and the spin-orbital interaction. The tensor interaction is written

$$\mathscr{S}_{(12)} f(r) \equiv \sum_{i,j} \sigma_i^{(1)} \sigma_j^{(2)} T_{ij} f(r), \tag{95}$$

where $f(r)$ is a radial function of finite range, and T_{ij} is the irreducible second-rank tensor

$$T_{ij} = 3x_i x_j/r^2 - \delta_{ij}.$$

The tensor force can be used to explain the quadrupole moment of the deuteron which requires a mixing of the $^3S_1$ and $^3D_1$ proton-neutron states.†

The spin-orbital interaction is used to explain the reversal of the order of certain levels in the shell model of the nucleus; for two nucleons the interaction is of the form

$$(\mathbf{S}.\mathbf{L})F(r), \tag{96}$$

where $\mathbf{L}$ is the orbital angular momentum and $F(r)$ is a radial function. Clearly an interaction which, in addition to (92), contains either (95) or (96) will give rise to polarization in nucleon-nucleon scattering.

In calculating the polarization it is convenient to use the eigenstates of the total spin S. These are given by

$$\left.\begin{aligned} |S_3 = M,\, S = 1\rangle &= \sum_{m_1, m_2} |m_1, m_2\rangle(\tfrac{1}{2}\tfrac{1}{2} m_1 m_2|1M) \\ |S_3 = 0,\, S = 0\rangle &= \sum_{m_1, m_2} |m_1, m_2\rangle(\tfrac{1}{2}\tfrac{1}{2} m_1 m_2|0\,0) \end{aligned}\right\}, \tag{97}$$

where $|m_1, m_2\rangle$ is the spin eigenstate for the first and second nucleons having spin components $m_1\hbar$, $m_2\hbar$ respectively. The Clebsch–Gordan coefficients are given in Table 4 below.

The spin-orbital interaction

Because‡ $$2(\mathbf{S}.\mathbf{L}) = (\mathbf{L}+\mathbf{S})^2 - \mathbf{L}^2 - \mathbf{S}^2,$$

the interaction (96) commutes with the total spin operator $\mathbf{S}^2$ and the orbital angular momentum operator $\mathbf{L}^2$. Eigenstates of motion under a potential which is made up from (92) and (96) can therefore be expressed as simultaneous eigenstates of the total angular momentum $\mathbf{J}^2 = (\mathbf{L}+\mathbf{S})^2$, its component $\mathbf{J}_3$, the spin $\mathbf{S}^2$, and the orbital angular momentum $\mathbf{L}^2$. Let the corresponding eigenvalues be J, M, S, L ($-J \leqslant M \leqslant J$), where $|L-S| \leqslant J \leqslant (L+S)$.

† See, for example, J. M. Blatt and V. F. Weisskopf, *Theoretical Nuclear Physics* (Wiley, New York, 1952), ch. 2.

‡ $\mathbf{S}$ and $\mathbf{L}$ are independent operators so $[\mathbf{S}, \mathbf{L}] = 0$. Also it is easy to see that $\mathbf{J}^2$ commutes with $\mathbf{L}^2$ and $\mathbf{S}^2$.

The normalized spin-angular eigenstates are given, for the singlet state ($S = 0$), by

$$W_J^{(M)} = Y_J^{(M)}(\theta, \phi)|S_3 = 0,\ S = 0\rangle \tag{98}$$

(where (θ, ϕ) is the direction of the vector joining the nucleons); and for the triplet state by

$$W_{L,J}^{(M)} = \sum_{m',m''} (L1m'm''|JM)Y_L^{(m')}(\theta,\phi).|S_3 = m'',\ S = 1\rangle$$
$$(L = |J-1|, J, J+1). \tag{99}$$

The Clebsch–Gordan coefficients $(L1m'm''|JM)$ are given in Table 4.

TABLE 4

The Clebsch–Gordan coefficients $(L1m'm''|JM)$

	$m'' = 1$	0	-1
$L = J-1$	$\left[\dfrac{(L+M)(L+M+1)}{(2L+1)(2L+2)}\right]^{\frac{1}{2}}$	$\left[\dfrac{(L-M+1)(L+M+1)}{(2L+1)(L+1)}\right]^{\frac{1}{2}}$	$\left[\dfrac{(L-M)(L-M+1)}{(2L+1)(2L+2)}\right]^{\frac{1}{2}}$
$L = J$	$-\left[\dfrac{(L+M)(L-M+1)}{2L(L+1)}\right]^{\frac{1}{2}}$	$\dfrac{M}{\{L(L+1)\}^{\frac{1}{2}}}$	$\left[\dfrac{(L-M)(L+M+1)}{2L(L+1)}\right]^{\frac{1}{2}}$
$L = J+1$	$\left[\dfrac{(L-M)(L-M+1)}{2L(2L+1)}\right]^{\frac{1}{2}}$	$-\left[\dfrac{(L-M)(L+M)}{L(2L+1)}\right]^{\frac{1}{2}}$	$\left[\dfrac{(L+M+1)(L+M)}{2L(2L+1)}\right]^{\frac{1}{2}}$

The complete eigenstate of type (J, M, L, S) will be of the form†

$$\left.\begin{aligned} &(1/r)u_J(r)W_J^{(M)} \quad \text{for the singlet state} \\ \text{and} \quad &(1/r)u_{LJ}(r)W_{LJ}^{(M)} \quad \text{for the triplet state} \end{aligned}\right\}. \tag{100}$$

The radial functions $u(r)$ are solutions of the radial differential equation; they are subject to the boundary condition that the probability density is to be finite at $r = 0$. In the non-relativistic approximation, the triplet state radial function obeys

$$\frac{d^2u_{LJ}(r)}{dr^2}+\left(k^2-\frac{L(L+1)}{r^2}\right)u_{LJ}(r)-\frac{m_N}{\hbar^2}V_{LJ}(r)u_{LJ}(r) = 0, \tag{101}$$

where k is the wave number, m_N is the nucleon's mass, and

$$V_{LJ}(r) = \int d\Omega\, \tilde{W}_{LJ}^{(M)} V W_{LJ}^{(M)}. \tag{102}$$

V is the nucleon-nucleon potential. The integral (102) which is over the angular variables, is independent of M. A similar equation determines the singlet state radial functions $u_J(r)$.

† The radial functions $u(r)$ are independent of M because the potential depends only on L, J and the radial distance r.

For interactions of finite range, these radial functions have the asymptotic form for large r:

$$\left.\begin{aligned} \frac{1}{r}u_J(r) &\sim \frac{1}{r}\sin(kr-\tfrac{1}{2}J\pi+\delta_J) \\ \frac{1}{r}u_{LJ}(r) &\sim \frac{1}{r}\sin(kr-\tfrac{1}{2}L\pi+\delta_{L,J}) \end{aligned}\right\}. \tag{103}$$

δ_J, δ_{LJ} are (real) phase angles.

The scattered wave

The scattered wave is derived by the same method as was used to describe the scattering of a fermion in a central field (Chapter III, § 8). The singlet state $S = 0$ is treated as for the scattering of particles without spin.† For the triplet case the incident wave may be written (using the notation of eqn. (3.67))

$$e^{ikx_3}|S_3, S=1\rangle = \frac{(2\pi\mathscr{R})^{\frac{1}{2}}}{k}\sum_{l=0}^{\infty} i^l(2l+1)^{\frac{1}{2}}Y_l^{(0)}(\theta,\phi)g_{lk}(r)|S_3, S=1\rangle, \tag{104}$$

where $|S_3, S = 1\rangle$ is the state vector for total spin component S_3 about the initial direction of relative motion O_3. By (99) (cf. eqn. (1.50))

$$Y_l^{(0)}(\theta,\phi)|S_3, S=1\rangle = \sum_{J=|l-1|}^{l+1}(l10S_3|JS_3)W_{lJ}^{(S_3)}. \tag{105}$$

Using (3.64) it is possible to write the asymptotic form of (104) for large r,

$$e^{ikx_3}|S_3, S=1\rangle \simeq \frac{1}{kr}\sum_{l=0}^{\infty}\sum_{J=|l-1|}^{l+1} i^l\{4\pi(2l+1)\}^{\frac{1}{2}}(l10S_3|JS_3)W_{lJ}^{(S_3)}\sin(kr-\tfrac{1}{2}l\pi). \tag{106}$$

Adding on suitable multiples of the eigensolutions (100) so as to suppress terms in e^{-ikr}, and subtracting the contribution of the incident wave (104), gives the scattered state spatial representative

$$\langle\mathbf{x}|\text{scatt}; k, S_3, S = 1\rangle = \frac{e^{ikr}}{r}\frac{1}{2ik}\sum_{l=0}^{\infty}\sum_{J=|l-1|}^{l+1}\{4\pi(2l+1)\}^{\frac{1}{2}}(l10S_3|JS_3)(e^{2i\delta_{lJ}}-1)W_{lJ}^{(S_3)}. \tag{107}$$

The scattering matrix

Defining the triplet part of the scattering matrix M by

$$\langle\mathbf{x}|\text{scatt}; k, S_3, S = 1\rangle = \frac{e^{ikr}}{r}\sum_{S_3'}|S_3', S = 1\rangle\langle S_3', S = 1|M|S_3, S = 1\rangle, \tag{108}$$

† See, for example, N. F. Mott and H. S. W. Massey, *Theory of Atomic Collisions* (Clarendon Press, 2nd edn., 1949), ch. ii.

where $|S_3', S=1\rangle$ is the final spin state, we have† (in the same notation as (21))

$$\langle S_3', S=1|M|S_3, S=1\rangle$$
$$= \frac{1}{2ik}\sum_{l=0}^{\infty}\sum_{J=|l-1|}^{l+1}\{4\pi(2l+1)\}^{\frac{1}{2}}(l10S_3|JS_3)(e^{2i\delta_{lJ}}-1)Y_l^{(m)}(\theta,\phi), \quad (109)$$

where $m = S_3 - S_3'$. The singlet state contribution to the scattering matrix is the simple expression‡

$$\langle S=0|M|S=0\rangle = \frac{1}{2ik}\sum_{j=0}^{\infty}(2J+1)(e^{2i\delta_J}-1)P_J(\cos\theta), \quad (110)$$

where δ_J are the singlet state phase shifts given by (103).§

The polarization

In the singlet state the spin state vector is unaltered by the scattering, so in this state there is no polarization of the scattered nucleon.||

Because no elements of M connect singlet and triplet states, the expression $\mathrm{tr}\{(\boldsymbol{\sigma}^{(1)}-\boldsymbol{\sigma}^{(2)})M\tilde{M}\}$ vanishes. We make use of this property in calculating the polarization produced in scattering. Assuming that the incident beam and the target are unpolarized, the polarization of the scattered nucleons is

$$\mathbf{P} = \mathrm{tr}(\boldsymbol{\sigma}^{(1)}M\tilde{M})/\mathrm{tr}(M\tilde{M}). \quad (111)$$

Remembering that $\mathbf{S} = \frac{1}{2}(\boldsymbol{\sigma}^{(1)}+\boldsymbol{\sigma}^{(2)})$,

we can write $\mathbf{P} = \mathrm{tr}(\mathbf{S}M\tilde{M})/\mathrm{tr}(M\tilde{M}). \quad (112)$

The singlet component of $\mathbf{S}$ vanishes, hence the numerator of (112) only contains contributions from the triplet state. Writing

$$M = M_{(3)}+M_{(0)},$$

where the triplet state part $M_{(3)}$ is given by (109), and the singlet state term is (110), we have

$$\mathbf{P} = \frac{\mathrm{tr}(\mathbf{S}M_{(3)}\tilde{M}_{(3)})}{M_{(0)}M_{(0)}^*+\mathrm{tr}(M_{(3)}\tilde{M}_{(3)})}. \quad (113)$$

The incident beam is along the O_3 axis, and we choose the azimuthal angle ϕ to be zero for the plane of scattering. As was seen above, the

† Using (99).

‡ Here we use the relation

$$Y_l^{(0)}(\theta) = \left(\frac{2l+1}{4\pi}\right)^{\frac{1}{2}} P_l(\cos\theta).$$

§ The scattering matrix in this representation can readily be expressed in terms of the coefficients $A,\ldots,F$ of (83). For details of the relations between these two forms see D. R. Swanson, *Phys. Rev.* **89** (1953) 740.

|| The initial system is in general a mixture of singlet and triplet states.

scattered beam is polarized along the normal to the plane of scattering, i.e. along the axis O_2. Deducing the spin matrix $\mathbf{S}$ from (48) we find that, for the unpolarized incident beam, scattering through an angle θ (in the centre of mass system) gives a polarization $P(\theta)$, where†

$$P(\theta)Q(\theta) = \tfrac{1}{4}\sqrt{2}\,\mathrm{im}\Big[\sum_{S'=-1}^{1} (M_{(3)})_{0S'}\{(M_{(3)})^*_{1S'}-(M_{(3)})^*_{-1,S'}\}\Big]. \tag{114}$$

The differential cross-section is given by

$$Q(\theta) = \tfrac{1}{4}\{|M_{(0)}|^2+\sum_{S,S'}|(M_{(3)})_{SS'}|^2\}. \tag{115}$$

For conciseness, in (114) and (115) we have written $(M_{(3)})_{SS'}$ for the elements of the matrix (109), etc.

The expressions (114) and (115) can be written as a sum of spherical harmonics using the formula (1.56). The summation over the magnetic quantum numbers is evaluated by Racah's technique‡ (cf. Chapter I, § 13). We get

$$\sum_{S'=-1}^{1} (M_{(3)})_{0S'}\{(M_{(3)})^*_{1S'}-(M_{(3)})^*_{-1S'}\}$$
$$= -\frac{(4\pi)^{\frac{1}{2}}}{k^2}\sum_{l,l'}\sum_{J,J'}(2l+1)(2l'+1)\Big\{\frac{(2J+1)(2J'+1)}{2L+1}\Big\}^{\frac{1}{2}}\times$$
$$\times(ll'00|L0)(l'101|J'1)(l100|J0)\times$$
$$\times(JJ'01|L1)W(J'l'Jl;\,1L)A_{lJ}A^*_{l'J'}\{Y_L^{(1)}(\theta,0)+Y_L^{(1)*}(\theta,0)\}, \tag{116}$$

where
$$A_{lJ} = \frac{1}{2i}(e^{2i\delta_{lJ}}-1)$$

and the values of l, l', J, J' are restricted to the sets

$$\left.\begin{aligned} l &= |J-1|,\ J+1; \qquad l' = |J'-1|,\ J',\ J'+1 \\ L &= |l-l'|,\ |l-l'|+2,\ \ldots,\ (l+l'-2),\ l+l' \end{aligned}\right\}. \tag{117}$$

The real coefficients $W(J'l'Jl;\,1L)$ are tabulated.§ The imaginary part of (116) is required to give the polarization (114). On writing

$$A_{lJ} = e^{i\delta_{lJ}}\sin(\delta_{lJ}),$$

it follows that the phases enter the polarization equation (114) in the form‖

$$\mathrm{im}(A_{lJ}A^*_{l'J'}) = \sin(\delta_{lJ})\sin(\delta_{l'J'})\sin(\delta_{lJ}-\delta_{l'J'}). \tag{118}$$

† Cf. L. J. B. Goldfarb and D. Feldman, *Phys. Rev.* **88** (1952) 1099.

‡ We use $(l'1m'S'|J'S'') = (-1)^{J'-1}\Big(\frac{2J'+1}{3}\Big)^{\frac{1}{2}}(J'l',-S''m'|1,\,-S')$

given by (1.59) and the formulae of Chapter I, § 13. § See p. 28, n. §.

‖ This is no longer true if, as in the tensor force case, we have to use complex phases. In that case (118) has to be modified.

The dependence on the scattering angle θ of the corresponding term in $P(\theta)Q(\theta)$ is of the form

$$\sin\theta\, f_{(L-1)}(\cos\theta),$$

where $f_{(L-1)}(\cos\theta)$ is a polynomial of degree $(L-1)$ in $\cos\theta$.

Because only triplet states contribute to the polarization, the orbital angular momenta l, l' contributing in $(p$–$p)$ scattering must be odd and L must be even. Therefore for $(p$–$p)$ scattering the polarization $P(\theta)$ is anti-symmetric about the scattering angle $\theta = \frac{1}{2}\pi$ in the centre of mass system. If we assume (as might be suggested by the symmetry of the differential cross-section about 90°, at energies around 100 MeV) that the neutron-proton interaction contains the Serber factor $\frac{1}{2}(1+P_x)$, only even values of l, l' can occur in $(p$–$n)$ scattering. Again, L must be even and $P(\theta)$ is anti-symmetric about $\theta = \frac{1}{2}\pi$. In fact the $(p$–$n)$ polarization shows some asymmetry about $\frac{1}{2}\pi$,† and we infer that there are some terms in (116) with odd L in the $(p$–$n)$ case.

Evaluation of the numerical constants occurring in (116) is tedious and the reader is referred to the very complete expressions given by Breit and his co-workers.‡ These authors give an expansion for $P(\theta)Q(\theta)$ which is sufficiently general to include any type of nucleon-nucleon interaction, and their formulae also allow for the effect of the Coulomb repulsion in $(p$–$p)$ scattering. As a simple example of the results we give the polarization for $(p$–$p)$ scattering which is obtained by ignoring all phases δ_{lJ} with $l \geqslant 2$, and ignoring the Coulomb effect; then we have§

$$P(\theta)Q(\theta) = \frac{\sin 2\theta}{k^2}\{3\sin\delta_{10}\sin\delta_{12}\sin(\delta_{10}-\delta_{12})+ \\ +(9/2)\sin\delta_{11}\sin\delta_{12}\sin(\delta_{11}-\delta_{12})\}. \quad (119)$$

The tensor force

We now discuss briefly how the polarization calculations are to be carried out when the nucleon-nucleon interaction includes a tensor force $\mathscr{S}_{12}f(r)$ (eqn. (95)) as well as forces of the types (92) and (96). Because the tensor force is an invariant, it commutes with the total angular momentum $\mathbf{J}^2$, and a component $\mathbf{J}_3$. Since T_{ij} is a tensor of the second rank, the tensor force does not commute with the orbital angular momentum; it can relate two-nucleon states of orbital angular momentum L to states of orbital angular momenta‖ $|L-2|$, L, $L+2$.

† See Fig. 44.

‡ G. Breit and J. B. Ehrman, *Phys. Rev.* **96** (1954) 805; M. H. Hall and A. M. Saperstein, ibid. 806.

§ A. Garren, *Phys. Rev.* **92** (1953) 213.

‖ Because $\mathscr{S}_{12}$ does not change parity, it cannot relate L to $L\pm 1$.

However, $\mathscr{S}_{12}$ commutes with the total spin $\mathbf{S}^2$ of the two nucleons.† Further, $\mathscr{S}_{12}$ has eigenvalue zero for the two-nucleon singlet state ($S = 0$), because this state must be an eigenstate of orbital angular momentum.‡ Therefore the tensor force gives no contribution in the singlet state.

For triplet states the scattered wave will have the orbital angular momentum values $L = J+1,\ J,\ |J-1|$ outside the range of the tensor force; within the range of the tensor force the orbital angular momentum components are mixed together.§ Instead of the eigenstates (110) we expect eigenstates of the form

$$\left.\begin{aligned}\psi^{(M)}_{J,(i)} &= (1/r)\big(u^{(i)}_{J-1,J}(r)W^{(M)}_{J-1,J}+u^{(i)}_{J+1,J}(r)W^{(M)}_{J+1,J}\big) \quad (i=1,2)\\ \psi^{(M)}_{J} &= (1/r)u_{JJ}(r)W^{(M)}_{JJ}\end{aligned}\right\}. \tag{120}$$

There are two linearly independent regular solutions $\psi^{(M)}_{J(i)}$ $(i = 1, 2)$. The radial functions u_{LJ} $(L \neq J)$ obey the simultaneous equations‖

$$\frac{d^2u_{LJ}}{dr^2}+\left(k^2-\frac{L(L+1)}{r^2}\right)u_{LJ}-\frac{m_N}{\hbar^2}\sum_{L'=J-1}^{J+1}V^{(J)}_{LL'}(r)u_{L'J}=0 \qquad (L = J\pm 1) \tag{121}$$

rather than (101). Here

$$V^{(J)}_{LL'}(r) = \int d\Omega\, \tilde{W}^{(M)}_{LJ} V W^{(M)}_{L'J},$$

where V is the total nucleon-nucleon potential.†† By time reversal invariance $V^{(J)}_{LL'}(r)$ is a real symmetric matrix in L, L'.

It is not possible to form two linear combinations of the solutions $\psi^{(M)}_{J(1)}$, $\psi^{(M)}_{J(2)}$ which are asymptotically dependent on $W^{(M)}_{J-1,J}$ or $W_{J+1,J}$ only. Scattering is described by finding linear combinations of the solutions (120) which, when added to the incident wave (106), cancel out the terms in e^{-ikr}.

The linear combinations of the solutions (120) which are to be used will depend on the value of the magnetic quantum number M ($M = S_3$), and they can be described by a set of complex‡‡ phase angles $\delta^{(M)}_{LJ}$.

† Because $\mathscr{S}_{12}$ preserves the permutation symmetry of the spin state vector.

‡ W. Rarita and J. Schwinger, *Phys. Rev.* **59** (1941) 436; see also J. Ashkin and Ta-You Wu, ibid. **73** (1948) 973, for a detailed analysis of the tensor force scattering formulae.

§ Because the tensor operator $\mathscr{S}_{12}$ obeys $(\mathscr{S}_{12})^2 = -2\mathscr{S}_{12}+(\boldsymbol{\sigma}^{(1)}+\boldsymbol{\sigma}^{(2)})^2$, the deuteron ground state (a mixture of $^3S_1$ and $^3D_1$ states) is of the form $\{u(r)+v(r)\mathscr{S}_{12}\}|S = 1, S_3\rangle$. Here $\mathscr{S}_{12}v(r)|S = 1, S_3\rangle$ has only an $L = 2$ component.

‖ A detailed discussion is given by D. R. Swanson, *Phys. Rev.* **89** (1953) 740.

†† $V^{(J)}_{LL'}(r)$ is independent of M, because V is an invariant.

‡‡ It should be noticed that the amplitudes of the asymptotic forms of $u^{(i)}_{J-1,J}(r)$ and $u^{(i)}_{J+1,J}(r)$ are not, in general, equal. Hence the *complex* phases.

Hence the scattered wave produced by a triplet state of spin M is

$$\langle \mathbf{x}|\text{scatt}; k, M, S=1\rangle = \frac{e^{ikr}}{r}\frac{1}{2ik}\sum_{L=0}^{\infty}\sum_{J=|L-1|}^{L+1}\{4\pi(2L+1)\}^{\frac{1}{2}}\times$$
$$\times(L10M|JM)(e^{2i\delta_{LJ}^{(M)}}-1)W_{LJ}^{(M)} \quad (|M| \leqslant 1). \quad (122)$$

It is easy to see by comparing (122), (106), and Table 4 that $\delta_{LJ}^{(M)} = \delta_{LJ}^{(-M)}$. Because $(J100|J0)$ vanishes, no term $\delta_{JJ}^{(0)}$ occurs. The complex phase angles $\delta_{LJ}^{(|M|)}$ are related to the asymptotic forms of the radial components $u_{LJ}^{(M)}(r)$,† and are determined by the potential V.

The triplet scattering matrix is now obtained on replacing $e^{2i\delta_{lJ}}$ in (109) by $e^{2i\delta_{lJ}^{(S_3)}}$, and the cross-section and polarization are then calculated as in the case of the spin-orbital force using (114) and (115).‡ In evaluating the polarization using (116) it should be remembered that the phases are in general complex and (118) is no longer valid. A convenient expression for the polarization has been given by C. A. Klein.§

Extensive calculations of cross-sections and polarizations based on spin orbit and tensor interactions have been made by various authors.|| †† Examples of the results are shown in Figs. 43 and 44. The Berkeley group have made a detailed phase shift analysis of (p–p) scattering at 310 MeV.‡‡

9. Multiple scattering of nucleons

So far we have examined, by a double scattering, the polarization produced in a beam which was initially unpolarized. More information can be obtained by examining the polarization produced in a beam which, before the scattering, was already polarized; this requires a triple scattering experiment.§§

We consider the scattering of nucleons by any homogeneous scatterer, remembering that (81) holds. The scatterers are assumed to be

† See D. R. Swanson, loc. cit.

‡ It is often found convenient to replace the two complex phase shifts $\delta_{LJ}^{(M)}$ by two real 'eigenphase shifts' (derived directly from (121)) together with a real mixing parameter (cf. J. M. Blatt and L. C. Biedenharn, *Rev. Mod. Phys.* **24** (1952) 258). Explicit forms for the elements of the scattering matrix M using this notation have been given by S. C. Wright, *Phys. Rev.* **99** (1955) 996.

§ C. A. Klein, *Nuovo Cim.* **2** (1955) 38.

|| For example, L. J. B. Goldfarb and D. Feldman, *Phys. Rev.* **88** (1952) 1099.

†† R. M. Thaler and J. Bengston, *Phys. Rev.* **94** (1954) 699, and A. Garren, ibid. **96** (1954) 1709, have also discussed the interference of the Coloumb interaction for p–p scattering.

‡‡ H. P. Stapp *et al.*, *Phys. Rev.* **105** (1957) 302.

§§ L. Wolfenstein, *Phys. Rev.* **96** (1954) 1654; R. Oehme, ibid. **98** (1955) 147.

unpolarized. If $\mathbf{P}^{(1)}$ and $\mathbf{P}^{(2)}$ are the nucleon polarizations before and after scattering respectively, we may write (30) in the form

$$Q^{(2)}\mathbf{P}^{(2)} = Q_0[P_2\,\mathbf{n}_2+\mathrm{tr}\{M(\boldsymbol{\sigma}.\mathbf{P}^{(1)})\tilde{M}\boldsymbol{\sigma}\}/\mathrm{tr}(M\tilde{M})], \tag{123}$$

where $Q_0 = \frac{1}{2}\mathrm{tr}(M\tilde{M})$ is the cross-section for scattering of an unpolarized beam, $Q^{(2)}$ is the cross-section for scattering of the polarized beam, and $P_2\,\mathbf{n}_2$ is the polarization produced in the scattering of an unpolarized beam. $\mathbf{n}_2$ is the unit normal to the plane of scattering† (formula (123) will be applied to the second scattering in a triple scattering experiment, cf. Fig. 45).

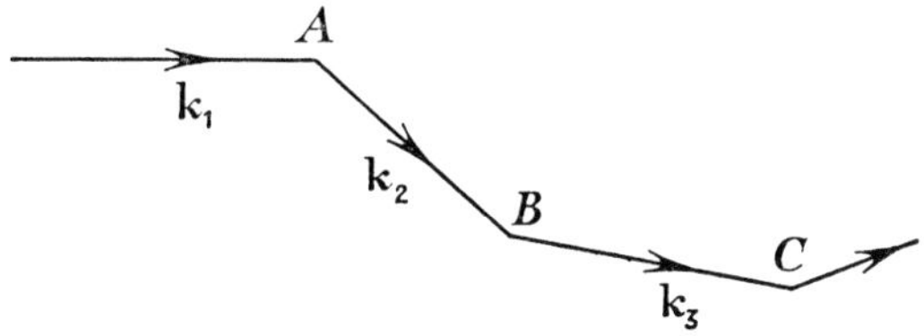

FIG. 45. Triple scattering.

The second term on the right of (123) is analysed using invariance arguments. Remembering that $\mathbf{P}^{(1)}$, $\mathbf{P}^{(2)}$, and $\mathbf{n}_2$ are axial vectors, and introducing the polar vector

$$\mathbf{s} = \mathbf{n}_2\times\mathbf{k}_3,$$

we can write the components of $\mathbf{P}^{(2)}$ (using the notation in Fig. 45)

$$Q^{(2)}(\mathbf{P}^{(2)}.\mathbf{n}_2) = Q_0\{P_2+D(\mathbf{P}^{(1)}.\mathbf{n}_2)\}, \tag{124}$$

$$Q^{(2)}(\mathbf{P}^{(2)}.\mathbf{s}) = Q_0\{A(\mathbf{P}^{(1)}.\mathbf{k}_2)+R(\mathbf{P}^{(1)}.\mathbf{n}_2\times\mathbf{k}_2)\}, \tag{125}$$

where D, A, R are functions of the energy and of $(\mathbf{k}_2.\mathbf{k}_3)$ only. The component of $\mathbf{P}^{(2)}$ along $\mathbf{k}_3$ cannot be detected by examining the cross-section for the third scattering (at C) and will not be written down. If the beam incident on the first scatterer at A is unpolarized then $\mathbf{P}^{(1)}$ is perpendicular to $\mathbf{k}_2$. Hence the coefficient A cannot be determined by a triple-scattering experiment.

Scattering in the plane

Let us consider the case in which $\mathbf{k}_1$, $\mathbf{k}_2$, $\mathbf{k}_3$ lie in a plane. Then $\mathbf{P}^{(1)}$ and $\mathbf{P}^{(2)}$ are parallel to $\mathbf{n}_2$, and by (124)

$$Q^{(2)}\mathbf{P}^{(2)} = \mathbf{n}_2\,Q_0(P_2\pm D|\mathbf{P}^{(1)}|),$$

where the $\pm$ sign is to be used according as $\mathbf{P}^{(1)}$ and $\mathbf{n}_2$ are in the same or in opposite directions. Hence, using (29),

$$\mathbf{P}^{(2)} = \mathbf{n}_2(P_2\pm D|\mathbf{P}^{(1)}|)/(1\pm|\mathbf{P}^{(1)}|P_2). \tag{126}$$

† The direction of $\mathbf{n}_2$ is given by $\mathbf{n}_2 = \mathbf{k}_2\times\mathbf{k}_3/|\mathbf{k}_2\times\mathbf{k}_3|$.

If both scatterings (at A and B) are to the left (or to the right), and if the beam incident on the second scatterer is completely polarized, i.e. $|\mathbf{P}^{(1)}| = 1$, then (126) gives

$$\mathbf{P}^{(2)} = \mathbf{n}_2 \frac{P_2+D}{1+P_2}. \tag{127}$$

Because $|\mathbf{P}^{(2)}| \leqslant 1$, it follows that $D \leqslant 1$. If $D = 1$, the beam is completely polarized after the second scattering, but if $D < 1$ the polarization is reduced, or even may have its sign reversed. Thus D gives a measure of the extent to which a second scattering in the same plane *preserves the polarization*. The behaviour of D as a function of energy and scattering angle can be found with the aid of (126), using the third scattering at C to determine $\mathbf{P}^{(2)}$. It is assumed that $|\mathbf{P}^{(1)}|$ and P_2 are already known from double-scattering experiments.

Scattering in orthogonal planes

A triple-scattering experiment can give further information when the planes of the first and second scatterings are perpendicular.† In this

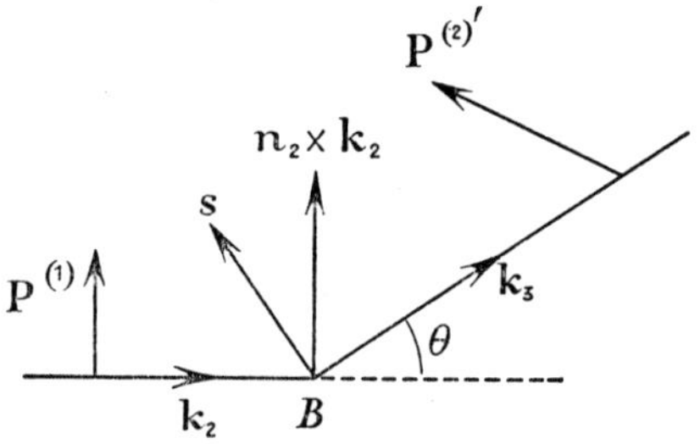

FIG. 46. Triple-scattering notation when the planes of the first and second scatterings are orthogonal.

case $\mathbf{P}^{(1)}$ lies in the plane of $\mathbf{k}_2$ and $\mathbf{k}_3$ (Fig. 46). It is easy to see that $Q^{(2)} = Q_0$, and by (124) the component of $\mathbf{P}^{(2)}$ perpendicular to the plane of scattering is $P_2\,\mathbf{n}_2$. The component of $\mathbf{P}^{(2)}$ in the plane of scattering is, by (125),

$$\mathbf{P}^{(2)\prime} = \pm R|\mathbf{P}^{(1)}|\mathbf{s}+G\mathbf{k}_3, \tag{128}$$

where $G\mathbf{k}_3$ is the undetectable component of $\mathbf{P}^{(2)}$ along $\mathbf{k}_3$. The signs $\pm$ are to be used according as $\mathbf{P}^{(1)}$ and $\mathbf{n}_2\times\mathbf{k}_2$ are in the same, or opposite, directions. R is thus a measure of the extent to which the component of polarization in the plane of scattering and normal to the momentum persists after scattering.

The coefficients D and R can easily be expressed in terms of the coefficients of the appropriate scattering matrix—such as the coefficients

† Triple-scattering experiments, by themselves, can give no more information.

of expression (83) for proton-proton scattering.† In this way information about D and R can add to our knowledge of the phase shifts. For example, if a nucleon beam with polarization $\mathbf{P}^{(1)}$ is scattered by un-

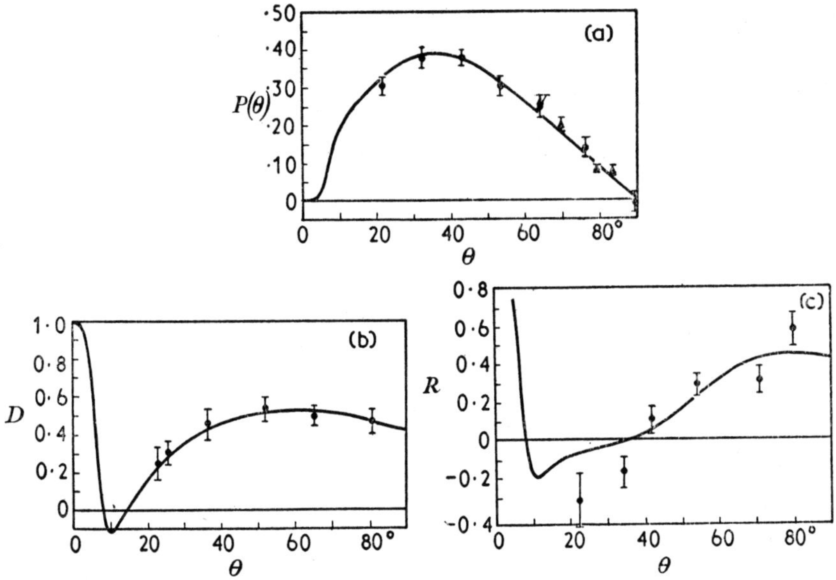

FIG. 47. (*a*), (*b*), (*c*) respectively show the polarization $P(\theta)$, and the coefficients D and R for elastic (p–p) scattering at about 310 MeV.† The curves are deduced from a set of phase shifts of Chamberlain *et al.*†

polarized spin zero targets, the polarization $\mathbf{P}^{(2)}$ can be expressed by the functions $f(\theta)$, $g(\theta)$ of (27), viz.

$$\mathbf{P}^{(2)} = \frac{2\,\mathrm{re}(fg^*)\mathbf{n}_2 + (|f|^2 - |g|^2)\mathbf{P}^{(1)} + 2\,\mathrm{im}(fg^*)\mathbf{n}_2 \times \mathbf{P}^{(1)} + 2|g|^2(\mathbf{n}_2 . \mathbf{P}^{(1)})\mathbf{n}_2}{|f|^2 + |g|^2 + 2\,\mathrm{re}(fg^*)(\mathbf{n}_2 . \mathbf{P}^{(1)})}. \tag{129}$$

The coefficients D and R have been determined by the Berkeley group‡ for proton-proton collisions at 310 MeV (lab.); together with the polarization they are shown in Fig. 47. The relation between D and R and the phase shifts can be found without difficulty.‡

The separation of the polarization and the depolarization coefficient D for nucleon-nucleon scattering into isotopic spin components $T = 0$ and $T = 1$ is easily carried out by the same method as was used on pp. 399 and 400 above.§

† O. Chamberlain, *et al*, *Phys. Rev.* **105** (1957) 288.
‡ H. P. Stapp, T. Ypsilantis, and N. Metropolis, ibid. 302.
§ See, for example, L. Wolfenstein, *Phys. Rev.* **101** (1956) 427.

10. Polarization relations in the process $p+p \to D+\pi^+$

In this process two polarization effects appear. If polarized protons are used, the distribution of the pions which are produced will show azimuthal asymmetry about the direction of the incident beam.† Further, with an unpolarized incident proton beam, the deuteron is polarized perpendicular to the plane containing the momenta of the deuteron and the pion. We discuss these effects for the energy region in which only low angular momenta values contribute to the reaction.

If the reaction is produced by a beam of protons hitting protons at rest, the threshold is a beam energy of around 280 MeV. This is readily seen by requiring that the two protons should have a total energy in the centre of mass system of at least $2Mc^2+\mu c^2-\Delta$, where M, μ are the proton and pion masses respectively, and Δ is the binding energy of the deuteron ($\Delta = 2{\cdot}2$ MeV). For beam energies T of up to 450 MeV, the total energy ϵ of the created pion in the centre of mass system is given by

$$\epsilon-\mu c^2 \simeq \tfrac{1}{2}(T-280)\ \text{MeV}.$$

We assume that it is legitimate to ignore the production of pions of angular momenta (relative to the deuteron) greater than unity, provided that $\eta = (p/c)$ is less than $0{\cdot}7$, where p is the momentum of the pion in the centre of mass system. This condition is satisfied for beam energies up to about 350 MeV. It ensures that the pion wavelength is greater than the size of the deuteron.‡

Isotopic spin

Ignoring effects which are not charge independent, the production of a pion in a nucleon-nucleon collision,

$$\mathcal{N}+\mathcal{N} \to \mathcal{N}+\mathcal{N}+\pi, \tag{130}$$

can occur with three distinct isotopic spin configurations. The corresponding cross-sections may be labelled $\sigma_{T,T'}$, where T, T' are the total isotopic spins of the nucleons in the initial and final states respectively.§ The three cross-sections are $\sigma_{1,1}$, $\sigma_{1,0}$, $\sigma_{0,1}$; the cross-section $\sigma_{1,0}$ may be divided into two parts $\sigma'_{1,0}$ and $\sigma_{1,0}(D)$, according as the two nucleons in the final state are free or bound to form a deuteron.‖ Here we are

† In the reverse process, $\pi^++D \to p+p$, we would expect polarization of the protons.

‡ Wave functions for pions of higher angular momenta will have a very small overlap with the deuteron provided $\eta < 10{\cdot}7$.

§ The interaction (130) is analysed in considerable detail by A. H. Rosenfeld, *Phys. Rev.* **96** (1954) 139. See also E. Fermi (Varenna Lectures), *Suppl. Nuovo Cim.* **1** (1955). A survey of experimental results is given by G. B. Yodh, *Phys. Rev.* **98** (1955) 1330.

‖ It is easy to see that $\sigma_{11} = \sigma(p+p \to p+p+\pi^0)$; $\sigma(p+p \to n+p+\pi^+) = \sigma_{11}+\sigma'_{10}$; $\sigma(n+p \to n+p+\pi^0) = \frac{1}{2}(\sigma'_{10}+\sigma_{01})$; $\sigma(n+p \to p+p+\pi^-) = \frac{1}{2}(\sigma_{11}+\sigma_{01})$, etc.

only concerned with $\sigma_{1,0}(D)$, the cross-section for the process

$$p+p \rightarrow D+\pi^{+}. \tag{131}$$

This is twice the cross-section for†

$$p+n \rightarrow D+\pi^{0}. \tag{132}$$

We shall discuss reaction (131), and show how it can give information about (p–p) scattering phase shifts, and the pion-nucleon interaction.

Angular momentum

With the assumptions made above, in the final state the pion can be in an s or p state relative to the deuteron. The deuteron is in the $^3S_1$ state, so the total angular momentum J can be 0, 1, or 2. The parity is positive or negative according as the pion is in the p or the s state. Remembering that initially the nucleons are in a state which is symmetric against charge exchange, the Pauli principle shows that they can be in the states $^1S_0$, $^3P_{0,1,2}$, $^1D_2$,... in the centre of mass system. The only possible transitions are

$$\left.\begin{aligned} {}^1S_0 &\rightarrow ({}^3S_1, p) \\ {}^3P_1 &\rightarrow ({}^3S_1, s) \\ {}^1D_2 &\rightarrow ({}^3S_1, p) \end{aligned}\right\}. \tag{133}$$

The terms on the right indicate the final states in (131), the subscripts on the left show the total angular momentum J.

Now we set up the state vector describing the outgoing system on the right of (131). Suppose we have three-component state vectors ψ_s ($s = 1, 0, -1$) which describe the (spin) states of the deuteron. They are eigenstates of the O_3 component of the spin operator, with eigenvalues $s\hbar$; the vectors ψ_s are normalized so that

$$\tilde{\psi}_s \cdot \psi_{s'} = \delta_{ss'}. \tag{134}$$

The angular momentum in the initial singlet states $^1S_0$, $^1D_2$ is given by the orbital angular momentum of the protons. This has the values $L = 0$, 2, respectively, and in both cases the component of angular momentum about the direction of the incident beam is zero. The outgoing wave produced by the $^1D_2$ state is obtained by combining the deuteron state vectors ψ_s with spherical harmonics $Y_1^{(s)}(\theta, \phi)$ representing

† The initial state in (132) contains equal amounts of the $T = 0$ and $T = 1$ states; only the $T = 1$ component can lead to $D+\pi^0$ because the deuteron has zero isotopic spin.

the p-wave pion.† The combination must give total angular momentum 2 and must have zero component of angular momentum about the incident beam direction. Taking the O_3 axis along this direction, the correct combination is

$$\sum_{s=-1}^{1} (11s,-s|20)\psi_s Y_1^{(-s)}(\theta,\phi).$$

The $^1S_0$ contribution is formed similarly.

The $^3P_1$ state is made up from an orbital angular momentum having $L = 1$ and zero component about O_3, and a spin function $\phi_{s'}$, representing the triplet spin state ($s' = +1, 0, -1$). For the outgoing wave ($^3S_1, s$), the deuteron state vector ψ_s must be combined with some other function so as to give the correct transformation properties; such a function is $Y_1^{(0)}(\theta=0)$, a spherical harmonic referring to the (fixed) direction of the incident beam. The correct combination is

$$(11s0|1s)\psi_s Y_1^{(0)}(0) \quad (s = +1, 0, -1).$$

The function $Y_1^{(0)}(0)$ may be omitted so long as the axes are not inverted.

Writing $\hbar k$ for the radial momentum of the final state in the centre of mass system, and letting r be the separation of the pion and the deuteron, the outgoing wave arising from the singlet states $^1S_0$ and $^1D_2$ is

$$\Psi_{\text{sing}} = \frac{e^{ikr}}{r} \sum_{s=-1}^{1} \{\alpha_0(11s,-s|00)+\alpha_2(11s,-s|20)\}\psi_s Y_1^{(-s)}(\theta,\phi). \tag{135}$$

The outgoing waves arising from the triplet states $^3P_1$ are

$$\Psi_{\text{trip},s} = \alpha_1(11s0|1s)\psi_s Y_0 \qquad (s = -1, 1) \tag{136}$$

(the factor $Y_0 = (4\pi)^{-\frac{1}{2}}$ is included in (136) to simplify the normalization). Only the spin values $s = -1, +1$ can occur in the triplet outgoing waves.

The coefficients α_0, α_1, α_2, which are independent of the angles, give the relative amplitudes and phases of the scattering matrix elements for the three reactions (133). Their energy dependence near the threshold can be estimated roughly by the usual phase space estimate. For the triplet case the final state contains two particles, both in s-states; we expect that the cross-section for this process (and thus $|\alpha_1|^2$) is proportional to η. The final states in the singlet case contain one s-state and one p-state particle. Hence we expect $|\alpha_0|^2$ and $|\alpha_3|^2$ to vary‡ as η^3.

† (θ, ϕ) is the direction of the outgoing pion relative to the incident beam, in the centre of mass system.

‡ Cf. E. Fermi, p. 414, n. §.

Pion-production cross-sections

With unpolarized protons in the initial state, there is no interference between the singlet and triplet processes; the differential cross-sections arising from (135) and (136) are to be calculated separately.† The differential cross-section $Q\,d\Omega$ for producing a pion in direction (θ, ϕ) is obtained by using (135), (136) and summing over the deuteron spin values. Because there is no interference between the singlet and triplet outgoing waves, the pion production cross-section Q is independent of the azimuthal angle ϕ; this is only true if the incident protons are not polarized. We get (in the c.m.s.)

$$Q\,d\Omega = \frac{d\Omega}{4\pi}[|\alpha_1|^2+|\alpha_0|^2+\tfrac{1}{2}|\alpha_2|^2+\sqrt{2}\,\mathrm{re}(\alpha_2\,\alpha_0^*)+ \\ +3\cos^2\theta\{\tfrac{1}{2}|\alpha_2|^2-\sqrt{2}\,\mathrm{re}(\alpha_2\,\alpha_0^*)\}]. \quad (137)$$

The total pion production cross-section is

$$\int Q\,d\Omega = |\alpha_0|^2+|\alpha_1|^2+|\alpha_2|^2.$$

The pion distributions arising from the $^3P_1$ state or the $^1S_0$ state alone are isotropic.‡ The distribution arising from the $^1D_2$ state alone is of the form $\frac{1}{3}+\cos^2\theta$.

Remembering the energy dependence of the $|\alpha_i|^2$, the differential cross-section is of the form

$$Q\,d\Omega = \frac{d\Omega}{4\pi}[A_1\,\eta+A_2\,\eta^3+A_3\,\eta^3\cos^2\theta]. \quad (138)$$

Experimental results of Crawford and Stevenson§ with (centre of mass) values of η between 0·38 and 0·58, and values of θ between 30° and 70°, have been fitted with the formula (138). These authors obtain $A_1 = 0{\cdot}14\pm0{\cdot}22$ mb, $A_2 = 0{\cdot}20\pm0{\cdot}08$ mb, $A_3 = 2{\cdot}44\pm0{\cdot}17$ mb. Because A_1 is not zero, we see that s-wave pion production is occurring as well as the p-wave production which is expected from the strong interaction of p-wave pions and nucleons.‖ The ratio of the terms in η^3 is $(A_2/A_3) \simeq 0{\cdot}08$. Clearly, the $^1S_0$ process contributes to the p-wave

† In working out the cross-section, the sum over all combinations of spins of the two protons equals the sum over the three components of the triplet spin and the singlet spin of the two particles.

‡ The $^1S_0$ state gives an isotropic distribution because we have summed over the deuteron spin.

§ F. S. Crawford and M. L. Stevenson, *Phys. Rev.* **97** (1955) 1305.

‖ An indirect estimate of the s-wave term $A_1\eta$ (starting from the reaction $\gamma+p \rightarrow n+\pi^+$) by a method due to Breuckner, Serber, and Watson (*Phys. Rev.* **81** (1951) 575) gives much the same value of A_1: for details see G. Bernardini and E. L. Goldwasser, ibid. **94** (1954) 729.

pion production as well as the $^1D_2$ process, which by itself would give $A_2/A_3 = \frac{1}{3}$.

The $T = \frac{3}{2}$, $J = \frac{3}{2}$ pion interaction† favours $^1D_2$.

The polarization phenomena

By determining the ratios of the coefficients in (138) we find

$$1+1/X \equiv (A_2+A_3)/A_2 = \left|\frac{\alpha_0}{\alpha_2}-\sqrt{2}\right|^2 \bigg/ \left|\frac{\alpha_0}{\alpha_2}+\frac{1}{\sqrt{2}}\right|^2$$

and
$$A_1/A_2 = |\alpha_1|^2/|\alpha_0+\alpha_2/\sqrt{2}|^2.$$

The relative phases of the α_i, and hence their values, are given by the polarization experiments. First we examine the polarization of the deuteron when the incident protons are unpolarized.‡ The deuterons can only be polarized perpendicular to the plane of the reaction products. Choosing $\phi = 0$ for this plane we have to evaluate $\langle S_2 \rangle$, where S_2 is the deuteron spin operator, which is given explicitly in § 5 above. The initial triplet state $^3P_1$ cannot contribute to the deuteron polarization, because the deuteron spin component is, in that case, determined by the spins in the unpolarized initial state. A simple calculation yields

$$\langle S_2 \rangle = -\frac{|\alpha_2|^2}{4\pi} 3\sqrt{2}\,\mathrm{im}\left(\frac{\alpha_0}{\alpha_2}\right)\sin\theta\cos\theta. \tag{139}$$

In the notation of § 5, the polarization P is $(2i/\sqrt{3})\langle \Omega_{11} \rangle$, because $\langle S_1 \rangle$ vanishes. The detection of the deuteron polarization is made by comparison with double-scattering experiments for deuterons.§ As was discussed in § 6, the value of $\langle \Omega_{21} \rangle$ appears to be small compared with $\langle \Omega_{11} \rangle$ at the energies involved|| (i.e. about 150 MeV (lab.) energy). Tripp has measured the polarization of the deuterons produced in interaction (131)†† for incident unpolarized protons of (lab.) energy 340 MeV; he finds $P = 0{\cdot}076 \pm 0{\cdot}059$. The difficulty of the experiment is reflected in the large limits of error.

Pion asymmetry

The phase of α_1/α_2 is involved in the asymmetry of the pion distribution in (131) when the incident protons are polarized. The angular

† A predominant $(\frac{3}{2}, \frac{3}{2})$ pion-nucleon interaction would give a much stronger $^1D_2$ than $^1S_0$ process, because of the angular momentum coupling.

‡ K. M. Watson and C. Richman, *Phys. Rev.* **83** (1951) 1256.

§ O. Chamberlain *et al.*, *Phys. Rev.* **95** (1954) 1104.

|| H. P. Stapp, *Univ. of California Radiation Lab. Report* No. 3098, gives theoretical reasons for believing that at these energies all the second-rank tensor components are small compared with the first-rank terms.

†† R. D. Tripp, *Phys. Rev.* **102** (1956) 862.

distribution of the pions is

$$Q(\theta,\phi)\,d\Omega = d\Omega\,\tfrac{1}{4}\{\mathrm{tr}(M\tilde{M})+\mathbf{P}^{(1)}.\,\mathrm{tr}(M\boldsymbol{\sigma}^{(1)}\tilde{M})\}, \tag{140}$$

where M is the scattering matrix, $\boldsymbol{\sigma}^{(1)}$ the spin operator for the incident proton, and tr indicates a summation over the deuteron spin states. $\mathbf{P}^{(1)}$ is the polarization of the incident proton beam. The scattering matrix M has to be related to the outgoing waves (135) and (136). The columns of M are labelled by ${}^3P_1$, ${}^1S_0$, ${}^1D_2$, the states of the incident protons. The rows are labelled by the spin s of the deuteron and the total angular momentum J. The matrix M reduces to two sub-matrices M_{sing} and M_{trip}. The matrix elements for the row with deuteron spin s ($s = 1,0,-1$) are

$$\begin{aligned} M_{\mathrm{sing}}&:\quad \alpha_0(11s,-s|00)Y_1^{(-s)}(\theta,\phi),\ \alpha_2(11s,-s|20)Y_1^{(-s)}(\theta,\phi),\\ M_{\mathrm{trip}}&:\quad \alpha_1(11s0|1s)(4\pi)^{-\frac{1}{2}} \end{aligned} \tag{141}$$

with an obvious notation.

Denoting the spin of the target proton by $\boldsymbol{\sigma}^{(2)}$, we see that

$$\mathrm{tr}\{M(\boldsymbol{\sigma}^{(1)}+\boldsymbol{\sigma}^{(2)})\tilde{M}\}$$

vanishes.† Therefore

$$\mathrm{tr}(M\boldsymbol{\sigma}^{(1)}\tilde{M}) = \tfrac{1}{2}\mathrm{tr}\{M(\boldsymbol{\sigma}^{(1)}-\boldsymbol{\sigma}^{(2)})\tilde{M}\}.$$

This shows that in the polarization term we need only consider interference between M_{sing} and M_{trip}, thus

$$\begin{aligned}\mathrm{tr}(M\boldsymbol{\sigma}^{(1)}\tilde{M}) &= \mathrm{tr}(M_{\mathrm{sing}}\boldsymbol{\sigma}^{(1)}\tilde{M}_{\mathrm{trip}})+\mathrm{tr}(M_{\mathrm{trip}}\boldsymbol{\sigma}^{(1)}\tilde{M}_{\mathrm{sing}})\\ &= 2\,\mathrm{re}\,\mathrm{tr}(M_{\mathrm{sing}}\boldsymbol{\sigma}^{(1)}\tilde{M}_{\mathrm{trip}}).\end{aligned}$$

Using the representation (3.34) for $\boldsymbol{\sigma}^{(1)}$, a simple calculation gives

$$\mathrm{tr}(M\sigma_1^{(1)}\tilde{M}) = \frac{1}{4\pi}\sqrt{2}\sin\theta\sin\phi\,|\alpha_2|^2\,\mathrm{im}\left\{\frac{\alpha_1^*}{\alpha_2^*}\left(\frac{\alpha_0}{\alpha_2}+\frac{1}{\sqrt{2}}\right)\right\}, \tag{142}$$

where $\sigma_1^{(1)}$ is the O_1 component of the proton spin operator. We are free to choose the O_1 axis along the direction of polarization of the incident proton (which is perpendicular to the incident beam). The differential cross-section $Q(\theta,\phi)$ for production of a pion in direction (θ,ϕ) becomes‡

$$Q(\theta,\phi)\,d\Omega \propto (A+\cos^2\theta+AP^{(1)}R\sin\theta\sin\phi)\,d\Omega, \tag{143}$$

where $$R = \sqrt{2}\frac{b}{1+b^2}\sin\{\psi-\arg(\alpha_1/\alpha_2)\}.$$

Here $\psi = \arg(\alpha_0/\alpha_2+1/\sqrt{2})$, $b = |\alpha_0+\alpha_2/\sqrt{2}|/|\alpha_1|$, and A is the ratio which appears when eqn. (137) is written $Q\,d\Omega = (\mathrm{const.})(A+\cos^2\theta)$.

† The singlet states give no contribution and the triplet state terms cancel.

‡ R. E. Marshak and A. M. L. Messiah, *Nuovo Cim.* **11** (1954) 337, and A. H. Rosenfeld, p. 414, n. §.

The asymmetry in (143):
$$\frac{P^{(1)}R\sin\theta}{1+(1/A)\cos^2\theta},$$
is greatest at the centre of mass angle $\theta = \frac{1}{2}\pi$, for which the average cross-section is least.

Crawford and Stevenson,† using a proton beam of (lab.) energy 314 MeV and producing pions with $\eta = 0{\cdot}41$, find a value
$$|R| = (0{\cdot}39 \pm 0{\cdot}05).$$

A relation for p–p scattering phases

It has been pointed out‡ that because the cross-section for reaction (131) just over the threshold is small compared with the proton-proton scattering cross-section, it is possible to use a time-reversal argument, similar to that relating pion-nucleon scattering and the photo-production of pions (Chapter VII, § 3). This immediately gives
$$\left.\begin{aligned}\arg(\alpha_0/\alpha_2) &= \delta(^1S_0)-\delta(^1D_2)+n\pi\\ \arg(\alpha_1/\alpha_2) &= \delta(^3P_1)-\delta(^1D_2)+n'\pi+\tfrac{1}{2}\pi\end{aligned}\right\}, \tag{144}$$
where n, n' are integers and $\delta(^1S_0)$, $\delta(^1D_2)$, $\delta(^3P_1)$ are the phases for proton-proton scattering in the states indicated, at the same energy. Comparison between the p–p phases and the values of $\arg(\alpha_0/\alpha_2)$, $\arg(\alpha_1/\alpha_2)$ as determined by the above polarization experiments has been made by Tripp;§ he uses (144) to resolve ambiguities in the values of $\arg(\alpha_0/\alpha_2)$, $\arg(\alpha_1/\alpha_2)$ deduced from the polarization experiments. The values he gets are in agreement with a strong Fermi type ($T = \frac{3}{2}$, $J = \frac{3}{2}$) pion-nucleon interaction; they give $|\alpha_0/\alpha_2|^2 \simeq 0{\cdot}1$, which shows an appreciable preference for the $^1D_2$ process rather than $^1S_0$.

Deviations from the simple energy dependence used above have been examined by Mescheryahov and Neganov‖ in the region above 450 MeV; little evidence of higher partial wave pions has been found. The polarization phenomena including the effect of higher partial waves have been worked out by Mandl and Regge.††

† See p. 417, n. §; also T. H. Fields *et al.*, *Phys. Rev.* **109** (1958) 1744.

‡ M. Gell-Mann and K. M. Watson, *Ann. Rev. Nuclear Sci.* **4** (Annual Reviews Inc., Stanford, Cal., 1954), p. 252.

§ R. D. Tripp, *Phys. Rev.* **102** (1956) 862.

‖ M. G. Mescheryahov and B. S. Neganov, *Dokl. Akad. Nauk SSSR.* **100** (1955) 677.

†† F. Mandl and T. Regge, *Phys. Rev.* **99** (1955) 1478.

IX

THE FOUNDATIONS OF FIELD QUANTIZATION

1. The action principle

THE quantization of fields which has been given in Chapter II (for bosons) and Chapter IV (for fermions) is based on a simple extension of the Poisson bracket method. When it is applied to fields, the method is not obviously Lorentz covariant, and it is not particularly straightforward or elegant. Powerful methods of field quantization which do not have these disadvantages have been given by Feynman and by Schwinger; they will be outlined in the present chapter.

Classical mechanics

Both of these authors' derivations start from the action principle of classical mechanics. It would be reasonable to say that the action principle is the fundamental law both of classical and of quantum mechanics; all the basic formulae may be derived *directly* from it. For a classical conservative dynamical system having Lagrangian L, the action function is†

$$W = \int\limits_A^B L\,dt; \tag{1}$$

the integration extends from a point A to a point B on the trajectory of the system. Suppose $q_1,\ldots, q_n$ are the general coordinates of the system. The action principle expresses the variation in W from an actual trajectory of the system to any adjacent trajectory; this variation is†

$$\delta W = \Big[\sum_{r=1}^{n} p_r\,\delta q_r - H\,\delta t\Big]_A^B, \tag{2}$$

where $(\delta t)_A$, $(\delta t)_B$, $(\delta q_r)_A$, $(\delta q_r)_B$ are the differences in time and coordinates between the end points of the new and the original trajectory. Also

$$p_r = \frac{\partial L}{\partial \dot{q}_r}, \qquad H = \sum_{r=1}^{n} p_r\,\dot{q}_r - L.$$

Thus, if we know W, the conjugate momenta p_r and the Hamiltonian H may be defined as the coefficients of the differentials in the variation formula (2). It also follows from (2) that for an actual trajectory, W is

† E. T. Whittaker, *Analytical Dynamics* (Cambridge University Press, 4th edn., 1937), ch. 9. W is frequently called the principal function.

a function only of the coordinates, momenta, and time at the end points; it does not depend on the intermediate values.

A classical transformation from dynamical variables (p_r, q_r) $(r = 1, 2,..., n)$ to new variables (P_r, Q_r) is canonical if the new variables (P_r, Q_r) form conjugate pairs; this will be the case if a function F exists such that†

$$\sum_{r=1}^{n} (P_r\,dQ_r - p_r\,dq_r) = dF. \tag{3}$$

We can write

$$P_r = \frac{\partial F}{\partial Q_r}, \qquad p_r = -\frac{\partial F}{\partial q_r} \qquad (r = 1, 2,..., n), \tag{4}$$

where $F \equiv F(Q, q)$. Comparing (2) and (3) it is clear that (for fixed t_A, t_B) the action W defines a canonical transformation between the variables $\{(p_r)_A, (q_r)_A\}$ and $\{(p_r)_B, (q_r)_B\}$. Clearly,

$$(p_r)_B = \frac{\partial W}{\partial (q_r)_B}, \qquad (p_r)_A = -\frac{\partial W}{\partial (q_r)_A}, \tag{5}$$

where W is expressed as a function of $(q_r)_A$, $(q_r)_B$.

Quantum mechanics

The importance of the action function W in quantum theory follows from some remarks of Dirac on the relation between canonical transformations in classical and in quantum mechanics.‡ In quantum mechanics the canonical transformation from the operators (p_r, q_r) to operators (P_r, Q_r) is

$$P_r = Sp_r S^{-1}, \qquad Q_r = Sq_r S^{-1}, \tag{6}$$

where S is a unitary operator. In quantum theory the variables (p_r, q_r) $(r = 1, 2,..., n)$ are canonical conjugates, provided

$$[p_r, p_s] = 0, \qquad [q_r, q_s] = 0, \qquad [p_r, q_s] = \frac{\hbar}{i}\delta_{rs}. \tag{7}$$

Transformations like (6) ensure that the commutators in (7) also hold for the new variables (P_r, Q_r). Dirac showed how the quantum theory transformation could be expressed in a form that is much more like (4). Let $|q'\rangle$, $|Q'\rangle$ be eigenvectors of the original and the new sets of coordinates. The transformation function $\langle Q'|q'\rangle$ between these eigenvectors is used to define an operator F in the *mixed representation*,

$$\langle Q'|q'\rangle = \exp\left\{\frac{i}{\hbar} F(Q', q')\right\}. \tag{8}$$

† E. T. Whittaker, op. cit., ch. 11.

‡ P. A. M. Dirac, *Quantum Mechanics* (Clarendon Press, 2nd edn., 1935), § 30.

For any representatives $\langle Q'|\,\rangle$, $\langle q'|\,\rangle$, we want to have

$$\langle Q'|P_r|\,\rangle = \frac{\hbar}{i}\frac{\partial}{\partial Q'_r}\langle Q'|\,\rangle, \qquad \langle q'|p_r|\,\rangle = \frac{\hbar}{i}\frac{\partial}{\partial q'_r}\langle q'|\,\rangle;$$

it follows that the canonical momenta are given in the mixed representation by

$$\left.\begin{aligned} \langle Q'|P_r|q'\rangle &= \frac{\partial F(Q',q')}{\partial Q'_r}\langle Q'|q'\rangle \\ \langle Q'|p_r|q'\rangle &= -\frac{\partial F(Q',q')}{\partial q'_r}\langle Q'|q'\rangle \end{aligned}\right\}. \tag{9}$$

If P_r, p_r can be written as functions $P_r(Q,q)$, $p_r(Q,q)$ of the operators Q, q, so that each Q is to the left of all the q, and if the operators $\partial F(Q,q)/\partial Q_r$, $\partial F(Q,q)/\partial q_r$ are written in the same way, then (9) gives the operator equations

$$P_r = \frac{\partial F(Q,q)}{\partial q_r}, \qquad p_r = -\frac{\partial F(Q,q)}{\partial q_r}. \tag{10}$$

(If $F(Q,q)$ itself is written with this ordering there should be no trouble in writing the partial derivatives similarly.) The relation between the classical transformation (4) and the canonical transformation of quantum theory, (10), is now obvious. Eqn. (8) which shows the connexion between the latter and the transformation function $\langle Q'|q'\rangle$ is very important in later developments.

The action in quantum mechanics

In classical mechanics the action W generates the canonical transformation (5). Let us consider the corresponding transformation in quantum mechanics. If the action is obtained as a function of the complete sets of commuting operators Q at T and q at t, and the terms are ordered† so that the Q are to the left of all the q, we have an operator which we shall call $W_0(Q,q;\,T,t)$. Starting from the operator equations (cf. (10))

$$P_r = \frac{\partial W_0(Q,q;\,T,t)}{\partial Q_r}, \qquad p_r = -\frac{\partial W_0(Q,q;\,T,t)}{\partial q_r}, \tag{11}$$

the argument given above may be reversed, so that corresponding to (8) we have the transformation function

$$\langle Q',T|q',t\rangle = C\exp\left\{\frac{i}{\hbar}W_0(Q',q';\,T,t)\right\}, \tag{12}$$

where C is a constant to be determined.

The meaning of this transformation function may be seen in two

† The final expression *includes* all the commutators introduced by the ordering.

ways. Considering the representative $\langle Q', T|\,\rangle$ of any state in terms of the set of commuting variables Q at time T, the transformation function makes possible the change in representation

$$\langle Q', T|\,\rangle = \int dq' \langle Q', T|q', t\rangle\langle q', t|\,\rangle, \tag{13}$$

where $\langle q', t|\,\rangle$ is the representative of the same state in terms of the set of commuting variables q. $\int dq'$ denotes the integration over the whole range of eigenvalues of the set q. The function $\langle Q', T|q', t\rangle$ shows how the representatives vary with time for a state in which the coordinates had the eigenvalues q' at t; in other words $\langle Q', T|q', t\rangle$, regarded as a function of Q' and T, is a Schrödinger wave function.

Alternatively, we may say that the transformation function varies with T so that it expresses the dynamical variables Q in terms of the values q of the same operators at time t, as required in the Heisenberg representation. Thus if t is kept fixed, the time dependence of any function A of the variables Q is given by

$$\langle q'', t|A(Q)|q', t\rangle = \iint \langle q'', t|Q'', T\rangle\, dQ''\langle Q''|A(Q)|Q'\rangle\, dQ'\langle Q', T|q', t\rangle.$$

The transformation function (12) must be unitary, and the value of C can readily be determined by this requirement. It will be convenient to include C in W_0 as an additive constant, and to write the transformation function as

$$\langle Q', T|q', t\rangle = \exp\left\{\frac{i}{\hbar} W_0(Q', q;\, T, t)\right\} = \langle Q', T|\exp\left\{\frac{i}{\hbar} W_0(Q, q;\, T, t)\right\}|q', t\rangle. \tag{14}$$

The effect of ordering the sets of operators Q and q to give $W_0(Q, q;\, T, t)$ must be examined carefully; the relation between Schwinger's method of developing field theory and Feynman's method (which is discussed in § 4 below) depends, to some extent, on the effect of the ordering. It should be noted that the ordered operator W_0, which we find, is not Hermitian;† in consequence, the transformation given by (14) is not obviously unitary.

Calculation of the action

Now we describe how to set up the ordered operator W_0. The differential equations used to define W_0 are taken over directly from the classical form. For simplicity, let us consider one degree of freedom.‡

† Cf. eqn. (17) below.

‡ Another example is given on p. 438.

Forgetting any difficulty about defining partial derivatives with respect to operators, W_0 is given by (cf. (2))

$$\left.\begin{aligned}\frac{\partial W_0(Q,q;\,T,t)}{\partial T} &= -H_0, & \frac{\partial W_0(Q,q;\,T,t)}{\partial t} &= H_0\\ \frac{\partial W_0(Q,q;\,T,t)}{\partial Q} &= P_0, & \frac{\partial W_0(Q,q;\,T,t)}{\partial q} &= -p_0\end{aligned}\right\}, \tag{15}$$

where H is the Hamiltonian, P the momentum at time T, and p that at time t. Using the equations of motion, H, P, and p have to be expressed in terms of the operators Q, q and the time difference $\tau = (T-t)$; finally, the operators have to be ordered so that the Q are to the left of all q, and this ordering is indicated by the subscripts 0 in (15). The order of the Q and q is changed by using their commutator, which is deduced from the equations of motion and the relation

$$[p,q] = \hbar/i.$$

The commutator $[Q,q]$ is a function of τ;† this has the consequence that the integral W_0 of eqn. (15) does not have the same dependence on τ as the operator derived by solving the equations (15) before they are ordered, and subsequently ordering the integral; in other words, for such equations, ordering and integrating are non-commuting operations. (This difficulty arises because partial derivatives with respect to both T and Q are necessary to define W_0.)

The free particle

A simple example‡ to illustrate this is free particle motion, with the Hamiltonian

$$H = \frac{p^2}{2m}.$$

The Heisenberg equations of motion enable us to write the constant momentum operator p in the form

$$p = \frac{m}{\tau}(Q-q), \quad \text{where } \tau = T-t.$$

Because p and q have the canonical commutation relation, we get

$$[Q,q] = \frac{\tau}{m}[p,q] = \frac{\hbar}{i}\frac{\tau}{m}.$$

The first equation of (15) is thus

$$\frac{\partial W_0(Q,q;\,T,t)}{\partial T} = -\frac{m}{2\tau^2}(Q^2-2Qq+q^2)-\frac{1}{2}\frac{\hbar}{i\tau}, \tag{16}$$

† See the example given on p. 438.

‡ This is due to J. Schwinger, *Phys. Rev.* **82** (1951) 927.

and it is easy to see that this, and the other three members of (15), are satisfied by

$$W_0(Q,q;\,T,t) = \frac{m}{2\tau}(Q^2-2Qq+q^2)+\tfrac{1}{2}\hbar i\log\tau+C', \tag{17}$$

where C' is a constant to be determined. Substituting in (14) gives

$$\langle Q',T|q',t\rangle = \frac{C}{\tau^{\frac{1}{2}}}\exp\left\{\frac{i}{\hbar}\frac{m}{2\tau}(Q'-q')^2\right\}, \tag{18}$$

where C is a constant. The unitary condition

$$\int \langle q'',t|Q',T\rangle dQ'\langle Q',T|q',t\rangle = \langle q'',t|q',t\rangle = \delta(q''-q')$$

requires

$$|C|^2 = \frac{m}{2\pi\hbar}.$$

The phase of C is determined by the initial condition

$$\lim_{T\to t}\langle Q',T|q',t\rangle = \delta(Q'-q'). \tag{19}$$

Including a small positive imaginary term in the mass m, so that it becomes $(m+i\epsilon)$ ($\epsilon > 0$, and small), the right-hand side of (18) vanishes as $\tau \to +0$, except for $Q' = q'$ where it is infinite. Using the integral

$$\lim_{\lambda\to+0}\int_{-\infty}^{\infty} e^{(i\alpha-\lambda)x^2}\,dx = \begin{cases} e^{\frac{1}{4}i\pi}\left(\dfrac{\pi}{\alpha}\right)^{\frac{1}{2}} & (\alpha > 0),\\[2ex] e^{-\frac{1}{4}i\pi}\left(\dfrac{\pi}{|\alpha|}\right)^{\frac{1}{2}} & (\alpha < 0),\end{cases} \tag{20}$$

it is clear that (19) is satisfied provided $C = (m/2\pi\hbar)^{\frac{1}{2}}e^{-\frac{1}{4}i\pi}$, so (letting $\epsilon \to 0$)

$$\langle Q',T|q',t\rangle = \left(\frac{m}{2\pi\hbar\tau}\right)^{\frac{1}{2}}e^{-\frac{1}{4}i\pi}\exp\left\{\frac{im}{2\hbar\tau}(Q'-q')^2\right\}. \tag{21}$$

The factor outside the exponential is present because $W_0(Q,q;\,T,t)$ (of eqn. (17)) is not Hermitian. If we had integrated the equations corresponding to (16), etc., before ordering the Q, q, i.e.

$$\frac{\partial W}{\partial T} = -\frac{m}{2\tau^2}(Q-q)^2, \quad \text{etc.},$$

the form corresponding to (17) would have been

$$W = -\frac{m}{2\tau}(Q-q)^2+C'.$$

Ordering this expression gives an additional term $\frac{1}{2}\hbar i$, instead of $\frac{1}{2}\hbar i\log\tau$ which is necessary to give the correct dependence on τ in (21).

Unambiguous evaluation of the action

The example which has just been discussed is particularly simple, as the commutator $[Q, q]$ is a number; in general, both the ambiguities and the difficulty of determining W_0, make (14) useless as a basic equation for quantum theory. There are two ways of avoiding the difficulty; Feynman, as will be shown in § 4, replaces $\langle Q', T|q', t\rangle$ in (14) by a decomposition into products of transformation functions $\langle q'_{(k)}, t^{(k)}|q'_{(k-1)}, t^{(k-1)}\rangle$, where the times $t^{(k-1)}$ and $t^{(k)}$ are close together. For such small time intervals, a modified form of (14) is possible. Schwinger's method can be understood by noticing that the equations (15) themselves are independent of the ordering of the operators; after ordering an operator A to give A_0 we still have $A = A_0$. Therefore, if we can avoid discussing large changes in the action, and only have to evaluate *infinitesimal changes* δW, we do not expect to have any ambiguity.

This required differential form can be derived from (14). On changing any of the variables in W_0 by small amounts,

$$\delta\langle Q', T|q', t\rangle = \frac{i}{\hbar}\delta W_0(Q', q;\, T, t)\exp\left\{\frac{i}{\hbar}W_0(Q', q';\, T, t)\right\}$$

$$= \frac{i}{\hbar}\delta W_0(Q', q';\, T, t)\langle Q', T|q', t\rangle$$

$$= \frac{i}{\hbar}\langle Q', T|\delta W_0(Q, q;\, T, t)|q', t\rangle.$$

Because the change in action is infinitesimal, the preceding equation may be written

$$\delta\langle Q', T|q', t\rangle = \frac{i}{\hbar}\langle Q', T|\delta W(Q, q; T, t)|q', t\rangle, \tag{22}$$

where the variation δW need not be ordered. In accordance with eqns. (15) (in which all the ordering subscripts are now to be dropped), and in analogy with classical mechanics, we assume

$$\delta W = \delta\left(\int_t^T L\, dt\right), \tag{23}$$

where L is the (Hermitian) Lagrangian operator. W is therefore Hermitian; this property preserves the unitary relation. If the unitary transformation connecting the eigenvectors is written

$$|Q'\rangle = U|q''\rangle,$$

then $\langle Q'|q'\rangle = \langle q''|\tilde{U}|q'\rangle$, so

$$\delta\langle Q'|q'\rangle = \langle q''|\delta\tilde{U}|q'\rangle = \langle Q'|U\,\delta\tilde{U}|q'\rangle. \tag{24}$$

By the unitary condition

$$(U+\delta U)(\tilde{U}+\delta\tilde{U}) = 1;$$

so, on neglecting the second-order term, $U\,\delta\tilde{U}$ is anti-Hermitian.

2. Schwinger's dynamical principle

The arguments of the last few pages have shown that (22) together with (23) is the quantum theory form of the action variation (2). Now forgetting the derivation of these equations, we may take (22) and (23) as the basic equations of quantum theory; it is only necessary to know a commuting set of operators q, and the Lagrangian operator L. A hint of the powerful method which is now available is given by the ease with which the laws of classical mechanics are deduced; if the operator sets Q and q commute, (22) shows that

$$\delta W(Q,q;\,T,t) = \delta\left(\int\limits_{(q,t)}^{(Q,T)} L\,dt\right)$$

depends only on the variations of q, Q, t, T (not on the intermediate values). This is the action principle of classical mechanics.

Schwinger writes down his *fundamental dynamical principle* for quantized fields† in a form coming directly from (22),

$$\delta\langle\phi'_{\sigma_1},\sigma_1|\phi'_{\sigma_2},\sigma_2\rangle = \frac{i}{\hbar}\langle\phi'_{\sigma_1},\sigma_1|\delta W(1,2)|\phi'_{\sigma_2},\sigma_2\rangle, \tag{25}$$

where σ_1 and σ_2 are space-like surfaces;‡ ϕ'_{σ_1} are the eigenvalues of a complete set ($\phi^{\alpha}_{\sigma_1}(u)$, $\alpha = 1,2,\ldots,n$) of field amplitudes on the surface σ_1, and similarly ϕ'_{σ_2} on σ_2; also

$$\delta W(1,2) = \delta\left(\frac{1}{c}\int\limits_{\sigma_2}^{\sigma_1} \mathscr{L}\{\phi^{\alpha}(x),\phi^{\alpha}_{\mu}(x)\}\,d^4x\right), \tag{26}$$

where $\mathscr{L}$ is the *Lorentz invariant* Lagrangian density. $\mathscr{L}$ is required to be a Hermitian function of the Hermitian field amplitudes $\phi^{\alpha}(x)$ and their first derivatives $\phi^{\alpha}_{\mu}(x)$, and is at most bilinear in the $\phi^{\alpha}_{\mu}(x)$. $\mathscr{L}$ is usually taken over from classical theory; where there is any ambiguity as to the order of two operators, the average of both orders is used.

† Strictly, this form only applies to boson fields; the slight generalization required for fermion fields is given below.

‡ A space-like surface σ is defined by the property that any pair of space-time points x_{μ}, x'_{μ} on σ obey $(x_{\mu}-x'_{\mu})^2 > 0$.

Writing the variation principle in the form (25) assumes that the $\phi^\alpha(u)$ at two different points u, u' on any space-like surface σ commute. Physical measurements at points whose separation is space-like can be made without mutual interference, and for boson fields the amplitudes $\phi^\alpha(u)$ can in principle be measured; thus it is reasonable to write the variation in the form (25), confining the discussion to boson fields for the present.

Boson fields

The form of (25) shows that $\delta W(1,2)$ can only depend on variations in the field variables on σ_1 and σ_2. If we change the operators $\phi^\alpha(x)$ by the variable amount $\delta_0\phi^\alpha(x)$ at points in the region D between σ_1 and σ_2, we get the *operator* Lagrange equations (everywhere in D),

$$\partial_\mu\left(\frac{\partial\mathscr{L}}{\partial\phi^\alpha_\mu}\right)-\frac{\partial\mathscr{L}}{\partial\phi^\alpha}=0 \quad (\alpha=1,2,\ldots,n). \tag{27}$$

In deriving (27) we must be careful about the order of the field variables and $\delta_0\phi^\alpha(x)$. Varying the field amplitudes $\phi^\alpha(x)$ by $\delta_0\phi^\alpha(x)$ will change any function $\mathscr{G}\{\phi^\alpha(x),\phi^\beta_\mu(x)\}$ by $\delta\mathscr{G}$; the expression for $\delta\mathscr{G}$ will in general contain terms in which $\delta_0\phi^\alpha(x)$ is between other operators, as well as terms in which $\delta_0\phi^\alpha(x)$ is at the right- or left-hand side of the expression. In order to use $\delta\mathscr{G}$ effectively, it is necessary to be able to move the operators $\delta_0\phi^\alpha(x)$ to the right-hand side (or the left-hand side) of all terms. We make the *assumption* that this can be done, but we do not specify the relations (involving a change of order of $\delta_0\phi^\alpha(x)$ and other field operators associated with the same space-time point x) which make it possible to move $\delta_0\phi^\alpha(x)$ to the right or the left.

A method due to Schwinger† shows that the assumption just made implies that $\delta_0\phi^\alpha(x)$ commutes with any field variable at x. Let us for the moment regard $\phi^\alpha(x)$ as independent variables over the four-dimensional region D between σ_1 and σ_2, and for convenience of notation introduce the integral

$$G=\int\limits_D d^4x\,\mathscr{G}\{\phi^\alpha(x),\phi^\beta_\mu(x)\}.$$

$\mathscr{G}$ can be written as the sum of two Hermitian operators (apart from an unimportant factor i), so we only consider Hermitian $\mathscr{G}$. We shall *assume* that any *boson* field (e.g. the charged pion field) can be expressed in terms of Hermitian field variables $\phi^\alpha(x)$. We shall now use such variables up to eqn. (29).

† J. Schwinger, *Phys. Rev.* **91** (1953) 713.

Varying $\phi^\alpha(x)$ over D and moving $\delta_0\phi^\alpha$ to the right or to the left gives the equivalent expressions†

$$\delta G = \int\limits_D \left(\frac{\delta G}{\delta\phi^\alpha(x)}\right)_r \delta_0\phi^\alpha(x)\, d^4x = \int\limits_D \delta_0\phi^\alpha(x)\left(\frac{\delta G}{\delta\phi^\alpha(x)}\right)_l d^4x, \tag{28}$$

where $(\delta G/\delta\phi^\alpha)_r$ and $(\delta G/\delta\phi^\alpha)_l$ are the right-hand and left-hand functional derivatives, respectively. Because $\mathscr{G}$ is Hermitian and $\delta_0\phi^\alpha(x)$ are independent, taking the Hermitian conjugate of (28) shows that

$$\left(\frac{\delta G}{\delta\phi^\alpha(x)}\right)_l = \left(\frac{\delta G}{\delta\phi^\alpha(x)}\right)_r. \tag{29}$$

The restriction to Hermitian $\mathscr{G}$ may now be removed, so (29) holds for any function $\mathscr{G}$ of the field variables at x. Hence $\delta_0\phi^\alpha(x)$ commutes with any function of the original field variables at the same point x.

It is now clear that the covariant equations of motion can be written in the form (27).

The general variation $\delta W(1,2)$

The variation $\delta W(1,2)$ must be examined in more detail. In addition to a change $\delta_0\phi^\alpha(x)$ in the operator $\phi^\alpha(x)$ at each point, the domain D lying between σ_1 and σ_2 is subjected to a small rigid displacement $\delta x_\nu(x)$ (i.e. a rotation and a translation). Rigidity requires

$$\partial_\mu \delta x_\nu + \partial_\nu \delta x_\mu = 0.$$

This displacement is introduced to give the mechanical invariants of the system. Using $\delta_0\phi^\alpha_\mu = \partial_\mu(\delta_0\phi^\alpha)$, and integrating by parts, gives

$$\delta W(1,2) = \frac{1}{c}\int\limits_D d^4x\, \delta_0\phi^\alpha\left\{\frac{\partial\mathscr{L}}{\partial\phi^\alpha} - \partial_\mu\left(\frac{\partial\mathscr{L}}{\partial\phi^\alpha_\mu}\right)\right\} +$$
$$+\frac{1}{c}\int\limits_{(\sigma_1)}\left\{\frac{\partial\mathscr{L}}{\partial\phi^\alpha_\mu}\delta_0\phi^\alpha + \mathscr{L}\,\delta x_\mu\right\} d\sigma_\mu - \frac{1}{c}\int\limits_{(\sigma_2)}\left\{\frac{\partial\mathscr{L}}{\partial\phi^\alpha_\mu}\delta_0\phi^\alpha + \mathscr{L}\,\delta x_\mu\right\} d\sigma_\mu. \tag{30}$$

Here

$$d\sigma_\mu = \frac{1}{i}(dx_2\,dx_3\,dx_4,\; dx_3\,dx_4\,dx_1,\; dx_4\,dx_1\,dx_2,\; dx_1\,dx_2\,dx_3)$$

is the 4-vector element of area‡ of the space-like surface concerned.

The surface variation

The lack of dependence of $\delta W(1,2)$ on the four-volume D gives (27). The variation $\delta\phi^\alpha(x)$ on the surface σ is made up§ from the variation

† The summation convention holds for repeated field indices. ‡ $x_4 = ict$.

§ W. Pauli, *Rev. Mod. Phys.* **13** (1941) 203; J. Schwinger, *Phys. Rev.* **82** (1951) 914.

$\delta_0 \phi^\alpha(x)$ together with the change in $\phi^\alpha(x)$ due to the displacement $x \to x+\delta x$ of the surface. The equivalent coordinate transformation is

$$x'_\mu - x_\mu = -\delta x_\mu, \quad \text{with } \delta x_\mu = \epsilon_\mu - \epsilon_{\mu\nu} x_\nu, \tag{31}$$

where ϵ_μ, $\epsilon_{\mu\nu} = -\epsilon_{\nu\mu}$ are the parameters of the infinitesimal transformation. The coordinate rotation gives a (proper) Lorentz transformation of the field variables which can be written

$$\{\phi^\alpha(x')\}' - \phi^\alpha(x) = \frac{i}{\hbar} \tfrac{1}{2} \epsilon_{\mu\nu} S^{\alpha\beta}_{\mu\nu} \phi^\beta(x), \tag{32}$$

where the constant numbers $S^{\alpha\beta}_{\mu\nu}$ are determined by the transformation properties of the field. Thus we get the variation on the surface

$$\delta\phi^\alpha(x) = \delta_0 \phi(x) + \phi^\alpha_\mu(x)\,\delta x_\mu + \frac{i}{\hbar} \tfrac{1}{2} \epsilon_{\mu\nu} S^{\alpha\beta}_{\mu\nu} \phi^\beta(x). \tag{33}$$

Writing

$$\pi^\alpha_\mu = \frac{1}{c} \frac{\partial \mathscr{L}}{\partial \phi^\alpha_\mu}, \tag{34}$$

the variation (30) becomes

$$\delta W(1,2) = \int\limits_{(\sigma_1)} \left\{\pi^\alpha_\mu \delta\phi^\alpha + \frac{1}{c} T_{\mu\nu} \delta x_\nu\right\} d\sigma_\mu - \int\limits_{(\sigma_2)} \left\{\pi^\alpha_\mu \delta\phi^\alpha + \frac{1}{c} T_{\mu\nu} \delta x_\nu\right\} d\sigma_\mu. \tag{35}$$

The symmetric stress-energy-momentum tensor $T_{\mu\nu}$ is given by†

$$\left.\begin{aligned} \frac{1}{c} T_{\mu\nu} &= \frac{1}{c} \mathscr{L} \delta_{\mu\nu} - \pi^\alpha_\mu \phi^\alpha_\nu - \partial_\lambda f_{\lambda\mu\nu} \\ \text{where‡} \quad f_{\lambda\mu\nu} &= \frac{1}{2i} \{\pi^\alpha_\mu S^{\alpha\beta}_{\lambda\nu} \phi^\beta + \pi^\alpha_\nu S^{\alpha\beta}_{\lambda\mu} \phi^\beta + \pi^\alpha_\lambda S^{\alpha\beta}_{\nu\mu} \phi^\beta\} \end{aligned}\right\}. \tag{36}$$

The mechanical invariants

The mechanical invariants are given by displacements which leave the Lagrangian $\mathscr{L}$ invariant; such displacements leave W unaltered and give $\delta W(1,2) = 0$. Putting $\delta\phi^\alpha = 0$, and picking out the coefficient of ϵ_μ (eqn. (31)) we get the Lorentz covariant form of the energy-momentum operators which are independent of the particular surface σ,

$$\mathbf{P}_\nu = \frac{1}{c} \int\limits_{(\sigma)} d\sigma_\mu T_{\mu\nu} \quad (\nu = 1,2,3,4). \tag{37}$$

These four constants ($\mathbf{P}_k$, $\mathbf{P}_4 = i\mathbf{P}_0$) are the components of the total energy-momentum 4-vector for any space-like surface σ. For a plane

† The derivation of $T_{\mu\nu}$ was first given by F. J. Belinfante, *Physica*, **6** (1939) 887; L. Rosenfeld, *Mém. Acad. R. Belg.* **6** (1940) 30.

‡ The mean of both orderings of the operators is to be used if there is any ambiguity in (36).

surface normal to the time axis, $d\sigma_\mu = (0,0,0,-i)d^3\mathbf{x}$, and the constants become

$$(1/ic)\int d^3\mathbf{x}\, T_{4\nu}.$$

From (37), it follows that for any closed surface S

$$\int\limits_S d\sigma_\mu\, T_{\mu\nu} = 0,$$

provided $d\sigma_\mu$ points outward everywhere on S. Using Green's theorem, we get the differential form of the conservation law

$$\partial_\mu T_{\mu\nu} = 0. \tag{38}$$

It is easy to see by the usual methods that the translation properties of any function f of the field variables are given by

$$\partial_\mu f = \frac{i}{\hbar}[f, \mathbf{P}_\mu]. \tag{39}$$

The six rotation components arising from $\epsilon_{\mu\nu}$ in (35) give the components of angular momentum, which are the six constants of motion

$$\left.\begin{aligned} \mathbf{P}_{\mu\nu} &= \frac{1}{c}\int\limits_{(\sigma)} d\sigma_\lambda\, M_{\lambda\mu\nu} \\ \text{where}\qquad M_{\lambda\mu\nu} &= x_\mu T_{\lambda\nu} - x_\nu T_{\lambda\mu} \end{aligned}\right\}. \tag{40}$$

The differential form of (40) is

$$\partial_\lambda M_{\lambda\mu\nu} = 0.$$

Substituting for $M_{\lambda\mu\nu}$ and using (38), we have $T_{\mu\nu} = T_{\nu\mu}$. The symmetry of the stress-energy tensor $T_{\mu\nu}$ is thus a result of the conservation of the generalized angular momentum, whenever there are no external forces which can induce angular momentum.

Charge conservation

So far we have used those boundary variations δW which are induced by translations and rotations of the coordinate system, to obtain conservation laws from the second term $T_{\mu\nu}\,\delta x_\nu$ in the integrands of (35). The simplest variation of the first term $\pi^\alpha_\mu\,\delta\phi^\alpha$ is associated with what Pauli calls 'gauge invariance of the first kind'† for non-Hermitian field variables. A non-Hermitian field variable $\phi^\alpha(x)$ will always be associated with its Hermitian conjugate variable $\tilde{\phi}^\alpha(x)$, so that the Hermitian Lagrangian can be written in terms of ϕ^α, $\tilde{\phi}^\alpha$. Treating the variables ϕ^α and their Hermitian conjugates $\tilde{\phi}^\alpha$ as independent, π^α_μ, $\tilde{\pi}^\alpha_\mu$ are given by (34) and its Hermitian conjugate. The gauge transformation consists

† W. Pauli, *Phys. Rev.* **58** (1940) 716.

in multiplying all non-Hermitian ϕ^α, $\tilde{\pi}^\alpha$ by $e^{i\lambda}$, and all $\tilde{\phi}^\alpha$, π^α by $e^{-i\lambda}$ (λ is real); this transformation will leave the Lagrangian invariant.

The infinitesimal transformation with parameter $\delta\lambda$ may be written

$$\delta\phi^\alpha(x) = i\,\delta\lambda\,\phi^\alpha(x), \qquad \delta\tilde{\phi}^\alpha(x) = -i\,\delta\lambda\,\tilde{\phi}^\alpha(x). \tag{41}$$

On substituting in (35), we obtain the constant of motion

$$F(\sigma) = i\,\delta\lambda \int\limits_{(\sigma)} (\pi_\mu^{\alpha'}\phi^{\alpha'} - \tilde{\pi}_\mu^{\alpha'}\tilde{\phi}^{\alpha'})\,d\sigma_\mu,$$

where the index α' indicates that the sum is taken over the complex field variables only.

The constant of motion may be written

$$Q = \frac{1}{c}\int\limits_{(\sigma)} d\sigma_\mu\, j_\mu(x), \tag{42}$$

where

$$j_\mu(x) = \frac{iec}{\hbar}(\pi_\mu^{\alpha'}\phi^{\alpha'} - \tilde{\pi}_\mu^{\alpha'}\tilde{\phi}^{\alpha'}) \tag{43}$$

is the charge current 4-vector. Q is the total charge. The differential form of the conservation law (42) (obtained by using Green's theorem) is the charge-current conservation law

$$\partial_\mu\, j_\mu(x) = 0. \tag{44}$$

The expression (43) for $j_\mu(x)$ for a mixture of non-Hermitian fields is only fully determined (apart from one constant e) if there is interaction between the fields; otherwise there can be one arbitrary constant like e for each non-Hermitian field.

Field variations

We return to (35) and consider only the field amplitude variation $\delta\phi^\alpha$. The canonical momentum operator $\pi^\alpha(x)$ is defined by

$$\pi^\alpha = n_\mu\,\pi_\mu^\alpha = \frac{1}{c} n_\mu \frac{\partial\mathscr{L}}{\partial\phi_\mu^\alpha},$$

where n_μ is the unit future pointing normal on the space-like surface. The fundamental variation formula (35) becomes

$$\delta W(1,2) = F(\sigma_1) - F(\sigma_2),$$

where

$$F(\sigma) = \int\limits_{(\sigma)} \pi^\alpha \delta\phi^\alpha\, d^3u. \tag{45}$$

d^3u is the element of three-volume on the surface σ.

Using (25) we can write

$$\delta\langle\phi'_{\sigma_1},\sigma_1|\phi''_{\sigma_2},\sigma_2\rangle = \frac{i}{\hbar}\langle\phi'_{\sigma_1},\sigma_1|\{F(\sigma_1) - F(\sigma_2)\}|\phi''_{\sigma_2},\sigma_2\rangle. \tag{46}$$

This can be expressed as infinitesimal changes in any representatives $\langle\phi'_{\sigma_1},\sigma_1|\ \rangle$, $\langle\phi''_{\sigma_2},\sigma_2|\ \rangle$,

$$\left.\begin{aligned}\delta\langle\phi'_{\sigma_1},\sigma_1|\ \rangle &= \frac{i}{\hbar}\langle\phi'_{\sigma_1},\sigma_1|F(\sigma_1)|\ \rangle\\ \delta\langle\phi''_{\sigma_2},\sigma_2|\ \rangle &= \frac{i}{\hbar}\langle\phi''_{\sigma_2},\sigma_2|F(\sigma_2)|\ \rangle\end{aligned}\right\}. \tag{47}$$

Such a change in the representatives of any state must be due to a change in the dynamical variables on σ_1 and σ_2. The variables $\phi^{\alpha}_{\sigma}(u)$, describing the system on a space-like surface σ, may be replaced by another set of dynamical variables $\xi_{\sigma}(u)$ on σ, which will describe the system equally well, provided each ξ_{σ} is related to the ϕ_{σ} by a unitary transformation,

$$\xi_{\sigma}(u) = K(\sigma)\phi_{\sigma}(u)\{K(\sigma)\}^{-1}; \tag{48}$$

the operator $K(\sigma)$ is unitary. The eigenvectors $|\xi'_{\sigma},\sigma\rangle$ are related to the original eigenvectors $|\phi'_{\sigma},\sigma\rangle$ by

$$|\xi'_{\sigma},\sigma\rangle = K(\sigma)|\phi'_{\sigma},\sigma\rangle,$$

and the eigenvalues of the two sets of variables are identical. The representatives are related in the contragredient way,

$$\langle\xi'_{\sigma},\sigma|\ \rangle = \langle\phi'_{\sigma},\sigma|\{K(\sigma)\}^{-1}|\ \rangle. \tag{49}$$

Thus the infinitesimal unitary transformation,

$$K(\sigma) = 1-\frac{i}{\hbar}F(\sigma), \tag{50}$$

gives

$$\delta\langle\phi'_{\sigma},\sigma|\ \rangle = \frac{i}{\hbar}\langle\phi'_{\sigma},\sigma|F(\sigma)|\ \rangle \tag{51}$$

as in (47).

The canonical commutators

Keeping the space-like surface σ fixed, eqn. (45) gives

$$F_{\phi}(\sigma) = \int\limits_{(\sigma)} \pi^{\alpha}(u)\delta\phi^{\alpha}(u)\,d^3u, \tag{52}$$

and (51) becomes

$$\delta\langle\phi'_{\sigma},\sigma|\ \rangle = \frac{i}{\hbar}\langle\phi'_{\sigma},\sigma|\int d^3u\;\delta\phi'^{\alpha}(u)\pi^{\alpha}(u)|\ \rangle.$$

This is a functional equation,

$$\frac{\delta}{\delta\phi'^{\alpha}(u)}\langle\phi'_{\sigma},\sigma|\ \rangle = \frac{i}{\hbar}\langle\phi'_{\sigma},\sigma|\pi^{\alpha}(u)|\ \rangle. \tag{53}$$

Thus the representative of $\pi^{\alpha}(u)|\ \rangle$ is

$$\frac{\hbar}{i}\frac{\delta}{\delta\phi'^{\alpha}(u)}\langle\phi'_{\sigma},\sigma|\ \rangle.$$

From (53) it follows that

$$\langle\phi'_\sigma,\sigma|[\pi^\alpha(u),\phi^\beta(u')]|\,\rangle = \frac{\hbar}{i}\left(\frac{\delta}{\delta\phi'^\alpha(u)}\phi'^\beta(u')\right)\langle\phi'_\sigma,\sigma|\,\rangle;$$

hence

$$[\pi^\alpha(u),\phi^\beta(u')] = \frac{\hbar}{i}\delta_{\alpha\beta}\,\delta^{(3)}(u-u'). \tag{54}$$

Using (53) it is also very easy to see that the canonical momenta $\pi^\alpha(u)$, $\pi^\beta(u')$ commute at all points (u), (u') on the surface σ.

The canonical transformations are obtained by the addition of a term $c\partial_\mu g_\mu(\phi^\alpha,\phi^\beta_\nu)$ to the Lagrangian density $\mathscr{L}$, g_μ being a 4-vector. This leaves the action unaltered, and therefore does not affect the equations of motion, but it changes the surface variations, so that in (45) we have

$$F(\sigma)\to F(\sigma)+\delta\left[\int\limits_{(\sigma)} d\sigma_\mu\, g_\mu(\phi^\alpha,\phi^\beta_\nu)\right].$$

Thus the infinitesimal unitary transformation (51) can be altered. An example of some interest occurs when

$$g_\mu = -\pi^\alpha_\mu\,\phi^\alpha;$$

this gives

$$F(\sigma) = -\int\limits_{(\sigma)} \phi^\alpha\delta\pi^\alpha\, d^3u \tag{55}$$

instead of (52). As the order of $\delta\phi^\alpha$ and π^α in (52) does not matter, the order of $\delta\pi^\alpha$ and ϕ^α in (55) may be changed. Using (55) we could develop the theory in the π^α-representation.

Fermion fields

Schwinger† generalizes the fundamental variation principle (25) to the form

$$\delta\langle\xi'_{\sigma_1},\sigma_1|\xi''_{\sigma_2},\sigma_2\rangle = \frac{i}{\hbar}\langle\xi'_{\sigma_1},\sigma_1|\delta W(1,2)|\xi''_{\sigma_2},\sigma_2\rangle, \tag{56}$$

where ξ_{σ_1}, ξ_{σ_2} are any complete sets of commuting operators on the space-like surfaces σ_1 and σ_2 respectively. In applying (56) to fermion fields, the Lagrangian operator $\mathscr{L}$ is to be anti-symmetrized by replacing the product of each pair of fermion field amplitudes ϕ^α by half the *difference* of the two orderings. The covariant equations (27) are derived by *assuming* that $\delta\phi^\alpha(x)$ anti-commutes with all single fermion field operators at x.

The stress-energy tensor $T_{\mu\nu}$, the Hamiltonian H, and the current density j_μ are readily determined. The method shows† that the com-

† J. Schwinger, loc. cit.

mutators (54) should be replaced by the anti-commutators

$$[\phi^{\beta}(u'), \pi^{\alpha}(u)]_{+} = -\frac{\hbar}{i}\delta_{\alpha\beta}\,\delta^{(3)}(u-u'). \qquad (57)$$

3. Examples

(*a*) *Neutral pion field*

$$\mathscr{L} = -\tfrac{1}{2}c^2\{(\partial_\nu \phi)^2+\mu^2\phi^2\}. \qquad (58)$$

The canonical momentum is

$$\pi = \dot{\phi}.$$

$S^{\alpha\beta}_{\mu\nu}$ vanishes because $\phi(x)$ is a pseudo-scalar, and (36) gives

$$T_{\mu\nu} = \tfrac{1}{2}c\{(\partial_\mu \phi)(\partial_\nu \phi)+(\partial_\nu \phi)(\partial_\mu \phi)\}+\delta_{\mu\nu}\mathscr{L}. \qquad (59)$$

In particular the momentum operator **P** is

$$\mathbf{P}_k = \frac{1}{ic}\int T_{4k}\,d^3\mathbf{x} = -\tfrac{1}{2}\int \{\pi(\partial_k \phi)+(\partial_k \phi)\pi\}\,d^3\mathbf{x}. \qquad (60)$$

The angular momentum operator is

$$\mathbf{M} = -\tfrac{1}{2}\int d^3\mathbf{x}\,\{\pi(\mathbf{x}\times\operatorname{grad}\phi)+(\mathbf{x}\times\operatorname{grad}\phi)\pi\}. \qquad (61)$$

(*b*) *The Dirac field*

$$\mathscr{L} = -\hbar c\bar{\psi}(\gamma^\mu\partial_\mu \psi+\kappa\psi) \quad (\bar{\psi} = \tilde{\psi}\gamma^4), \qquad (62)$$

or, in a more symmetric form,

$$\mathscr{L} = -\tfrac{1}{2}\hbar c\bar{\psi}(\gamma^\mu\partial_\mu \psi+\kappa\psi)+\tfrac{1}{2}\hbar c\{(\partial_\mu \bar{\psi})\gamma^\mu-\kappa\bar{\psi}\}\psi. \qquad (63)$$

Expression (63) is Hermitian. By (36),

$$T_{\mu\nu} = \tfrac{1}{4}\hbar c\{\bar{\psi}\gamma^\mu\partial_\nu \psi+\bar{\psi}\gamma^\nu\partial_\mu \psi-(\partial_\nu \bar{\psi})\gamma^\mu\psi-(\partial_\mu \bar{\psi})\gamma^\nu\psi\}. \qquad (64)$$

Using Dirac's equation (3.3), $G_k = T_{4k}/ic$ is given by†

$$\mathbf{G} = (\hbar/2i)\{\tilde{\psi}\operatorname{grad}\psi-(\operatorname{grad}\tilde{\psi})\psi\}+(\hbar/4)\operatorname{curl}(\tilde{\psi}\boldsymbol{\sigma}'\psi).$$

The momentum operator is‡

$$\mathbf{P} = \frac{\hbar}{2i}\int d^3\mathbf{x}\,\{\tilde{\psi}(\operatorname{grad}\psi)-(\operatorname{grad}\tilde{\psi})\psi\}. \qquad (65)$$

The angular momentum operator

$$\mathbf{M} = \int d^3\mathbf{x}\,\mathbf{x}\times\mathbf{G}$$

can be written

$$\mathbf{M} = \mathbf{M}^0+\mathbf{M}^{\mathrm{sp}} \qquad (66)$$

† $\boldsymbol{\sigma}'$ is the 4×4 matrix (3.10) or (3.35).

‡ The integral of $\operatorname{curl}(\tilde{\psi}\boldsymbol{\sigma}'\psi)$ vanishes by the boundary conditions.

with (cf. (4.40), (4.41))

$$\left.\begin{aligned}\mathbf{M}^0 &= \tfrac{1}{2}\int d^3\mathbf{x}\,\{\tilde{\psi}(\mathbf{L}\psi)-(\mathbf{L}\tilde{\psi})\psi\}\\ \mathbf{M}^{\mathrm{sp}} &= \tfrac{1}{2}\hbar\int d^3\mathbf{x}\;\tilde{\psi}\boldsymbol{\sigma}'\psi\end{aligned}\right\}. \tag{67}$$

Here $\mathbf{L} = (\hbar/i)(\mathbf{x}\times\mathrm{grad})$.

4. Feynman's principle

Feynman's method† of developing the basic equations of quantum field theory is not so closely related to the original methods of Heisenberg and Pauli‡ as is the scheme due to Schwinger, and it requires more abstract mathematical ideas. However, the method is a powerful research tool and it leads almost directly to a number of valuable results.

Dirac pointed out§ that eqn. (14) may be written in terms of the transformation functions $\langle q'(k),t^{(k)}|q'(k-1),t^{(k-1)}\rangle$ connecting the eigenstates $|q'(k-1),t^{(k-1)}\rangle$ of the complete set of commuting variables $q(k-1)$ at time $t^{(k-1)}$, with the eigenstates $|q'(k),t^{(k)}\rangle$ of the set of commuting variables $q(k)$ at time $t^{(k)}$. Choosing $(n-1)$ intermediate times $t^{(k)}$ $(k = 1,2,\ldots,n-1)$, so that

$$t < t^{(1)} < t^{(2)} < \ldots < t^{(n-1)} < T,$$

we may write

$$\begin{aligned}\langle Q',T|q',t\rangle = \int\ldots\int \langle Q',T|q'(n-1),t^{(n-1)}\rangle\,dq'(n-1)\times\\ \times\langle q'(n-1),t^{(n-1)}|q'(n-2),t^{(n-2)}\rangle\ldots\times\\ \times\langle q'(2),t^{(2)}|q'(1),t^{(1)}\rangle\,dq'(1)\,\langle q'(1),t^{(1)}|q,t\rangle,\end{aligned} \tag{68}$$

where $\int\ldots dq'(k)$ denotes integration over the eigenvalues of the set $q(k)$. Eqn. (68) is just the repeated application of the basic formula for a change of representation in a quantum system. We assume that n is large and all the time intervals $(t^{(k)}-t^{(k-1)})$ are very small.

One-dimensional motion of a particle

It is necessary to examine the eqns. (15) to see whether they give a suitable expression for the operator W_0 to use in the substitution for

$$\begin{aligned}&\langle q'(k),t^{(k)}|q'(k-1),t^{(k-1)}\rangle\\ &\quad= \langle q'(k),t^{(k)}|\exp\left[\frac{i}{\hbar}W_0\{q(k),q(k-1);\,t^{(k)},t^{(k-1)}\}\right]|q'(k-1),t^{(k-1)}\rangle\end{aligned} \tag{69}$$

† R. P. Feynman, *Rev. Mod. Phys.* **20** (1948) 367–87 (for the non-relativistic case), and *Phys. Rev.* **80** (1950) 440–57, especially §§ 8, 9 (for the relativistic field treatment).

‡ W. Heisenberg and W. Pauli, *Z. Phys.* **56** (1929) 1; **59** (1930) 168.

§ P. A. M. Dirac, *Quantum Mechanics* (Clarendon Press, 2nd edn., 1935), eqn. (24), p. 125.

for small $(t^{(k)}-t^{(k-1)})$. It is useful to discuss, as an example, the single-particle problem having the Hamiltonian

$$H = \frac{p^2}{2m}+V(q),$$

where $V(q)$ is a function of the position operator q, and p is the momentum operator. The momentum and coordinate are $p(1)$, $q(1)$ at $t^{(1)}$, and $p(2)$, $q(2)$ at $t^{(2)}$, and $\tau = t^{(2)}-t^{(1)}$ is small. The simultaneous commutators are

$$[p(1),q(1)] = \hbar/i, \qquad [p(2),q(2)] = \hbar/i. \tag{70}$$

Remembering that H may be written in terms either of $p(1)$ and $q(1)$, or of $p(2)$ and $q(2)$, the equations of motion are

$$\dot{q}(1) = \frac{i}{\hbar}[H,q(1)] = \frac{1}{m}p(1),$$

$$\ddot{q}(1) = \frac{i}{\hbar}[H,\dot{q}(1)] = -\frac{1}{m}\frac{dV}{dq}(1), \quad \text{etc.}$$

Hence

$$\left.\begin{aligned} q(2) &= q(1)+\frac{\tau}{m}p(1)-\frac{\tau^2}{2m}\frac{dV}{dq}(1)+O(\tau^3) \\ q(1) &= q(2)-\frac{\tau}{m}p(2)-\frac{\tau^2}{2m}\frac{dV}{dq}(2)+O(\tau^3) \end{aligned}\right\}. \tag{71}$$

Eqns. (71) may be used to write the momenta in terms of the coordinates $q(1)$, $q(2)$. Ordering of operators can be done with the aid of the commutator

$$[q(2),q(1)] = \frac{\hbar}{i}\frac{\tau}{m}+O(\tau^3), \tag{72 a}$$

which follows directly from (70) and (71). Thus

$$\left.\begin{aligned} p(2) &= \frac{m}{\tau}\{q(2)-q(1)\}-\tfrac{1}{2}\tau\frac{dV}{dq}(2)+O(\tau^2) \\ p(1) &= \frac{m}{\tau}\{q(2)-q(1)\}+\tfrac{1}{2}\tau\frac{dV}{dq}(1)+O(\tau^2) \end{aligned}\right\}. \tag{72 b}$$

In terms of $q(1)$, $q(2)$, and τ, the first equation of (15),

$$\frac{\partial W_0}{\partial t^{(2)}} = -\frac{1}{2m}\{p(2)\}^2-V\{q(2)\},$$

becomes

$$\frac{\partial W_0}{\partial t^{(2)}} = -\frac{1}{2m}\left\{\frac{m^2}{\tau^2}[\{q(2)\}^2-2q(2)q(1)+\{q(1)\}^2]-m\frac{dV}{dq}(2)[q(2)-q(1)]\right\}+$$
$$+\frac{m}{2\tau^2}[q(1),q(2)]-V\{q(2)\}+O(\tau).$$

From the equations of motion and (71) we have

$$V\{q(2)\}-V\{q(1)\} = \frac{dV}{dq}(2)\,[q(2)-q(1)]+O(\tau^2)$$

and, with (72 a), this gives the ordered equation

$$\frac{\partial W_0}{\partial t^{(2)}} = -\frac{m}{2\tau^2}[\{q(2)\}^2-2q(2)q(1)+\{q(1)\}^2]-\tfrac{1}{2}[V\{q(1)\}+V\{q(2)\}]-\frac{\hbar}{2i\tau}+O(\tau). \tag{73}$$

Eqns. (15) also give

and

$$\left.\begin{aligned} \frac{\partial W_0}{\partial t^{(1)}} &= -\frac{\partial W_0}{\partial t^{(2)}} \\ \frac{\partial W_0}{\partial q(2)} &= p(2) \\ \frac{\partial W_0}{\partial q(1)} &= -p(1) \end{aligned}\right\}. \tag{74}$$

The integral of (73) and (74) is (using (72 b))

$$W_0 = \frac{m}{2\tau}[\{q(2)\}^2-2q(2)q(1)+\{q(1)\}^2]-\frac{\hbar}{2i}\log\tau-$$
$$-\tfrac{1}{2}\tau[V\{q(1)\}+V\{q(2)\}]+A+O(\tau^2), \tag{75}$$

where A is an arbitrary constant. Thus (14) gives

$$\langle q'(2),t^{(2)}|q'(1),t^{(1)}\rangle$$
$$= \frac{C}{\tau^{\frac{1}{2}}}\exp\left\{\frac{i}{\hbar}\left[\frac{m}{2\tau}\{q'(2)-q'(1)\}^2-\tfrac{1}{2}\tau[V\{q'(1)\}+V\{q'(2)\}]+O(\tau^2)\right]\right\}, \tag{76}$$

where C is a constant. The value of C is determined by the boundary condition

$$\lim_{\tau\to 0}\langle q'(2),t^{(2)}|q'(1),t^{(1)}\rangle = \delta\{q'(2)-q'(1)\}$$

and, as in (21), this gives

$$\langle q'(2),t^{(2)}|q'(1),t^{(1)}\rangle$$
$$= \left(\frac{m}{2\pi\hbar\tau}\right)^{\frac{1}{2}}e^{-\frac{1}{4}i\pi}\exp\left\{\frac{i}{\hbar}\left[\frac{m}{2\tau}\{q'(2)-q'(1)\}^2-\right.\right.$$
$$\left.\left.-\tfrac{1}{2}\tau[V\{q'(1)\}+V\{q'(2)\}]+O(\tau^2)\right]\right\}. \tag{77}$$

A simple calculation will verify that the transformation function (77) is unitary up to terms in the exponent which are proportional to τ.

The argument of the exponential in (77) is $(i/\hbar)$ times the action associated with the classical motion from $q(1)$ to $q(2)$; the velocity is given the constant value required to take the particle from $q(1)$ to $q(2)$ in time τ, and the potential energy is taken as the average of the initial and the final values.

Dividing the interval $T-t$ into a large number (n) of intervals of length τ and substituting (77) in (68) gives the transformation function which describes the quantum mechanical behaviour of the system:

$$\langle Q',T|q',t\rangle = \frac{1}{N}\int\limits_{(-\infty)}^{(\infty)}\!\!\cdots\!\!\int \exp\Big\{\frac{i}{\hbar}W\{Q',q'(n-1)\}\Big\}\,dq'(n-1)\times$$

$$\times\exp\Big\{\frac{i}{\hbar}W\{q'(n-1),q'(n-2)\}\Big\}\ldots dq'(1)\exp\Big\{\frac{i}{\hbar}W\{q'(1),q'\}\Big\}, \quad (78)$$

where

$$W\{q'(k),q'(k-1)\} = \frac{m}{2\tau}\{q'(k)-q'(k-1)\}^2-\tfrac{1}{2}\tau[V\{q'(k)\}+V\{q'(k-1)\}]. \quad (79)$$

In writing (78) it has been assumed that for sufficiently small values of τ the $O(\tau^2)$ terms in (77) are negligible. All the intermediate values $q'(k)$ $(k = 1,2,\ldots,n-1)$ of the coordinate are to be integrated over the infinite range $(-\infty,\infty)$; the normalizing factor N is given by

$$\frac{1}{N} = \Big(\frac{m}{2\pi\hbar\tau}\Big)^{\frac{1}{2}(n-1)}e^{-\frac{1}{4}i(n-1)\pi}. \quad (80)$$

Combining the exponential factors, eqn. (78) may be written

$$\langle Q',T|q',t\rangle = \frac{1}{N}\int\limits_{(-\infty)}^{(\infty)}\!\!\cdots\!\!\int\times$$

$$\times\exp\Big\{\frac{i}{\hbar}W\{Q',q'(n-1),\ldots,q'(k),\ldots,q'(1),q'\}\Big\}\,dq'(n-1)\ldots dq'(1), \quad (81)$$

where $W\{Q',q'(n-1),\ldots,q'(k),\ldots,q'(1),q\}$ is the *classical* action associated with the *path* from q' to Q' passing through $q'(1)$, $q'(2),\ldots$, $q'(k),\ldots$, $q'(n-1)$. This path is not an actual trajectory of the particle because the intermediate values $q'(k)$ are arbitrary.

Dirac has remarked† that by the action principle of classical mechanics (§ 1, eqn. (2)) $W\{Q',q'(n-1),\ldots,q'(k),\ldots,q'(1),q'\}$ is stationary for variations of the intermediate values $q'(k)$ about the actual classical trajectory; therefore, the principle of stationary phase shows that as $\hbar\to 0$ the only contribution to the integral in (81) comes from values of $q'(k)$ $(k = 1,2,\ldots,n-1)$ in the immediate neighbourhood of the classical trajectory. In this way (81) expresses the classical motion in the limit $\hbar\to 0$. The probability distribution for $q'(k)$ at some inter-

† See p. 437, n. §.

mediate time $t^{(k)}$ is zero, except for the value of $q'(k)$ corresponding to the Newtonian trajectory.

Integration over paths

Feynman generalizes (81), replacing the paths

$$q', q'(1),..., q'(k),..., q'(n-1), Q'$$

which are open polygons, by continuous curves† joining q' to Q'; this gives *Feynman's principle* for the quantum mechanical behaviour of a particle:

$$\langle Q', T|q', t\rangle = \frac{1}{\bar{N}} \int\limits_{(\text{paths } C(q',Q'))} d\Omega_c \exp\left\{\frac{i}{\hbar} W\{C(q', Q')\}\right\}. \quad (82)$$

$\bar{N}$ is a normalizing factor, $C(q', Q')$ is a path from q' to Q', and $W\{C(q', Q')\}$ is the *classical* action associated with that path. $W\{C(q',Q')\}$ may be calculated by integrating (79) over the infinitesimal time intervals τ which make up the interval $(T-t)$. $d\Omega_c$ is a suitably chosen measure (or weight function) for the paths, and we have now to discuss how this measure can be defined, and what set of paths is to be included in the integration.

There are obvious difficulties in defining the integral on the right of (82) if we try to include all possible paths $C(q', Q')$ joining q' at t to Q' at T. For this set of paths the values $q'(t')$ at each of the non-enumerable set of times t' $(t < t' < T)$ are arbitrary, and taking over the notation of (81), we write (82) as

$$\langle Q', T'|q', t'\rangle = \frac{1}{\bar{N}} \int\limits_{(\text{all } C(q',Q'))} \exp\left\{\frac{i}{\hbar} W\{Q', q'(t'), q'\}\right\} \prod_{t \leqslant t' \leqslant T} dq'(t'), \quad (83)$$

where $W\{Q', q'(t'), q'\}$ is the action associated with the path defined by $q'(t')$ $(t \leqslant t' \leqslant T)$. We do not know what meaning to attach to the formal expression (83) which implies a multiple integral in a non-enumerable number of dimensions; it is doubtful whether such an expression would be of any value to a physicist if its meaning were known.

The polygonal paths $(q', q'(1),..., q'(n-1), Q')$ used in (81) have discontinuous *velocities* $\dot{q}'(t')$ at $t' = t^{(k)}$ $(k = 1, 2,..., n-1)$, but such polygons can easily be approximated by continuous paths having continuous velocities, and it is easy to see (remembering (79)) that the effect of this approximation on the action may be made negligible. It is clear that

† A path can be visualized by plotting $q'(t')$ against t' for $t < t' < T$.

amongst the *paths* included in (83), those which have discontinuous velocities $\dot{q}'(t')$ for all t' $(t \leqslant t' \leqslant T)$ must be a large set; it is safe to assume that this set is not relevant to physics.

A set of paths, for which we expect to have suitable mathematical techniques, and which appears to be comprehensive enough for physical requirements, is given by

$$q'(t') = q'_0(t') + \sum_{n=0}^{\infty} a_n P_n(t'), \tag{84}$$

where a_n are constants and $P_n(t')$ form a set of independent normal orthogonal differentiable functions obeying

$$P_n(t) = P_n(T) = 0, \quad \text{for all } n; \tag{85}$$

also,†

$$q'_0(t') = \frac{1}{T-t}\{(T-t')q' + (t'-t)Q'\}.$$

For example,

$$P_n(t') = \frac{1}{n\pi}(2(T-t))^{\frac{1}{2}}\sin\{\omega_n(t'-t)\}, \qquad \omega_n = \frac{n\pi}{T-t} \quad (n = 1, 2, 3, \ldots)$$

is a suitable set of functions. Eqn. (84) may be regarded as giving a representation of $q'(t') - q'_0(t')$ on the Hilbert space defined by the set of functions $P_n(t)$.

The precise form of the fundamental equation (82) can now be derived from (81) by taking the limit $n \to \infty$, while keeping all the intervals $(t^{(k)} - t^{(k-1)})$ equal. It is convenient to replace $(n-1)$ in (81) by n; then, using (84), the variables of integration $q'(1), \ldots, q'(n)$ are to be replaced by $a_1, \ldots, a_n$. Thus,

$$\prod_{k=1}^{n} dq'(k) = \frac{\partial(q)}{\partial(a)} \prod_{k=1}^{n} da_1 \ldots da_n,$$

where $\partial(q)/\partial(a)$ is the Jacobian of the transformation, and is given by

$$\frac{\partial(q)}{\partial(a)} = \det\{P_j(t^{(k)})\} \quad (j, k = 1, 2, \ldots, n).$$

The Jacobian is independent of the a_k, and, in the limit $n \to \infty$, (81) becomes

$$\langle Q', T | q', t \rangle = \frac{1}{\overline{N}} \int_{(-\infty)}^{(\infty)} \!\!\cdots\!\! \int \exp\left\{\frac{i}{\hbar} W(a_1, a_2, \ldots)\right\} \prod_{k=1}^{\infty} da_k, \tag{86}$$

where $\overline{N}$ is to be determined (apart from a phase factor) by the unitary condition. The classical action W is now a function of the a_k. In

† Another natural choice for $q'(t')$ is the classical trajectory joining q' at t to Q' at T. With this choice $W(a_1, a_2, \ldots)$ of (86) is bilinear in the a_i $(i = 1, 2, \ldots)$ by the action principle; the classical trajectory is then obviously given in the limit $\hbar \to 0$.

practice, with a suitably chosen set $P_n(t')$, we may expect all but a finite number of the coefficients a_n to be unimportant.

An example

A simple example to illustrate (86) is the motion of a free particle for which we have already found the transformation function (21). Using (84),

$$L = \tfrac{1}{2}m(\dot{q}')^2 = \tfrac{1}{2}m\Big[(\dot{q}'_0)^2+2\sum_{n=0}^{\infty} a_n \dot{q}'_0 \dot{P}_n(t')+\Big\{\sum_{n=0}^{\infty} a_n \dot{P}_n(t')\Big\}^2\Big],$$

so
$$W(a) = \int_t^T L\,dt' = \tfrac{1}{2}m\Big\{(\dot{q}'_0)^2(T-t)+\sum_{n=0}^{\infty} a_n^2\Big\}. \tag{87}$$

Here we have used the particular form for $P_n(t')$ shown opposite, together with

$$\dot{q}'_0 = \frac{Q'-q'}{T-t}.$$

Substituting (87) in (86), the integration over each a_n gives a constant factor, so

$$\langle Q', T|q', t\rangle = C\exp\Big\{\frac{i}{\hbar}\frac{m}{2(T-t)}(Q'-q')^2\Big\}, \tag{88}$$

where C is to be determined by the unitary condition; this expression then becomes identical with (21). The integrals over a_n, viz.

$$\prod_{n=0}^{\infty}\int_{-\infty}^{\infty} da_n \exp\Big(\frac{i}{\hbar}\frac{m}{2}a_n^2\Big), \tag{89}$$

have to be evaluated with the aid of the convergence device as in (20). On making the integrations in (89) we get an infinite product which does not converge. A suitable definition of $\bar{N}$ in (86) removes this difficulty. Feynman has shown† how (81) or (82) may be used to describe the motion of a forced simple harmonic oscillator.

Feynman's principle for boson fields

Feynman's principle for quantizing boson fields‡ is obtained by generalizing (82). Using the notation of § 2, the transformation function required to describe the propagation of the field between the space-like surfaces σ_2 and σ_1 ($\sigma_2 < \sigma_1$) is $\langle\phi'_{\sigma_1}, \sigma_1|\phi'_{\sigma_2}, \sigma_2\rangle$. It is necessary to define a configuration C of the classical field variables§ $\phi^\alpha(x_\mu)$ in the

† R. P. Feynman, *Rev. Mod. Phys.* **20** (1948) 367 (especially § 13), and *Phys. Rev.* **80** (1950) 440 (§ 3).

‡ R. P. Feynman, *Phys. Rev.* **80** (1950) 440 (§§ 8, 9).

§ It is convenient in discussing Feynman's principle to use real (or Hermitian) field components $\phi^\alpha(x_\mu)$.

space-time region D between σ_1 and σ_2. To each point (x_μ) of this region we ascribe a value of each of the classical field amplitudes $\phi^\alpha(x_\mu)$, such that the set of values is continuous on passing from one point (x_μ) to another, and so that the values on σ_1 and σ_2 are the sets ϕ'_{σ_1} and ϕ'_{σ_2}, respectively. For each configuration C we can define a *classical* action $W(C)$, which is obtained by integrating the classical Lagrangian density $\mathscr{L}$ over the region D.

The generalization of (82) is

$$\langle\phi'_{\sigma_1},\sigma_1|\phi'_{\sigma_2},\sigma_2\rangle = \frac{1}{\bar{N}}\int\limits_{R_c} d\Omega_c \exp\Bigl\{\frac{i}{\hbar}W(C)\Bigr\}, \tag{90}$$

where $d\Omega_c$ is a suitably chosen measure (or weight) for summing over the configurations, and R_c is the set of configurations which is included in the summation. $\bar{N}$ is a normalizing constant, to be determined by the unitary condition on the transformation function. The set R_c and the measure $d\Omega_c$ are obtained by arguments similar to those applied to (82). It is unphysical to let R_c include configurations which have a large number of discontinuities in the derivatives and we assume that it is sufficient to use an expansion of the classical field variables analogous to (84),

$$\phi^\alpha(x_\mu) = \phi_0^\alpha(x_\mu)+\sum_{n=1}^{\infty} a_n P_n(x_\mu), \tag{91}$$

where $(P_n(x_\mu))$ forms a complete normal orthogonal set of functions in the region D, obeying the boundary conditions

$$P_n(\sigma_1) = P_n(\sigma_2) = 0.$$

$\phi_0^\alpha(x_\mu)$ is continuous and differentiable, and obeys the boundary conditions $\phi_0^\alpha(\sigma_1) = \phi'^\alpha_{\sigma_1}$, $\phi_0^\alpha(\sigma_2) = \phi'^\alpha_{\sigma_2}$.

The measure could be defined as

$$\prod_{(\text{all } x_\mu \text{ in } D)} \prod_\alpha d\phi^\alpha(x_\mu) \tag{92}$$

if that quantity existed; but it is easy to see, following the argument given above in the particle case, that on using the representation $(a_1, a_2, a_3,...)$ of the configuration C given by (91), we must replace (90) by

$$\langle\phi'_{\sigma_1},\sigma_1|\phi'_{\sigma_2},\sigma_2\rangle = \frac{1}{\bar{N}}\int\cdots\int \prod_{n=1}^{\infty} da_n . \exp\Bigl\{\frac{i}{\hbar}W(a_1,a_2,...)\Bigr\}. \tag{93}$$

$\bar{N}$ is the necessary normalizing constant, and the action has been expressed in terms of the coefficients a_n. In the form (93), Feynman's principle (90) has been given a precise meaning; this form is frequently used in calculations.

The sum over cells

It is also possible to replace (92) by an expression in which the field amplitudes appear explicitly. This is achieved by dividing the space-time region D into a large number of very small cells of equal volume. Limiting the configurations C occurring in R_c to those in which the classical field amplitudes $\phi^{\alpha}(x_\mu)$ vary very little *within* any cell, we may replace (92) by

$$\prod_{(i)} \prod_{(\alpha)} d\phi'^{\alpha}(i),$$

where $\phi^{\alpha}(i)$ denotes the field value in cell i, and $\prod_{(i)}$ is the product taken over all cells in D. With this notation (90) can be written

$$\langle \phi'_{\sigma_1}, \sigma_1 | \phi'_{\sigma_2}, \sigma_2 \rangle = \frac{1}{N'} \int_{R_c} \exp\left\{\frac{i}{\hbar} W(C)\right\} \prod_{(i)} \prod_{(\alpha)} d\phi'^{(\alpha)}(i). \tag{94}$$

N' is a normalizing constant, and $W(C)$ is the classical action associated with the configuration C.

The integral on the right of (94) is sometimes called a *functional integral*† because it results naturally from an attempt to replace the variables with respect to which an integration is made, by functions of these variables. Field amplitudes are functions of space-time points, so a sum over the configurations of the field requires a summation over a set of functions, one associated with each cell in D. There are obvious mathematical difficulties in the way of any attempt to extend the concept of functional integration as used in (94) to the limiting case in which the cells shrink to points x_μ; it is doubtful whether such an extension is desirable on physical grounds.

Normalizing factor and the unitary condition

The normalizing factor N' in (94) (or $\bar{N}$ in (93)) is independent of the initial and final values of the field amplitudes ϕ'_{σ_2} and ϕ'_{σ_1}, and depends only on the space-time domain D. This may be seen by the reasoning which led to (80). The transformation function $\langle \phi'_{\sigma_1}, \sigma_1 | \phi'_{\sigma_2}, \sigma_2 \rangle$ is to be expressed as an integrated product of transformation functions $\langle \phi'_{\sigma'}, \sigma' | \phi'_{\sigma}, \sigma \rangle$ relating to space-like surfaces σ' and σ which lie close together, as in (78). For boson fields which we are considering, the Lagrangian density is quadratic in the time derivatives of the field variables, so a simple extension of (79) gives the action between σ and σ'. The normalizing factor (80) is dependent on the *first* term in

† The idea of a 'functional integral' appears to have been first used explicitly by S. F. Edwards and R. E. Peierls, *Proc. Roy. Soc.* A, **224** (1954) 24.

(79), and a similar relation will hold in the field case—hence N' in (94) depends only on the domain D.

There is another (somewhat less precise) method of showing that N' is independent of the field variables. The unitary condition may be written

$$\int \langle \phi'_{\sigma_1}, \sigma_1 | \phi''_{\sigma_2}, \sigma_2 \rangle^* \, d\phi'_{\sigma_1} \langle \phi'_{\sigma_1}, \sigma_1 | \phi'_{\sigma_2}, \sigma_2 \rangle = \delta(\phi'_{\sigma_2} - \phi''_{\sigma_2}), \tag{95}$$

where $\int ... d\phi'_{\sigma_1}$ denotes integration over all the eigenvalues attached to three-dimensional cells on σ_1 and $\delta(\phi'_{\sigma_2} - \phi''_{\sigma_2})$ is a product of δ-functions, one for each field variable and each spatial cell on σ_2. Substituting (94) into (95), the product of the exponential terms gives

$$\exp\left\{\frac{i}{\hbar}\{W(C') - W(C'')\}\right\} = \exp\left\{\frac{i}{\hbar} W(C' - C'')\right\}, \tag{96}$$

where C' is a field configuration leading from ϕ'_{σ_2} to ϕ'_{σ_1}, and C'' a configuration leading from ϕ''_{σ_2} to ϕ'_{σ_1}; $(C' - C'')$ is the configuration leading from ϕ'_{σ_2} to ϕ''_{σ_2}, via ϕ'_{σ_1}. $(C' - C'')$ is not an actual trajectory. $W(C' - C'')$ must be made stationary against variations both in C' and C''; hence the exponential on the right of (96) oscillates, and will not give any large contributions when substituted in (95), except when $C' = C''$. It is only possible to have $C' = C''$ if $\phi'_{\sigma_2} = \phi''_{\sigma_2}$; hence we expect the substitution of (94) into (95) to give a multiple of a δ-function on the left of (95). N' is chosen to make this multiple unity.

The decomposition of the normalizing constant N' of (94) for subdivisions of the space-time region D is readily shown. The unitary condition (95)—on using the normal orthogonal property of the eigenvectors on σ_2, viz.

$$\langle \phi''_{\sigma_2}, \sigma_2 | \phi'_{\sigma_2}, \sigma_2 \rangle = \delta(\phi'_{\sigma_2} - \phi''_{\sigma_2}), \tag{97}$$

may be written

$$\int\limits_{(\sigma)} |\phi'_{\sigma}, \sigma\rangle \, d\phi'_{\sigma} \langle \phi'_{\sigma}, \sigma| = I. \tag{98}$$

Here I is the identity operator, and the index σ_1 has been replaced by σ to show the general validity of (98). In this equation the integral is taken over each field amplitude ϕ^α at each three-dimensional cell into which σ is divided; the grain of this subdivision into cells is to some extent arbitrary, but it should be such that variations of the field inside a cell may be ignored in practice. Choosing a space-like surface σ between σ_1 and σ_2, the region D is divided into two regions, the earlier and the later being called D_2 and D_1 respectively. The action $W(C)$ is then the sum of contributions $W(C_2)$ and $W(C_1)$ from these two regions, and those space-time cells of R_c (eqn. (94)) which are intersected by σ

may be replaced (for the purposes of the integration in (94)) by three-dimensional cells on σ. By (98),

$$\langle\phi'_{\sigma_1},\sigma_1|\phi'_{\sigma_2},\sigma_2\rangle = \int\limits_{(\sigma)} d\phi'_{\sigma}\langle\phi'_{\sigma_1},\sigma_1|\phi'_{\sigma},\sigma\rangle\langle\phi'_{\sigma},\sigma|\phi'_{\sigma_2},\sigma_2\rangle, \tag{99}$$

so if N'_1 and N'_2 are the normalizing factors associated with D_1 and D_2, we have

$$N' = N'_1 . N'_2. \tag{100}$$

Field operators

Feynman remarks† that the fundamental equation (90) leads directly to an expression for the matrix element of any functional F of the field amplitudes $\phi^{\alpha}(x_{\mu})$ in the region D. Let us consider first the operator $\phi^{\alpha}(x_{\mu})$ at some point x_{μ} in D; its matrix element in the mixed representation defined by the eigenvector sets $|\phi'_{\sigma_1},\sigma_1\rangle$, $|\phi'_{\sigma_2},\sigma_2\rangle$ may, with the help of (98), be written

$$\langle\phi'_{\sigma_1},\sigma_1|\phi^{\alpha}(x_{\mu})|\phi'_{\sigma_2},\sigma_2\rangle = \int\limits_{(\sigma)} d\phi'_{\sigma}\langle\phi'_{\sigma_1},\sigma_1|\phi^{\alpha}(x_{\mu})|\phi'_{\sigma},\sigma\rangle\langle\phi'_{\sigma},\sigma|\phi'_{\sigma_2},\sigma_2\rangle, \tag{101}$$

where x_{μ} lies on the surface σ. Because $\phi^{\alpha}(x_{\mu})|\phi'_{\sigma},\sigma\rangle = \phi'^{\alpha}(x_{\mu})|\phi'_{\sigma},\sigma\rangle$, where $\phi'^{\alpha}(x_{\mu})$ is an eigenvalue of the operator $\phi^{\alpha}(x_{\mu})$, the integral in (101) is identical with that in (99) except for the integration over the variable $\phi'^{\alpha}(x_{\mu})$. An argument almost identical with that showing how (99) was related to (94), enables us to write (101) as

$$\langle\phi'_{\sigma_1},\sigma_1|\phi^{\alpha}(x_{\mu})|\phi'_{\sigma_2},\sigma_2\rangle = \frac{1}{N'}\int\limits_{R_c} \phi'^{\alpha}(x_{\mu})\exp\left\{\frac{i}{\hbar}W(C)\right\}\prod_{(i)}\prod_{(\alpha)} d\phi'^{\alpha}(i). \tag{102}$$

The most general form of this equation is

$$\langle\phi'_{\sigma_1},\sigma_1|\phi^{\alpha}(x_{\mu})|\phi'_{\sigma_2},\sigma_2\rangle = \frac{1}{N}\int\limits_{R_c} d\Omega_c\,\phi'^{(\alpha)}(x_{\mu})\exp\left\{\frac{i}{\hbar}W(C)\right\}. \tag{103}$$

Eqn. (81) gave the transformation function as an expression which contained classical variables rather than operators; (103) does the same for the matrix elements of the operator $\phi^{\alpha}(x_{\mu})$.

The product of operators

Now we consider what happens when the product of two field amplitudes $\phi'^{\alpha}(x_{\mu})$, $\phi'^{\beta}(x'_{\mu})$ replaces $\phi'^{\alpha}(x_{\mu})$ in the integral in (102), viz.

$$\frac{1}{N'}\int\limits_{R_c} \phi'^{\alpha}(x_{\mu})\phi'^{\beta}(x'_{\mu})\exp\left\{\frac{i}{\hbar}W(C)\right\}\prod_{(i)}\prod_{(\alpha)} d\phi'^{\alpha}(i), \tag{104}$$

† R. P. Feynman, *Phys. Rev.* **80** (1950) 440, § 8.

where (x_μ) and (x'_μ) are both in the region D. If a space-like surface σ can be drawn through (x_μ) and (x'_μ), the argument from (101) to (102) can be retraced to show that (104) is the matrix element

$$\langle\phi'_{\sigma_1},\sigma_1|\phi^\alpha(x_\mu)\phi^\beta(x'_\mu)|\phi'_{\sigma_2},\sigma_2\rangle = \langle\phi'_{\sigma_1},\sigma_1|\phi^\beta(x'_\mu)\phi^\alpha(x_\mu)|\phi_{\sigma_2},\sigma_2\rangle. \quad (105)$$

The matrix element must in this case be independent of the order of the operators, because the order of the classical field variables in (104) is unimportant. The boson field variables should, therefore, commute when their separation is space-like. If x_μ is to the future of x'_μ, space-like surfaces σ and σ' are drawn through these points respectively. Dividing the integration in (104) into parts relating to the three space-time regions (σ_1,σ), (σ,σ'), (σ',σ_2) and using (100), the integral may be written

$$\int\limits_{(\sigma)} d\phi'_\sigma \int\limits_{(\sigma')} d\phi'_{\sigma'}\,\phi'^\alpha(x_\mu)\phi'^\beta(x'_\mu)\langle\phi'_{\sigma_1},\sigma_1|\phi'_\sigma,\sigma\rangle\langle\phi'_\sigma,\sigma|\phi'_{\sigma'},\sigma'\rangle\langle\phi'_{\sigma'},\sigma'|\phi'_{\sigma_2},\sigma_2\rangle$$
$$= \langle\phi'_{\sigma_1},\sigma_1|\phi^\alpha(x_\mu)\phi^\beta(x'_\mu)|\phi'_{\sigma_2},\sigma_2\rangle.$$

Thus in general we have

$$\langle\phi'_{\sigma_1},\sigma_1|T\{\phi^\alpha(x_\mu)\phi^\beta(x'_\mu)\}|\phi'_{\sigma_2},\sigma_2\rangle$$
$$= \frac{1}{N'}\int\limits_{R_c} \phi'^\alpha(x_\mu)\phi'^\beta(x'_\mu)\exp\left\{\frac{i}{\hbar}W(C)\right\}\prod_{(i)}\prod_{(\alpha)} d\phi^{(\alpha)}(i), \quad (106)$$

where T is the chronological operator† which arranges boson operators in temporal order with the latest to the left. It is obvious that if the points $(x_\mu^{(1)}),\ldots,(x_\mu^{(n)})$ lie in D, then, similarly,‡

$$\langle\phi'_{\sigma_1},\sigma_1|T\{\phi^{\alpha_1}(x_\mu^{(1)})\ \ldots\ \phi^{\alpha_n}(x_\mu^{(n)})\}|\phi'_{\sigma_2},\sigma_2\rangle$$
$$= \frac{1}{N'}\int\limits_{R_c} d\Omega_c\,\phi'^{\alpha_1}(x_\mu^{(1)})\ \ldots\ \phi'^{\alpha_n}(x_\mu^{(n)})\exp\left\{\frac{i}{\hbar}W(C)\right\}. \quad (107)$$

Derivatives

Eqn. (103) is linear in $\phi'^\alpha(x_\mu)$ and it may be used to give the matrix element of any derivative $\partial_\nu\phi^\alpha(x_\mu)$ of the operator $\phi^\alpha(x_\mu)$, thus

$$\langle\phi'_{\sigma_1},\sigma_1|\partial_\nu\phi^\alpha(x_\mu)|\phi'_{\sigma_2},\sigma_2\rangle = \frac{1}{N}\int\limits_{R_c} d\Omega_c\,\partial_\nu\phi'^\alpha(x_\mu)\exp\left\{\frac{i}{\hbar}W(C)\right\}. \quad (108)$$

In a similar way higher-order derivatives of the field amplitude operators, such as $\partial_\lambda\partial_\nu\phi^\alpha(x_\mu)$, are formed.

† See Chapter II, § 5, etc.

‡ A careful discussion of the Feynman principle is given by J. C. Polkinghorne, *Proc. Roy. Soc.* A, **230** (1955) 272.

The classical Lagrangian equations of motion of an important class of fields may be written

$$(\partial_\nu^2-\kappa_\alpha^2)\phi'^\alpha(x_\mu) = -s'^{(\alpha)}(x_\mu), \tag{109}$$

where κ_α are constants, and $s'^{(\alpha)}(x_\mu)$ is the product of several field amplitudes $\phi'^\beta(x_\mu)$ (the notation ϕ', s' is used to emphasize that these variables are not operators). Multiplying the left-hand side of (109) by $\exp\{(i/\hbar)W(C)\}$, and integrating over the configurations in R_c, eqns. (103), (107), and (108) show that the field operators also obey the equations

$$(\partial_\nu^2-\kappa_\alpha^2)\phi^\alpha(x_\mu) = -s^{(\alpha)}(x_\mu).$$

The canonical momentum

Polkinghorne has shown† that (94) can be used to derive the canonical momentum operator $\pi^\alpha(u)$. Taking (53) as the definition of $\pi^\alpha(u)$, then

$$\frac{\delta}{\delta\phi'^\alpha_{\sigma_1}(u_1)}\langle\phi'_{\sigma_1},\sigma_1|\phi'_{\sigma_2},\sigma_2\rangle = \frac{i}{\hbar}\langle\phi'_{\sigma_1},\sigma_1|\pi^\alpha(u_1)|\phi'_{\sigma_2},\sigma_2\rangle, \tag{110}$$

where u_1 is a point on σ_1. The functional derivative on the left is found by adding to the $\phi'^\alpha(x_\mu)$ values of each configuration C, a function $\xi(x_\mu)$ which vanishes on σ_2 and takes the value ξ' on σ_1. Assuming $\xi(x_\mu)$ is small, and varies slowly, the change in the action $W(C)$ associated with a configuration C is

$$W(C)\to W(C)+\frac{1}{c}\int\limits_D d^4x\left\{\frac{\partial\mathscr{L}}{\partial\phi'^\alpha}\xi(x_\mu)+\frac{\partial\mathscr{L}}{\partial\phi'^\alpha_\nu}\partial_\nu\,\xi(x_\mu)\right\},$$

where $\mathscr{L}$ is the classical Lagrangian density. Using the classical equations of motion, this becomes

$$W(C)\to W(C)+\frac{1}{c}\int\limits_{(\sigma_1)} d^3u_1\,\xi(u_1)n_\nu\frac{\partial\mathscr{L}}{\partial\phi'^\alpha_\nu}.$$

Considering only Lagrangian densities $\mathscr{L}$ such that the order of the operators in $(\partial\mathscr{L}/\partial\phi^\alpha_\nu)$ is unambiguous, and using (94), (107), and (108), the change in the transformation function may be written

$$\langle\phi'^\alpha_{\sigma_1}+\xi,\sigma_1|\phi'_{\sigma_2},\sigma_2\rangle-\langle\phi'_{\sigma_1},\sigma_1|\phi'_{\sigma_2},\sigma_2\rangle$$
$$= \frac{i}{\hbar c}\int\limits_{(\sigma_1)} d^3u_1\,\xi(u_1)\langle\phi'_{\sigma_1},\sigma_1|n_\nu\frac{\partial\mathscr{L}}{\partial\phi^\alpha_\nu}|\phi'_{\sigma_2},\sigma_2\rangle.$$

Now, by (110), we have the operator relation

$$\pi^\alpha(u) = \frac{1}{c}n_\nu\frac{\partial\mathscr{L}}{\partial\phi^\alpha_\nu(u)} \tag{111}$$

as in § 2.

† J. Polkinghorne, loc. cit.

The definition of π^{α} by (110) leads immediately to the canonical commutation relations (54) between the field amplitudes and the canonical momenta for boson fields. This completes the basic formalism of the Feynman principle for boson fields.

Evaluation of propagators

We give a simple example which shows how the method is applied.† We evaluate the propagator (106) for a neutral pion field having the Lagrangian (58). The field amplitude $\phi(x_{\mu})$ is expanded (cf. (91)) thus:

$$\phi(x_{\mu}) = \sum_{n} a_n \phi_n(x_{\mu}), \tag{112}$$

where the set of functions $\phi_n(x)$ are Green's functions which for some arbitrary y obey‡

$$\tfrac{1}{2}\phi_n(y)\left(\frac{\partial^2}{\partial x_{\nu}^2} - \mu^2 + i\epsilon\right)\phi_n(x) = -\delta^4(x-y) \tag{113}$$

and $$\tfrac{1}{2}\int d^4x\,\{(\partial_{\nu}\phi_m)(\partial_{\nu}\phi_n) + (\mu^2 - i\epsilon)\phi_m\phi_n\} = \delta_{mn}. \tag{114}$$

ϵ is a small positive constant which is introduced to give convergence in the action integral. This normalization implies that in (93) (with $\hbar = c = 1$)

$$\exp\{iW(a_1, a_2, ...)\} = \exp\left(-i\sum_{n} a_n^2\right).$$

The integral (106) gives the vacuum expectation value when (112) is substituted; this is because (112) only allows fluctuations about zero mean field. Thus

$$\langle 0|T\{\phi(x_{\mu})\phi(y_{\mu})\}|0\rangle = \frac{\sum_{n,m} \phi_n(x_{\mu})\phi_m(y_{\mu}) \int_{-\infty}^{\infty} a_n a_m \exp(-i\sum_{s} a_s^2) \prod_{j} da_j}{\prod_{j} \int \exp(-ia_j^2)\, da_j}$$

$$= (-\tfrac{1}{2}i)\sum_{n} \phi_n(x_{\mu})\phi_n(y_{\mu}). \tag{115}$$

Applying the operator $(-\partial_{x_{\nu}}^2 + \mu^2 - i\epsilon)$ to (115) and using (113), it is easy to verify that the propagator $\langle 0|T\{\phi(x_{\mu})\phi(y_{\mu})\}|0\rangle$ defined in this way agrees with (2.61).

Non-trivial applications of Feynman's functional integration to pions interacting with a nucleon source have been given by Edwards and Peierls.§

The application of the functional integration method to fermion

† P. T. Matthews and A. Salam, *Nuovo Cim.* **2** (1955) 120.

‡ S. F. Edwards, *Phil. Mag.* **47** (1954) 758.

§ S. F. Edwards and R. E. Peierls, *Proc. Roy. Soc.* A, **224** (1954) 24; S. F. Edwards, *Suppl. Nuovo Cim.* **2** (1956) 711.

fields† is complicated by the anti-commuting character of the field amplitudes; the interpretation of the method encounters considerable difficulties in this case.‡

† K. Symanzik, *Z. Naturforsch.* **9a** (1954) 809; P. T. Matthews and A. Salam, loc. cit.

‡ D. J. Candlin, *Nuovo Cim.* **4** (1956) 231; W. K. Burton and A. H. de Borde, ibid. 254.

APPENDIX

GREEN'S FUNCTIONS AND INVARIANT FUNCTIONS

WE give the various Green's functions and invariant functions which are used in solving the field equations. The notation is Lorentz invariant; as usual $x \equiv x_\mu = (\mathbf{x}, x_4)$ with $x_4 = ix_0 = ict$, and $d^4x = d^3\mathbf{x}dx_0$. We start with the electromagnetic case.

Electromagnetic field

This field may be described by the four-potential $A_\mu = (\mathbf{A}, A_4)$ with $A_4 = i\phi$. These potentials obey

$$\partial_\mu^2 A_\nu = -\frac{1}{c}j_\nu, \tag{A.1}$$

where j_ν ($j_4 = ic\rho$) is the four-current which is the source of the field. Here rational units are used, so that the electric field intensity near a point charge e placed at $\mathbf{x} = 0$ is $e/4\pi\mathbf{x}^2$, and $e^2/4\pi\hbar c = 137{\cdot}04$. A typical member of eqns. (A.1) is

$$\partial_\mu^2 \phi(x_\nu) = -\rho(x_\nu). \tag{A.2}$$

If ρ is independent of time, i.e. $\rho = \rho(\mathbf{x})$, a solution of (A.2) is given by the electrostatic potential

$$\phi(\mathbf{x}, t) = \frac{1}{4\pi}\int_{-\infty}^{\infty} d^3\mathbf{x}'\frac{\rho(\mathbf{x}')}{|\mathbf{x}-\mathbf{x}'|}. \tag{A.3}$$

For $\rho(x_\nu)$ varying with time, the best known solution of (A.2) is the *retarded potential*

$$\phi_{\text{ret}}(\mathbf{x}, t) = \frac{1}{4\pi}\int_{-\infty}^{\infty} d^3\mathbf{x}'\frac{\rho\{\mathbf{x}', t'=t-(1/c)|\mathbf{x}-\mathbf{x}'|\}}{|\mathbf{x}-\mathbf{x}'|}. \tag{A.4}$$

The physical meaning of the retarded potential is that a change in the value of ρ at $\mathbf{x}'$ can only affect the value of ϕ_{ret} at $\mathbf{x}$ at a time $(1/c)|\mathbf{x}-\mathbf{x}'|$ later. Writing (A.4) as an integral over all space time gives

$$\phi_{\text{ret}}(x) = \int_{-\infty}^{\infty} d^4x'\,D_{\text{ret}}(x-x')\rho(x'), \tag{A.5}$$

where

$$D_{\text{ret}}(x) = \frac{1}{4\pi|\mathbf{x}|}\delta(x_0-|\mathbf{x}|). \tag{A.6}$$

The function $D_{\text{ret}}(x)$ is called the retarded Green's function for the electromagnetic field.

Now we prove that the retarded Green's function obeys the equation

$$\partial_\mu^2 D_{\text{ret}}(x) = -\delta^4(x), \tag{A.7}$$

where $\delta^4(x) = \delta^3(\mathbf{x})\delta(x_0)$. It is easy to see that any function of the form $\phi = \frac{1}{|\mathbf{x}|}f(x_0-|\mathbf{x}|)$ obeys

$$\partial_\mu^2 \phi(x) = 0, \tag{A.8}$$

except possibly at $x_\mu = 0$. The behaviour of $\partial_\mu^2 D_{\text{ret}}$ at the origin can be found by integrating this function over any space-time volume V which contains the origin. Green's theorem applied to this integral gives

$$\int\limits_V \partial_\mu^2 D_{\text{ret}}(x)\, d^4x = \int\limits_S n_\mu \partial_\mu D_{\text{ret}}\, d\sigma, \tag{A.9}$$

where S is the three-dimensional boundary, n_μ its unit outward normal, and $d\sigma$ its element of volume. S may be chosen to consist of the two time planes $\pm x_0$ $(x_0 > 0)$, together with any surface joining these planes and lying in the region $x_\mu^2 > 0$. By (A.6), $\partial_\mu D_{\text{ret}}$ vanishes on each of these surfaces except the plane $+x_0$. On this plane $n_\mu = (0,0,0,-i)$, $d\sigma = d^3\mathbf{x}$, and

$$n_\mu \partial_\mu D_{\text{ret}}(x) = -\frac{1}{4\pi|\mathbf{x}|}\delta'(x_0-|\mathbf{x}|).$$

The surface integral to the right of (A.9) thus reduces to

$$-\int\limits_0^\infty 4\pi\mathbf{x}^2\, d|\mathbf{x}|\, \frac{1}{4\pi|\mathbf{x}|}\delta'(x_0-|\mathbf{x}|) = -1 \quad (x_0 > 0);$$

this completes the proof of (A.7). Operating on both sides of (A.5) with ∂_μ^2, it is obvious that $\phi_{\text{ret}}(x)$ obeys (A.2).

The differential operator ∂_μ^2 occurring in (A.2) is unaltered by exchanging past and future $(x_4 \to -x_4)$, so, as well as the retarded solution, there is also an advanced potential

$$\phi_{\text{adv}}(\mathbf{x},t) = \frac{1}{4\pi}\int\limits_{-\infty}^{\infty} d^3\mathbf{x}'\frac{\rho\{\mathbf{x}',t'=t+(1/c)|\mathbf{x}-\mathbf{x}'|\}}{|\mathbf{x}-\mathbf{x}'|}$$

$$= \int\limits_{-\infty}^{\infty} d^4x'\, D_{\text{adv}}(x-x')\rho(x'), \tag{A.10}$$

where
$$D_{\text{adv}}(x) = \frac{1}{4\pi|\mathbf{x}|}\delta(x_0+|\mathbf{x}|). \tag{A.11}$$

It is obvious that $D_{\text{adv}}(x)$ obeys (A.7). The important distinction between

ϕ_{ret} and ϕ_{adv} lies in the boundary conditions they satisfy. If $\rho(x)$ vanishes outside a finite region of space time, $\phi_{\text{ret}}(x)$ vanishes as $t \to -\infty$, while $\phi_{\text{adv}}(x)$ vanishes as $t \to +\infty$. $\phi_{\text{ret}}(x)$ is looked on as the field *produced* by the source $\rho(x)$; about $\phi_{\text{adv}}(x)$ we can only say that it is a solution so chosen that it vanishes ultimately. This possibility of choosing solutions of (A.2) to obey various boundary conditions exists because from any solution of (A.2) we may obtain another by adding a solution of the homogeneous equation (A.8).

It follows that the difference $(\phi_{\text{adv}}(x)-\phi_{\text{ret}}(x))$ is a solution of (A.8), and the corresponding function† $D(x)$, given by

$$D(x) = D_{\text{adv}}(x)-D_{\text{ret}}(x), \tag{A.12}$$

obeys

$$\partial_\mu^2 D(x) = 0. \tag{A.13}$$

The functions D_{ret}, D_{adv}, D will now be written in explicitly Lorentz invariant forms. Using the relation‡

$$\delta(x_\mu^2) = \delta(x_0^2-\mathbf{x}^2) = \frac{1}{2|\mathbf{x}|}\{\delta(x_0-|\mathbf{x}|)+\delta(x_0+|\mathbf{x}|)\}, \tag{A.14}$$

and introducing the step function

$$\theta(x) = \begin{cases} 1 & (x_0 > 0), \\ 0 & (x_0 < 0), \end{cases} \tag{A.15}$$

it follows from (A.6) and (A.11) that

$$\left.\begin{aligned} D_{\text{ret}}(x) &= \frac{1}{2\pi}\theta(x)\delta(x_\mu^2) \\ D_{\text{adv}}(x) &= \frac{1}{2\pi}\theta(-x)\delta(x_\mu^2) \end{aligned}\right\}. \tag{A.16}$$

$\theta(x)$ is not an invariant, but when it is multiplied into any function which vanishes for $x_\mu^2 > 0$, the product is invariant under *proper* Lorentz transformations; thus (A.16) shows the invariant character of D_{ret} and D_{adv}. Further, introducing

$$\epsilon(x) = \begin{cases} 1 & (x_0 > 0), \\ -1 & (x_0 < 0), \end{cases} \tag{A.17}$$

we have $\epsilon(x) = \theta(x)-\theta(-x)$, and (A.12) gives

$$D(x) = -\frac{1}{2\pi}\epsilon(x)\delta(x_\mu^2), \tag{A.18}$$

which is again obviously invariant.

† $D(x)$ is *not* a Green's function; it satisfies (A.13), *not* (A.7).

‡ P. A. M. Dirac, *Principles of Quantum Mechanics* (Clarendon Press, 3rd edn., 1947), ch. 4.

The general solution of the eqn. (A.1) for the electromagnetic potentials can now be written

$$A_\mu(x) = A_\mu^{\text{in}}(x) + \frac{1}{c}\int_{-\infty}^{\infty} d^4x'\, D_{\text{ret}}(x-x')j_\mu(x'), \tag{A.19}$$

where $A_\mu^{\text{in}}(x)$ is any solution of the homogeneous equation

$$\partial_\nu^2 A_\mu^{\text{in}}(x) = 0. \tag{A.20}$$

A_μ^{in} is the *incoming* wave and, if j_μ vanishes outside a finite region of space time, then $A_\mu(x) \to A_\mu^{\text{in}}(x)$ as $t \to -\infty$. Corresponding to (A.19), the advanced Green's function solution is

$$A_\mu(x) = A_\mu^{\text{out}}(x) + \frac{1}{c}\int_{-\infty}^{\infty} d^4x'\, D_{\text{adv}}(x-x')j_\mu(x'), \tag{A.21}$$

where $A_\mu^{\text{out}}(x)$ satisfies (A.20). Under the same condition on j_μ, we have $A_\mu(x) \to A_\mu^{\text{out}}(x)$ as $t \to +\infty$.

As well as (A.1), the electromagnetic potentials A_μ will be subject to the Lorentz condition

$$\partial_\mu A_\mu(x) = 0. \tag{A.22}$$

This requires that

$$\partial_\mu A_\mu^{\text{in}}(x) = 0. \tag{A.23}$$

We use (A.19). If j_μ vanishes outside a finite region of space time, we have

$$\partial_{x_\mu} \int_{-\infty}^{\infty} d^4x'\, D_{\text{ret}}(x-x')j_\mu(x') = \int_{-\infty}^{\infty} d^4x'\, D_{\text{ret}}(x-x')\partial_\mu\, j_\mu(x').$$

The conservation law for charge and current

$$\partial_\mu j_\mu = 0$$

then implies (A.23). Eqns. (A.19) and (A.21) may be used, on eliminating $A_\mu(x)$, to describe the scattering of an incoming electromagnetic wave $A_\mu^{\text{in}}(x)$ by a known distribution of charge and current $j_\mu(x)$, to give an outgoing electromagnetic wave $A_\mu^{\text{out}}(x)$.

There are two other Green's functions which are important in field theory. A function $\bar{D}(x)$ which is symmetric between past and future can be formed from the advanced and retarded potentials,

$$\begin{aligned}\bar{D}(x) &= \tfrac{1}{2}\{D_{\text{adv}}(x)+D_{\text{ret}}(x)\} \\ &= \frac{1}{4\pi}\{\theta(x)+\theta(-x)\}\delta(x_\mu^2) = \frac{1}{4\pi}\delta(x_\mu^2).\end{aligned} \tag{A.24}$$

This function will be important when the time direction does not matter.

The other Green's function is the Feynman function $D_F(x)$ which appears in calculations of scattering matrix elements. For $x_0 > 0$ and $x_0 < 0$ it is respectively equal to the positive and negative frequency functions $2iD^{(+)}(x)$ and $-2iD^{(-)}(x)$, where $D(x)$ is given by (A.12).† The positive and negative frequency components of field operators respectively destroy and create particles (cf. Chapters II and IV). The function $D_F(x-x')$ is associated with the creation of particles at an earlier time x_0', and their destruction at a later time x_0. As was seen in Chapter II, §§ 5, 11, and Chapter IV, § 4, Green's functions of this type describe the *causal* propagation of disturbances in quantized fields.

Frequency splitting

Before deriving $D_F(x)$ we must examine the splitting of a field variable, or operator, into positive and negative frequency Fourier components. We consider $A_\mu(x)$; the positive and negative frequency components $A_\mu^{(+)}(x)$, $A_\mu^{(-)}(x)$ are given by

$$A_\mu(x) = A_\mu^{(+)}(x)+A_\mu^{(-)}(x), \tag{A.25}$$

where

$$\left.\begin{aligned} A_\mu^{(+)}(x) &= \int\limits_0^\infty d\omega\, \mathscr{A}_\mu(\mathbf{x},\omega)e^{-i\omega x_0} \\ A_\mu^{(-)}(x) &= \int\limits_{-\infty}^0 d\omega\, \mathscr{A}_\mu(\mathbf{x},\omega)e^{-i\omega x_0} \end{aligned}\right\}. \tag{A.26}$$

It is necessary to find conditions for frequency splitting to be unique (i.e. Lorentz invariant) and complete. If a matrix element of $A_\mu(x)$ describes the destruction of a photon in one Lorentz frame of reference, it must describe the destruction of a photon (of different frequency and momentum) in any other Lorentz frame; thus if $A_\mu(x)$ transforms into $A'_\mu(x)$ under any proper Lorentz transformation, $A_\mu^{(+)}(x)$ must transform into the positive frequency part $A_\mu'^{(+)}(x)$ of $A'_\mu(x)$.

Schwinger‡ has discussed the required conditions. We consider, for example, *any* invariant function $\phi(x_\mu)$, and define $\phi^{(+)}(x_\mu)$ by

$$\phi^{(+)}(x_\mu) = \frac{1}{2\pi i}\int\limits_{C_+} \frac{d\tau}{\tau}\phi(x_\mu-\tau\epsilon_\mu), \tag{A.27}$$

where C_+ is a contour in the complex τ plane running from $-\infty$ to $+\infty$ along the real axis, avoiding the origin by going around a small semicircle underneath it (Fig. 48). ϵ_μ is a future-pointing time-like vector ($\epsilon_\mu^2 < 0$, $\epsilon_0 > 0$).

† This is an invariant statement because for $x_\mu^2 > 0$, $D^{(+)}(x)+D^{(-)}(x) = 0$.
‡ J. Schwinger, *Phys. Rev.* **74** (1948) 1492.

Suppose a Fourier analysis of the space and time components of $\phi(x_\mu)$ gives

$$\phi(x_\mu) = \int_{-\infty}^{\infty} d^4k\, a(k_\mu)e^{ik_\mu x_\mu}, \tag{A.28}$$

where k_μ $(\mu = 1,2,3,4)$ denotes the four Fourier variables, with $k_4 = ik_0$ and $d^4k = d^3\mathbf{k}dk_0$; then, by (A.27),

$$\phi^{(+)}(x_\mu) = \frac{1}{2\pi i}\int_{-\infty}^{\infty} d^4k\, a(k_\mu)e^{ik_\mu x_\mu}\int_{C_+} e^{-i\tau k_\mu \epsilon_\mu}\frac{d\tau}{\tau}. \tag{A.29}$$

The integral over τ in (A.29) can be evaluated by closing the contour

FIG. 48. The contour C_+.

C_+ by an infinite semicircle in the τ plane. For $k_\mu \epsilon_\mu > 0$ this semicircle is in the lower half-plane, and for $k_\mu \epsilon_\mu < 0$ it is in the upper half-plane. Thus,

$$\frac{1}{2\pi i}\int_{C_+} e^{-i\tau k_\mu \epsilon_\mu}\frac{d\tau}{\tau} = \begin{cases} 0 & (k_\mu \epsilon_\mu > 0), \\ 1 & (k_\mu \epsilon_\mu < 0). \end{cases} \tag{A.30}$$

It follows that in any particular Lorentz frame we can find the positive frequency part (and similarly the negative frequency part) of a function $\phi(x_\mu)$ by using (A.27). For the frequency splitting to be unique (i.e. independent of any particular Lorentz frame), we require $k_\mu \epsilon_\mu$ to preserve its sign under Lorentz transformations. It is necessary that in the Fourier expansion of $\phi(x_\mu)$ (eqn. (A.28)), no terms should appear for which $k_\mu^2 > 0$. This gives an invariant sign of k_0 and of

$$k_\mu \epsilon_\mu = -k_0 \epsilon_0\left(1 - \frac{\mathbf{k}.\boldsymbol{\epsilon}}{k_0 \epsilon_0}\right)$$

(because the only restriction on ϵ_μ is $|\boldsymbol{\epsilon}| < \epsilon_0$). In this discussion it does not matter whether $\phi(x_\mu)$ is an invariant or a spinor, a vector or a tensor.

The negative frequency part of $\phi(x_\mu)$ is given by

$$\phi^{(-)}(x_\mu) = \frac{1}{2\pi i}\int_{C_+} \frac{d\tau}{\tau}\phi(x_\mu + \tau\epsilon_\mu). \tag{A.31}$$

Hence, completeness:

$$\phi(x_\mu) = \phi^{(+)}(x_\mu) + \phi^{(-)}(x_\mu).$$

In analysing the potentials of electromagnetic waves, only $a(k_\mu)$ (in (A. 28)) with $k_\mu^2 = 0$ occur, while for free meson waves only $a(k_\mu)$ with

$k_\mu^2+\kappa^2 = 0$ (κ real) will occur. Therefore the interaction representation operators† for these fields can be split uniquely into positive and negative frequency components. The same holds for $D(x)$ (and $D^{(1)}(x)$).

Although $D_{\text{ret}}(x)$ and $D_{\text{adv}}(x)$ do not have unique positive and negative frequency parts, we could choose any reference frame and define the Green's function $D_F(x)$ by‡

$$D_F(x) = \frac{2}{i}\{D_{\text{ret}}^{(+)}(x)+D_{\text{adv}}^{(-)}(x)\}. \tag{A.32}$$

Remembering the definitions (A.6) and (A.11), it is clear that because x_0 only appears in the δ-functions, we have

$$D_{\text{ret}}^{(+)}(x) = \frac{1}{4\pi|\mathbf{x}|}\delta^{(+)}(x_0-|\mathbf{x}|), \quad D_{\text{adv}}^{(-)}(x) = \frac{1}{4\pi|\mathbf{x}|}\delta^{(-)}(x_0+|\mathbf{x}|). \tag{A.33}$$

As the frequency splitting relates to a particular frame of reference it is not Lorentz invariant. However, it is easy to see from (A.37) that the *sum* of $D_{\text{ret}}^{(+)}(x)$ and $D_{\text{adv}}^{(-)}(x)$ (and therefore $D_F(x)$) is invariant.

The functions $\delta^{(+)}$, $\delta^{(-)}$

Using the integral representation§ for the δ-function

$$\delta(a) = \frac{1}{2\pi}\int\limits_{-\infty}^{\infty} e^{-ias}\,ds, \tag{A.34}$$

it is clear that because of the way in which x_0 appears in (A.33), we must write

$$\delta^{(+)}(a) = \frac{1}{2\pi}\int\limits_{0}^{\infty} e^{-ias}\,ds, \qquad \delta^{(-)}(a) = \frac{1}{2\pi}\int\limits_{-\infty}^{0} e^{-ias}\,ds. \tag{A.35}$$

Eqns. (A.35) will now be used to define functions $\delta^{(+)}(a)$ and $\delta^{(-)}(a)$ for any real a. We have

$$\delta^{(+)}(a)+\delta^{(-)}(a) = \delta(a),$$

$$\delta^{(+)}(a)-\delta^{(-)}(a) = \lim_{\lambda\to+0}\frac{1}{2\pi i}\left(\frac{1}{a+i\lambda}+\frac{1}{a-i\lambda}\right). \tag{A.36}$$

Thus
$$\delta^{(\pm)}(a) = \tfrac{1}{2}\delta(a)\pm\frac{1}{2\pi i a}. \tag{A.37}$$

From (A.36) it follows that where $\delta^{(+)}(a)$ or $\delta^{(-)}(a)$ appears in an integral,

† See Chapter II, § 3.

‡ The physical significance of this definition was pointed out by M. Fiertz, *Helv. phys. Acta*, **23** (1950) 731.

§ P. A. M. Dirac, *Quantum Mechanics* (Clarendon Press, 3rd edn., 1947).

the contribution from the term $(1/a)$ is to be evaluated as a Cauchy principal value; this is because $(1/a)$ in (A.37) is the average of two terms, one of which has a small positive imaginary part and the other a small negative imaginary part.

The function $\delta^{(+)}(a)$ was first used† in working out an approximation describing the scattering of a spinless particle of momentum $\mathbf{p}_0$ and energy E_0 by a fixed potential V. The state vector $|\rangle$ describing the particle satisfies

$$(E_0-T-V)|\rangle = 0,$$

where T is the kinetic energy operator. Taking the representatives $\langle\mathbf{p}|\rangle$ of the scattered wave with respect to eigenstates of momentum $\mathbf{p}$, and using the Born approximation, gives

$$(E_0-E_p)\langle\mathbf{p}|\rangle = \langle\mathbf{p}|V|\mathbf{p}_0\rangle; \tag{A.38}$$

E_p is the kinetic energy associated with momentum $\mathbf{p}$. Dirac showed that, if $|\mathbf{x}|$ is the distance from the scatterer, the solution of (A.38) which, to order $1/|\mathbf{x}|$, contains only outward spreading waves† is

$$\langle\mathbf{p}|\rangle = -\langle\mathbf{p}|V|\mathbf{p}_0\rangle 2\pi i\delta^{(+)}(E_p-E_0). \tag{A.39}$$

That (A.39) is the correct solution is seen by writing out the scattered state representative in configuration space (i.e. the wave function)

$$\langle\mathbf{x}|\rangle = (2\pi\hbar)^{-\frac{3}{2}} \int\limits_{-\infty}^{\infty} d^3\mathbf{p}\, e^{i(\mathbf{p}.\mathbf{x})/\hbar}\langle\mathbf{p}|\rangle$$

and showing that, on integration over the angular distribution of $\mathbf{p}$, the coefficient of the term $(1/|\mathbf{x}|)\exp(-i|\mathbf{p}||\mathbf{x}|)$ vanishes, and the only large term remaining in $\langle\mathbf{x}|\rangle$ is, apart from angular factors, of the form $(1/|\mathbf{x}|)\exp(i|\mathbf{p}||\mathbf{x}|)$. A solution of (A.38) representing a wave having incoming components only is obtained from (A.39) on replacing $-\delta^{(+)}(E_p-E_0)$ by $\delta^{(-)}(E_p-E_0)$. It is shown below that the momentum space form (A.64) of D_F can be discussed in terms of these $\delta^{(+)}$ functions.

Returning to (A.32) and using (A.33), (A.37), and (A.14), we simplify $D_F(x)$ to give‡

$$D_F(x_\mu) = \frac{1}{2\pi i}\left\{\delta(x_\mu^2)-\frac{1}{\pi i}\frac{1}{x_\mu^2}\right\}$$

$$= \frac{1}{\pi i}\delta^{(-)}(x_\mu^2). \tag{A.40}$$

As the argument of $\delta^{(-)}(x_\mu^2)$ is quadratic in x_0, the minus sign no longer indicates the negative frequency part with respect to x_0.

† P. A. M. Dirac, loc. cit.

‡ Notice that $\delta^{(-)}(x_\mu^2) = \delta^{(+)}(-x_\mu^2)$.

Another useful function is given by the difference in the Green's functions $\frac{1}{2}iD_F$ and $\bar{D}$. Defining $D^{(1)}(x)$ by

$$\tfrac{1}{2}iD^{(1)}(x) = \tfrac{1}{2}iD_F(x) - \bar{D}(x), \tag{A.41}$$

on using (A.12), (A.24), and (A.32), we have

$$D^{(1)}(x) = i\{D^{(+)}(x) - D^{(-)}(x)\}. \tag{A.42}$$

The operation of taking positive and negative frequency parts is linear, so the *homogeneous* eqn. (A.13) is obeyed by $D(x)$, $D^{(+)}(x)$, $D^{(-)}(x)$, and $D^{(1)}(x)$. By (A.24), (A.40), and (A.41),

$$D^{(1)}(x) = \frac{1}{2\pi^2 x_\mu^2}. \tag{A.43}$$

Meson fields

A typical field variable $\phi(x_\mu)$ obeys the equation

$$(\partial_\mu^2 - \kappa^2)\phi(x) = -s(x), \tag{A.44}$$

where $s(x)$ is the source. Because the propagation is dispersive, the retarded solution $\phi_{\text{ret}}(x_\mu)$ is influenced by sources *within* the past light cone whose vertex is at x_μ. The retarded solution is

$$\phi_{\text{ret}}(x) = \int_{-\infty}^{\infty} d^4x'\, D_{\text{ret}(\kappa)}(x-x')s(x'),$$

where† $$D_{\text{ret}(\kappa)}(x) = \frac{1}{2\pi}\theta(x)\delta(x_\mu^2) - \frac{\kappa}{4\pi}\eta(x)\frac{J_1\{\kappa\sqrt{(-x_\mu^2)}\}}{\sqrt{(-x_\mu^2)}}. \tag{A.45}$$

Here $$\eta(x) = \begin{cases} +1, & \text{for } x_\mu^2 \leqslant 0,\ x_0 > 0, \\ 0, & \text{otherwise,} \end{cases} \tag{A.46}$$

and J_1 is the ordinary Bessel function of order one.‡ For small s,

$$J_1(s) = \tfrac{1}{2}s + O(s^3),$$

and for large s, $$J_1(s) \sim \frac{\sin(s - \frac{1}{4}\pi)}{\sqrt{(\frac{1}{2}\pi s)}} + O(s^{-\frac{3}{2}}).$$

On the future light cone $D_{\text{ret}(\kappa)}(x)$ differs from $D_{\text{ret}}(x)$ of (A.6) by the constant $(-\kappa^2/8\pi)$, and for large positive values of $(-x_\mu^2)\kappa^2$ (with $x_0 > 0$), the form of $D_{\text{ret}(\kappa)}$ is

$$\frac{\kappa^2}{(2\pi)^{\frac{1}{2}}} \frac{\sin\{-\kappa\sqrt{(-x_\mu^2)} + \frac{1}{4}\pi\}}{\{\kappa\sqrt{(-x_\mu^2)}\}^{\frac{3}{2}}}.$$

† See E. Schrödinger, *Proc. R. Irish Acad.* A, **47** (1941) 1, where other references are given.

‡ The first term in (A.45) is just (A.6).

Changing the sign of x_0 in (A.45) gives the advanced Green's function

$$D_{\mathrm{adv}(\kappa)}(x) = \frac{1}{2\pi}\theta(-x)\delta(x_\mu^2) - \frac{\kappa}{4\pi}\eta(-x)\frac{J_1\{\kappa\surd(-x_\mu^2)\}}{\surd(-x_\mu^2)}. \tag{A.47}$$

Defining the function $D_{(\kappa)}(x)$ by eqn. (A.12),† and $\bar{D}_\kappa(x)$ by (A.24)† gives

$$\bar{D}_\kappa(x) = \frac{1}{4\pi}\delta(x_\mu^2) - \frac{\kappa}{8\pi}\{\eta(x)+\eta(-x)\}\frac{J_1\{\kappa\surd(-x_\mu^2)\}}{\surd(-x_\mu^2)} \tag{A.48}$$

and‡

$$D_\kappa(x) = -\frac{1}{2\pi}\epsilon(x)\delta(x_\mu^2) + \frac{\kappa}{4\pi}\{\eta(x)-\eta(-x)\}\frac{J_1\{\kappa\surd(-x_\mu^2)\}}{\surd(-x_\mu^2)}. \tag{A.49}$$

$\bar{D}_\kappa(x)$ and $D_\kappa(x)$ both vanish for $x_\mu^2 > 0$. The function $D_\kappa^{(1)}(x)$ defined by eqn. (A.42)† has been evaluated‡ by Dirac; it is

$$D_\kappa^{(1)}(x) = \left\{\begin{array}{ll} \dfrac{\kappa}{4\pi}\dfrac{1}{\surd(-x_\mu^2)}N_1\{\kappa\surd(-x_\mu^2)\} & (x_\mu^2 < 0) \\ -\dfrac{\kappa}{4\pi}\dfrac{1}{\surd(x_\mu^2)}H_1^{(1)}\{i\kappa\surd(x_\mu^2)\} & (x_\mu^2 > 0) \end{array}\right\}, \tag{A.50}$$

where N_1 is the Bessel function of the second kind and of first order, and $H_1^{(1)}$ is the Hankel function of the first kind and first order.

The function
$$D_{F(\kappa)}(x) = \frac{2}{i}\bar{D}_\kappa(x) + D_\kappa^{(1)}(x) \tag{A.51}$$

can now be written down explicitly; for most purposes it is more convenient to use the momentum space transform of D_F.

The functions $D_{\mathrm{ret}(\kappa)}(x)$, $D_{\mathrm{adv}(\kappa)}(x)$, $\bar{D}_\kappa(x)$, $\frac{1}{2}iD_{F(\kappa)}(x)$ are Green's functions obeying the typical equation

$$(\partial_\mu^2 - \kappa^2)\bar{D}_\kappa(x) = -\delta^4(x), \tag{A.52}$$

and they are specified by the *boundary* conditions

$$\left.\begin{array}{ll} D_{\mathrm{ret}(\kappa)}(x) = 0, \quad x_0 < 0; & D_{\mathrm{adv}(\kappa)}(x) = 0, \quad x_0 > 0 \\ \bar{D}_\kappa(-x) = \bar{D}_\kappa(x) \quad \text{and} & \bar{D}_\kappa(x) = 0, \quad x_\mu^2 > 0 \\ D_{F(\kappa)}(x) = 2iD_\kappa^{(+)}(x), & x_0 > 0 \\ D_{F(\kappa)}(x) = -2iD_\kappa^{(-)}(x), & x_0 < 0\S \end{array}\right\}. \tag{A.53}$$

The functions $D_\kappa(x)$ and $D_\kappa^{(1)}(x)$ (or $D_\kappa^{(+)}(x)$ and $D_\kappa^{(-)}(x)$) obey the homogeneous equation

$$(\partial_\mu^2 - \kappa^2)D_\kappa(x) = 0, \tag{A.54}$$

† The subscript κ being added to each function.

‡ P. A. M. Dirac, *Proc. Camb. Phil. Soc.* **30** (1934) 150.

§ These relations for $D_{F(\kappa)}(x)$ are readily proved by deforming the contour $I(C_F)$ in the momentum representation shown in Fig. 49, p. 463.

and have the symmetry properties

$$\left.\begin{aligned} D_\kappa(\mathbf{x},x_0) &= D_\kappa(-\mathbf{x},x_0) = -D_\kappa(\mathbf{x},-x_0) \\ D^{(1)}_\kappa(\mathbf{x},x_0) &= D^{(1)}_\kappa(-\mathbf{x},x_0) = D^{(1)}_\kappa(\mathbf{x},-x_0) \\ D^{(+)}_\kappa(\mathbf{x},x_0) &= -D^{(-)}_\kappa(\mathbf{x},x_0) \quad \text{for } x_\mu^2 > 0 \end{aligned}\right\}. \tag{A.55}$$

Finally, the definitions (A.48) and (A.49) show that

$$\bar{D}_\kappa(x) = -\tfrac{1}{2}\epsilon(x)D_\kappa(x). \tag{A.56}$$

Integrating (A.52) with respect to x_0 from $(\mathbf{x}, -\epsilon)$ to $(\mathbf{x}, +\epsilon)$, where ϵ is small and positive, gives

$$\lim_{\epsilon\to+0}\left(-\frac{\partial\bar{D}_\kappa}{\partial x_0}\bigg|_{\mathbf{x},-\epsilon}+\frac{\partial\bar{D}}{\partial x_0}\bigg|_{\mathbf{x},\epsilon}\right) = \delta^3(\mathbf{x})$$

and, using (A.56), this becomes

$$\frac{1}{c}\frac{\partial D_\kappa(\mathbf{x},0)}{\partial t} = -\delta^3(\mathbf{x}). \tag{A.57}$$

Momentum representation

The product $\delta^4(x)$ appearing in (A.52) is Lorentz invariant, and it may be expressed by an integral over all the space of 4-vectors k_μ. Thus

$$\delta^4(x) = (2\pi)^{-4}\int_{-\infty}^{\infty} d^4k\, e^{ik_\mu x_\mu}. \tag{A.58}$$

Now we prove that $\bar{D}_\kappa(x)$ has an integral expression

$$\bar{D}_\kappa(x) = (2\pi)^{-4}P\int_{-\infty}^{\infty}\frac{e^{ik_\mu x_\mu}}{k_\mu^2+\kappa^2}\,d^4k, \tag{A.59}$$

where P indicates the principal value. It is clear that the integral in (A.59) obeys equation (A.52), so it gives a Green's function. The integral is real and Lorentz invariant, and it is unaltered on replacing x_μ by $-x_\mu$; also,

$$P\int_{-\infty}^{\infty} dk_0\,\frac{e^{-ik_0x_0}}{\mathbf{k}^2+\kappa^2-k_0^2} = \frac{\pi\epsilon(x)}{\sqrt{(\mathbf{k}^2+\kappa^2)}}\sin\{x_0\sqrt{(\mathbf{k}^2+\kappa^2)}\}, \tag{A.60}$$

so the integral vanishes when $x_0 = 0$. Therefore, by Lorentz invariance, it must vanish at all points outside the light cone. These conditions show† that this Green's function is $\bar{D}_\kappa(x)$.

† The difference of two functions satisfying these conditions must obey (A.54). The only solution of (A.54) which depends on x_μ^2 only is readily seen to be $D^{(1)}_\kappa$. It is non-zero for $x_\mu^2 > 0$.

Using (A.56), (A.59), and (A.60) gives

$$D_\kappa(x) = -(2\pi)^{-3} \int\limits_{-\infty}^{\infty} d^3\mathbf{k}\, e^{i\mathbf{k}.\mathbf{x}} \frac{\sin\{x_0\sqrt{(\mathbf{k}^2+\kappa^2)}\}}{\sqrt{(\mathbf{k}^2+\kappa^2)}}. \tag{A.61}$$

It follows that $D_\kappa(x)$ may be written as an integral in the four-dimensional k_μ space, provided k_0 is allowed to take complex values. The integration is performed by first integrating over the k_0 contour C_D (see

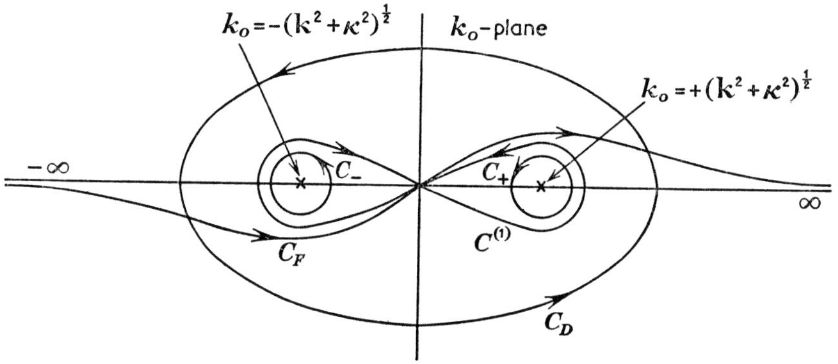

FIG. 49. Contours in the complex k_0 plane for the integral I.

Fig. 49) and then over all values of **k**, and a simple calculation shows that

$$D_\kappa(x) = (2\pi)^{-4} \int\limits_{C_D} dk_0 \int\limits_{-\infty}^{\infty} d^3\mathbf{k} \frac{e^{ik_\mu x_\mu}}{k_\mu^2+\kappa^2}. \tag{A.62}$$

The contour C_D encloses both poles of the integrand and, denoting the integral (A.62) by $I(C_D)$ and similar integrals with contours C_+ and C_- in the k_0 plane by $I(C_+)$ and $I(C_-)$ respectively, then

$$I(C_D) = I(C_+)+I(C_-). \tag{A.63}$$

$I(C_+)$ gives a contribution only for $k_0 = (\mathbf{k}^2+\kappa^2)^{\frac{1}{2}} > 0$, so $I(C_+)$ is the positive frequency part of $I(C_D)$, i.e. $D_\kappa^{(+)}(x) = I(C_+)$, and similarly $D_\kappa^{(-)}(x) = I(C_-)$. It follows from (A.42) that $D_\kappa^{(1)}(x) = iI(C^{(1)})$.

The principal value integral (A.59) is given by a contour in the k_0 plane (Fig. 49) consisting of the real axis except for small segments about each of the poles. The three portions of the real axis obtained in this way can be joined up by a semicircle beneath the point

$$k_0 = -(\mathbf{k}^2+\kappa^2)^{\frac{1}{2}},$$

and a semicircle above the point $k_0 = +(\mathbf{k}^2+\kappa^2)^{\frac{1}{2}}$, and the resulting contour gives the same integral as C_F in Fig. 49. Thus we have

$$I(C_F) = \bar{D}_\kappa+\tfrac{1}{2}iD^{(1)}.$$

By (A.41), $$\tfrac{1}{2}iD_F = I(C_F)$$

or $$\tfrac{1}{2}iD_F(x) = \lim_{\epsilon\to+0}(2\pi)^{-4}\int_{-\infty}^{\infty} d^4k\,\frac{e^{ik_\mu x_\mu}}{k^2+\kappa^2-i\epsilon}, \tag{A.64}$$

where the small positive constant ϵ is used to enable us to revert to *real* k_0 in the integrand; this device is due to Feynman.†

Writing out the denominator of (A.64) in partial fractions and evaluating the contributions from the semicircles in the contour C_F, it is easy to see (using (A.37)) that

$$\tfrac{1}{2}iD_F(x) = \frac{i}{(2\pi)^3}\int_{-\infty}^{\infty} d^4k\,\frac{e^{ik_\mu x_\mu}}{2E_{\mathbf{k}}}\{\delta^{(+)}(E_{\mathbf{k}}-k_0)+\delta^{(+)}(E_{\mathbf{k}}+k_0)\}, \tag{A.65}$$

where $E_{\mathbf{k}} = (\mathbf{k}^2+\kappa^2)^{\frac{1}{2}}$. Integrating (A.65) first over $\mathbf{k}$, it is seen by comparing with (A.39) that for large $|\mathbf{x}|$, the largest terms arising from both $\delta^{(+)}$ functions have radial dependence $(1/|\mathbf{x}|)e^{i|\mathbf{k}||\mathbf{x}|}$. The time dependence is $e^{-ik_0x_0}$, and, because the chief contribution to $\delta^{(+)}(E_{\mathbf{k}}-k_0)$ arises from $k_0 \simeq E_{\mathbf{k}}$, this term gives *outgoing* waves of *positive* frequency. The chief contribution to $\delta^{(+)}(E_{\mathbf{k}}+k_0)$ comes from $k_0 \simeq -E_{\mathbf{k}}$, so this term gives *incoming* waves of *negative* frequency.

Using (A.14), we can write the above integrals over the complex k_0 plane for $D^{(+)}$, $D^{(-)}$, etc., as the following integrals over *real* $(\mathbf{k}, k_0)$,

$$\left.\begin{aligned}
D_\kappa^{(+)}(x) &= \frac{-i}{(2\pi)^3}\int_{-\infty}^{\infty} d^4k\, e^{ik_\mu x_\mu}\delta(k_\mu^2+\kappa^2)\theta(k)\\
D_\kappa^{(-)}(x) &= \frac{i}{(2\pi)^3}\int_{-\infty}^{\infty} d^4k\, e^{ik_\mu x_\mu}\delta(k_\mu^2+\kappa^2)\theta(-k)\\
D_\kappa(x) &= \frac{-i}{(2\pi)^3}\int_{-\infty}^{\infty} d^4k\, e^{ik_\mu x_\mu}\delta(k_\mu^2+\kappa^2)\epsilon(k)\\
D_\kappa^{(1)}(x) &= \frac{1}{(2\pi)^3}\int_{-\infty}^{\infty} d^4k\, e^{ik_\mu x_\mu}\delta(k_\mu^2+\kappa^2)
\end{aligned}\right\}. \tag{A.66}$$

Other useful forms can readily be derived from these formulae; in particular, from (A.59) and (A.66),

$$D_{F(\kappa)}(x) = \frac{1}{4\pi^3}\int_{-\infty}^{\infty} d^4k\, e^{ik_\mu x_\mu}\delta^{(+)}(k_\mu^2+\kappa^2). \tag{A.67}$$

† R. P. Feynman, *Phys. Rev.* **76** (1949) 749. In his notation D_F becomes K.

Field variables in terms of values on a space-like surface

Finally we notice how, when there is no source present, we can express a field variable at any space-time point in terms of its values and the values of its normal derivatives on any space-like surface σ. Such a surface has a unit normal n_μ (pointing to the future side), and a 4-vector element of area $d\sigma_\mu = n_\mu \, d\sigma$, where $d\sigma$ is the three-dimensional element of area. In terms of differential lengths,

$$d\sigma_\mu = \frac{1}{i}(dx_2\,dx_3\,dx_4,\, dx_3\,dx_4\,dx_1,\, dx_4\,dx_1\,dx_2,\, dx_1\,dx_2\,dx_3).$$

Now eqn. (A.57) may be written in Lorentz invariant form as

$$\int\limits_{(\sigma)} \frac{\partial D_\kappa(x)}{\partial x_\mu} d\sigma_\mu = 1, \tag{A.68}$$

where the integral is taken over any space-like surface σ which passes through the coordinate origin. Eqn. (A.68) is obviously Lorentz invariant and, choosing a coordinate system such that its time axis lies along n_μ at the origin, (A.68) is equivalent to (A.57) (remembering $D_\kappa(x) = 0 \;\; (x_\mu^2 > 0)$).

We suppose a field variable $\phi(x)$ obeys the homogeneous equation

$$(\partial_\mu^2 - \kappa^2)\phi(x) = 0, \tag{A.69}$$

and that the values of $\phi(x)$ and $n_\mu \partial_\mu \phi(x)$ on a space-like surface σ are known. We assert that the value of ϕ at any point x'_μ is given in terms of these variables by

$$\phi(x') = \int\limits_{(\sigma)} d\sigma \{D_\kappa(x'-x) n_\mu \partial_\mu \phi(x) - \phi(x) n_\mu \partial_{x\mu} D_\kappa(x'-x)\}. \tag{A.70}$$

Remembering that $D_\kappa(\mathbf{x}, 0) = 0$, it follows from (A.68) that (A.70) is true if x'_μ lies on σ. If x'_μ does not lie on σ, we choose a space-like σ' through x'_μ, and evaluate the difference in the values of the integral (A.70) when taken over σ and over σ'. Using Green's theorem, this difference may be written

$$\int\limits_V d^4x \{D_\kappa(x'-x)(\partial_\mu^2 - \kappa^2)\phi(x) - \phi(x)(\partial_{x\mu}^2 - \kappa^2) D_\kappa(x'-x)\}.$$

V is the space-time region lying between σ and σ'. By (A.54) and (A.69) it is obvious that this vanishes, and (A.70) is proved.

Dirac's wave equation

We discuss the solution of the equation

$$(\gamma^\mu \partial_\mu + \kappa)\psi(x) = -\eta(x), \tag{A.71}$$

where $\eta \equiv \eta_\alpha(x)$ ($\alpha = 1, 2, 3, 4$) is a spinor source function. The notation of Chapter III is used. There is a solution of the form

$$\psi(x) = \psi_{\text{in}}(x) + \int_{-\infty}^{\infty} d^4x' S_{\text{ret}}(x-x')\eta(x'), \tag{A.72}$$

where $\psi_{\text{in},\alpha}(x)$ ($\alpha = 1, 2, 3, 4$) is some solution of the homogeneous Dirac equation

$$(\gamma^\mu \partial_\mu + \kappa)\psi_{\text{in}}(x) = 0. \tag{A.73}$$

We require

$$(\gamma^\mu \partial_\mu + \kappa)S_{\text{ret}}(x) = -\delta^4(x), \tag{A.74}$$

and

$$S_{\text{ret}}(x) = 0 \quad (x_0 < 0). \tag{A.75}$$

Disturbances in the fermion field cannot be propagated faster than light, so we also require

$$S_{\text{ret}}(x) = 0 \quad (x_\mu^2 > 0). \tag{A.76}$$

We note that

$$(\gamma^\mu \partial_\mu + \kappa)(\gamma^\mu \partial_\mu - \kappa) = \partial_\mu^2 - \kappa^2.$$

Writing

$$S_{\text{ret}}(x) = (\gamma^\mu \partial_\mu - \kappa)D_{\text{ret}(\kappa)}(x), \tag{A.77}$$

where $D_{\text{ret}(\kappa)}(x)$ is given by (A.45), it is easy to see that (A.74), (A.75), and (A.76) are satisfied.

Corresponding to (A.21) there is also an advanced solution of (A.71) given by

$$\psi(x) = \psi_{\text{out}}(x) + \int_{-\infty}^{\infty} d^4x\, S_{\text{adv}}(x-x')\eta(x'), \tag{A.78}$$

where $\psi_{\text{out}}(x)$ obeys the homogeneous equation (A.73), and $S_{\text{adv}}(x)$ is a 4×4 matrix, such that

$$(\gamma^\mu \partial_\mu + \kappa)S_{\text{adv}}(x) = -\delta^4(x) \tag{A.79}$$

and

$$S_{\text{adv}}(x) = 0 \quad (x_0 > 0); \qquad S_{\text{adv}}(x) = 0 \quad (x_\mu^2 > 0). \tag{A.80}$$

Eqns. (A.79) and (A.80) are satisfied by substituting (cf. (A.47))

$$S_{\text{adv}}(x) = (\gamma^\mu \partial_\mu - \kappa)D_{\text{adv}(\kappa)}(x). \tag{A.81}$$

We saw in Chapter III that under a Lorentz transformation

$$x'_\mu = a_{\mu\nu} x_\nu,$$

the fermion variables ψ_α become $(\Lambda\psi)_\alpha$, where Λ is a 4×4 matrix obeying

$$\Lambda^{-1}\gamma^\mu \Lambda = a_{\mu\nu}\gamma^\nu.$$

Thus $\gamma^\mu \partial_\mu$ is an invariant, and by (A.77) and (A.81) $S_{\text{ret}}(x)$ and $S_{\text{adv}}(x)$ are invariants under proper Lorentz transformations.

Eqn. (A.71) is not invariant under the simple time reversal substitution $x_0 \to -x_0$ but, as was shown in Chapters III and VII, ψ has to be replaced by $\gamma^4\gamma^5\psi$ under time reversal, and under inversion of space and time $(x_\mu \to -x_\mu)$ ψ has to be replaced by $\gamma^5\psi$.† This has the consequence that the advanced Green's function is not obtained from the retarded function on replacing x_0 by $-x_0$, as was the case for boson fields, but we have

$$S_{\text{adv}}(x_\mu) = \gamma^5 S_{\text{ret}}(-x_\mu)\gamma^5 \tag{A.82}$$

and

$$S_{\text{adv}}(\mathbf{x}, x_0) = \gamma^4\gamma^5 S_{\text{ret}}(\mathbf{x}, -x_0)\gamma^5\gamma^4. \tag{A.83}$$

The adjoint fermion field variable $\bar{\psi}(x)$ (where $\bar{\psi} = \tilde{\psi}\gamma^4$) obeys the equation

$$\bar{\psi}(\overleftarrow{\partial}_\mu \gamma^\mu - \kappa) = \bar{\eta}(x), \tag{A.84}$$

where $\overleftarrow{\partial}_\mu$ acts to the left and $\bar{\eta}(x)$ is an adjoint spinor source function $(\bar{\eta} = \tilde{\eta}\gamma^4)$. From (A.74) and (A.82),

$$(\gamma^\mu\partial_\mu - \kappa)S_{\text{adv}}(-x) = \delta^4(x).$$

Using (A.81) this may be written

$$S_{\text{adv}}(-x_\mu)(\gamma^\mu\overleftarrow{\partial}_\mu - \kappa) = \delta^4(x). \tag{A.85}$$

The *retarded* solution of (A.84) is therefore

$$\left.\begin{aligned} \bar{\psi}(x) &= \bar{\psi}_{\text{in}}(x) + \int_{-\infty}^{\infty} d^4x'\, \bar{\eta}(x')S_{\text{adv}}(x'-x), \\ \text{where} \quad \bar{\psi}_{\text{in}}(x)(\overleftarrow{\partial}_\mu \gamma^\mu - \kappa) &= 0. \end{aligned}\right\} \tag{A.86}$$

There is a similar form for the advanced solution of (A.84).

When discussing the quantum field properties we require a causal Green's function. As on p. 458 we choose a particular frame of reference and define the (invariant) Feynman function $S_F(x)$ by

$$\tfrac{1}{2}iS_F(x) = S^{(+)}_{\text{ret}}(x) + S^{(-)}_{\text{adv}}(x). \tag{A.87}$$

It is easy to see that

$$S_F(x) = (\gamma^\mu\partial_\mu - \kappa)D_{F(\kappa)}(x). \tag{A.88}$$

(Eqn. (A.27) gives the prescription for taking positive (and negative) frequency parts, and it is clear that it does not matter whether we act on a function with $(\gamma^\mu\partial_\mu)$ before or after taking its positive (negative) frequency part.) Because $\tfrac{1}{2}iD_{F(\kappa)}(x)$ satisfies (A.52), we have

$$(\gamma^\mu\partial_\mu + \kappa)\{\tfrac{1}{2}iS_F(x)\} = -\delta^4(x). \tag{A.89}$$

Eqn. (A.98) below shows the frequency properties of $S_F(x)$.

Another Green's function which is sometimes of use is

$$\bar{S}(x) = (\gamma^\mu\partial_\mu - \kappa)\bar{D}_\kappa(x). \tag{A.90}$$

Also $\quad \bar{S}(x) = 0$ for $x_\mu^2 > 0$, and $\bar{S}(-x_\mu) = \gamma^5\bar{S}(x_\mu)\gamma^5$. $\qquad$ (A.91)

† Of course, the spinor source function $\eta(x)$ of eqn. (A.71) must transform like $\psi(x)$.

Differences between these Green's functions give solutions of the homogeneous Dirac equation: for example,

$$S(x) = S_{\mathrm{adv}}(x) - S_{\mathrm{ret}}(x) = (\gamma^{\mu}\,\partial_{\mu} - \kappa)D_{\kappa}(x) \tag{A.92}$$

satisfies

$$(\gamma^{\mu}\partial_{\mu} + \kappa)S(x) = 0 \tag{A.93}$$

and

$$S(x) = 0 \quad (x_{\mu}^{2} > 0); \qquad S(-x_{\mu}) = -\gamma^{5}S(x_{\mu})\gamma^{5}. \tag{A.94}$$

The (matrix) function

$$S^{(1)}(x) = i\{S^{(+)}(x) - S^{(-)}(x)\} = (\gamma^{\mu}\,\partial_{\mu} - \kappa)D^{(1)}(x) \tag{A.95}$$

also satisfies (A.93), and $S^{(1)}(-x) = \gamma^{5}S^{(1)}(x)\gamma^{5}$.

The relation analogous to (A.68) is

$$\int\limits_{(\sigma)} \gamma^{\mu}S(x)\,d\sigma_{\mu} = \int\limits_{(\sigma)} S(x)\gamma^{\mu}\,d\sigma_{\mu} = 1, \tag{A.96}$$

where the integration is over any space-like surface σ which passes through the coordinate origin. Because of (A.92) the only contribution to (A.96) arises from the neighbourhood of the origin, and we can choose a coordinate system with the time axis in the direction of the normal n_{μ} to σ at the origin. Either integral in (A.96) then reduces to

$$\int\limits_{(\sigma)} \frac{\partial D}{\partial x_{4}}\,d\sigma_{4}$$

and, by (A.57), this equals unity.

Because $\partial D/\partial x_{4}$ is an even function of x_{μ}, it is possible to replace $S(x)$ by $S(-x)$ in both integrals. In this form (A.96) may be used to enable us to write down the solution $\psi(x')$ of the *homogeneous* Dirac equation (A.73) in terms of the values of $\psi(x)$ on a given space-like surface σ:

$$\psi(x') = \int\limits_{(\sigma)} S(x'-x)\gamma^{\mu}\psi(x)\,d\sigma_{\mu}. \tag{A.97}$$

If x'_{μ} lies on σ, (A.94) and (A.96) show that (A.97) is true; also (A.93) shows that $\psi(x')$ satisfies the homogeneous equation (A.73) for any x'_{μ}.

Eqn. (A.97) can readily be written in another useful form. Deforming the contour $I(C_{F})$ of Fig. 49 we get the *invariant* result†

$$\tfrac{1}{2}iS_{F}(x) = \begin{Bmatrix} -S^{(+)}(x) & (x_{0} > 0) \\ +S^{(-)}(x) & (x_{0} < 0) \end{Bmatrix}. \tag{A.98}$$

Thus, if we choose two space-like surfaces σ_{1} and σ_{2} with σ_{1} to the past of x'_{μ} and σ_{2} to the future of x'_{μ}, on taking positive and negative

† It is invariant because for $x_{\mu}^{2} > 0$, $S^{(+)}(x) = -S^{(-)}(x)$.

frequency parts of (A.97), we get

$$\left.\begin{aligned} \psi^{(+)}(x') &= -\tfrac{1}{2}i \int\limits_{(\sigma_1)} S_F(x'-x)\gamma^\mu\psi(x)\,d\sigma_\mu \\ \psi^{(-)}(x') &= \tfrac{1}{2}i \int\limits_{(\sigma_2)} S_F(x'-x)\gamma^\mu\psi(x)\,d\sigma_\mu \end{aligned}\right\}; \tag{A.99}$$

combining these two formulae gives a new form for $\psi(x')$,

$$\psi(x') = \tfrac{1}{2}i\Bigl(\int\limits_{(\sigma_2)} - \int\limits_{(\sigma_1)}\Bigr) d\sigma_\mu S_F(x'-x)\gamma^\mu\psi(x). \tag{A.100}$$

Eqn. (A.100), which has been used by Feynman,† expresses the fermion field $\psi(x')$ in terms of positive frequency components coming from the past, and negative frequency components coming from the future. Feynman expresses this in the form: electron components of the wave function propagate forwards in time, while positron components propagate backwards in time.

Momentum representation

It follows directly from the momentum representations (A.64) and (A.59) for D_F and $\bar{D}$, that

$$\tfrac{1}{2}iS_F(x) = \lim_{\epsilon\to+0}(2\pi)^{-4}\int\limits_{-\infty}^{\infty} d^4k\, e^{ik_\mu x_\mu}\frac{i\gamma^\mu k_\mu - \kappa}{k_\mu^2+\kappa^2-i\epsilon} \tag{A.101}$$

and

$$\bar{S}(x) = (2\pi)^{-4}P\int\limits_{-\infty}^{\infty} d^4k\, e^{ik_\mu x_\mu}\frac{i\gamma^\mu k_\mu - \kappa}{k_\mu^2+\kappa^2}. \tag{A.102}$$

Also, using (A.67),

$$S_F(x) = \frac{1}{4\pi^3}\int\limits_{-\infty}^{\infty} d^4k\, e^{ik_\mu x_\mu}(i\gamma^\mu k_\mu - \kappa)\delta^{(+)}(k_\mu^2+\kappa^2), \tag{A.103}$$

while (A.92) and (A.66) gives

$$S(x) = -\frac{i}{(2\pi)^3}\int\limits_{-\infty}^{\infty} d^4k\, e^{ik_\mu x_\mu}(i\gamma^\mu k_\mu - \kappa)\epsilon(k)\delta(k_\mu^2+\kappa^2). \tag{A.104}$$

The functions $S^{(+)}$, $S^{(-)}$, $S^{(1)}$ can readily be written in similar forms. Finally, we notice that S_F can be expressed in the symbolic form

$$\tfrac{1}{2}iS_F(x) = \lim_{\epsilon\to+0}\frac{(-1)}{(2\pi)^4}\int d^4k\frac{e^{ikx}}{i\gamma k+\kappa-i\epsilon}. \tag{A.105}$$

Eqn. (A.105) can be written down directly, by operational methods, from the inhomogeneous equation for $S_F(x)$:

$$(\gamma^\mu\partial_\mu+\kappa-i\epsilon)S_F(x) = 2i\delta^4(x) \quad (\epsilon\to+0). \tag{A.106}$$

† R. P. Feynman, *Phys. Rev.* **76** (1949) 749.

The device of replacing κ by $\kappa - i\epsilon$, as used in eqn. (A.106), specifies uniquely that the solution is the S_F Green's function.

In the presence of an electromagnetic field $A_\mu(x)$, the fermion Green's function $G(x, x')$ has to satisfy

$$\left[\gamma^\mu\left\{\partial_{x_\mu} + \frac{ie}{\hbar c} A_\mu(x)\right\} - \kappa\right] G(x, x') = -\delta^4(x - x'). \qquad \text{(A.107)}$$

This equation could be used to describe the behaviour of spin-$\frac{1}{2}$ fermions when both a source function and an electromagnetic field have to be taken into account.

Table of Particles (1958 *data*)

Class	*Symbol and charge*	*Observed anti-particle*	*Attribut*	*Mass* (*in* m_e)	(*in MeV*)	*Spin*/$\hbar$	*Magnetic moment*	*Mean life* (*sec.*)	*Most common decay modes*	*Branching ratios* (%)
BARYONS—HEAVY FERMIONS	Ξ^-		-2	2585 ± 6	1321 ± 3	?	?	$\sim3\times10^{-10}$	$\Lambda^0+\pi^-$	
	(1)Ξ^0		-2	?				?	$\Lambda^0+\pi^0$	
	Σ^-		-1	$2341{\cdot}6\pm0{\cdot}8$	$1196{\cdot}5\pm0{\cdot}4$			$(1{\cdot}72\pm0{\cdot}2)\times$ $\times10^{-10}$	$n+\pi^-$	
	Σ^0		-1	(2)$2329{\cdot}9\pm0{\cdot}3$	$1190{\cdot}5\pm1{\cdot}5$	$\frac{1}{2}$	?	$<10^{-12}$	$\Lambda^0+\gamma$ (fast decay)	
	Σ^+		-1	$2327{\cdot}9\pm0{\cdot}6$	$1189{\cdot}5\pm0{\cdot}3$			$(0{\cdot}8\pm0{\cdot}2)\times$ $\times10^{-10}$	$p+\pi^0$ $n+\pi^+$	46 ± 6 54 ± 6
	Λ^0	(3)$\bar{\Lambda}^0$	-1 1	$2182{\cdot}5\pm0{\cdot}4$	$1115{\cdot}2\pm0{\cdot}2$	$\frac{1}{2}$	?	$(2{\cdot}6\pm0{\cdot}2)\times$ $\times10^{-10}$	$\Lambda^0\rightarrow p+\pi^-$ $n+\pi^+$	63 ± 4 37 ± 4
	n	$\bar{n}$	0	$1838{\cdot}65$ $\pm0{\cdot}04$	$939{\cdot}51\pm0{\cdot}02$	$\frac{1}{2}$	$-1{\cdot}913\,\frac{e\hbar}{2M_pc}$	$(1{\cdot}1\pm0{\cdot}2)\times10^3$	$n\rightarrow p+e^-+\bar{\nu}$	
	p	$\bar{p}$	0	$1836{\cdot}12$ $\pm0{\cdot}04$	$938{\cdot}21\pm0{\cdot}02$	$\frac{1}{2}$	$2{\cdot}793\times\frac{e\hbar}{2M_pc}$	stable ($>4\times10^{23}$ years)(4)		
MESONS—MEDIUM BOSONS	K^+	K^-	1 -1	$967{\cdot}0\pm0{\cdot}4$	$494{\cdot}0\pm0{\cdot}2$	0	0(5)	$(1{\cdot}3\pm0{\cdot}1)10^{-8}$	$K^+\rightarrow$ $\mu^++\nu$(6) $\pi^++\pi^0$ $\pi^-+2\pi^+$ $\pi^++2\pi^0$ $e^++\nu+\pi^0$(7) $\mu^++\nu+\pi^0$	 59 26 5·6 1·7 4 3
	K^0	$\bar{K}_0$	1 -1	965 ± 5	$493\pm2{\cdot}5$	0	0	$K^0\,(1{\cdot}0\pm0{\cdot}1)\times$ $\times10^{-10}$ $K_2^0\,(9{\cdot}0\pm3)\times$ $\times10^{-8}$	$K_1^0\rightarrow\pi^++\pi^-$ $2\pi^0$ $K_2^0\rightarrow$ $\pi^++\pi^-+\pi^0$ $e^\pm+\pi^\mp+\nu$ $\mu^\pm+\pi^\mp+\nu$	76 24 ~30 ~30 ~30
	π^+	π^-	0	$273{\cdot}27\pm0{\cdot}12$	$139{\cdot}63\pm0{\cdot}06$	0	0	$(2{\cdot}56\pm0{\cdot}1)\times$ $\times10^{-8}$	$\pi^+\rightarrow\mu^++\nu$(7) $\pi^-\rightarrow\mu^-+\bar{\nu}$	
	π^0		0	$264{\cdot}27\pm0{\cdot}3$	$135{\cdot}04\pm0{\cdot}16$	0	0	$<10^{-15}$	$\pi^0\rightarrow2\gamma$ $e^++e^-+\gamma$ (fast decays)	98·8 1·2
LEPTONS(8)—LIGHT FERMIONS	μ^+	μ^-	0	$206{\cdot}86\pm0{\cdot}11$	$105{\cdot}70\pm0{\cdot}06$	$\frac{1}{2}$	$(1{\cdot}0026\pm$ $\pm0{\cdot}0008)$(9)$\times$ $\times\frac{e\hbar}{2m_\mu c}$	$(2{\cdot}22\pm0{\cdot}02)\times$ $\times10^{-6}$	$\mu^+\rightarrow$ $e^++\nu+\bar{\nu}$ $\mu^-\rightarrow$ $e^-+\nu+\bar{\nu}$	
	e^+	e^-	0	1	0·510976	$\frac{1}{2}$	$(1{\cdot}00115\pm$ $\pm0{\cdot}00002)\times$ $\times\frac{e\hbar}{2m_ec}$	stable	*Remarks*	
	$\bar{\nu}$	ν	0	$<0{\cdot}0005$		$\frac{1}{2}$	0(10)	stable	$\bar{\nu}$ is right-handed ν is left-handed	
PHOTON	γ		0	0		1	0	stable	We can only detect spin components $\hbar$ and $-\hbar$ about the momentum	

The *isotopic spin* assignment is that (Ξ^0, Ξ^-), (p, n), (K^+, K^0), and $(\bar{K}^0, K^-)$ are doublets, and $(\Sigma^+, \Sigma^0, \Sigma^-)$ and (π^+, π^0, π^-) are triplets. Λ^0 is a singlet.

(1) *Annual High Energy Physics Conference* (C.E.R.N. Geneva, 1958), p. 160.
(2) M. L. Stevenson, *Phys. Rev.* **111** (1958) 1707.
(3) Ref. (1) above, p. 153. The decay is $\bar{\Lambda}^0\rightarrow\bar{p}+\pi^+$.
(4) F. Reines *et al.*, *Phys. Rev.* **109** (1958) 609.
(5) Spin 0 particles cannot have a magnetic moment.
(6) The charge conjugate decays are expected for K^-.
(7) Lepton conservation is assumed.
(8) For lepton conservation the lower particle in each pair is the lepton, the upper is the anti-lepton.
(9) T. Coffin *et al.*, *Phys. Rev.* **109** (1958) 973. Reducing the mass m_μ to $206{\cdot}58m_e$ would give agreement with the theoretical value

$$\left\{1+\frac{\alpha}{2\pi}+0{\cdot}75\left(\frac{\alpha}{\pi}\right)^2\right\}\frac{e\hbar}{2m_\mu c}.$$

(10) By the 2-component theory.

AUTHOR INDEX

SUBJECT INDEX

PRINTED IN GREAT BRITAIN
AT THE UNIVERSITY PRESS, OXFORD
BY VIVIAN RIDLER
PRINTER TO THE UNIVERSITY